Mathematics

SCOTT FORESMAN • ADDISON WESLEY

Authors

Randall I. Charles

Warren Crown

Francis (Skip) Fennell

Janet H. Caldwell
Mary Cavanagh
Dinah Chancellor
Alma B. Ramirez

Jeanne F. Ramos
Kay Sammons
Jane F. Schielack

William Tate
Mary Thompson
John A. Van de Walle

Consulting Mathematicians

Edward J. Barbeau
Professor of Mathematics
University of Toronto
Toronto, Ontario, Canada

David M. Bressoud
DeWitt Wallace Professor
of Mathematics
Macalester College
Saint Paul, Minnesota

Gary Lippman
Professor of Mathematics
and Computer Science
California State University Hayward
Hayward, California

Editorial Offices: Glenview, Illinois • Parsippany, New Jersey • New York, New York

Sales Offices: Parsippany, New Jersey • Duluth, Georgia • Glenview, Illinois
Coppell, Texas • Ontario, California • Mesa, Arizona

Teacher's Edition
Available online and on CD-ROM

Grade 1 • Volume 2 (Chapters 4-6)

Reading Consultants

Peter Afflerbach
Professor and Director of
The Reading Center
University of Maryland
College Park, Maryland

Donald J. Leu
John and Maria Neag
Endowed Chair in Literacy
and Technology
University of Connecticut
Storrs, Connecticut

ESL Consultant

Jim Cummins
Professor of Curriculum
Ontario Institute for Studies in Education
University of Toronto
Toronto, Ontario, Canada

Professional Development Consultant

David C. Geary
Chair and Middlebush Professor
Department of Psychological Sciences
University of Missouri
Columbia, Missouri

ISBN: 0-328-11716-1

1 2 3 4 5 6 7 8 9 10 V064 12 11 10 09 08 07 06 05 04

The
SCOTT FORESMAN
Difference

SCOTT FORESMAN • ADDISON WESLEY

Mathematics

You can count on us.

The difference that counts . . .

Our all-new scientifically research-based program has been designed to make math simpler to teach, easier to learn, and more accessible to every student. With the Scott Foresman Difference, students, teachers, and parents can all say: "I get it!"

Pre-Kindergarten

Count on our unique, **scientifically research-based** Pre-K math program to help early math learners bloom. **Field tested for eight years** in diverse classrooms, it has been proven to build essential math background.

Pre-K *Kindergarten* *Grade 1*

Kindergarten

We follow up in Kindergarten with a flexible, **research-based,** full-day curriculum that successfully **develops and extends mathematical thinking.** Stories, games, and center activities teach your students basic math understandings.

Grade 2 *Grade 3* *Grade 4*

Grades 1 and 2

To help your students comprehend and successfully apply basic facts, our **research-based program** begins with an **understanding of number** and what the number sentence means. This leads to **algebra success.**

Grades 3 through 6

In the upper grades, the Scott Foresman Difference is evident from cover-to-cover. From **instruction right on the student page** to daily assessment and **customized intervention,** our **research-based program** ensures that your students **achieve progress and test success.**

Grade 5 *Grade 6*

and the research that proves it.

Completely planned, written, and reviewed by the authors, our program is backed by more than 100 years of research into what really works in the classroom. Four phases of research were integrated into the program's development by the authors, who are all recognized experts in the acquisition of mathematical learning.

1 Ongoing Research

The proven effectiveness of Scott Foresman, Addison Wesley, and Silver Burdett Ginn previous math programs provides a longitudinal research base that spans more than 100 years. Pretest and posttest results show that these programs improve students' math proficiency.

2 Scientific Research Base

An experienced authorship team provided expertise in synthesizing and contributing to a rich body of scientific evidence. Research-based techniques were embedded into the program's instructional materials, assessments, and professional development.

3 Formative Research

Classroom field studies, school administrators, mathematics teachers, and reviewers contributed valuable recommendations as the program was designed and written. Pretest and posttest scores were part of the information gathered during program development.

4 Summative Research

Scientific evidence, including longitudinal studies in the classroom, further validate the efficacy of our program. Control group research designs and test score data ensure that the program is of the highest quality and predictive of success.

Authors

Randall I. Charles
Professor Emeritus,
Department of Mathematics
and Computer Science
San Jose State University
San Jose, California

Dinah Chancellor
Coordinator of Math, Science,
Gifted/Talented, Title IV
Carroll ISD
Southlake, Texas

William Tate
Professor and Chair of the
Department of Education
College of Arts and Sciences
Washington University
St. Louis, Missouri

Warren Crown
Professor of Mathematics
Education
Rutgers University
New Brunswick, New Jersey

Alma B. Ramírez
Senior Research Associate,
Mathematics
Case Methods Project
WestEd
Oakland, California

Mary Thompson
Mathematics Instructional Specialist
New Orleans Public Schools Louisiana
New Orleans, Louisiana

Francis (Skip) Fennell
Professor of Education
McDaniel College
Westminster, Maryland

Jeanne F. Ramos
Administrative Coordinator,
K–12 Mathematics
Los Angeles Unified School
District
Los Angeles, California

John Van de Walle
Professor Emeritus of Mathematics
Education/Consultant
Virginia Commonwealth University
Richmond, Virginia

Janet H. Caldwell
Professor of Mathematics
Rowan University
Glassboro, New Jersey

Kay Sammons
Supervisor of Mathematics
Howard County Public Schools
Ellicott City, Maryland

Mary Cavanagh
Project Coordinator, Math,
Science and Beyond
Solano Beach School District
San Diego County, California

Jane F. Schielack
Associate Professor of Mathematics
Texas A&M University
College Station, Texas

Consulting Mathematicians

Edward J. Barbeau
Professor of Mathematics
University of Toronto
Toronto, Ontario, Canada

David M. Bressoud
DeWitt Wallace Professor of Mathematics
Macalester College
Saint Paul, Minnesota

Gary Lippman
Professor of Mathematics and Computer Science
California State University Hayward
Hayward, California

Reading Consultants

Peter Afflerbach
Professor and Director of the Reading Center
University of Maryland
College Park, Maryland

Donald J. Leu
John and Maria Neag Endowed Chair
in Literacy and Technology
University of Connecticut
Storrs, Connecticut

ESL Consultant

Jim Cummins
Professor of Curriculum
Ontario Institute for Studies in Education
University of Toronto
Toronto, Ontario, Canada

Professional Development Consultant

David C. Geary
Chair and Middlebush Professor
Department of Psychological Sciences
University of Missouri
Columbia, Missouri

Reviewers

Mary Bacon
Mathematics Specialist
East Baton Rouge Parish School System
Baton Rouge, Louisiana

Cheryl Baker
Mathematics Teacher
Norton Middle School
Norton, Ohio

Marcelline A. Barron
Curriculum Leader Math and Science, Grades K–5
Fairfield Public Schools
Fairfield, Connecticut

Mary Connery-Simmons
Mathematics Specialist
Springfield Massachusetts Public Schools
Springfield, Massachusetts

Anthony C. Dentino
Supervisor of Curriculum
Brick Township Schools
Brick, New Jersey

Donna McCollum Derby
Teacher
Kernersville Elementary School
Kernersville, North Carolina

Dawn Evans
Mathematics Teacher
Bret Harte Elementary School
Chicago, Illinois

Terri Geaudreau
Title I Math Facilitator
Bemiss Elementary
Spokane, Washington

Sister Helen Lucille Habig, RSM
Assistant Superintendent of Catholic Schools
Archdiocese of Cincinnati
Cincinnati, Ohio

Sam Hanson
Teacher
Totem Falls Elementary
Snohomish, Washington

Allison Harris
Professional Development School Coach
Seattle Public Schools
Seattle, Washington

Kim Hill
Teacher
Hayes Grade Center
Ada, Oklahoma

Pamela Renee Hill
Teacher
Durham Public Schools
Durham, North Carolina

Martha Knight
Teacher
Oak Mountain Elementary
Birmingham, Alabama

Catherine Kuhns
Teacher
Country Hills Elementary
Coral Springs, Florida

Madeleine A. Madsen
District Curriculum Resource
District Community Consolidated School District 59
Arlington Heights, Illinois

Susan Mayberger
Supervisor of English as a Second Language/Director of Migrant Education
Omaha Public Schools
Omaha, Nebraska

Judy Peede
Elementary Lead Math Teacher
Wake County Schools
Raleigh, North Carolina

Lynda M. Penry
Teacher
Wright Elementary
Fort Walton Beach, Florida

Jolyn D. Raleigh
District Math Curriculum Specialist, Grades K–2
Granite School District
Salt Lake City, Utah

Deanna P. Rigdon
District Math Curriculum Specialist, Grades 3–4
Granite School District
Salt Lake City, Utah

Thomas Romero
Principal
Adams Elementary
Wapato, Washington

Wendy Siegel
Mathematics Coordinator, Grades K–12
Orchard Park Middle School
Orchard Park, New York

Sandra Smith
Teacher
Cheat Lake Elementary
Morgantown, West Virginia

Vickie H. Smith
Assistant Principal
Phoenix Academic Magnet Elementary School
Alexandria, Louisiana

Rochelle A. Solomon
Mathematics Resource Teacher
Cleveland Municipal School District
Cleveland, Ohio

Frank L. Sparks
Curriculum Design and Support Specialist, Secondary Mathematics
New Orleans Public Schools
New Orleans, Louisiana

Beth L. Spivey
Lead Teacher, Elementary Mathematics
Wake County Public School System
Raleigh, North Carolina

Paula Spomer
Teacher
Chisholm Elementary
Edmond, Oklahoma

Robert Trammel
Math Consultant
Fort Wayne Community Schools
Fort Wayne, Indiana

Annemarie Tuffner
Mathematics Lead Teacher, Grades K–12
Neshaminy School District
Langhorne, Pennsylvania

Ann Watts
Mathematics Specialist
East Baton Rouge Parish School System
Baton Rouge, Louisiana

Judy L. Wright
Curriculum and Staff Development Specialist
Columbus Public Schools
Columbus, Ohio

Theresa Zieles
Teacher
Indianapolis Public School #88
Indianapolis, Indiana

National Math Advisory Board

F. William Amorosi
Saugus Public Schools
Saugus, Massachusetts

Linda Bailey
Oklahoma City, Oklahoma

Mary Bording
Huntsville Public Schools
Huntsville, Alabama

Patti Bridwell
Austin, Texas

Merry Brown
Lake Jackson, Texas

Gayle D. Coleman
St. Louis Public Schools
St. Louis, Missouri

Steven T. Cottrell
Davis School District
Farmington, Utah

Brenda DeBorde
Grand Prairie ISD
Grand Prairie, Texas

Toni Lynn De Vore
Wood County Schools
Parkersburg, West Virginia

Sandra Eliason
Orland School District 135
Orland Park, Illinois

Larue Evans
Cherry Hill Elementary Schools
Cherry Hill, New Jersey

Ann R. Flanagan
Sachem Central School District
Holbrook, New York

Nancy C. French
Davenport Community School District
Davenport, Iowa

Marguerite Hart
Indianapolis, Indiana

Cathy Hutchins
Laird Elementary School
Tempe, Arizona

Nancy B. Knight
Mount Laurel Township Schools
Mount Laurel, New Jersey

Suzzanne Legg
Kansas City Public Schools
Kansas City, Kansas

Gale Levow
Community School District 8
Bronx, New York

Lynda M. Penry
Wright Elementary
Fort Walton Beach, Florida

Patricia Paluch Pockl
Ohio County Schools
Wheeling, West Virginia

Sylvia O. Reeder-Tucker
Prince George's County Public Schools
Capitol Heights, Maryland

Beverly Kendrick Ross
Kyrene School District
Tempe, Arizona

Kathy Ross
New Orleans, Louisiana

Edward J. Sahagian
North Bergen School District
North Bergen, New Jersey

Kathleen Savage
Mesa Public Schools
Mesa, Arizona

Beth Ann Schefelker
Henry David Thoreau Elementary
Milwaukee Public Schools
Milwaukee, Wisconsin

Dana Smith Simmons
Flint Community Schools
Flint, Michigan

Toni Vela
Laredo, ISD
Laredo, Texas

Julie Victory
Pocono Mountain School District
Swiftwater, Pennsylvania

Jesse Warren
South Bend Community School Corporation
South Bend, Indiana

Nancy Zirkelbach
Cloverdale Elementary
Bonneville School District #93
Idaho Falls, Idaho

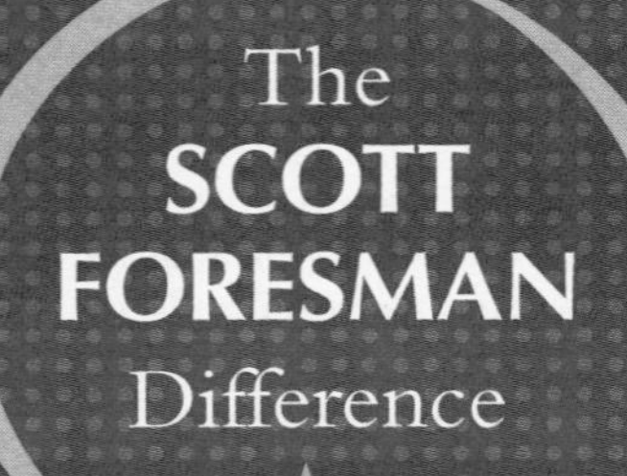

We truly teach for understanding.

Research shows that teaching for understanding is the best test prep you can provide. That's why every program claims to teach for understanding. But our program is different.

Includes instruction right on the student page

Everything your students need to "get it" is always accessible. Students are able to engage in deeper, independent learning while parents can help at home.

Instructional Stories

At the primary level, Read-Together Math Stories in the Student Edition and in Big Book format actually teach math concepts. Your students build math background while improving their reading fluency.

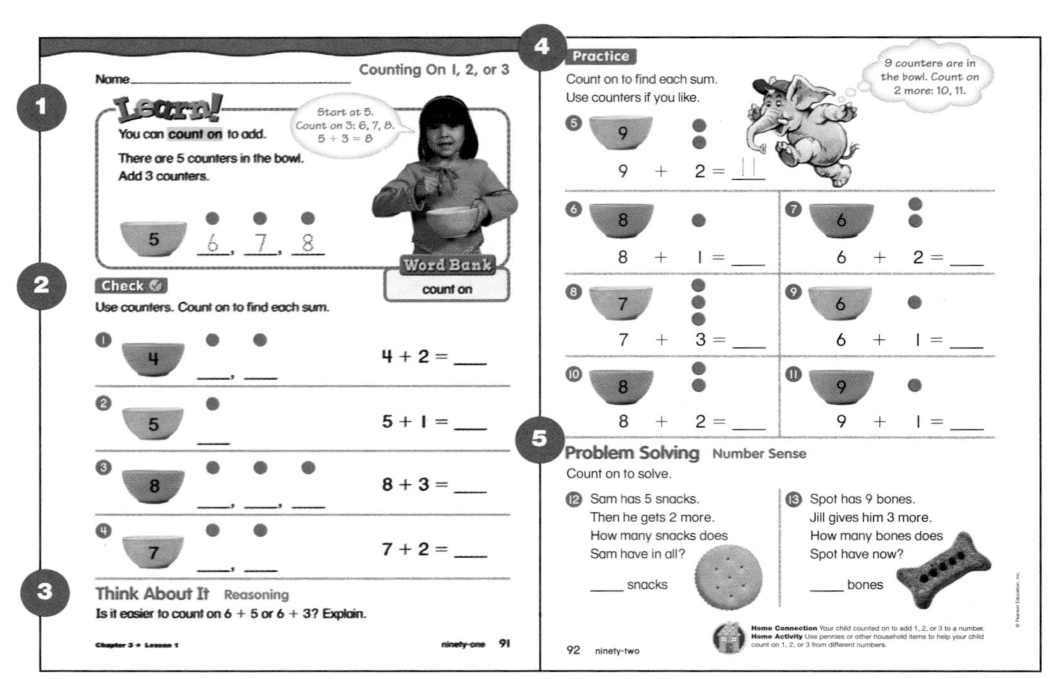

Name______ Counting On 1, 2, or 3

1 Learn!
You can count on to add.
There are 5 counters in the bowl.
Add 3 counters.
Start at 5. Count on 3: 6, 7, 8. 5 + 3 = 8
5 6, 7, 8
Word Bank
count on

2 Check
Use counters. Count on to find each sum.
1. 4 ___, ___ 4 + 2 = ___
2. 5 ___ 5 + 1 = ___
3. 8 ___, ___, ___ 8 + 3 = ___
4. 7 ___, ___ 7 + 2 = ___

3 Think About It Reasoning
Is it easier to count on 6 + 5 or 6 + 3? Explain.

Chapter 3 • Lesson 1 ninety-one 91

4 Practice
Count on to find each sum.
Use counters if you like.
9 counters are in the bowl. Count on 2 more: 10, 11.
5. 9 + 2 = 11
6. 8 + 1 = ___
7. 6 + 2 = ___
8. 7 + 3 = ___
9. 6 + 1 = ___
10. 8 + 2 = ___
11. 9 + 1 = ___

5 Problem Solving Number Sense
Count on to solve.
12. Sam has 5 snacks. Then he gets 2 more. How many snacks does Sam have in all? ___ snacks
13. Spot has 9 bones. Jill gives him 3 more. How many bones does Spot have now? ___ bones

Home Connection Your child counted on to add 1, 2, or 3 to a number.
Home Activity Use pennies or other household items to help your child count on 1, 2, or 3 from different numbers.

92 ninety-two

1. Learn
Introduces concepts and vocabulary clearly

2. Check
Quickly assesses your students' grasp of the new concept before practice

3. Think About It
Gives your students a chance to verbalize and clarify understanding before practice begins

4. Practice
Provides instruction with more examples your students can explore with manipulatives

5. Problem Solving
Engages your students with daily problem-solving activities

6. Magnetic Manipulatives
Fun, no-mess manipulatives your students can hold up to display their work and help you check for understanding

Identifies explicitly what your students need to achieve

Lessons in the Student Edition clearly explain the mathematics your students need to understand and the skills they need to master. Step-by-step instruction guides their thinking when they need it most.

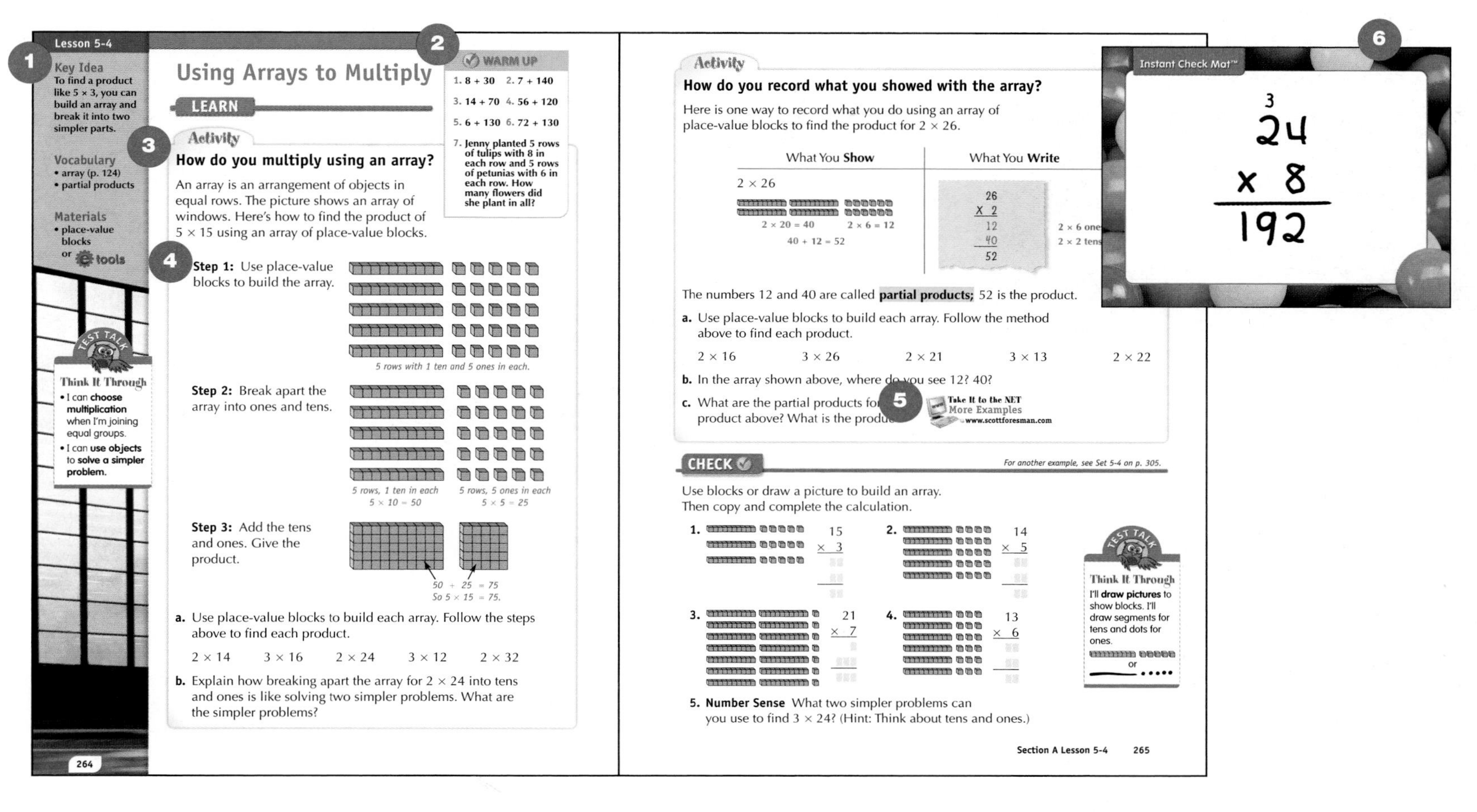
Lesson 5-4

Key Idea
To find a product like 5 × 3, you can build an array and break it into two simpler parts.

Vocabulary
• array (p. 124)
• partial products

Materials
• place-value blocks or tools

Think It Through
• I can choose multiplication when I'm joining equal groups.
• I can use objects to solve a simpler problem.

Using Arrays to Multiply

LEARN

WARM UP
1. 8 + 30 2. 7 + 140
3. 14 + 70 4. 56 + 120
5. 6 + 130 6. 72 + 130
7. Jenny planted 5 rows of tulips with 8 in each row and 5 rows of petunias with 6 in each row. How many flowers did she plant in all?

Activity

How do you multiply using an array?

An array is an arrangement of objects in equal rows. The picture shows an array of windows. Here's how to find the product of 5 × 15 using an array of place-value blocks.

Step 1: Use place-value blocks to build the array.

5 rows with 1 ten and 5 ones in each.

Step 2: Break apart the array into ones and tens.

5 rows, 1 ten in each
5 × 10 = 50

5 rows, 5 ones in each
5 × 5 = 25

Step 3: Add the tens and ones. Give the product.

50 + 25 = 75
So 5 × 15 = 75.

a. Use place-value blocks to build each array. Follow the steps above to find each product.

2 × 14 3 × 16 2 × 24 3 × 12 2 × 32

b. Explain how breaking apart the array for 2 × 24 into tens and ones is like solving two simpler problems. What are the simpler problems?

264

Activity

How do you record what you showed with the array?

Here is one way to record what you do using an array of place-value blocks to find the product for 2 × 26.

What You Show	What You Write
2 × 26 2 × 20 = 40 2 × 6 = 12 40 + 12 = 52	26 × 2 12 2 × 6 ones 40 2 × 2 tens 52

The numbers 12 and 40 are called **partial products;** 52 is the product.

a. Use place-value blocks to build each array. Follow the method above to find each product.

2 × 16 3 × 26 2 × 21 3 × 13 2 × 22

b. In the array shown above, where do you see 12? 40?

c. What are the partial products for the product above? What is the product?

Take It to the NET More Examples www.scottforesman.com

CHECK

For another example, see Set 5-4 on p. 305.

Use blocks or draw a picture to build an array. Then copy and complete the calculation.

1. 15 × 3 2. 14 × 5 3. 21 × 7 4. 13 × 6

Think It Through
I'll draw pictures to show blocks. I'll draw segments for tens and dots for ones.

5. **Number Sense** What two simpler problems can you use to find 3 × 24? (Hint: Think about tens and ones.)

Section A Lesson 5-4 265

Instant Check Mat™

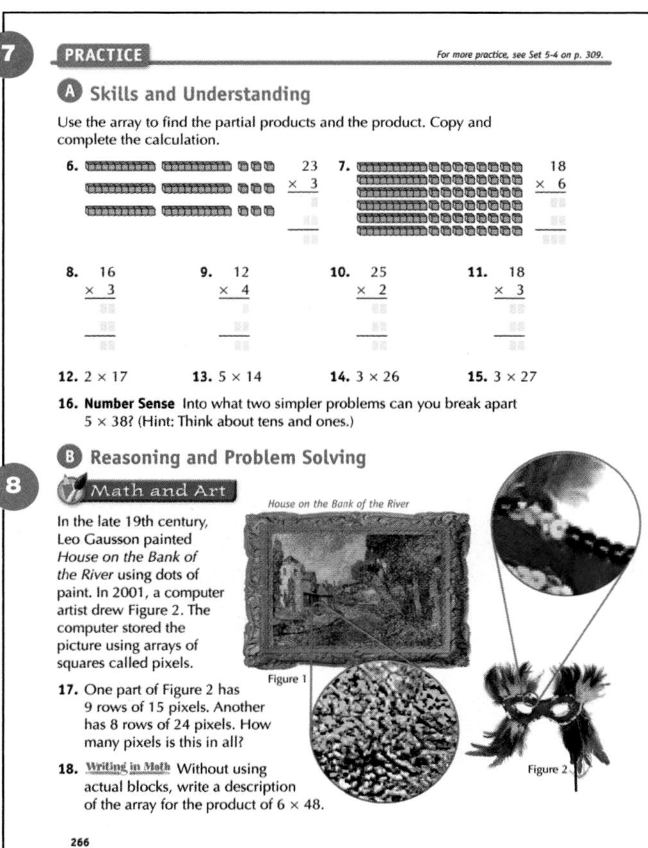
PRACTICE

For more practice, see Set 5-4 on p. 309.

A Skills and Understanding

Use the array to find the partial products and the product. Copy and complete the calculation.

6. 23 × 3 7. 18 × 6

8. 16 × 3 9. 12 × 4 10. 25 × 2 11. 18 × 3

12. 2 × 17 13. 5 × 14 14. 3 × 26 15. 3 × 27

16. **Number Sense** Into what two simpler problems can you break apart 5 × 38? (Hint: Think about tens and ones.)

B Reasoning and Problem Solving

Math and Art

In the late 19th century, Leo Gausson painted *House on the Bank of the River* using dots of paint. In 2001, a computer artist drew Figure 2. The computer stored the picture using arrays of squares called pixels.

House on the Bank of the River

Figure 1

Figure 2

17. One part of Figure 2 has 9 rows of 15 pixels. Another has 8 rows of 24 pixels. How many pixels is this in all?

18. Writing in Math Without using actual blocks, write a description of the array for the product of 6 × 48.

266

1. **Key Idea**
Identifies important mathematics concepts clearly right at the start

2. **Warm Up**
Activates prior knowledge of skills your students will need in the upcoming lesson

3. **Focus Questions**
Sets up instruction for your students' understanding

4. **Guided Instruction**
Makes concepts easier for your students to grasp with step-by-step instruction and clear models right on the student page

5. **Take It to the Net**
Provides online access to test prep, more practice, and more examples

6. **Instant Check Mat™**
See all your students' work at a glance and assess their understanding instantly

7. **Built-in Leveled Practice**
Allows you to customize instruction to match your students' abilities

8. **Curriculum Connections**
Encourages your students to transfer the concepts they acquire to other subject areas

Monitors understanding every step of the way

With embedded assessment opportunities right on the student page, it's easy to gauge your students' progress on an ongoing basis. This frees you to focus your time and energy on helping each student acquire the skills and understanding needed for test success.

Before the Lesson

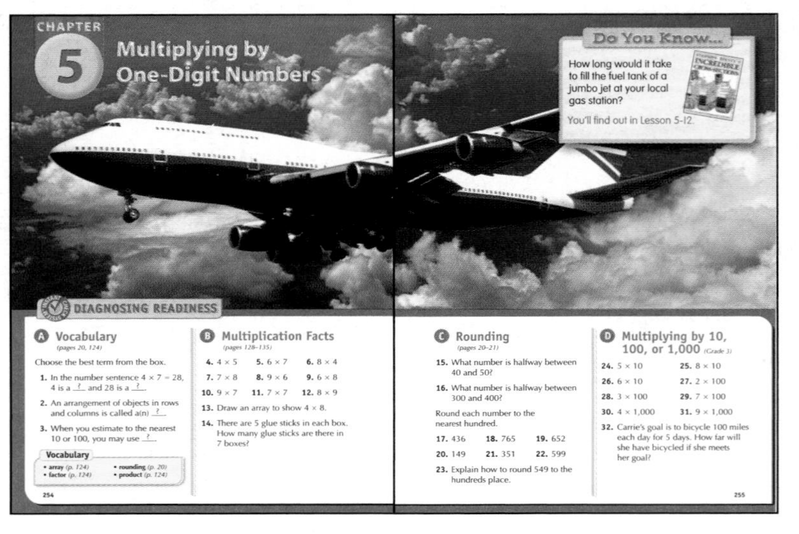
CHAPTER 5 Multiplying by One-Digit Numbers

Do You Know...
How long would it take to fill the fuel tank of a jumbo jet at your local gas station?
You'll find out in Lesson 5-12.

DIAGNOSING READINESS

A Vocabulary (pages 20, 124)
Choose the best term from the box.
1. In the number sentence 4 × 7 = 28, 4 is a _?_ and 28 is a _?_.
2. An arrangement of objects in rows and columns is called a(n) _?_.
3. When you estimate to the nearest 10 or 100, you may use _?_.
Vocabulary
• array (p. 124) • factor (p. 124) • rounding (p. 20) • product (p. 124)

B Multiplication Facts (pages 128–135)
4. 4 × 5 5. 6 × 7 6. 8 × 4
7. 7 × 8 8. 9 × 6 9. 6 × 8
10. 9 × 7 11. 7 × 7 12. 8 × 9
13. Draw an array to show 4 × 8.
14. There are 5 glue sticks in each box. How many glue sticks are there in 7 boxes?

C Rounding (pages 20–21)
15. What number is halfway between 40 and 50?
16. What number is halfway between 300 and 400?
Round each number to the nearest hundred.
17. 436 18. 765 19. 652
20. 149 21. 351 22. 599
23. Explain how to round 549 to the hundreds place.

D Multiplying by 10, 100, or 1,000 (Grade 3)
24. 5 × 10 25. 8 × 10
26. 6 × 10 27. 2 × 100
28. 3 × 100 29. 7 × 100
30. 4 × 1,000 31. 9 × 1,000
32. Carrie's goal is to bicycle 100 miles each day for 5 days. How far will she have bicycled if she meets her goal?

254 255

Diagnosing Readiness

Helps you assess your students' knowledge of vocabulary, skills, and concepts, and then prescribe individualized intervention prior to chapter lessons

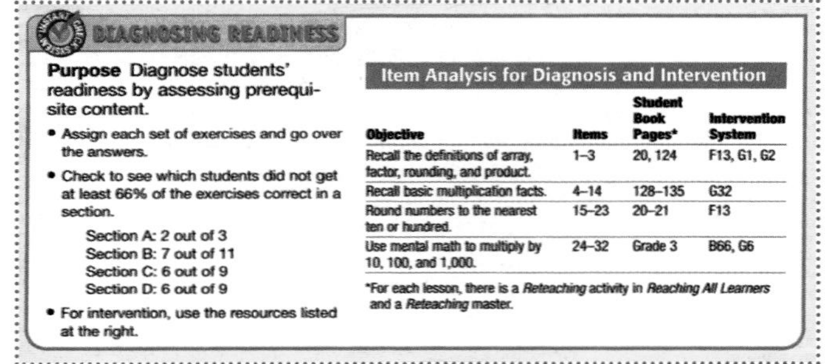
DIAGNOSING READINESS

Purpose Diagnose students' readiness by assessing prerequisite content.

- Assign each set of exercises and go over the answers.
- Check to see which students did not get at least 66% of the exercises correct in a section.
  - Section A: 2 out of 3
  - Section B: 7 out of 11
  - Section C: 6 out of 9
  - Section D: 6 out of 9
- For intervention, use the resources listed at the right.

Item Analysis for Diagnosis and Intervention

Objective	Items	Student Book Pages*	Intervention System
Recall the definitions of array, factor, rounding, and product.	1–3	20, 124	F13, G1, G2
Recall basic multiplication facts.	4–14	128–135	G32
Round numbers to the nearest ten or hundred.	15–23	20–21	F13
Use mental math to multiply by 10, 100, and 1,000.	24–32	Grade 3	B66, G6

*For each lesson, there is a *Reteaching* activity in *Reaching All Learners* and a *Reteaching* master.

Every assessment aligns with customized intervention in the Teacher's Edition

During the Lesson

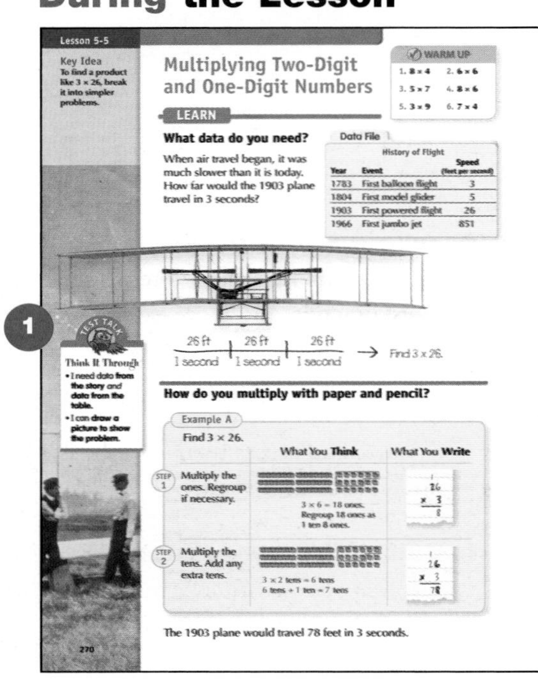
Lesson 5-5

Key Idea: To find a product like 3 × 26, break it into simpler problems.

Multiplying Two-Digit and One-Digit Numbers

WARM UP
1. 8 × 4 2. 6 × 6
3. 5 × 7 4. 8 × 6
5. 3 × 9 6. 7 × 4

LEARN

What data do you need?

When air travel began, it was much slower than it is today. How far would the 1903 plane travel in 3 seconds?

Data File — History of Flight

Year	Event	Speed (feet per second)
1783	First balloon flight	3
1804	First model glider	5
1903	First powered flight	26
1966	First jumbo jet	851

Think It Through
• I need data from the story and data from the table.
• I can draw a picture to show the problem.

26 ft 26 ft 26 ft
1 second 1 second 1 second → Find 3 × 26.

How do you multiply with paper and pencil?

Example A
Find 3 × 26.

	What You Think	What You Write
STEP 1 Multiply the ones. Regroup if necessary.	3 × 6 = 18 ones. Regroup 18 ones as 1 ten 8 ones.	
STEP 2 Multiply the tens. Add any extra tens.	3 × 2 tens = 6 tens. 6 tens + 1 ten = 7 tens	78

The 1903 plane would travel 78 feet in 3 seconds.

270

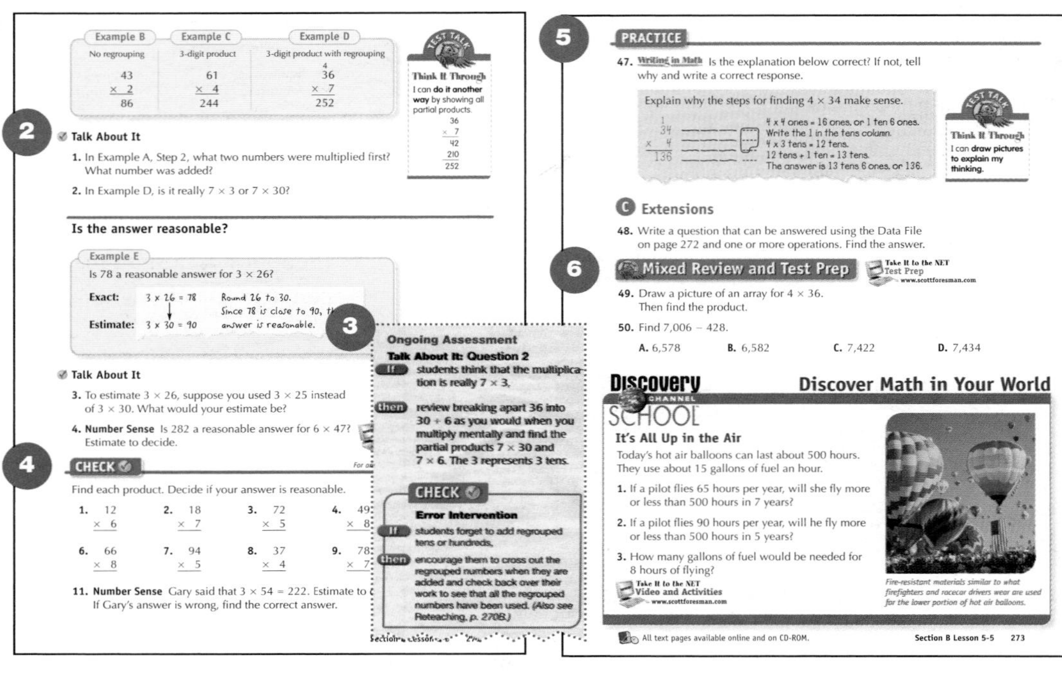
Example B: No regrouping — 43 × 2 = 86
Example C: 3-digit product — 61 × 4 = 244
Example D: 3-digit product with regrouping — 36 × 7 = 252

Think It Through
I can do it another way by showing all partial products.

Talk About It
1. In Example A, Step 2, what two numbers were multiplied first? What number was added?
2. In Example D, is it really 7 × 3 or 7 × 30?

Is the answer reasonable?

Example E
Is 78 a reasonable answer for 3 × 26?
Exact: 3 × 26 = 78
Estimate: 3 × 30 = 90
Round 26 to 30. Since 78 is close to 90, my answer is reasonable.

Talk About It
3. To estimate 3 × 26, suppose you used 3 × 25 instead of 3 × 30. What would your estimate be?
4. Number Sense Is 282 a reasonable answer for 6 × 47? Estimate to decide.

CHECK
Find each product. Decide if your answer is reasonable.
1. 12 × 6 2. 18 × 7 3. 72 × 5
6. 66 × 8 7. 94 × 5 8. 37 × 4
11. Number Sense Gary said that 3 × 54 = 222. Estimate to decide if Gary's answer is wrong, find the correct answer.

Ongoing Assessment
Talk About It: Question 2
If students think that the multiplication is really 7 × 3,
then review breaking apart 36 into 30 + 6 as you would when you multiply mentally and find the partial products 7 × 30 and 7 × 6. The 3 represents 3 tens.

CHECK
Error Intervention
If students forget to add regrouped tens or hundreds,
then encourage them to cross out the regrouped numbers when they are added and check back over their work to see that all the regrouped numbers have been used. (Also see Reteaching, p. 270B.)

PRACTICE
47. Writing in Math Is the explanation below correct? If not, tell why and write a correct response.
Explain why the steps for finding 4 × 34 make sense.
4 × 4 ones = 16 ones, or 1 ten 6 ones. Write the 1 in the tens column.
4 × 3 tens = 12 tens.
12 tens + 1 ten = 13 tens.
The answer is 13 tens 6 ones, or 136.

Think It Through
I can draw pictures to explain my thinking.

C Extensions
48. Write a question that can be answered using the Data File on page 272 and one or more operations. Find the answer.

Mixed Review and Test Prep
49. Draw a picture of an array for 4 × 36. Then find the product.
50. Find 7,006 − 428.
A. 6,578 B. 6,582 C. 7,422 D. 7,434

Discovery Channel School — Discover Math in Your World
It's All Up in the Air
Today's hot air balloons can last about 500 hours. They use about 15 gallons of fuel an hour.
1. If a pilot flies 65 hours per year, will she fly more or less than 500 hours in 7 years?
2. If a pilot flies 90 hours per year, will he fly more or less than 500 hours in 5 years?
3. How many gallons of fuel would be needed for 8 hours of flying?

All text pages available online and on CD-ROM.

Section B Lesson 5-5 273

1. Test Talk—Think It Through
Gives your students practice in the type of thinking and problem-solving strategies they'll use on tests

2. Talk About It
Supplies your students with an informal assessment opportunity that lets them verbalize their understanding

3. If . . . Then
Provides instant intervention before your students get too far off track

4. Check
Sees if your students "get it" before beginning independent practice

5. Writing in Math
Prepares your students for open-ended and short- or extended-response questions on state and national tests

6. Mixed Review and Test Prep
Helps your students keep their test-taking skills sharp

Aligns all assessments with immediate and systematic remediation

Our unique Item Analysis for Diagnosis and Intervention in the Teacher's Edition lets you quickly assess your students' understanding of math concepts and prescribe individualized intervention.

After the Lesson *at the End of Each Section . . .*

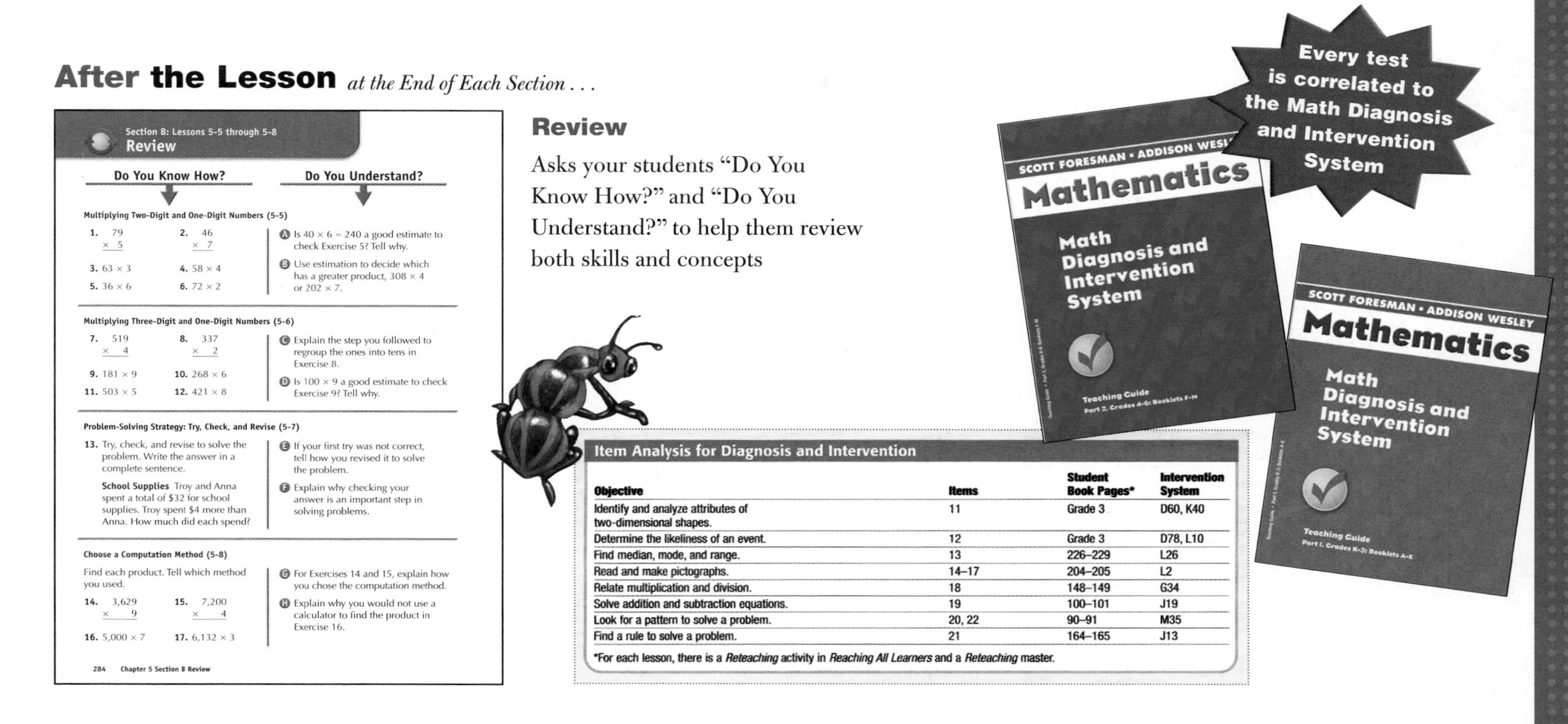
Section B: Lessons 5-5 through 5-8
Review

Do You Know How? | Do You Understand?

Multiplying Two-Digit and One-Digit Numbers (5-5)

1. 79 × 5
2. 46 × 7
3. 63 × 3
4. 58 × 4
5. 36 × 6
6. 72 × 2

A Is 40 × 6 = 240 a good estimate to check Exercise 5? Tell why.
B Use estimation to decide which has a greater product, 308 × 4 or 202 × 7.

Multiplying Three-Digit and One-Digit Numbers (5-6)

7. 519 × 4
8. 337 × 2
9. 181 × 9
10. 268 × 6
11. 503 × 5
12. 421 × 8

C Explain the step you followed to regroup the ones into tens in Exercise 8.
D Is 100 × 9 a good estimate to check Exercise 9? Tell why.

Problem-Solving Strategy: Try, Check, and Revise (5-7)

13. Try, check, and revise to solve the problem. Write the answer in a complete sentence.
School Supplies Troy and Anna spent a total of $32 for school supplies. Troy spent $4 more than Anna. How much did each spend?

E If your first try was not correct, tell how you revised it to solve the problem.
F Explain why checking your answer is an important step in solving problems.

Choose a Computation Method (5-8)

Find each product. Tell which method you used.

14. 3,629 × 9
15. 7,200 × 4
16. 5,000 × 7
17. 6,132 × 3

G For Exercises 14 and 15, explain how you chose the computation method.
H Explain why you would not use a calculator to find the product in Exercise 16.

284 Chapter 5 Section B Review

Item Analysis for Diagnosis and Intervention

Objective	Items	Student Book Pages*	Intervention System
Identify and analyze attributes of two-dimensional shapes.	11	Grade 3	D60, K40
Determine the likeliness of an event.	12	Grade 3	D78, L10
Find median, mode, and range.	13	226–229	L26
Read and make pictographs.	14–17	204–205	L2
Relate multiplication and division.	18	148–149	G34
Solve addition and subtraction equations.	19	100–101	J19
Look for a pattern to solve a problem.	20, 22	90–91	M35
Find a rule to solve a problem.	21	164–165	J13

*For each lesson, there is a *Reteaching* activity in *Reaching All Learners* and a *Reteaching* master.

Review

Asks your students "Do You Know How?" and "Do You Understand?" to help them review both skills and concepts

After the Lesson *at the End of Each Chapter . . .*

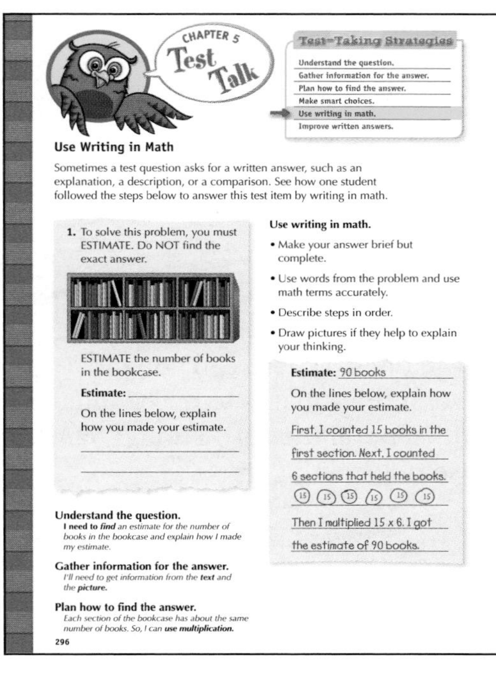

Test Talk

Gives your students in-depth instruction and practice on the test-taking strategies introduced at the beginning of the Student Edition

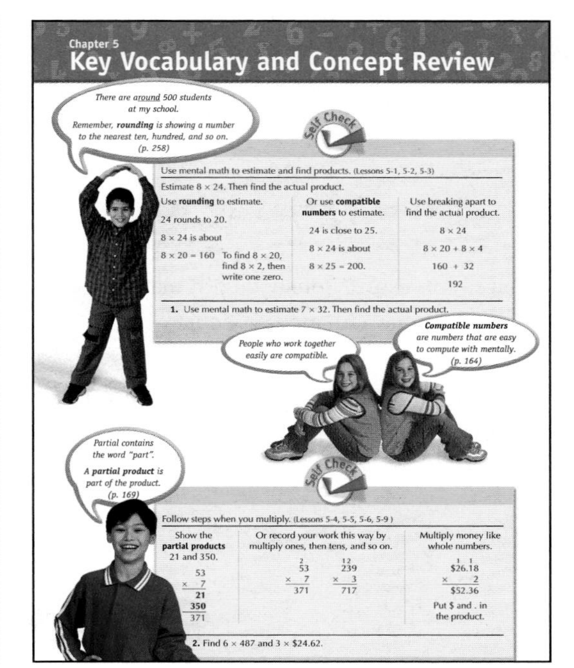

Key Vocabulary and Concept Review

Checks your students' understanding of math concepts and provides them with real-world vocabulary connections

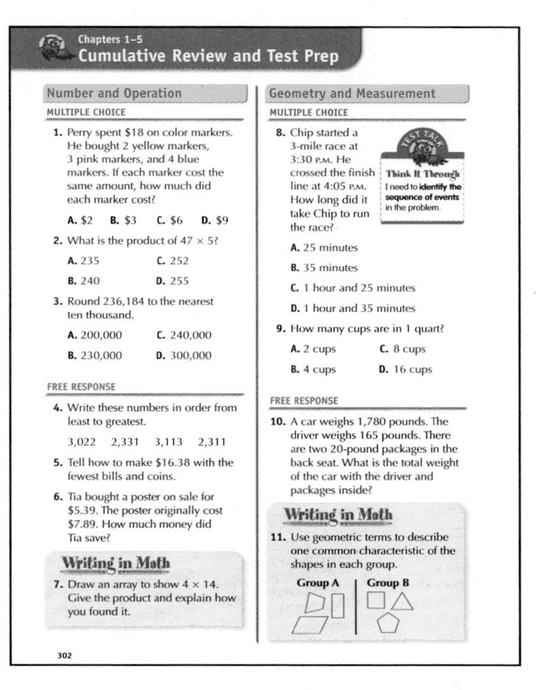

Cumulative Review and Test Prep

Provides ongoing assessment and practice of previously taught content

The SCOTT FORESMAN Difference

We create better problem solvers.

Problem solving is incredibly important to math proficiency and test success. That's why every program has a problem-solving component. But our program is different.

Connects reading and writing to problem solving

Research shows math performance is often connected to literacy. We apply familiar reading and writing strategies to math and explain to your students how these strategies can help them become more successful problem solvers.

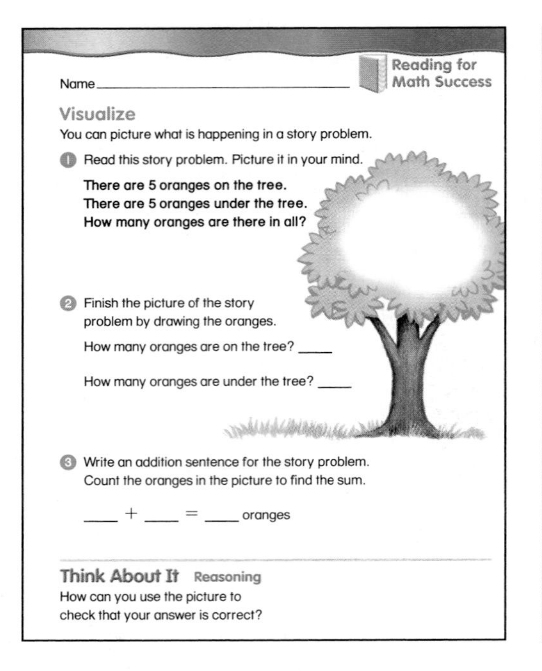

Name ______ Reading for Math Success

Visualize

You can picture what is happening in a story problem.

1. Read this story problem. Picture it in your mind.
   There are 5 oranges on the tree.
   There are 5 oranges under the tree.
   How many oranges are there in all?
2. Finish the picture of the story problem by drawing the oranges.
   How many oranges are on the tree? ____
   How many oranges are under the tree? ____
3. Write an addition sentence for the story problem. Count the oranges in the picture to find the sum.
   ____ + ____ = ____ oranges

Think About It Reasoning
How can you use the picture to check that your answer is correct?

Reading for Math Success

Identifies a reading strategy your students already know and shows them how to apply the strategy to math word problems

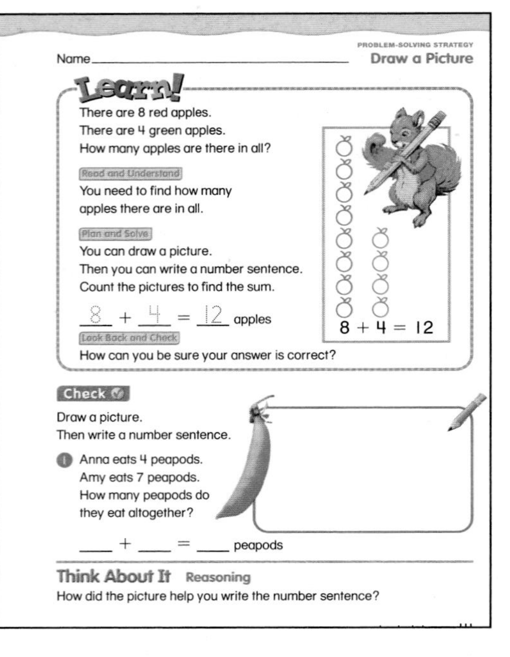

Name ______ PROBLEM-SOLVING STRATEGY Draw a Picture

Learn!

There are 8 red apples.
There are 4 green apples.
How many apples are there in all?

Read and Understand
You need to find how many apples there are in all.

Plan and Solve
You can draw a picture.
Then you can write a number sentence.
Count the pictures to find the sum.

8 + 4 = 12 apples

8 + 4 = 12

Look Back and Check
How can you be sure your answer is correct?

Check
Draw a picture.
Then write a number sentence.

1. Anna eats 4 peapods.
   Amy eats 7 peapods.
   How many peapods do they eat altogether?
   ____ + ____ = ____ peapods

Think About It Reasoning
How did the picture help you write the number sentence?

Problem-Solving Strategy

Teaches your students how and when to use the reading strategy to solve problems, and then provides an opportunity for them to demonstrate what they have learned

Problem of the Day Transparencies Flip Chart

Reinforces previously taught math content and enhances specific problem-solving skills and strategies each day for whole-class or small group problem-solving

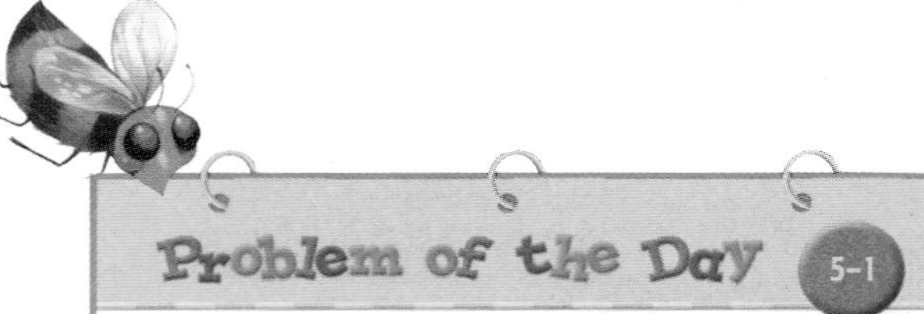

Problem of the Day 5-1

The figure below has a perimeter of 18 units. Where can you move two of the squares to make a figure with a perimeter of 12 units? (Hint: Use objects.)

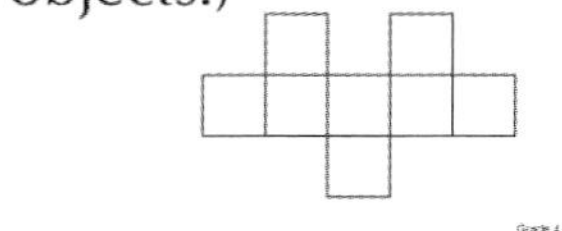

Links techniques to understanding and solving word problems

By linking reading and writing to math, students become more adept at understanding word problems and identifying what they need to do. Your students will improve their abilities to recognize and organize the important details and learn how to describe their solutions by writing clear, concise, and accurate answers.

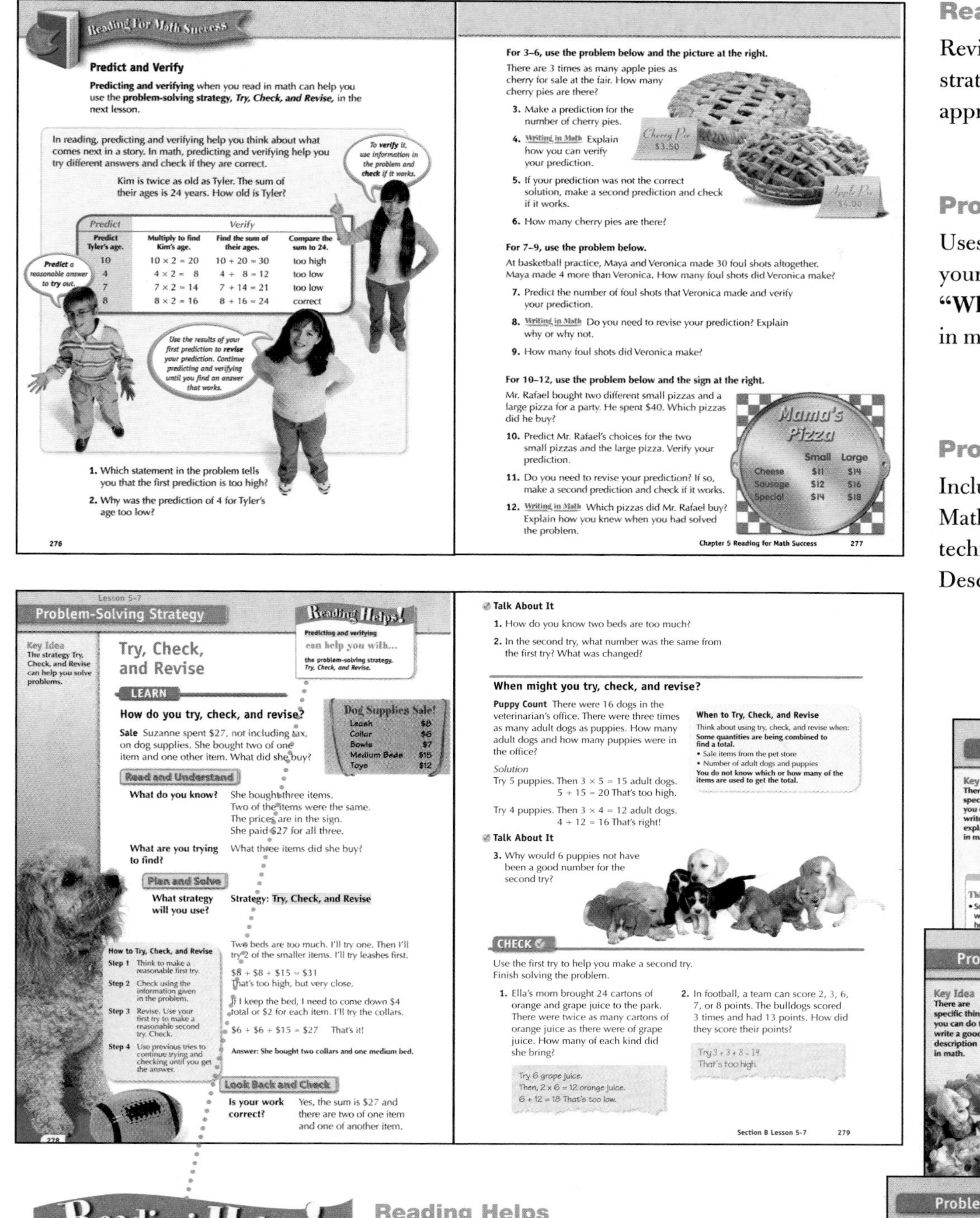

Reading For Math Success

Predict and Verify

Predicting and verifying when you read in math can help you use the **problem-solving strategy, *Try, Check, and Revise,*** in the next lesson.

In reading, predicting and verifying help you think about what comes next in a story. In math, predicting and verifying help you try different answers and check if they are correct.

Kim is twice as old as Tyler. The sum of their ages is 24 years. How old is Tyler?

Predict	Verify		
Predict Tyler's age.	Multiply to find Kim's age.	Find the sum of their ages.	Compare the sum to 24.
10	10 × 2 = 20	10 + 20 = 30	too high
4	4 × 2 = 8	4 + 8 = 12	too low
7	7 × 2 = 14	7 + 14 = 21	too low
8	8 × 2 = 16	8 + 16 = 24	correct

1. Which statement in the problem tells you that the first prediction is too high?
2. Why was the prediction of 4 for Tyler's age too low?

276

For 3–6, use the problem below and the picture at the right.

There are 3 times as many apple pies as cherry for sale at the fair. How many cherry pies are there?

3. Make a prediction for the number of cherry pies.
4. Writing in Math Explain how you can verify your prediction.
5. If your prediction was not the correct solution, make a second prediction and check if it works.
6. How many cherry pies are there?

For 7–9, use the problem below.

At basketball practice, Maya and Veronica made 30 foul shots altogether. Maya made 4 more than Veronica. How many foul shots did Veronica make?

7. Predict the number of foul shots that Veronica made and verify your prediction.
8. Writing in Math Do you need to revise your prediction? Explain why or why not.
9. How many foul shots did Veronica make?

For 10–12, use the problem below and the sign at the right.

Mr. Rafael bought two different small pizzas and a large pizza for a party. He spent $40. Which pizzas did he buy?

10. Predict Mr. Rafael's choices for the two small pizzas and the large pizza. Verify your prediction.
11. Do you need to revise your prediction? If so, make a second prediction and check if it works.
12. Writing in Math Which pizzas did Mr. Rafael buy? Explain how you knew when you had solved the problem.

Mama's Pizza

	Small	Large
Cheese	$11	$14
Sausage	$12	$16
Special	$14	$18

Chapter 5 Reading for Math Success 277

Lesson 5-7

Problem-Solving Strategy

Key Idea
The strategy Try, Check, and Revise can help you solve problems.

Try, Check, and Revise

Reading Helps! Predicting and verifying can help you with... the problem-solving strategy, Try, Check, and Revise.

LEARN

How do you try, check, and revise?

Sale Suzanne spent $27, not including tax, on dog supplies. She bought two of one item and one other item. What did she buy?

Dog Supplies Sale!	
Leash	$8
Collar	$6
Bowls	$7
Medium Beds	$15
Toys	$12

Read and Understand

What do you know? She bought three items. Two of the items were the same. The prices are in the sign. She paid $27 for all three.

What are you trying to find? What three items did she buy?

Plan and Solve

What strategy will you use? Strategy: Try, Check, and Revise

How to Try, Check, and Revise
Step 1 Think to make a reasonable first try.
Step 2 Check using the information given in the problem.
Step 3 Revise. Use your first try to make a reasonable second try. Check.
Step 4 Use previous tries to continue trying and checking until you get the answer.

Two beds are too much. I'll try one. Then I'll try 2 of the smaller items. I'll try leashes first.
$8 + $8 + $15 = $31
That's too high, but very close.
If I keep the bed, I need to come down $4 total or $2 for each item. I'll try the collars.
$6 + $6 + $15 = $27 That's it!

Answer: She bought two collars and one medium bed.

Look Back and Check

Is your work correct? Yes, the sum is $27 and there are two of one item and one of another item.

278

Talk About It

1. How do you know two beds are too much?
2. In the second try, what number was the same from the first try? What was changed?

When might you try, check, and revise?

Puppy Count There were 16 dogs in the veterinarian's office. There were three times as many adult dogs as puppies. How many adult dogs and how many puppies were in the office?

Solution
Try 5 puppies. Then 3 × 5 = 15 adult dogs. 5 + 15 = 20 That's too high.
Try 4 puppies. Then 3 × 4 = 12 adult dogs. 4 + 12 = 16 That's right!

When to Try, Check, and Revise
Think about using try, check, and revise when:
Some quantities are being combined to find a total.
• Sale items from the pet store
• Number of adult dogs and puppies
You do not know which or how many of the items are used to get the total.

Talk About It

3. Why would 6 puppies not have been a good number for the second try?

CHECK

Use the first try to help you make a second try. Finish solving the problem.

1. Ella's mom brought 24 cartons of orange and grape juice to the park. There were twice as many cartons of orange juice as there were of grape juice. How many of each kind did she bring?
Try 6 grape juice. Then, 2 × 6 = 12 orange juice. 6 + 12 = 18 That's too low.

2. In football, a team can score 2, 3, 6, 7, or 8 points. The bulldogs scored 3 times and had 13 points. How did they score their points?
Try 3 + 3 + 8 = 14. That's too high.

Section B Lesson 5-7 279

Predicting and Verifying

can help you with...

the problem-solving strategy, *Try, Check, and Revise.*

Reading Helps

Provides quick, memorable reminders that teach your students to recognize how reading skills and strategies connect with problem solving

Reading for Math Success

Reviews reading comprehension skills and strategies and provides a clear connection to appropriate math strategies

Problem-Solving Strategy

Uses explicit and systematic instruction to focus your students' thinking on exactly **"How"** and **"When"** to use specific problem solving strategies in math

Problem-Solving Skill

Includes lessons that reinforce the Writing in Math exercises by teaching your students specific techniques for Writing to Explain, Writing to Describe, and Writing to Compare

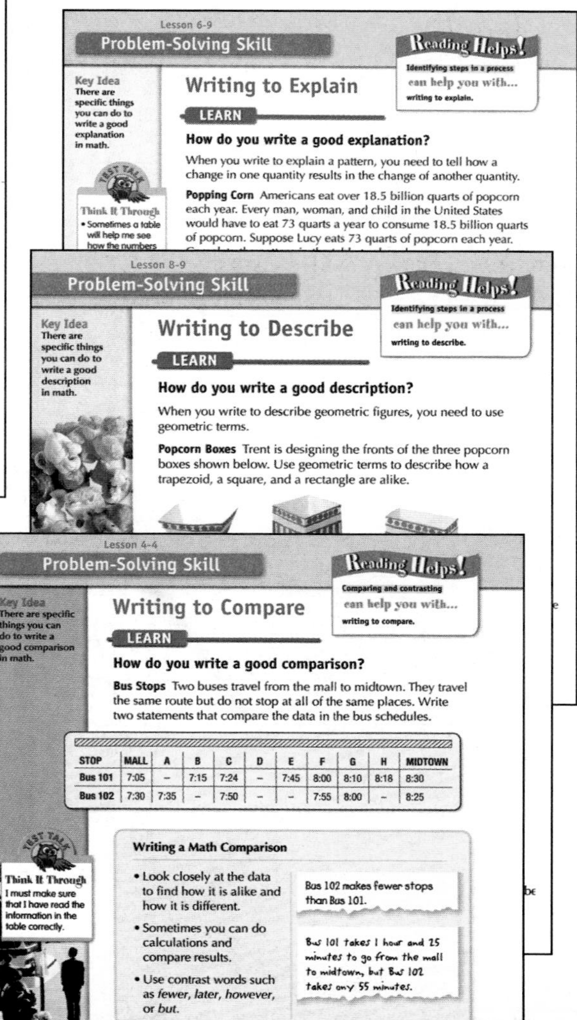

Lesson 6-9

Problem-Solving Skill

Key Idea
There are specific things you can do to write a good explanation in math.

Writing to Explain

Reading Helps! Identifying steps in a process can help you with... writing to explain.

LEARN

How do you write a good explanation?

When you write to explain a pattern, you need to tell how a change in one quantity results in the change of another quantity.

Popping Corn Americans eat over 18.5 billion quarts of popcorn each year. Every man, woman, and child in the United States would have to eat 73 quarts a year to consume 18.5 billion quarts of popcorn. Suppose Lucy eats 73 quarts of popcorn each year.

Think It Through
• Sometimes a table will help me see how the numbers

Lesson 8-9

Problem-Solving Skill

Key Idea
There are specific things you can do to write a good description in math.

Writing to Describe

Reading Helps! Identifying steps in a process can help you with... writing to describe.

LEARN

How do you write a good description?

When you write to describe geometric figures, you need to use geometric terms.

Popcorn Boxes Trent is designing the fronts of the three popcorn boxes shown below. Use geometric terms to describe how a trapezoid, a square, and a rectangle are alike.

Lesson 4-4

Problem-Solving Skill

Key Idea
There are specific things you can do to write a good comparison in math.

Writing to Compare

Reading Helps! Comparing and contrasting can help you with... writing to compare.

LEARN

How do you write a good comparison?

Bus Stops Two buses travel from the mall to midtown. They travel the same route but do not stop at all of the same places. Write two statements that compare the data in the bus schedules.

STOP	MALL	A	B	C	D	E	F	G	H	MIDTOWN
Bus 101	7:05	–	7:15	7:24	–	7:45	8:00	8:10	8:18	8:30
Bus 102	7:30	7:35	–	7:50	–	–	7:55	8:00	–	8:25

Think It Through
I must make sure that I have read the information in the table correctly.

Writing a Math Comparison

• Look closely at the data to find how it is alike and how it is different.
• Sometimes you can do calculations and compare results.
• Use contrast words such as *fewer, later, however,* or *but.*

Bus 102 makes fewer stops than Bus 101.

Bus 101 takes 1 hour and 25 minutes to go from the mall to midtown, but Bus 102 takes only 55 minutes.

Provides real-world applications

Our unique partnerships with Discovery Channel School™ and Dorling Kindersley provide your students with rich real-world applications that answer the common question: "When am I ever going to use this?"

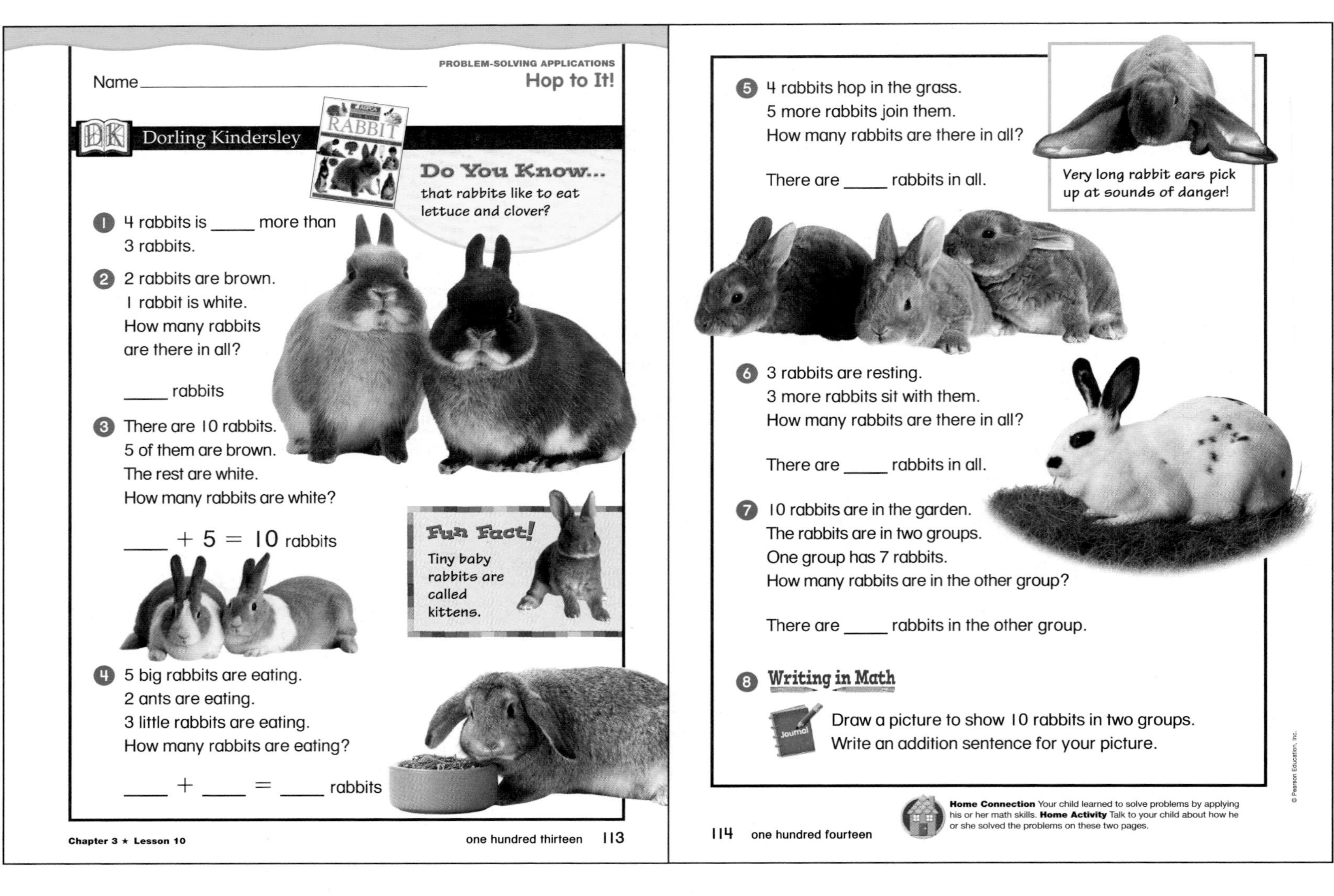
PROBLEM-SOLVING APPLICATIONS

Hop to It!

Name ____________________

Dorling Kindersley

Do You Know... that rabbits like to eat lettuce and clover?

1. 4 rabbits is _____ more than 3 rabbits.
2. 2 rabbits are brown. 1 rabbit is white. How many rabbits are there in all?

   _____ rabbits
3. There are 10 rabbits. 5 of them are brown. The rest are white. How many rabbits are white?

   ____ + 5 = 10 rabbits

Fun Fact! Tiny baby rabbits are called kittens.

4. 5 big rabbits are eating. 2 ants are eating. 3 little rabbits are eating. How many rabbits are eating?

   ____ + ____ = ____ rabbits

Chapter 3 ★ Lesson 10 — one hundred thirteen 113

5. 4 rabbits hop in the grass. 5 more rabbits join them. How many rabbits are there in all?

   There are _____ rabbits in all.

Very long rabbit ears pick up at sounds of danger!

6. 3 rabbits are resting. 3 more rabbits sit with them. How many rabbits are there in all?

   There are _____ rabbits in all.
7. 10 rabbits are in the garden. The rabbits are in two groups. One group has 7 rabbits. How many rabbits are in the other group?

   There are _____ rabbits in the other group.
8. **Writing in Math**

   Draw a picture to show 10 rabbits in two groups. Write an addition sentence for your picture.

Home Connection Your child learned to solve problems by applying his or her math skills. **Home Activity** Talk to your child about how he or she solved the problems on these two pages.

114 one hundred fourteen

© Pearson Education, Inc.

Problem-Solving Applications

Dorling Kindersley provides visually stunning ways for your students to see how math concepts apply to the world around them.

Math Leveled Literature Library also available!

TIMES TABLES!
Multiplication made fun
x2=
x3=
x4=
x5=
x6=
Wendy Clemson & David Clemson

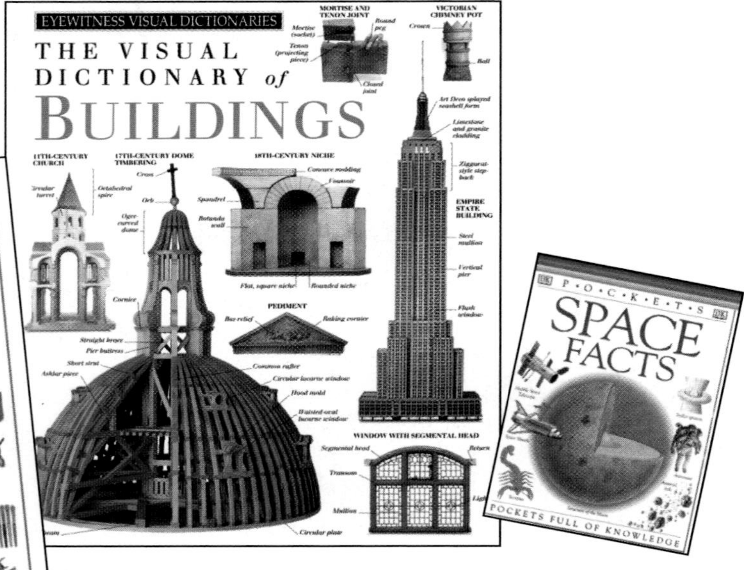

EYEWITNESS VISUAL DICTIONARIES
THE VISUAL DICTIONARY of BUILDINGS
POCKETS
SPACE FACTS
POCKETS FULL OF KNOWLEDGE

DK Literature Library

Engaging nonfiction books from Dorling Kindersley, the world-famous publisher of the DK Eyewitness Books, provide real-world, high-interest data for problem solving.

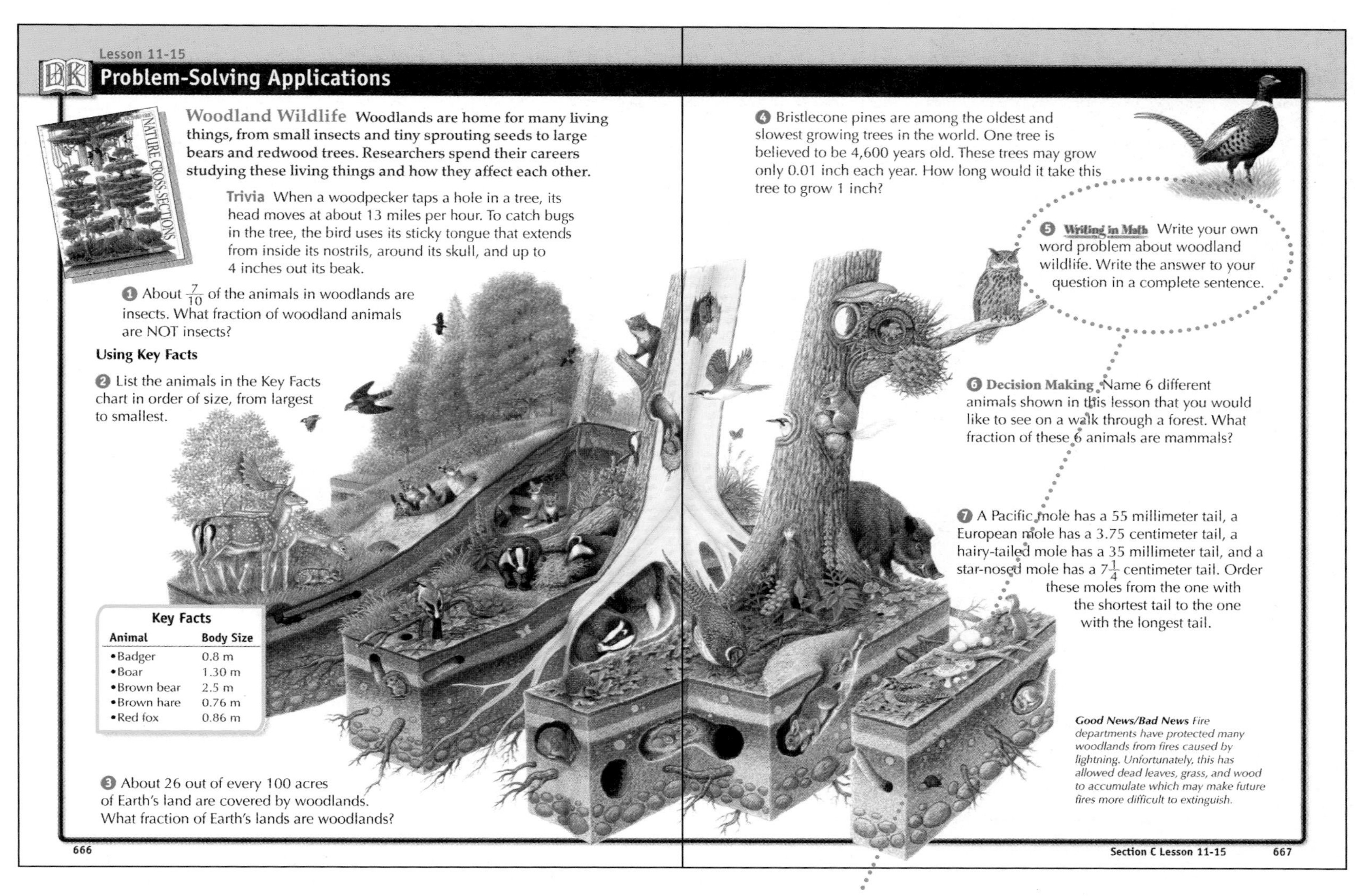

Lesson 11-15
Problem-Solving Applications
Woodland Wildlife Woodlands are home for many living things, from small insects and tiny sprouting seeds to large bears and redwood trees. Researchers spend their careers studying these living things and how they affect each other.
Trivia When a woodpecker taps a hole in a tree, its head moves at about 13 miles per hour. To catch bugs in the tree, the bird uses its sticky tongue that extends from inside its nostrils, around its skull, and up to 4 inches out its beak.
1 About 7/10 of the animals in woodlands are insects. What fraction of woodland animals are NOT insects?
Using Key Facts
2 List the animals in the Key Facts chart in order of size, from largest to smallest.
Key Facts
Animal Body Size
Badger 0.8 m
Boar 1.30 m
Brown bear 2.5 m
Brown hare 0.76 m
Red fox 0.86 m
3 About 26 out of every 100 acres of Earth's land are covered by woodlands. What fraction of Earth's lands are woodlands?
4 Bristlecone pines are among the oldest and slowest growing trees in the world. One tree is believed to be 4,600 years old. These trees may grow only 0.01 inch each year. How long would it take this tree to grow 1 inch?
5 Writing in Math Write your own word problem about woodland wildlife. Write the answer to your question in a complete sentence.
6 Decision Making Name 6 different animals shown in this lesson that you would like to see on a walk through a forest. What fraction of these 6 animals are mammals?
7 A Pacific mole has a 55 millimeter tail, a European mole has a 3.75 centimeter tail, a hairy-tailed mole has a 35 millimeter tail, and a star-nosed mole has a 7 1/4 centimeter tail. Order these moles from the one with the shortest tail to the one with the longest tail.
Good News/Bad News Fire departments have protected many woodlands from fires caused by lightning. Unfortunately, this has allowed dead leaves, grass, and wood to accumulate which may make future fires more difficult to extinguish.
666
Section C Lesson 11-15 667

Writing in Math

Gives your students a chance to explain their thinking and improve their writing skills and helps them become better problem solvers

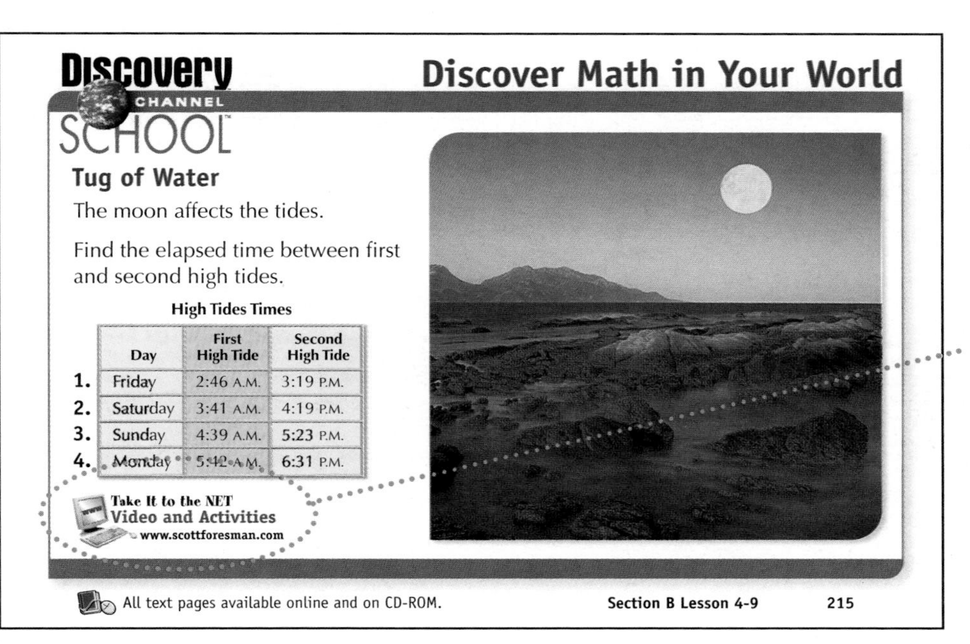

Discovery Channel School™
Tug of Water
The moon affects the tides.
Find the elapsed time between first and second high tides.
High Tides Times
Day | First High Tide | Second High Tide
1. Friday 2:46 A.M. 3:19 P.M.
2. Saturday 3:41 A.M. 4:19 P.M.
3. Sunday 4:39 A.M. 5:23 P.M.
4. Monday 5:42 A.M. 6:31 P.M.

Helps your students discover math in their world with engaging real-world applications in every chapter

Take It to the NET

Shows your students how math connects to the world outside the classroom with online real-world video links from Discovery Channel School

The SCOTT FORESMAN Difference

We meet the needs of all teachers.

Teachers need help simplifying the planning and instruction process and saving time. Every program offers teacher resources and classroom support for their materials. But our program is different.

Teaches important content before the test

Exclusive daily warm-up activities in Pacing for Test Success cover all the important content in later chapters and prepare your students for test success.

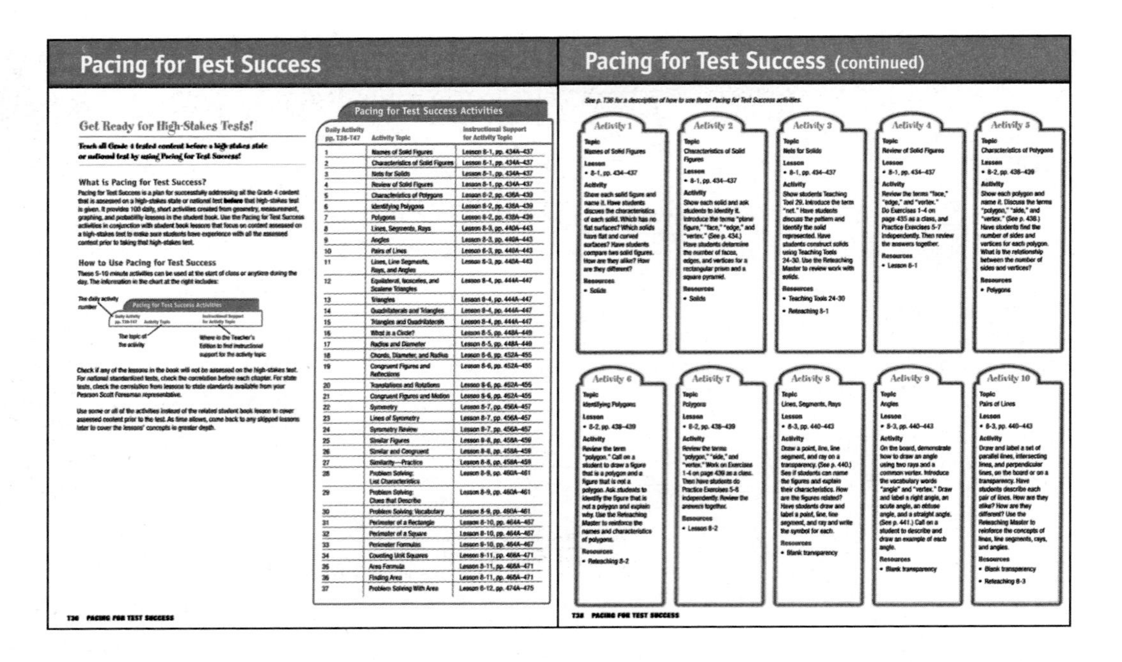
Pacing for Test Success

Get Ready for High-Stakes Tests!

What Is Pacing for Test Success?

How to Use Pacing for Test Success

Pacing for Test Success Activities

Pacing for Test Success (continued)

Simplifies the planning process

Everything you need to create effective lessons is organized into an easy-to-read Lesson Planner. From ongoing assessment opportunities to Student Edition resources, you'll always be completely prepared for every lesson.

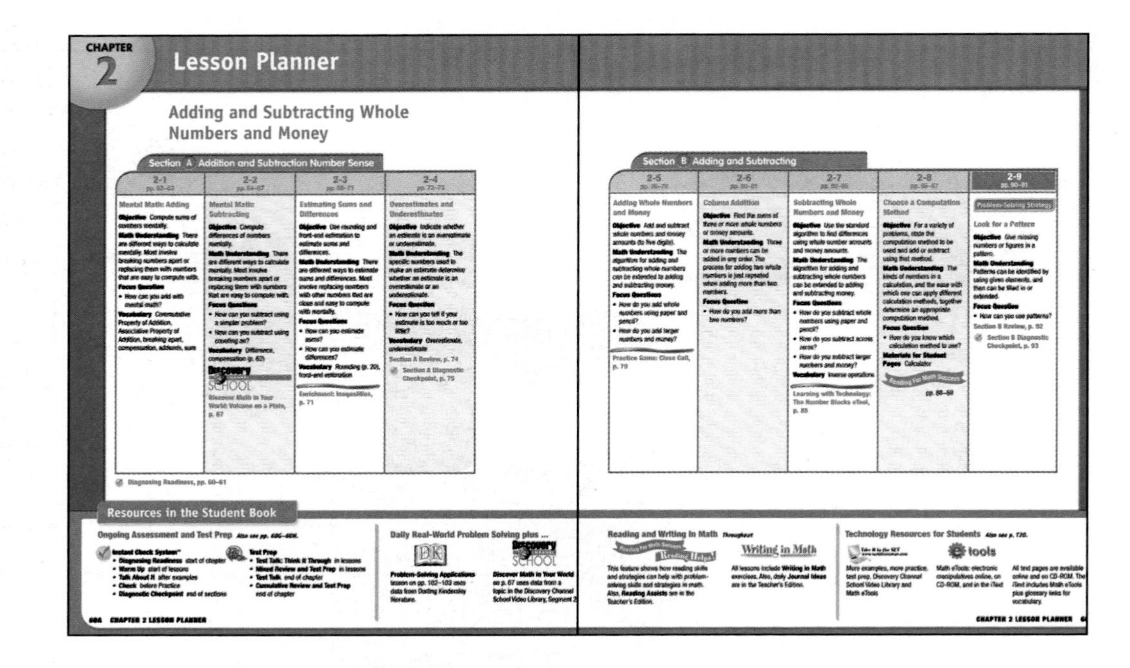
CHAPTER 2

Lesson Planner

Adding and Subtracting Whole Numbers and Money

Section A Addition and Subtraction Number Sense

Section B Adding and Subtracting

Resources in the Student Book

Reaches all learners with differentiated instruction options

Customize your instruction to meet the individual needs of all your students. Research-based suggestions for approaching lessons allow you to reach every child effectively and individually.

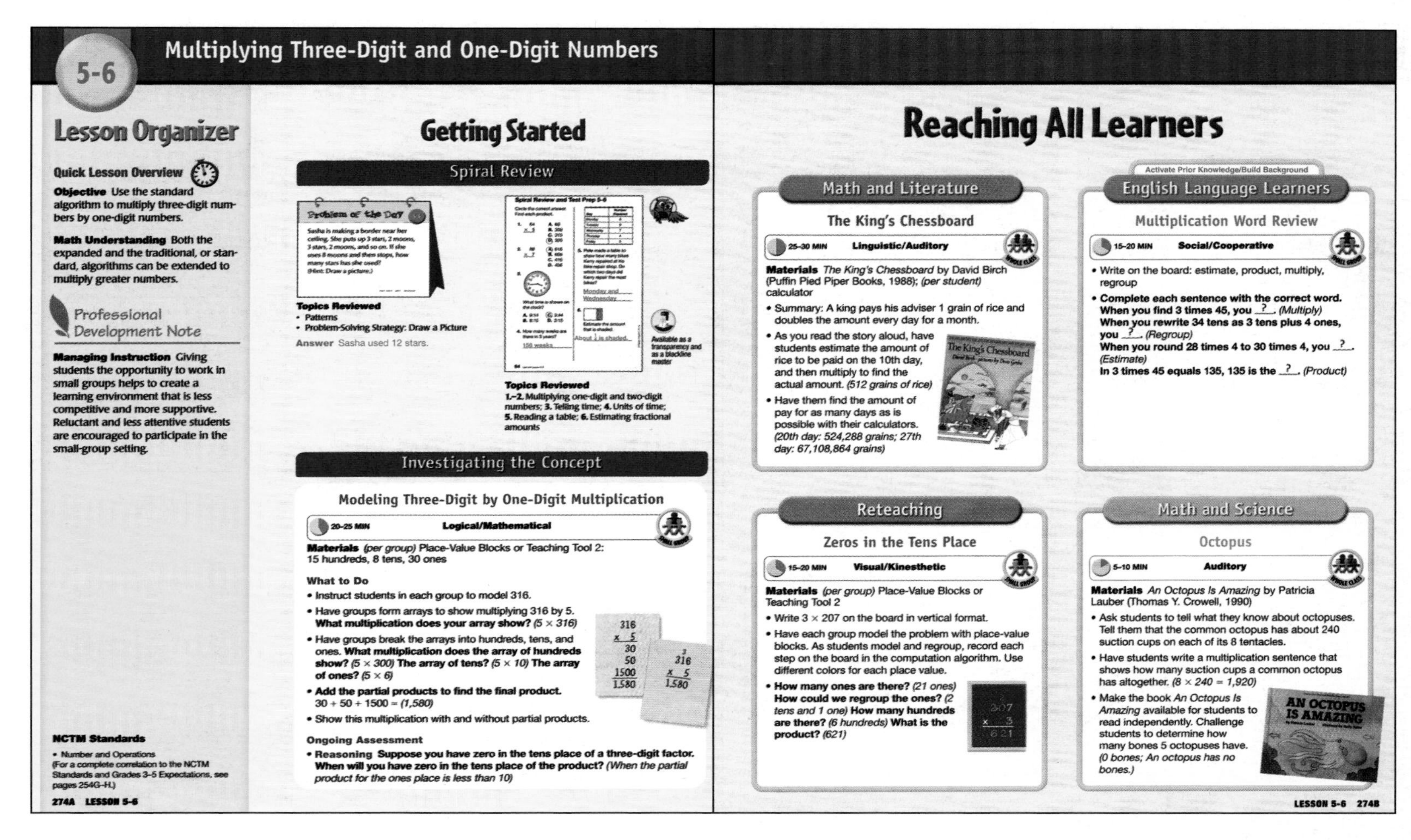

5-6 Multiplying Three-Digit and One-Digit Numbers

Lesson Organizer

Quick Lesson Overview

Objective Use the standard algorithm to multiply three-digit numbers by one-digit numbers.

Math Understanding Both the expanded and the traditional, or standard, algorithms can be extended to multiply greater numbers.

Professional Development Note

Managing Instruction Giving students the opportunity to work in small groups helps to create a learning environment that is less competitive and more supportive. Reluctant and less attentive students are encouraged to participate in the small-group setting.

NCTM Standards

- Number and Operations

(For a complete correlation to the NCTM Standards and Grades 3–5 Expectations, see pages 254G–H.)

274A LESSON 5-6

Getting Started

Spiral Review

Problem of the Day

Sasha is making a border near her ceiling. She puts up 3 stars, 2 moons, 3 stars, 2 moons, and so on. If she uses 8 moons and then stops, how many stars has she used? (Hint: Draw a picture.)

Topics Reviewed
- Patterns
- Problem-Solving Strategy: Draw a Picture

Answer Sasha used 12 stars.

Spiral Review and Test Prep 5-6

Available as a transparency and as a blackline master

Topics Reviewed

1.–2. Multiplying one-digit and two-digit numbers; **3.** Telling time; **4.** Units of time; **5.** Reading a table; **6.** Estimating fractional amounts

Investigating the Concept

Modeling Three-Digit by One-Digit Multiplication

20–25 MIN **Logical/Mathematical**

Materials *(per group)* Place-Value Blocks or Teaching Tool 2: 15 hundreds, 8 tens, 30 ones

What to Do
- Instruct students in each group to model 316.
- Have groups form arrays to show multiplying 316 by 5. **What multiplication does your array show?** *(5 × 316)*
- Have groups break the arrays into hundreds, tens, and ones. **What multiplication does the array of hundreds show?** *(5 × 300)* **The array of tens?** *(5 × 10)* **The array of ones?** *(5 × 6)*
- **Add the partial products to find the final product.** 30 + 50 + 1500 = *(1,580)*
- Show this multiplication with and without partial products.

316
× 5
30
50
1500
1,580

316
× 5
1,580

Ongoing Assessment
- **Reasoning Suppose you have zero in the tens place of a three-digit factor. When will you have zero in the tens place of the product?** *(When the partial product for the ones place is less than 10)*

Reaching All Learners

Math and Literature

The King's Chessboard

25–30 MIN **Linguistic/Auditory**

Materials *The King's Chessboard* by David Birch (Puffin Pied Piper Books, 1988); *(per student)* calculator
- Summary: A king pays his adviser 1 grain of rice and doubles the amount every day for a month.
- As you read the story aloud, have students estimate the amount of rice to be paid on the 10th day, and then multiply to find the actual amount. *(512 grains of rice)*
- Have them find the amount of pay for as many days as is possible with their calculators. *(20th day: 524,288 grains; 27th day: 67,108,864 grains)*

Activate Prior Knowledge/Build Background

English Language Learners

Multiplication Word Review

15–20 MIN **Social/Cooperative**
- Write on the board: estimate, product, multiply, regroup
- **Complete each sentence with the correct word.**
  When you find 3 times 45, you ___?___. *(Multiply)*
  When you rewrite 34 tens as 3 tens plus 4 ones, you ___?___. *(Regroup)*
  When you round 28 times 4 to 30 times 4, you ___?___. *(Estimate)*
  In 3 times 45 equals 135, 135 is the ___?___. *(Product)*

Reteaching

Zeros in the Tens Place

15–20 MIN **Visual/Kinesthetic**

Materials *(per group)* Place-Value Blocks or Teaching Tool 2
- Write 3 × 207 on the board in vertical format.
- Have each group model the problem with place-value blocks. As students model and regroup, record each step on the board in the computation algorithm. Use different colors for each place value.
- **How many ones are there?** *(21 ones)* **How could we regroup the ones?** *(2 tens and 1 one)* **How many hundreds are there?** *(6 hundreds)* **What is the product?** *(621)*

207
× 3
621

Math and Science

Octopus

5–10 MIN **Auditory**

Materials *An Octopus Is Amazing* by Patricia Lauber (Thomas Y. Crowell, 1990)
- Ask students to tell what they know about octopuses. Tell them that the common octopus has about 240 suction cups on each of its 8 tentacles.
- Have students write a multiplication sentence that shows how many suction cups a common octopus has altogether. *(8 × 240 = 1,920)*
- Make the book *An Octopus Is Amazing* available for students to read independently. Challenge students to determine how many bones 5 octopuses have. *(0 bones; An octopus has no bones.)*

LESSON 5-6 274B

Lesson Organizer

Quick lesson overviews include math objectives and understanding while Professional Development Notes improve your teaching methods

Getting Started

Includes daily suggestions for spiral review and investigating the concept

SCOTT FORESMAN • ADDISON WESLEY
Mathematics
Grade 4
Every Student Learns
With a forward by Dr. Jim Cummins

Reaching All Learners

Meet the diverse needs in your classroom with fun and stimulating activities that are easy to incorporate directly into your lesson plan

- Math Vocabulary
- Reading in Math
- Writing in Math
- Oral Language in Math
- Math and Literature
- English Language Learners
- Reteaching
- Math and Technology
- Advanced Learners
- Students with Special Needs
- Cross-Curriculum Connections

Every Student Learns

Lesson-specific suggestions help your students overcome language barriers to access math content

Teaching Support

Simplifies the instruction process

Our lessons include all the resources you need right at the point of use to help you keep all your lessons on track.

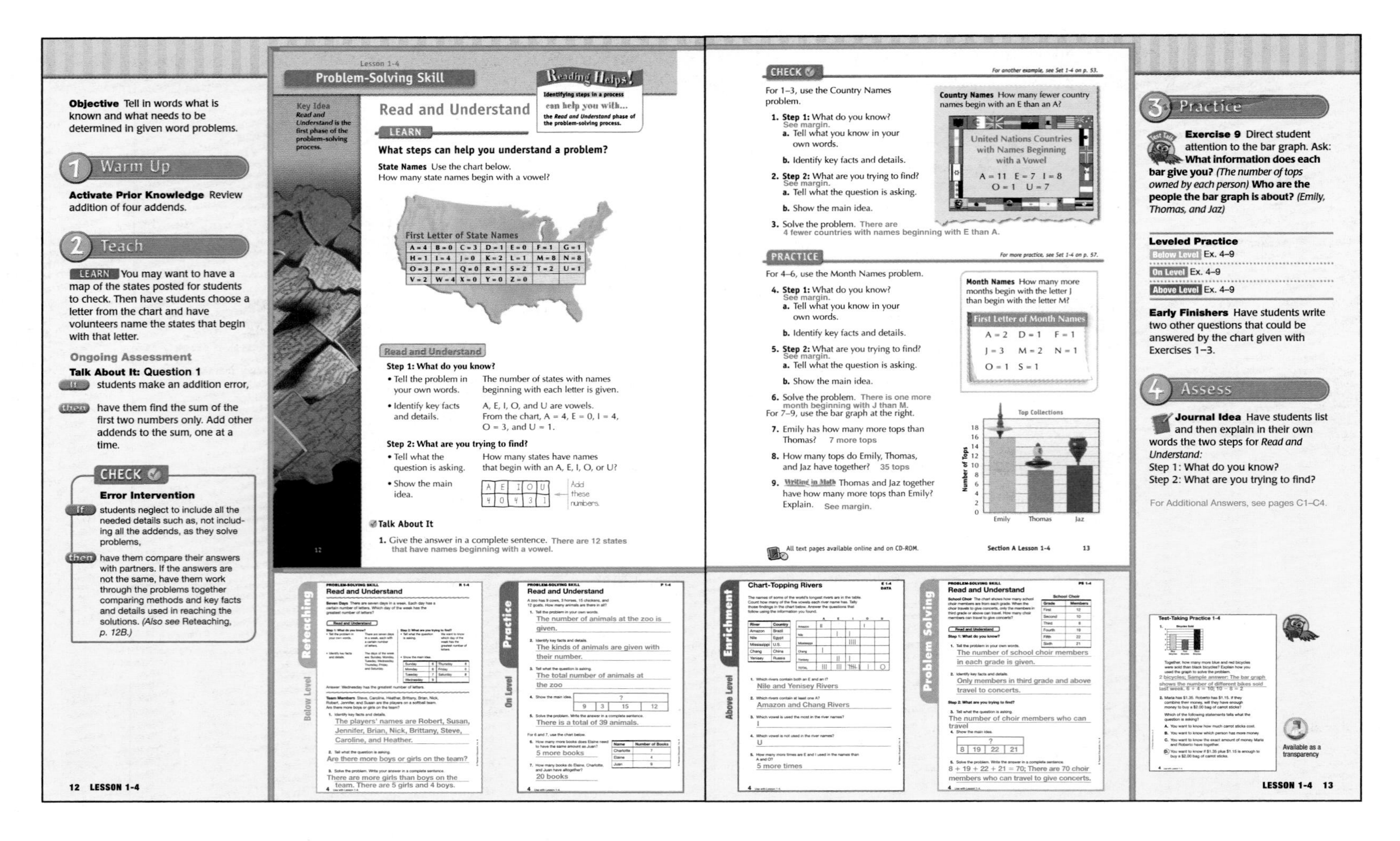

Objective Tell in words what is known and what needs to be determined in given word problems.

1 Warm Up

Activate Prior Knowledge Review addition of four addends.

2 Teach

LEARN You may want to have a map of the states posted for students to check. Then have students choose a letter from the chart and have volunteers name the states that begin with that letter.

Ongoing Assessment

Talk About It: Question 1

If students make an addition error, **then** have them find the sum of the first two numbers only. Add other addends to the sum, one at a time.

CHECK

Error Intervention

If students neglect to include all the needed details such as, not including all the addends, as they solve problems, **then** have them compare their answers with partners. If the answers are not the same, have them work through the problems together comparing methods and key facts and details used in reaching the solutions. *(Also see Reteaching, p. 12B.)*

Lesson 1-4

Problem-Solving Skill

Key Idea *Read and Understand* is the first phase of the problem-solving process.

Read and Understand

Reading Helps! Identifying steps in a process can help you with... the *Read and Understand* phase of the problem-solving process.

LEARN

What steps can help you understand a problem?

State Names Use the chart below. How many state names begin with a vowel?

First Letter of State Names

A = 4	B = 0	C = 3	D = 1	E = 0	F = 1	G = 1
H = 1	I = 4	J = 0	K = 2	L = 1	M = 8	N = 8
O = 3	P = 1	Q = 0	R = 1	S = 2	T = 2	U = 1
V = 2	W = 4	X = 0	Y = 0	Z = 0		

Read and Understand

Step 1: What do you know?

- Tell the problem in your own words. — The number of states with names beginning with each letter is given.
- Identify key facts and details. — A, E, I, O, and U are vowels. From the chart, A = 4, E = 0, I = 4, O = 3, and U = 1.

Step 2: What are you trying to find?

- Tell what the question is asking. — How many states have names that begin with an A, E, I, O, or U?
- Show the main idea. — A E I O U / 4 0 4 3 1 — Add these numbers.

Talk About It

1. Give the answer in a complete sentence. There are 12 states that have names beginning with a vowel.

12

CHECK For another example, see Set 1-4 on p. 53.

For 1–3, use the Country Names problem.

Country Names How many fewer country names begin with an E than an A?

United Nations Countries with Names Beginning with a Vowel: A = 11, E = 7, I = 8, O = 1, U = 7

1. **Step 1:** What do you know? See margin.
   a. Tell what you know in your own words.
   b. Identify key facts and details.
2. **Step 2:** What are you trying to find? See margin.
   a. Tell what the question is asking.
   b. Show the main idea.
3. Solve the problem. There are 4 fewer countries with names beginning with E than A.

PRACTICE For more practice, see Set 1-4 on p. 57.

For 4–6, use the Month Names problem.

Month Names How many more months begin with the letter J than begin with the letter M?

First Letter of Month Names: A = 2, D = 1, F = 1, J = 3, M = 2, N = 1, O = 1, S = 1

4. **Step 1:** What do you know? See margin.
   a. Tell what you know in your own words.
   b. Identify key facts and details.
5. **Step 2:** What are you trying to find? See margin.
   a. Tell what the question is asking.
   b. Show the main idea.
6. Solve the problem. There is one more month beginning with J than M.

For 7–9, use the bar graph at the right.

7. Emily has how many more tops than Thomas? 7 more tops
8. How many tops do Emily, Thomas, and Jaz have together? 35 tops
9. **Writing in Math** Thomas and Jaz together have how many more tops than Emily? Explain. See margin.

Top Collections (Number of Tops: Emily, Thomas, Jaz)

All text pages available online and on CD-ROM. Section A Lesson 1-4 13

3 Practice

Exercise 9 Direct student attention to the bar graph. Ask: **What information does each bar give you?** *(The number of tops owned by each person)* **Who are the people the bar graph is about?** *(Emily, Thomas, and Jaz)*

Leveled Practice

Below Level Ex. 4–9

On Level Ex. 4–9

Above Level Ex. 4–9

Early Finishers Have students write two other questions that could be answered by the chart given with Exercises 1–3.

4 Assess

Journal Idea Have students list and then explain in their own words the two steps for *Read and Understand:*

Step 1: What do you know?

Step 2: What are you trying to find?

For Additional Answers, see pages C1–C4.

Reteaching — Below Level: Read and Understand

Practice — On Level: Read and Understand

Enrichment — Above Level: Chart-Topping Rivers

Problem Solving: Read and Understand

Test-Taking Practice 1-4

Available as a transparency

12 LESSON 1-4 — LESSON 1-4 13

Four manageable and familiar steps

1 Warm Up

Helps you activate prior knowledge

2 Teach

Suggests how to introduce the math concept, assess your students, and intervene if necessary

3 Practice

Uses leveled exercises to help you reach every student in your classroom

4 Assess

Provides specific strategies for checking your students' understanding before moving on

Ongoing Assessment

Provides multiple checkpoints in each lesson with immediate intervention for your students who may be struggling with the concept

Blackline Masters

Leveled Practice and Problem-Solving blackline masters are shown right at the point of use along with the Test-Taking Practice Transparencies.

Supports professional development every day

We include the professional development resources you need to be more effective and successful in the classroom, no matter what your experience level may be.

Successful Beginnings

Professional Development Needs Assessment

Shows your school how to interpret student achievement test scores, assess staff development needs, and implement a professional development program that incorporates research-based best practices

On-Site Inservice

Occurs at the beginning of the school year to introduce the program philosophy and explain the Teacher's Edition and program components

Chapter Facilitator Guides

Provides workshop or discussion-group leaders the support they need on content and instruction for every chapter

In the Teacher's Edition

Professional Development

Appears at the beginning of each chapter and includes a Skills Trace as well as Math Background and Teaching Tips for each section in the chapter

Professional Development Note

Provides insights for every lesson, every day, on Math Background, How Children Learn Math, Effective Questioning Techniques, Managing Instruction, or Research Base

Professional Development Note

Managing Instruction Giving students the opportunity to work in small groups helps to create a learning environment that is less competitive and more supportive. Reluctant and less attentive students are encouraged to participate in the small-group setting.

Ongoing Professional Development

Professional Development Series

Contains a set of three modules with videos of real classroom lessons and all the resources necessary for presenting a two- to three-hour workshop on specific math content or for doing independent study

Math Across the Grades

Gives you more in-depth math background for every strand

★ Look for **LessonLab BreakThrough™ Professional Development** on page T20.

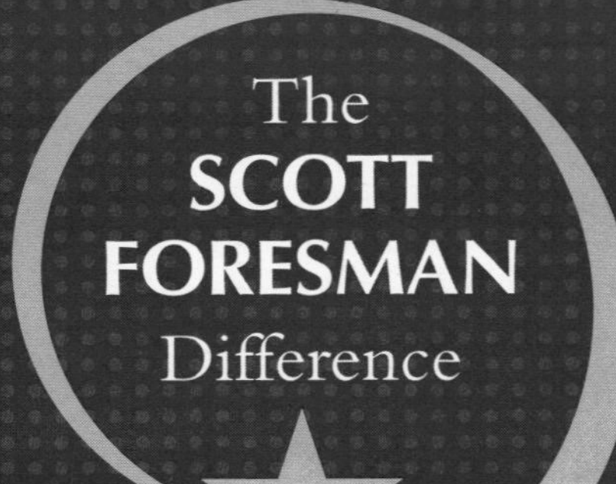
The
SCOTT
FORESMAN
Difference

We offer integrated technology solutions.

Technology is not only changing the nature of mathematics, it also is changing students' needs for success in the 21st century. Most math programs feature technology. But our program is different.

Integrates technology with curriculum

We bring technology and curriculum together, providing technology solutions for all students, teachers, and parents that directly improve student learning and increase test success.

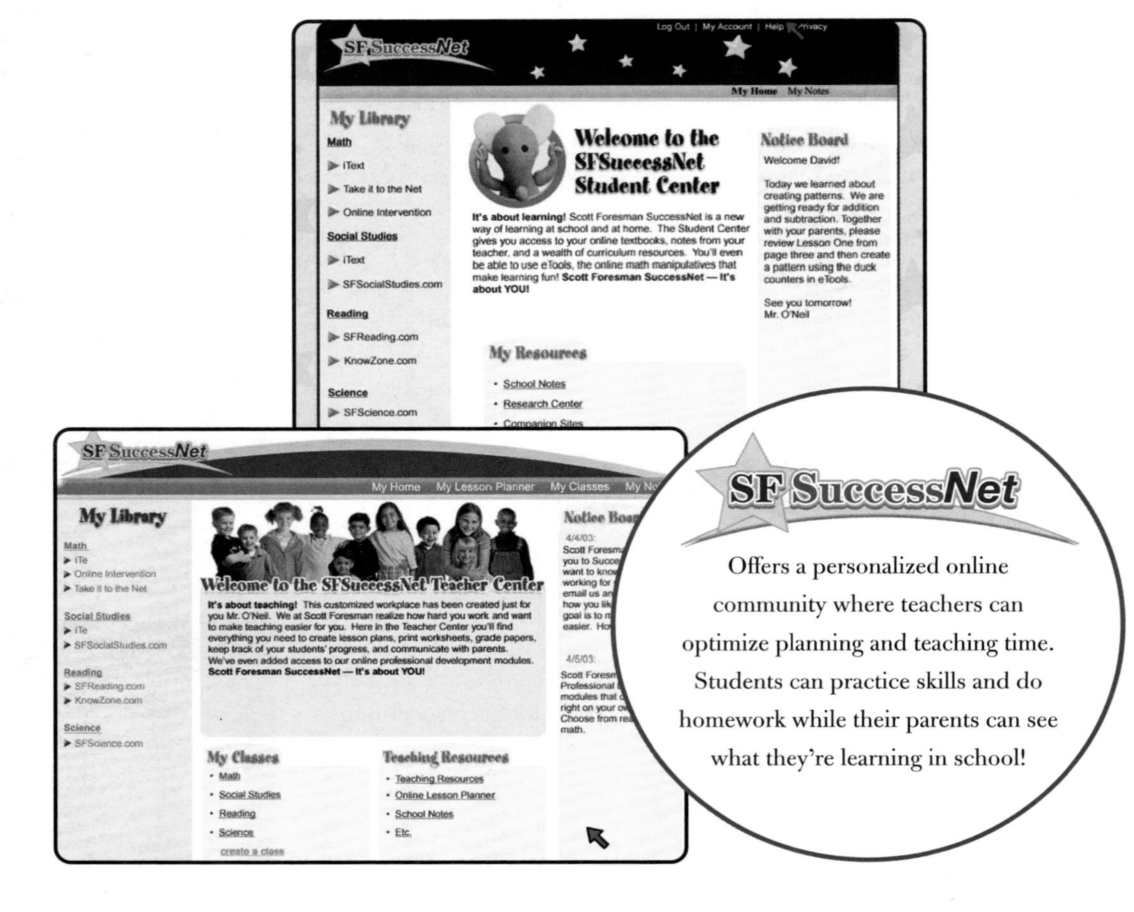
SF SuccessNet
Welcome to the SFSuccessNet Student Center
My Library
Notice Board
My Resources
Welcome to the SFSuccessNet Teacher Center
My Classes
Teaching Resources
SF SuccessNet
Offers a personalized online community where teachers can optimize planning and teaching time. Students can practice skills and do homework while their parents can see what they're learning in school!

Professional Development

Professional Development Series

Enables you to grow as an educator and help all your students succeed with videos that show flexible ways to implement research-based best practices for instruction

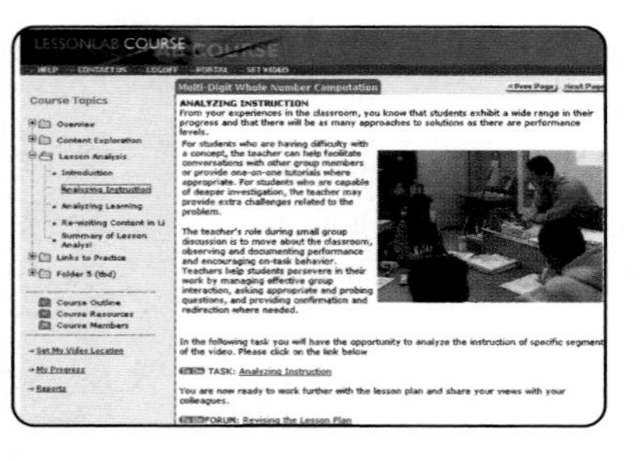

LessonLab BreakThrough™ Professional Development

Utilizes cutting-edge, interactive, online technology to provide facilitated professional development designed exclusively for our program

Teach and assess efficiently with versatile resources

Our technology options make it easy for you to monitor your students' progress and provide each of them with individualized intervention.

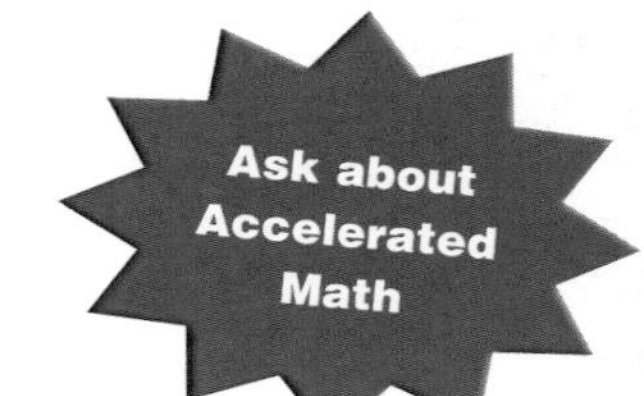

Teacher Resources

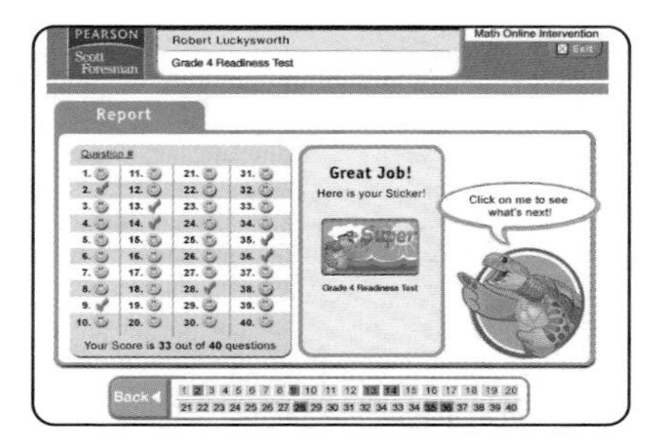

Math Online Intervention

Helps diagnose your entire class with online diagnostic tests that assess every student and prescribe individualized intervention with reports to monitor adequate yearly progress

Student Resources

Scott Foresman's Web Site "Take It to the NET"

Provides your students with access to more examples, more practice, test prep, videos, and Math eTools tied directly to their lessons

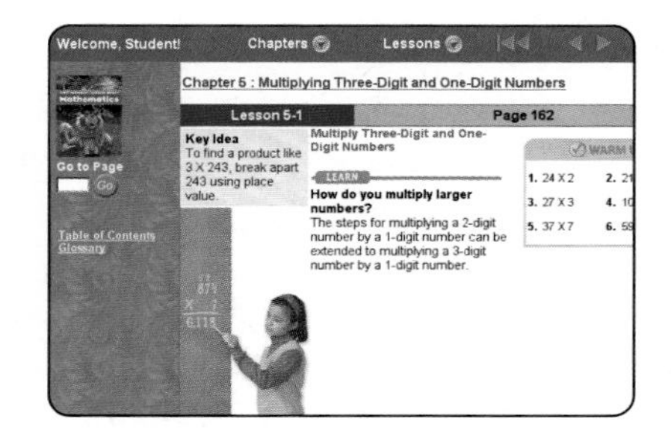

Online Student Edition

Gives your students easy access to their textbooks online or on CD-ROM from any home computer—a great solution to heavy backpacks!

Online Teacher's Edition

Provides complete access to your entire Teacher's Edition, an online lesson planner, and selected ancillary pdf files online or on CD-ROM

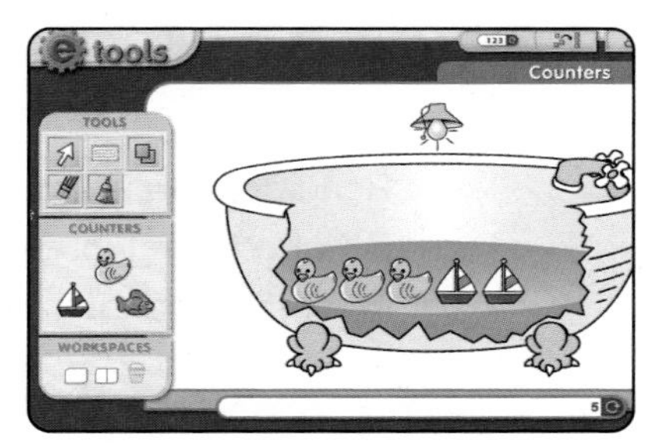

Math eTools

Helps your students grasp difficult math concepts with electronic manipulatives and software tools online or on CD-ROM

Discovery Channel School™ Video Library

Engages your students with online, CD-ROM, or videocassette segments for every chapter in the Student Edition, helping them discover math in their world

ExamView® Test Generator

Allows you to create and print customized tests quickly and easily with varied questions and test formats that assess your students' math understanding of key concepts and skills

MindPoint™ Quiz Show CD-ROM

Uses multiple-choice questions in a fun format to give your students additional math practice

Digital Learning CD-ROM powered by KnowledgeBox®

Supplies an interactive, completely customizable, educational multimedia center where your students can play games, watch videos, take tutorials, or participate in sing-alongs

Components

Teaching for Understanding

Pre-K Program (Pre-K)
Student Big Book (K)
Student Edition Chapter Booklets (K)
Student Edition (K–6)
Practice Masters/Workbook (K–6)
Reteaching Masters/Workbook (1–6)
Enrichment Masters/Workbook (K–6)
Homework Workbook (1–6)
Instant Check Mat (K–6)
Workmats (K–2)
Assessment Sourcebook (K–6)
Test-Taking Practice Transparencies (1–6)
Spiral Review and Test Prep Masters/Workbook (1–6)
Spiral Review and Test Prep Transparencies (1–6)
Math Diagnosis and Intervention System (K–6)
SAT 9/10 Practice and Test Prep (1–6)
TerraNova Practice and Test Prep (1–6)
ITBS Practice and Test Prep (3–6)
Benchmark Tests (3–6)
Review from Last Year Masters (1–6)

Problem-Solving Connections

Problem-Solving Masters/Workbook (1–6)
Problem of the Day Transparencies/Flip Chart (K–6)
Math Vocabulary Kit (K–6)
Discovery Channel School™ Masters/Videos (1–6)
Read-Together Math Stories Big Books (K–2)
DK Literature Library (Pre-K–6)
Math Leveled Literature Library (K–6)

Teaching Support

Teacher's Edition (Pre-K–6)
Teaching Tool Masters (K–6)
Every Student Learns (K–6)
Home-School Connection (K–6)
Chapter File Folders (K–6)
Classroom Manipulatives Kit (Pre-K–6)
Overhead Manipulatives Kit (K–6)
Solution Manual (3–6)
Student Magnetic Manipulatives Kit (K–6)
Teacher Magnetic Manipulatives Kit (K–2)
Math Games (K–6)
Calendar Time Kit (K–5)
Professional Development Series (K–6)
Chapter Facilitator Guide (K–6)
Math Across the Grades (K–Algebra)

Technology

SuccessNet Portal (K–6)
Math eTools (Pre-K–6)
Digital Learning CD-ROM
powered by KnowledgeBox® (1–6)
Online Student Edition (1–6)
MindPoint™ Quiz Show (1–6)
Discovery Channel School™ Video Library (1–6)
www.scottforesman.com (K–6)
Online Teacher's Edition (K–6)
LessonLab's BreakThrough™ Mathematics (K–6)
Professional Development Series (K–6)
Math Online Intervention (1–6)
ExamView® Test Generator (1–6)

Table of Contents

Volume 1: Chapters 1-3

Volume 2: Chapters 4-6

Volume 3: Chapters 7-9

Volume 4: Chapters 10-12

** Shown in Volumes 1-4 of the Teacher's Edition*

*** Shown in Volume 1 of the Teacher's Edition*

Pacing Guide

The pacing suggested below assumes one day for most lessons plus time for assessment for a total of 180 days.
You may need to adjust pacing to meet the needs of your students and your district curriculum.

- Chapter 1 ..... 16 days
- Chapter 2 ..... 16 days
- Chapter 3 ..... 11 days
- Chapter 4 ..... 10 days
- Chapter 5 ..... 19 days
- Chapter 6 ..... 12 days
- Chapter 7 ..... 14 days
- Chapter 8 ..... 20 days
- Chapter 9 ..... 12 days
- Chapter 10 ..... 22 days
- Chapter 11 ..... 15 days
- Chapter 12 ..... 13 days

CHAPTER 1

Table of Contents

Patterns and Readiness for Addition and Subtraction

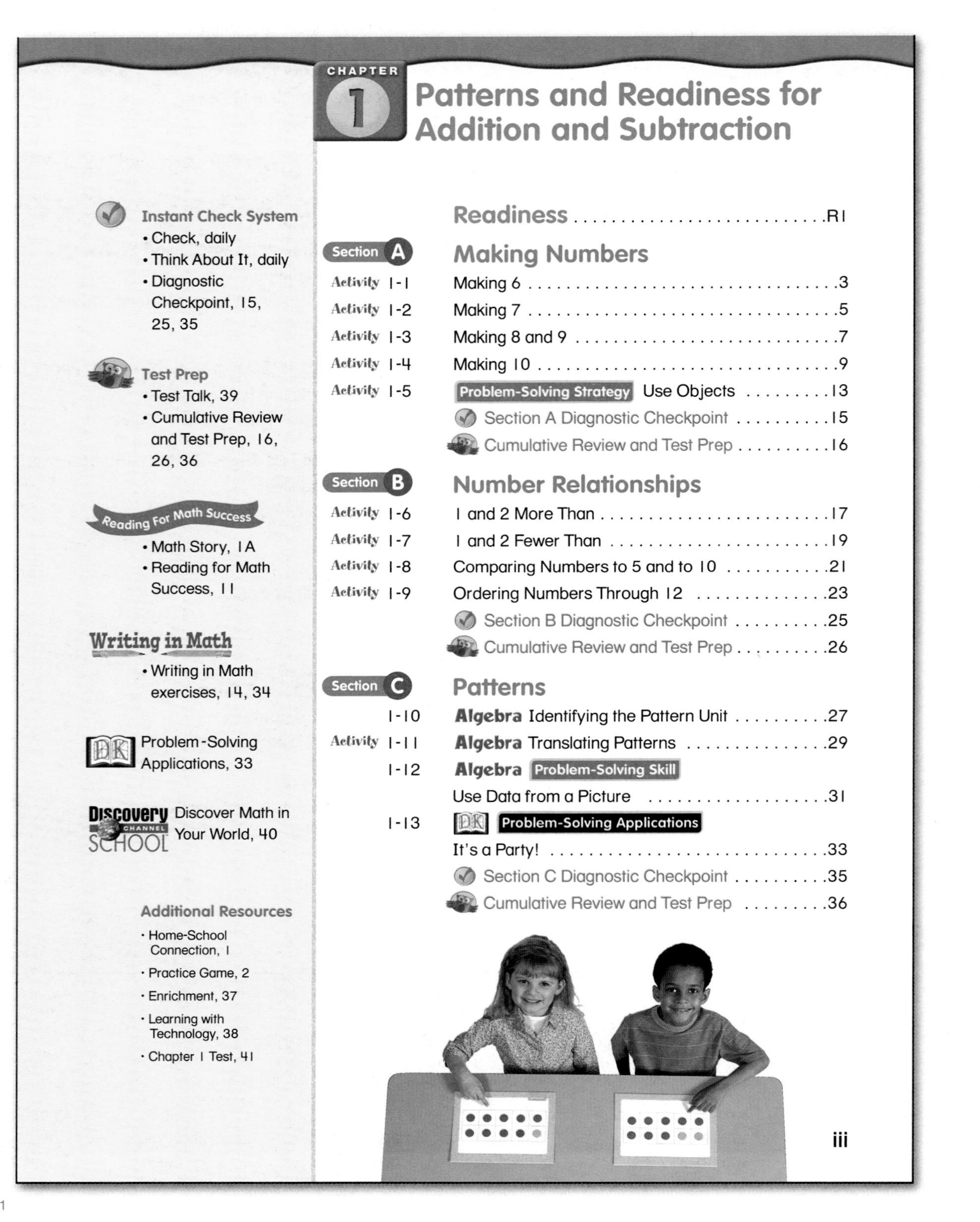

CHAPTER 1

Patterns and Readiness for Addition and Subtraction

Instant Check System
- Check, daily
- Think About It, daily
- Diagnostic Checkpoint, 15, 25, 35

Test Prep
- Test Talk, 39
- Cumulative Review and Test Prep, 16, 26, 36

Reading For Math Success
- Math Story, 1A
- Reading for Math Success, 11

Writing in Math
- Writing in Math exercises, 14, 34

DK Problem-Solving Applications, 33

Discovery Channel School: Discover Math in Your World, 40

Additional Resources
- Home-School Connection, 1
- Practice Game, 2
- Enrichment, 37
- Learning with Technology, 38
- Chapter 1 Test, 41

iii

EC NTL 12 11 10 9 8 7 6 5 4 3 2 1

CHAPTER 2

Table of Contents

Understanding Addition and Subtraction

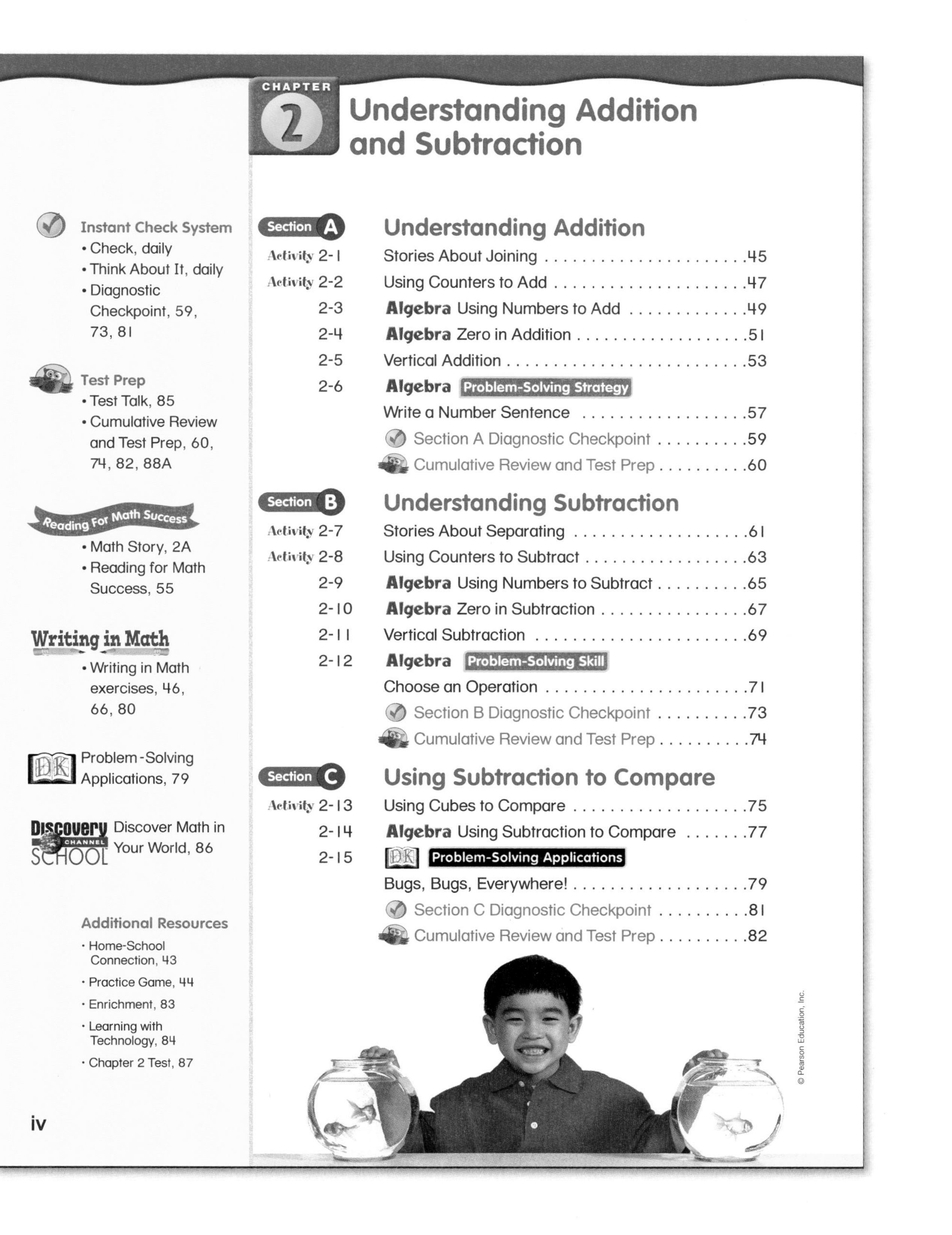

CHAPTER 2

Understanding Addition and Subtraction

Instant Check System
- Check, daily
- Think About It, daily
- Diagnostic Checkpoint, 59, 73, 81

Test Prep
- Test Talk, 85
- Cumulative Review and Test Prep, 60, 74, 82, 88A

Reading For Math Success
- Math Story, 2A
- Reading for Math Success, 55

Writing in Math
- Writing in Math exercises, 46, 66, 80

DK Problem-Solving Applications, 79

Discovery Channel School Discover Math in Your World, 86

Additional Resources
- Home-School Connection, 43
- Practice Game, 44
- Enrichment, 83
- Learning with Technology, 84
- Chapter 2 Test, 87

iv

CHAPTER 3

Table of Contents

Strategies for Addition Facts to 12

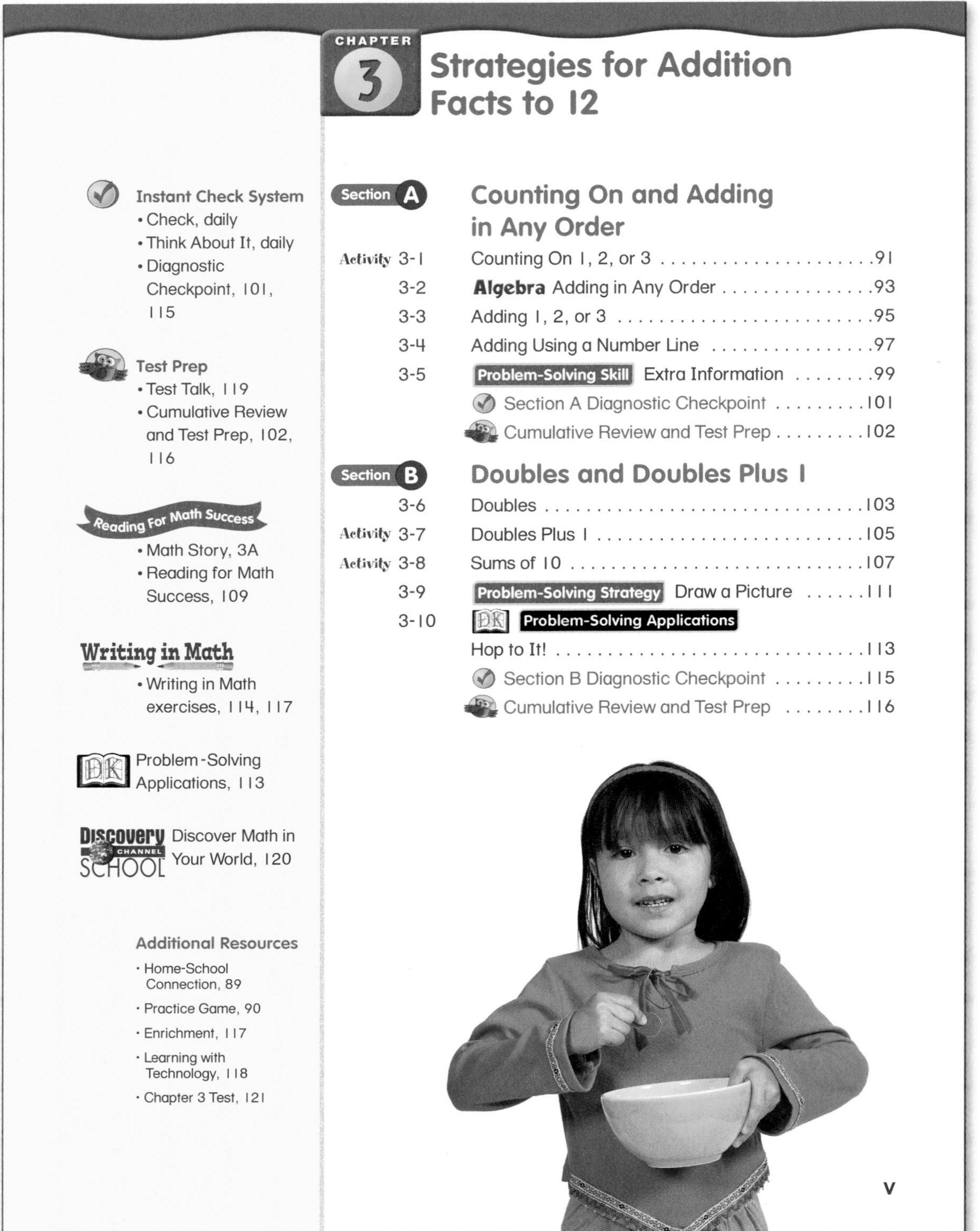

CHAPTER 3

Strategies for Addition Facts to 12

Instant Check System
- Check, daily
- Think About It, daily
- Diagnostic Checkpoint, 101, 115

Test Prep
- Test Talk, 119
- Cumulative Review and Test Prep, 102, 116

Reading For Math Success
- Math Story, 3A
- Reading for Math Success, 109

Writing in Math
- Writing in Math exercises, 114, 117

DK Problem-Solving Applications, 113

Discovery Channel School Discover Math in Your World, 120

Additional Resources
- Home-School Connection, 89
- Practice Game, 90
- Enrichment, 117
- Learning with Technology, 118
- Chapter 3 Test, 121

v

Table of Contents

Strategies for Subtraction Facts to 12

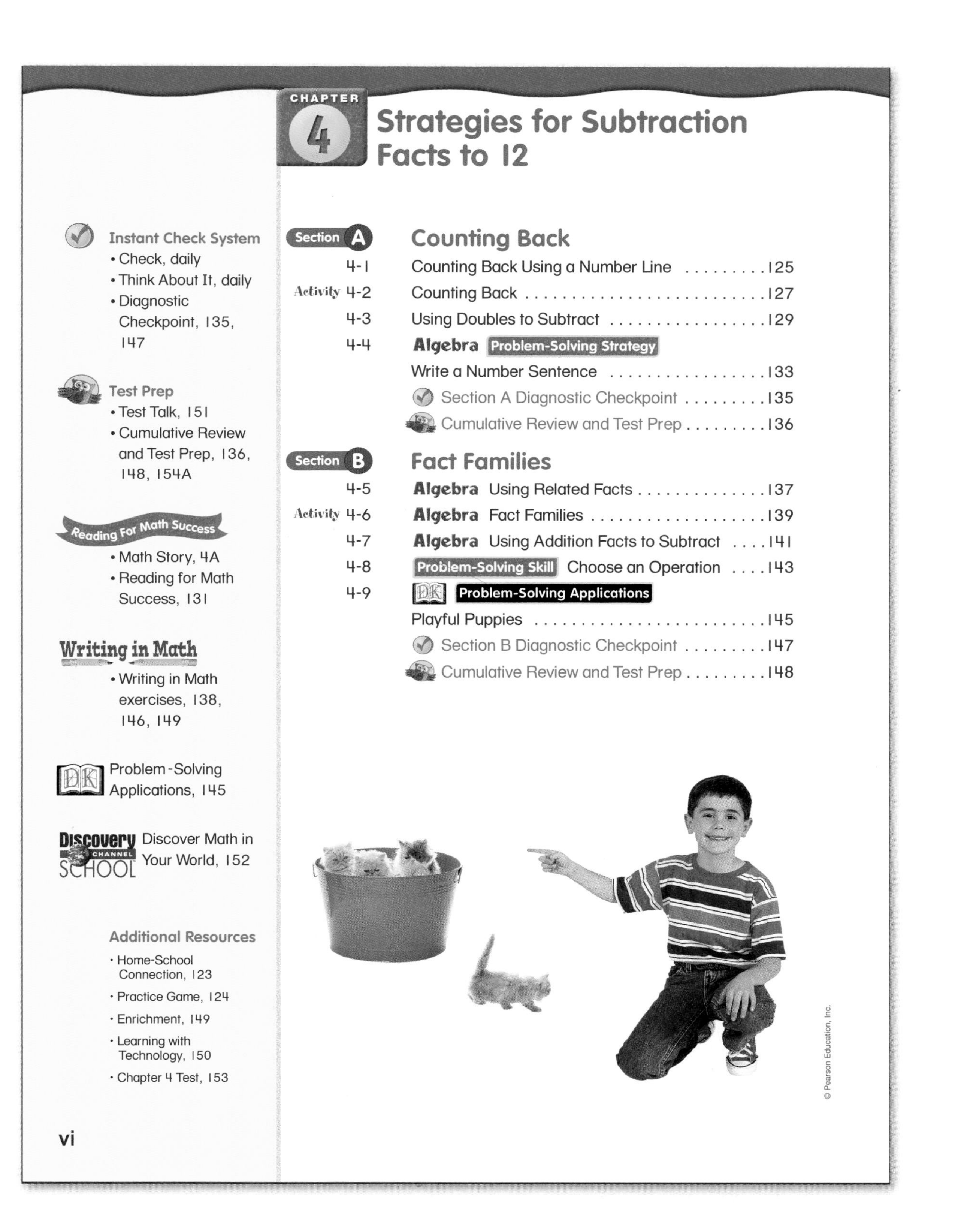

CHAPTER 4

Strategies for Subtraction Facts to 12

Instant Check System
- Check, daily
- Think About It, daily
- Diagnostic Checkpoint, 135, 147

Test Prep
- Test Talk, 151
- Cumulative Review and Test Prep, 136, 148, 154A

Reading For Math Success
- Math Story, 4A
- Reading for Math Success, 131

Writing in Math
- Writing in Math exercises, 138, 146, 149

Problem-Solving Applications, 145

Discovery Channel School Discover Math in Your World, 152

Additional Resources
- Home-School Connection, 123
- Practice Game, 124
- Enrichment, 149
- Learning with Technology, 150
- Chapter 4 Test, 153

vi

Table of Contents

Geometry and Fractions

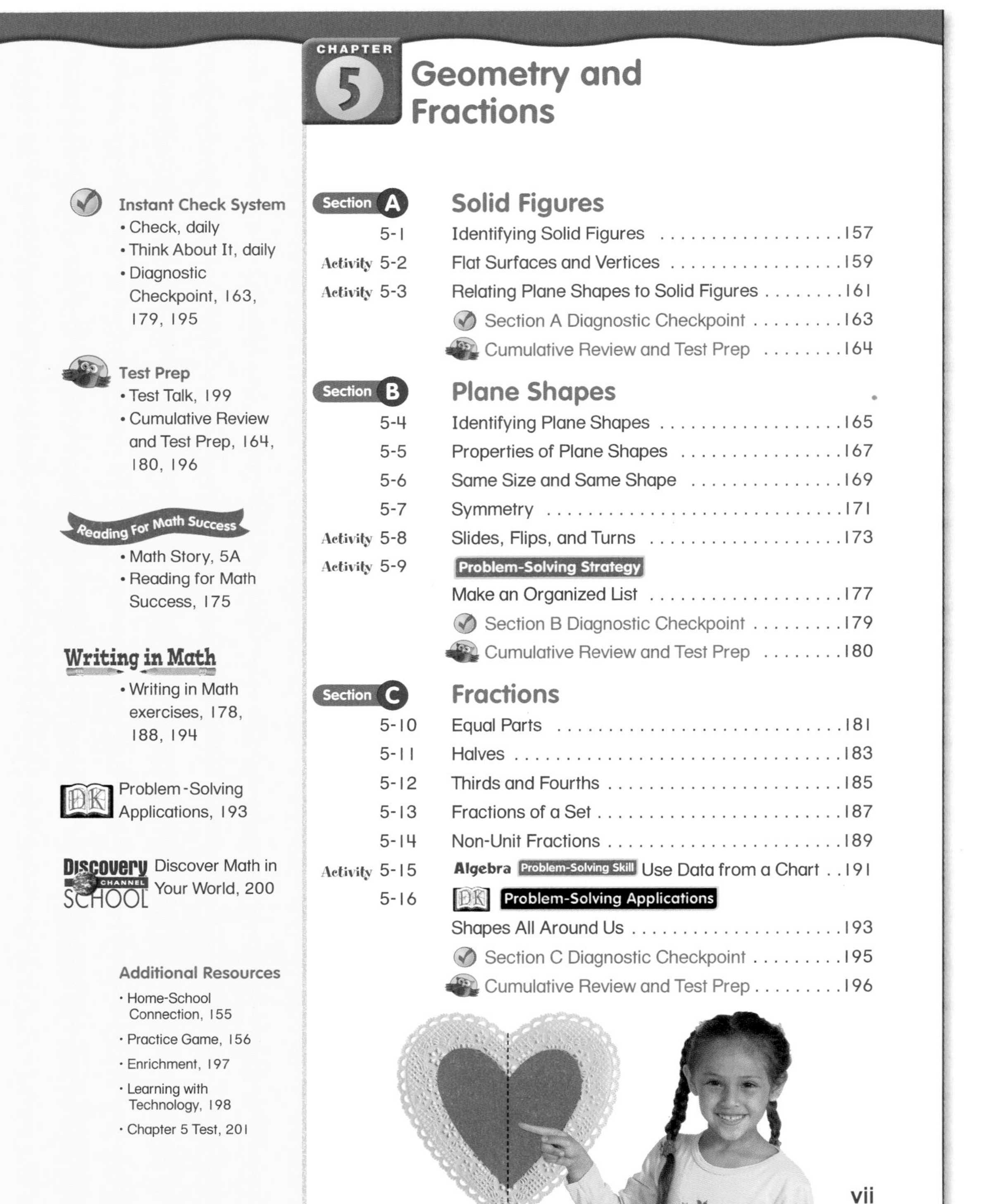

CHAPTER 5

Geometry and Fractions

Instant Check System
- Check, daily
- Think About It, daily
- Diagnostic Checkpoint, 163, 179, 195

Test Prep
- Test Talk, 199
- Cumulative Review and Test Prep, 164, 180, 196

Reading For Math Success
- Math Story, 5A
- Reading for Math Success, 175

Writing in Math
- Writing in Math exercises, 178, 188, 194

DK Problem-Solving Applications, 193

Discovery Channel School Discover Math in Your World, 200

Additional Resources
- Home-School Connection, 155
- Practice Game, 156
- Enrichment, 197
- Learning with Technology, 198
- Chapter 5 Test, 201

vii

CHAPTER 6 Table of Contents

Time

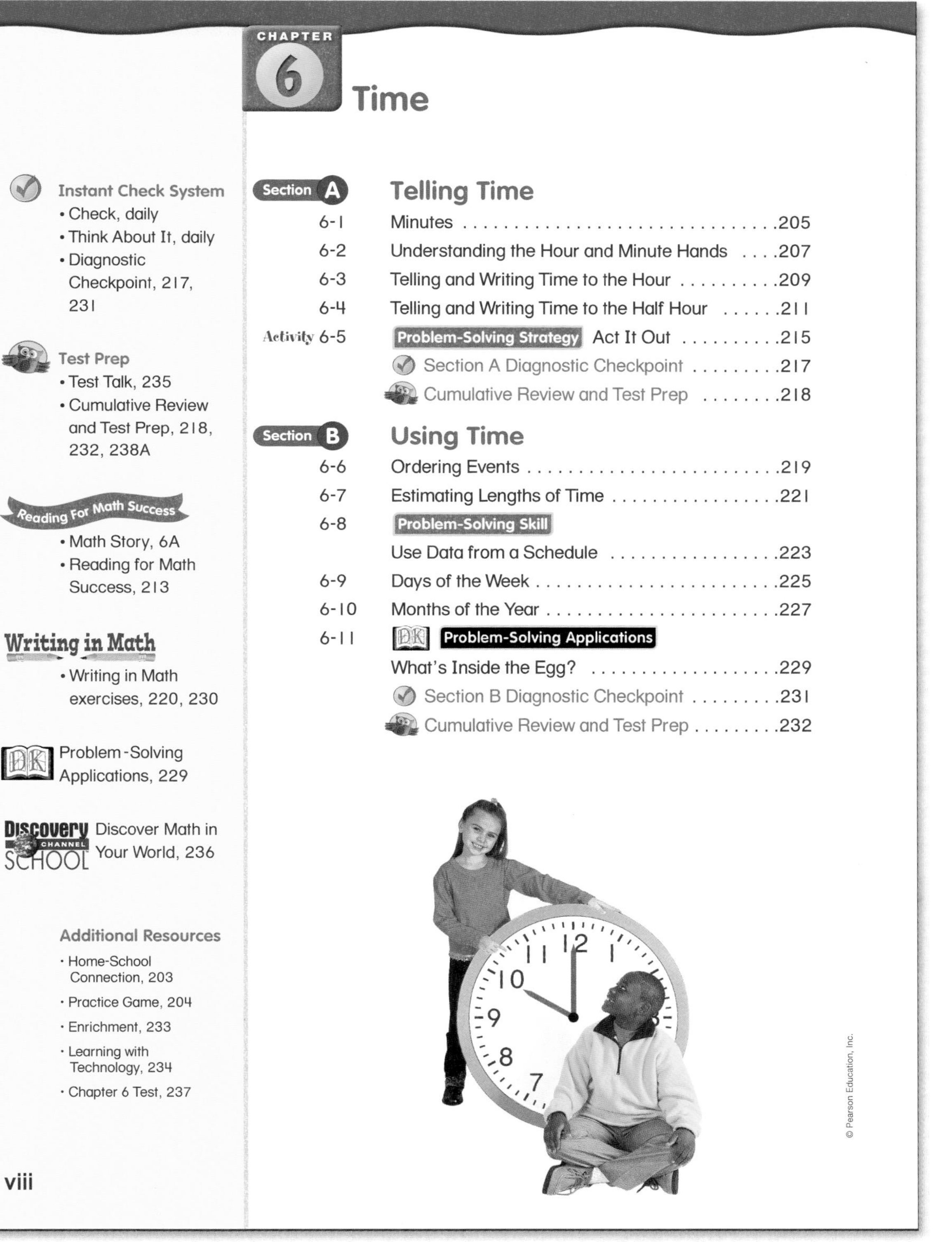

CHAPTER 6 Time

Instant Check System
- Check, daily
- Think About It, daily
- Diagnostic Checkpoint, 217, 231

Test Prep
- Test Talk, 235
- Cumulative Review and Test Prep, 218, 232, 238A

Reading For Math Success
- Math Story, 6A
- Reading for Math Success, 213

Writing in Math
- Writing in Math exercises, 220, 230

Problem-Solving Applications, 229

Discovery Channel School Discover Math in Your World, 236

Additional Resources
- Home-School Connection, 203
- Practice Game, 204
- Enrichment, 233
- Learning with Technology, 234
- Chapter 6 Test, 237

CHAPTER 7

Table of Contents

Counting to 100

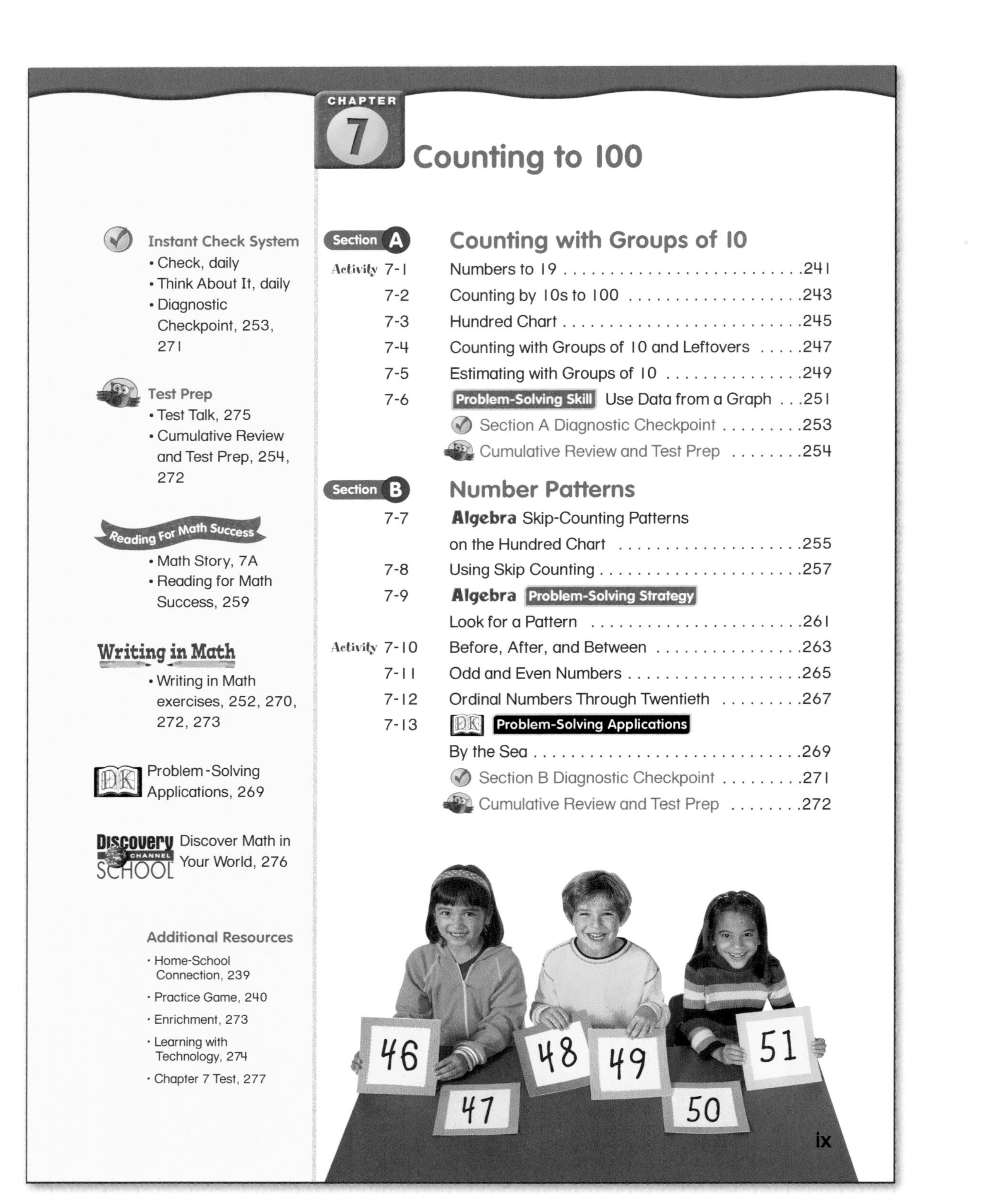

CHAPTER 7

Counting to 100

Instant Check System
- Check, daily
- Think About It, daily
- Diagnostic Checkpoint, 253, 271

Test Prep
- Test Talk, 275
- Cumulative Review and Test Prep, 254, 272

Reading For Math Success
- Math Story, 7A
- Reading for Math Success, 259

Writing in Math
- Writing in Math exercises, 252, 270, 272, 273

DK Problem-Solving Applications, 269

Discovery Channel School Discover Math in Your World, 276

Additional Resources
- Home-School Connection, 239
- Practice Game, 240
- Enrichment, 273
- Learning with Technology, 274
- Chapter 7 Test, 277

ix

Table of Contents

Place Value, Data, and Graphs

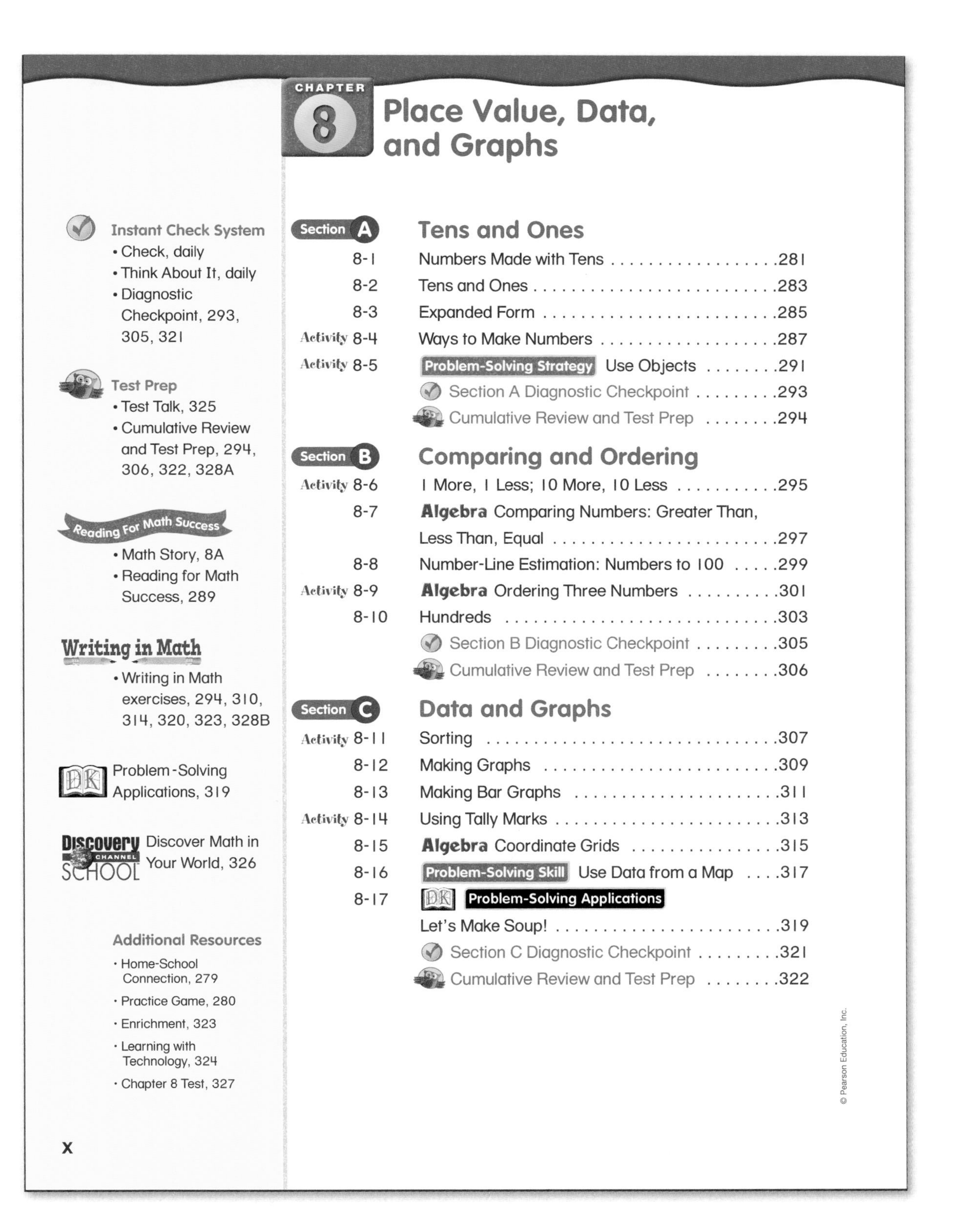

CHAPTER 8

Place Value, Data, and Graphs

Instant Check System
- Check, daily
- Think About It, daily
- Diagnostic Checkpoint, 293, 305, 321

Test Prep
- Test Talk, 325
- Cumulative Review and Test Prep, 294, 306, 322, 328A

Reading For Math Success
- Math Story, 8A
- Reading for Math Success, 289

Writing in Math
- Writing in Math exercises, 294, 310, 314, 320, 323, 328B

DK Problem-Solving Applications, 319

Discovery Channel School Discover Math in Your World, 326

Additional Resources
- Home-School Connection, 279
- Practice Game, 280
- Enrichment, 323
- Learning with Technology, 324
- Chapter 8 Test, 327

CHAPTER 9 Table of Contents

Money

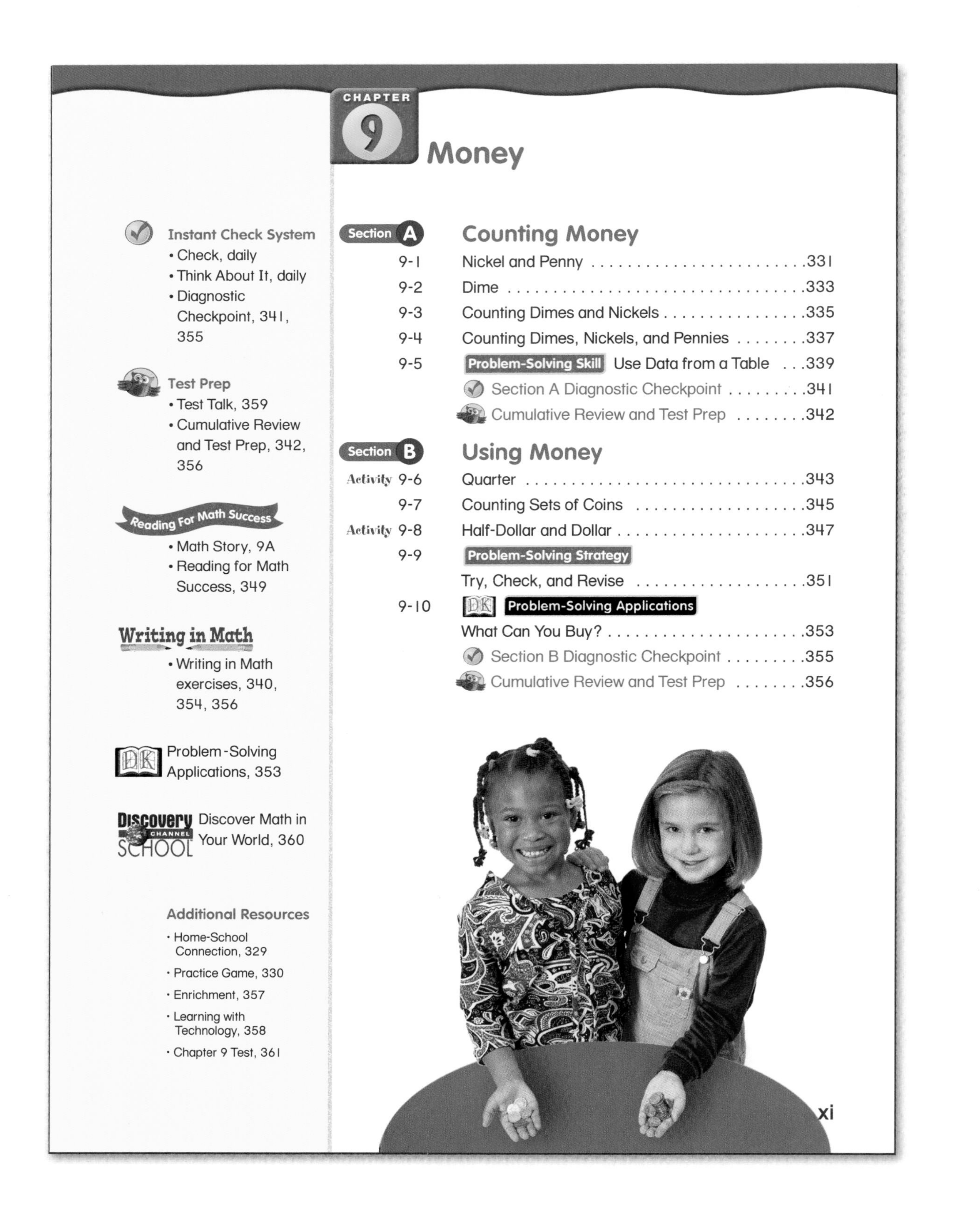

CHAPTER 9

Money

Instant Check System
- Check, daily
- Think About It, daily
- Diagnostic Checkpoint, 341, 355

Test Prep
- Test Talk, 359
- Cumulative Review and Test Prep, 342, 356

Reading For Math Success
- Math Story, 9A
- Reading for Math Success, 349

Writing in Math
- Writing in Math exercises, 340, 354, 356

Problem-Solving Applications, 353

Discovery Channel School Discover Math in Your World, 360

Additional Resources
- Home-School Connection, 329
- Practice Game, 330
- Enrichment, 357
- Learning with Technology, 358
- Chapter 9 Test, 361

xi

CHAPTER 10

Table of Contents

Measurement and Probability

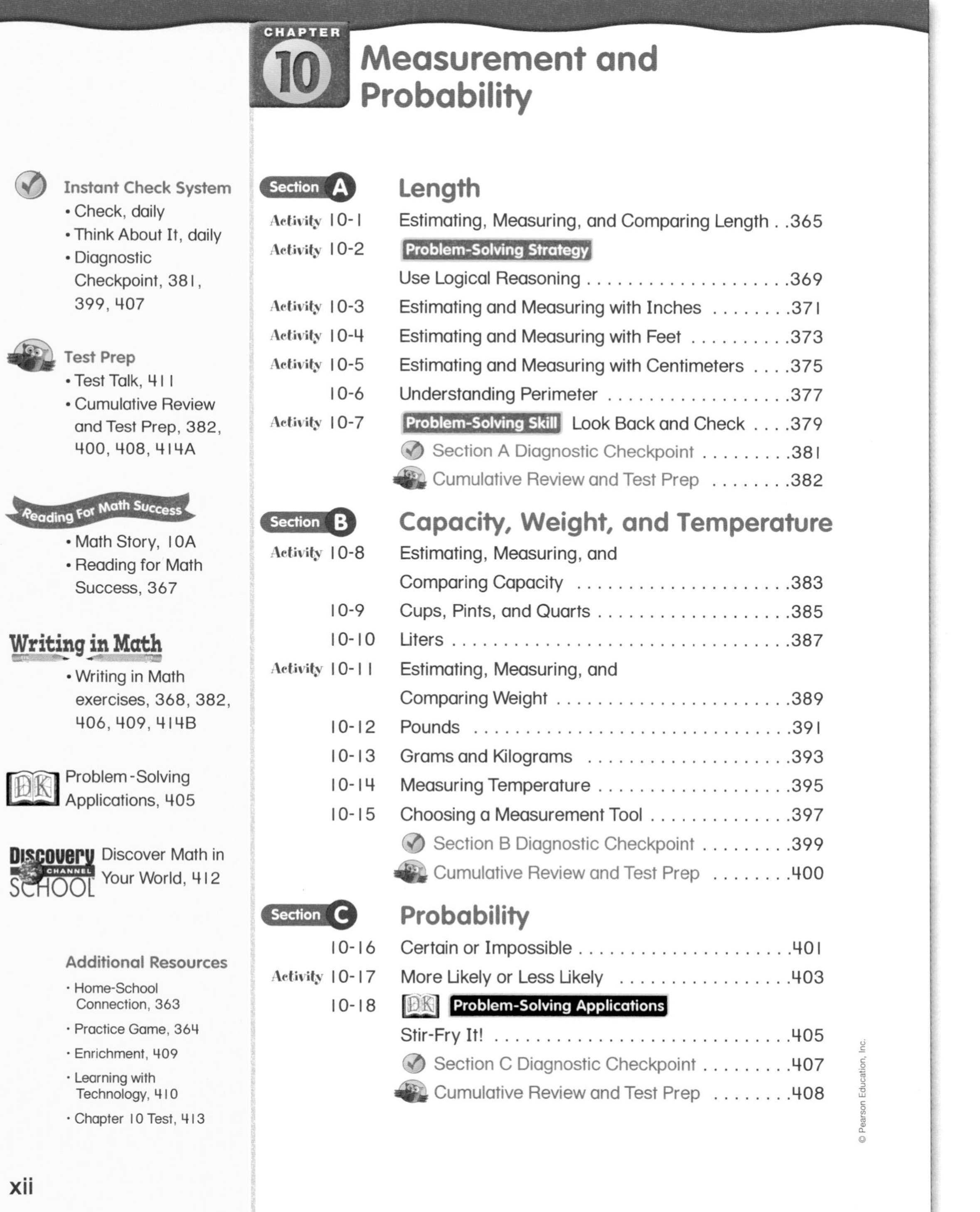

CHAPTER 10

Measurement and Probability

Instant Check System
- Check, daily
- Think About It, daily
- Diagnostic Checkpoint, 381, 399, 407

Test Prep
- Test Talk, 411
- Cumulative Review and Test Prep, 382, 400, 408, 414A

Reading For Math Success
- Math Story, 10A
- Reading for Math Success, 367

Writing in Math
- Writing in Math exercises, 368, 382, 406, 409, 414B

DK Problem-Solving Applications, 405

Discovery Channel School Discover Math in Your World, 412

Additional Resources
- Home-School Connection, 363
- Practice Game, 364
- Enrichment, 409
- Learning with Technology, 410
- Chapter 10 Test, 413

xii

Chapter 11 Table of Contents

Addition and Subtraction Facts to 18

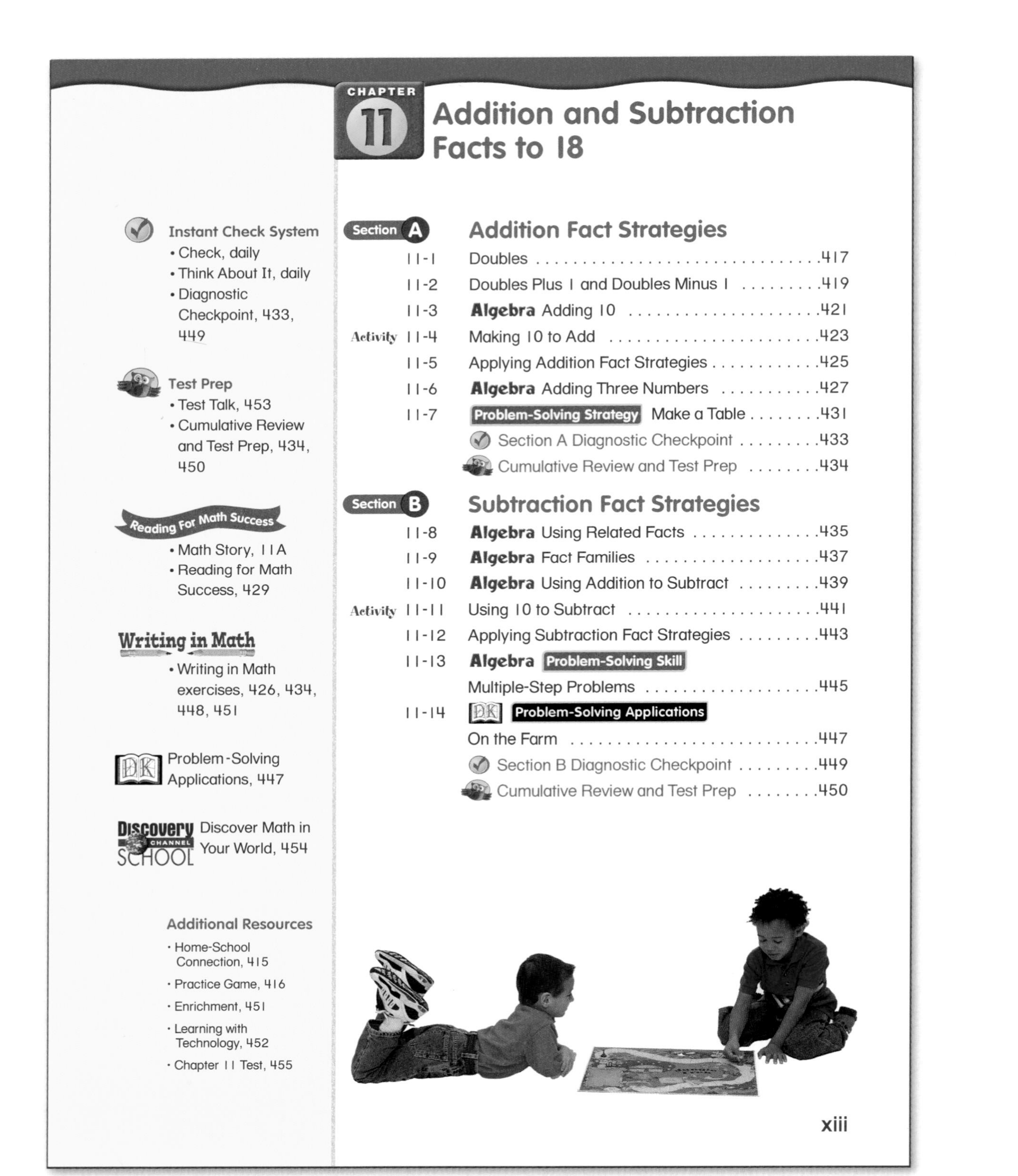

Chapter 11

Addition and Subtraction Facts to 18

Instant Check System
- Check, daily
- Think About It, daily
- Diagnostic Checkpoint, 433, 449

Test Prep
- Test Talk, 453
- Cumulative Review and Test Prep, 434, 450

Reading For Math Success
- Math Story, 11A
- Reading for Math Success, 429

Writing in Math
- Writing in Math exercises, 426, 434, 448, 451

DK Problem-Solving Applications, 447

Discovery Channel School Discover Math in Your World, 454

Additional Resources
- Home-School Connection, 415
- Practice Game, 416
- Enrichment, 451
- Learning with Technology, 452
- Chapter 11 Test, 455

CHAPTER 12

Table of Contents

Two-Digit Addition and Subtraction

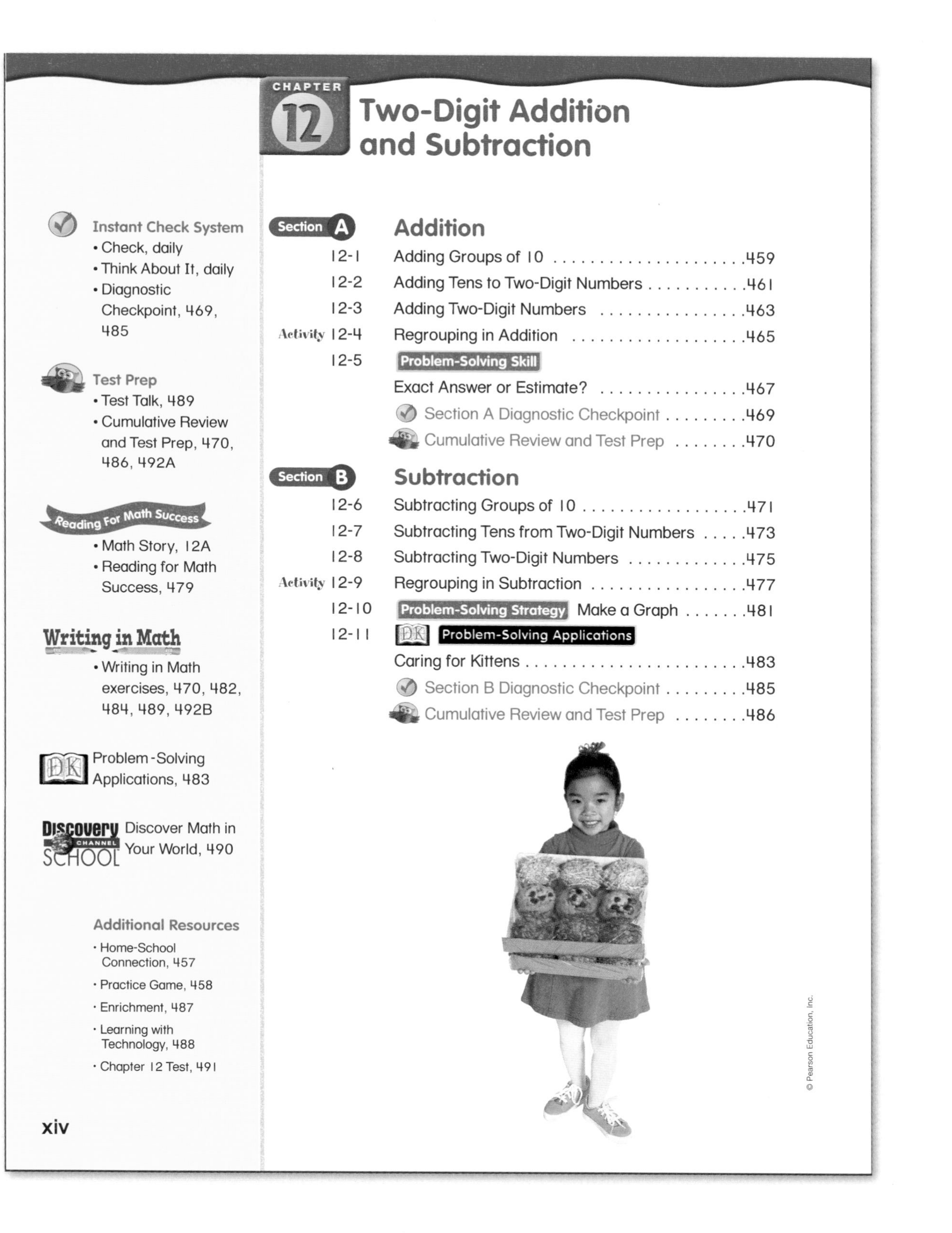

CHAPTER 12

Two-Digit Addition and Subtraction

Instant Check System
- Check, daily
- Think About It, daily
- Diagnostic Checkpoint, 469, 485

Test Prep
- Test Talk, 489
- Cumulative Review and Test Prep, 470, 486, 492A

Reading For Math Success
- Math Story, 12A
- Reading for Math Success, 479

Writing in Math
- Writing in Math exercises, 470, 482, 484, 489, 492B

DK Problem-Solving Applications, 483

Discovery Channel School Discover Math in Your World, 490

Additional Resources
- Home-School Connection, 457
- Practice Game, 458
- Enrichment, 487
- Learning with Technology, 488
- Chapter 12 Test, 491

CHAPTER 4

Lesson Planner

Strategies for Subtraction Facts to 12

Suggested Pacing: 10 days

Section A Counting Back

4-1 pp. 125–126	4-2 pp. 127–128	4-3 pp. 129–130	4-4 pp. 133–134
Counting Back Using a Number Line **Objective** Use a number line to count back 1 or 2. **Math Understanding** Moving to the left on a number line is one way to show subtraction. **Vocabulary** Count back	**Counting Back** **Objective** Find differences by counting back 1 or 2. **Math Understanding** When counting back, the last number said tells how many are left. **Materials for Student Pages** *(per child)* 12 counters	**Using Doubles to Subtract** **Objective** Find differences by using doubles facts. **Math Understanding** Doubles facts can be used to find differences for their related subtraction facts. Reading For Math Success pp. 131–132	Problem-Solving Strategy **Algebra Write a Number Sentence** **Objective** Solve problems by writing subtraction sentences. **Math Understanding** Writing a number sentence is one strategy that can be used to solve a problem. **Section A Diagnostic Checkpoint, p. 135** **Cumulative Review and Test Prep, p. 136**

Math Story: ***Count Back, Jack*****, pp. 4A–4F** **Home-School Connection, p. 123**

Practice Game: ***Counting Back*****, p. 124**

Resources in the Student Book

Ongoing Assessment and Test Prep *Also see* pp. 123G–123H.

Instant Check System™
- **Check** before Practice
- **Think About It** after examples
- **Diagnostic Checkpoint** end of sections

Test Prep
- **Test Talk** end of chapter
- **Cumulative Review and Test Prep** end of sections

Daily Real-World Problem Solving plus ...

Problem-Solving Applications lesson on pp. 145–146 uses data from Dorling Kindersley literature.

Discover Math in Your World on p. 152 uses data from a topic in the Discovery Channel School Video Library, Segment 4.

Notes

Reading and Writing in Math *Throughout*

This feature shows how reading skills and strategies can help with problem-solving skills and strategies in math.
Also, **Reading Assists** are in the Teacher's Edition.

Writing in Math

Some lessons include **Writing in Math** exercises. Also, daily **Journal Ideas** are in the Teacher's Edition.

Technology Resources for Students *Also see* p. T20.

Take It to the NET
More Activities
www.scottforesman.com

More activities, Discovery Channel School Video Library, and Math eTools

Math eTools: electronic manipulatives online, on CD-ROM, and in the Online Student's Edition

All text pages are available online and on CD-ROM. The Online Student's Edition includes Math eTools plus glossary links for vocabulary.

Strategies for Subtraction Facts to 12 (continued)

Section B Fact Families

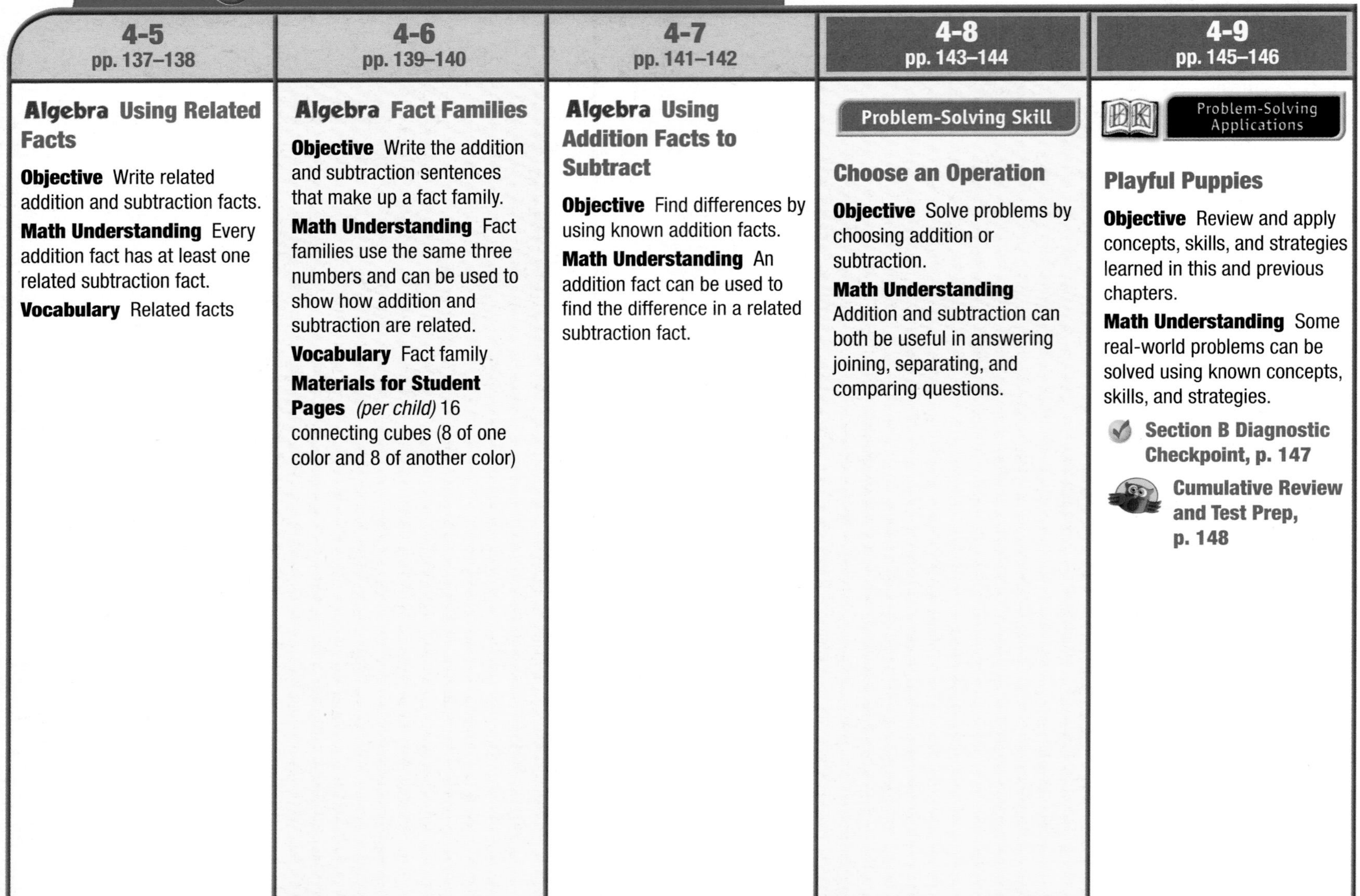

4-5 pp. 137–138	4-6 pp. 139–140	4-7 pp. 141–142	4-8 pp. 143–144	4-9 pp. 145–146
Algebra Using Related Facts **Objective** Write related addition and subtraction facts. **Math Understanding** Every addition fact has at least one related subtraction fact. **Vocabulary** Related facts	**Algebra Fact Families** **Objective** Write the addition and subtraction sentences that make up a fact family. **Math Understanding** Fact families use the same three numbers and can be used to show how addition and subtraction are related. **Vocabulary** Fact family **Materials for Student Pages** *(per child)* 16 connecting cubes (8 of one color and 8 of another color)	**Algebra Using Addition Facts to Subtract** **Objective** Find differences by using known addition facts. **Math Understanding** An addition fact can be used to find the difference in a related subtraction fact.	Problem-Solving Skill **Choose an Operation** **Objective** Solve problems by choosing addition or subtraction. **Math Understanding** Addition and subtraction can both be useful in answering joining, separating, and comparing questions.	DK Problem-Solving Applications **Playful Puppies** **Objective** Review and apply concepts, skills, and strategies learned in this and previous chapters. **Math Understanding** Some real-world problems can be solved using known concepts, skills, and strategies. **Section B Diagnostic Checkpoint, p. 147** **Cumulative Review and Test Prep, p. 148**

Additional Resources for ...

Reaching All Learners

- **Practice** Masters/Workbook, every lesson
- **Reteaching** Masters/Workbook, every lesson
- **Enrichment** Masters/Workbook, every lesson
- **Every Student Learns** A teacher resource with daily suggestions for helping students overcome language barriers to learning math
- **Spiral Review and Test Prep** Transparencies and Masters/Workbook, every lesson
- **Math Games** Use *Bubble Mania* anytime after Lesson 4-6.
- **Investigation** See pp. 123I–123J.

Problem Solving

- **Problem Solving** Masters/Workbook, every lesson
- **Problem of the Day** Flipchart/Transparencies, every lesson
- **Discovery Channel School** Masters, follow-up to Segment 4 in the Discovery Channel School Video Library

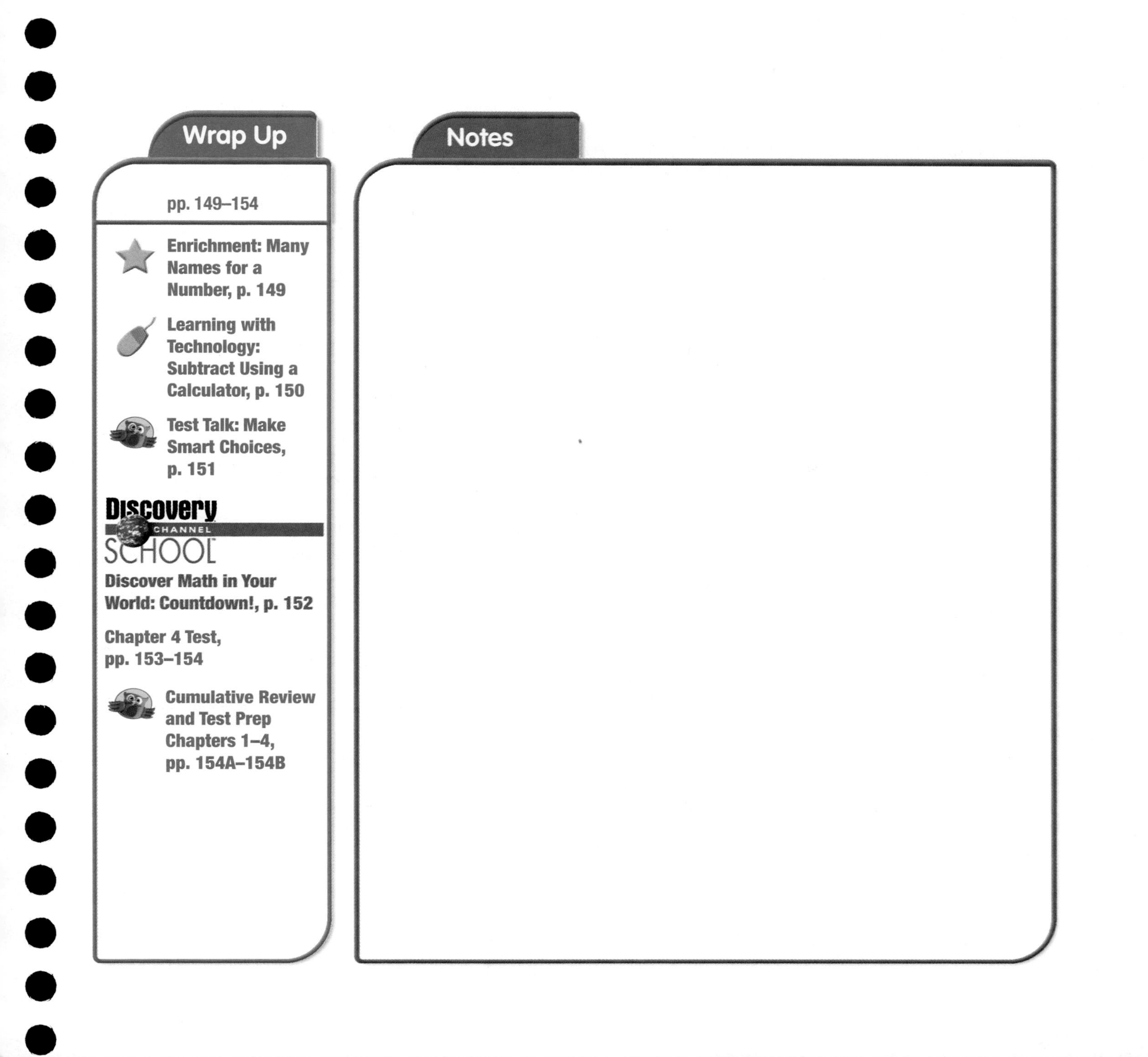

Wrap Up
pp. 149–154
Enrichment: Many Names for a Number, p. 149
Learning with Technology: Subtract Using a Calculator, p. 150
Test Talk: Make Smart Choices, p. 151
Discovery Channel School
Discover Math in Your World: Countdown!, p. 152
Chapter 4 Test, pp. 153–154
Cumulative Review and Test Prep Chapters 1–4, pp. 154A–154B
Notes

Reading in Math

- **Vocabulary Kit** Word Cards plus transparencies and activities for instructional word walls and for small groups
- **Dorling Kindersley Literature Library** Books with interesting data

Assessment, Intervention, and Test Prep

- **Assessment Sourcebook** See pp. 123G–123H.
- **Math Diagnosis and Intervention System** See pp. 123G–123H.
- **Test-Taking Practice** Transparencies, every lesson
- **SAT 9, SAT 10, TerraNova Practice and Test Prep** Includes practice tests, correlations, and more

Teacher Support

- **Teaching Tools** Masters: paper manipulatives and more
- **Home-School Connection** Masters, use Chapter 4 Family Letter at the start of the chapter. Use Study Buddies 7 and 8 after Lessons 4-1 and 4-6.
- **Professional Development Resources** See p. T18.
- **Technology Resources** See p. T20.

CHAPTER 4 Professional Development

Skills Trace - Strategies for Subtraction Facts to 12

BEFORE Chapter 4	DURING Chapter 4	AFTER Chapter 4
Grade K introduced subtraction strategies by expressing a number as two parts and the relationship between two numbers as 1 or 2 fewer. **Chapter 2 in Grade 1** developed the meanings of addition and subtraction.	**Chapter 4** introduces mental math strategies, including counting back and using doubles for learning basic subtraction facts to 12. Identifying fact families for related addition and subtraction facts is also introduced.	**Chapter 11 in Grade 1** develops mental math strategies for learning basic subtraction facts to 18. **Grade 2** develops mental math strategies for learning basic subtraction facts and applies them to subtract two- and three-digit numbers.

Math Background and Teaching Tips

Section A

Counting Back
pp. 125–136

Fact strategies are mental techniques for subtracting with basic facts, aimed at achieving basic fact mastery. They provide a bridge from understanding the meaning of subtraction to being able to automatically recall basic subtraction facts.

Understanding Subtraction → Fact Strategies → Fact Mastery

Counting Back

Properties of whole numbers provide the basis for the development of these fact strategies. Number relationships children worked with in Chapter 1, as well as the number line model of those relationships, provide the basis for the counting back strategy.

TIP! Develop Efficiency *Help children use subtraction-fact strategies to bridge their understanding of subtraction to quick and accurate recall of basic facts by providing opportunities for them to practice over time.*

Similar to addition, counting back is an accurate subtraction-fact strategy only when the number being subtracted is 1, 2, or 3. Facts like 6 − 2, 11 − 3, and 8 − 1 are examples.

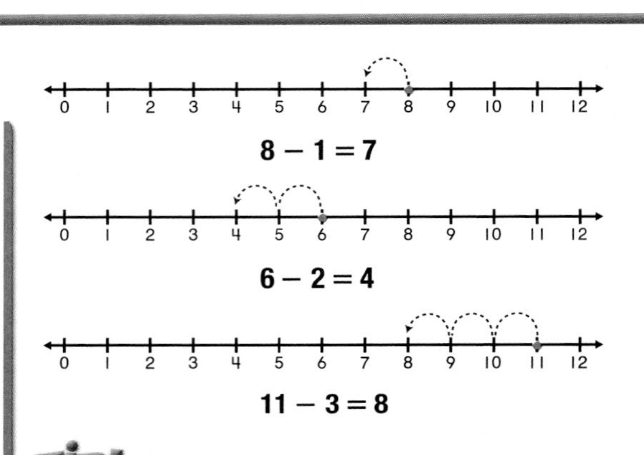

TIP! Use Representations *Encourage children to use the number line to facilitate their understanding of the counting-back strategy. Children should move from using the number line to counting back mentally as soon as they are ready.*

Using Doubles

This subtraction strategy is based on the inverse relationship of addition and subtraction. An addition double can help with a subtraction double.

Since 6 + 6 = 12,
then 12 − 6 = 6.

Since 8 + 8 = 16,
then 16 − 8 = 8.

Math Understandings

- Moving to the left on a number line is one way to show subtraction.
- When counting back, the last number said tells how many are left.
- Doubles facts can be used to find differences for their related subtraction facts.
- Writing a number sentence is one strategy that can be used to solve a problem.

Equality

It is important that children understand that an addition or subtraction sentence can be expressed with the equal sign in varying positions.

6 + 2 = 8	9 − 5 = 4
8 = 6 + 2	4 = 9 − 5

This understanding of equality will help lay the foundation for future success in working with algebraic concepts.

Section B

Fact Families

pp. 137–148

Subtraction facts can be easily mastered by thinking of a related addition fact. To find $8 - 5$, think "5 plus what number equals 8?" This part-part-whole mat illustrates this subtraction.

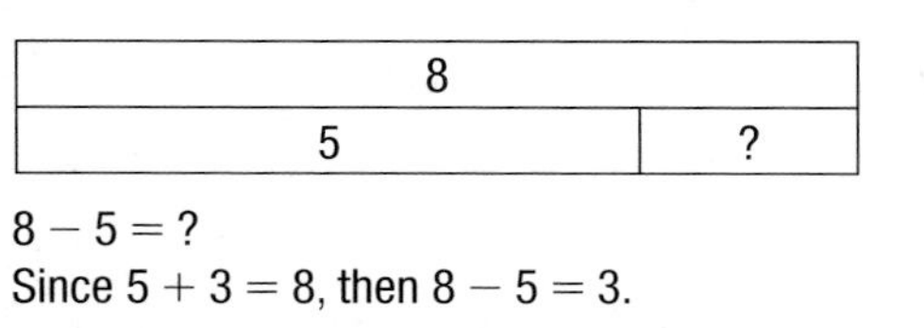

8	
5	?

$8 - 5 = ?$
Since $5 + 3 = 8$, then $8 - 5 = 3$.

This strategy is possible because of the inverse relationship of addition and subtraction.

If $a - b = c$, then $a = b + c$.
If $a = b + c$, then $a - b = c$.

"Fact families" help emphasize the inverse relationship between addition and subtraction.

Notice how fact families use the commutative (order) property of addition.

9	
3	6

$6 + 3 = 9$ $\quad$ $9 - 3 = 6$
$3 + 6 = 9$ $\quad$ $9 - 6 = 3$

TIP! Reinforce Big Ideas *Guide children to notice how the two addition sentences in a fact family represent the order property of addition. When one fact is known, it can be used to find the sum for the related addition fact.*

Thinking Addition to Subtract

Because of the inverse relationship of addition and subtraction, addition can be used to solve subtraction facts. To find $15 - 7$, think "7 plus what number equals 15?"

Since $7 + 8 = 15$,
then $15 - 7 = 8$ and $15 - 8 = 7$.

In problem solving, children will choose an operation. The types of problems include joining, separating, and comparing. For each problem, emphasize visualization of the action of the problem so that children picture clearly what they know and what they need to find out.

Joining Problems

These are problems in which two amounts are joined to form a total amount.

> Andrew planted 5 flower seeds in one pot and 7 flower seeds in another pot. How many seeds did Andrew plant?
>
> $5 + 7 = \square$

In this problem, two known amounts are combined to find the unknown sum. In other joining problems, the amount added or the initial amount may be unknown.

Separating Problems

In these problems an amount is taken away from an initial amount.

Math Understandings

- Every addition fact has at least one related subtraction fact.
- Fact families use the same numbers and can be used to show how addition and subtraction are related.
- An addition fact can be used to find the difference in a related subtraction fact.
- Addition and subtraction can both be useful in answering joining, separating, and comparing questions.

> Karen had 16 tulip bulbs. She planted 7 tulip bulbs in the garden. How many tulip bulbs does Karen have left?
>
> $16 - 7 = \square$

In this problem, the amount left is unknown. In other separating problems, the amount taken away or the initial amount may be unknown.

Comparing Problems

In these problems, two amounts are compared to find the amount greater or less.

> Lisette has 11 ride tickets left. Ty has 8 ride tickets left. Lisette has how many more tickets than Ty?
>
> $11 - 8 = \square$

In this problem, the difference between the two amounts is unknown. In other comparing problems, either of the amounts to be compared may be unknown.

CHAPTER 4

Assessment, Intervention, Test Prep

Assessment Resources

DIAGNOSING READINESS

Start of Year Diagnosing Readiness for Grade 1, Assessment Sourcebook pp. 43–46 and in Online Intervention

Start of Chapter Diagnosing Readiness for Chapter 4, Assessment Sourcebook pp. 93–94 and in Online Intervention

Start of Lesson Warm Up, Teacher's Edition pp. 125, 127, 129, 133, 137, 139, 141, 143, 145

Instant Check System™

ONGOING ASSESSMENT

Before Independent Practice Check and Think About It, Student Book, every lesson

After a Section Diagnostic Checkpoint, pp. 135, 147 and in Online Intervention

Basic-Facts Timed Test 4 Assessment Sourcebook, p. 30

FORMAL EVALUATION

Chapter Tests Chapter 4 Test, Student Book pp. 153–154; Assessment Sourcebook Forms A and B Free Response pp. 95–98, Forms C and D Multiple Choice pp. 99–106, Performance Assessment p. 7; Multiple-Choice Chapter Test in Online Intervention

Cumulative Tests Chapters 1–3, 1–6, 1–9, 1–12, Assessment Sourcebook, pp. 89–92, 135–138, 181–184, 227–230; Online Intervention

Test Generator Computer-generated tests; can be customized

Correlation to Assessments, Intervention, and Standardized Tests

	Assessments		Intervention	Standardized Tests				
Lessons	Diagnostic Checkpoint	Chapter Test	Math Diagnosis and Intervention System	SAT 9/10	ITBS	CTBS	CAT	MAT
4-1 Counting Back Using a Number Line	p. 135: Ex. 5	Ex. 1	Booklet B: B24	/•		•	•	•
4-2 Counting Back	p. 135: Ex. 1, 2	Ex. 3, 4	Booklet B: B25	•/•	•	•	•	•
4-3 Using Doubles to Subtract	p. 135: Ex. 3, 4	Ex. 5, 6	Booklet B: B26	•/•	•	•	•	•
4-4 Problem-Solving Strategy: Write a Number Sentence	p. 135: Ex. 6	Ex. 10	Booklet E: E36	•/•	•	•	•	•
4-5 Using Related Facts	p. 147: Ex. 1	Ex. 2	Booklet B: B27	•/•	•	•	•	•
4-6 Fact Families	p. 147: Ex. 2	Ex. 9	Booklet B: B28	•/•	•	•	•	•
4-7 Using Addition Facts to Subtract	p. 147: Ex. 4, 5	Ex. 7, 8	Booklet B: B29	•/•	•	•	•	•
4-8 Problem-Solving Skill: Choose an Operation	p. 147: Ex. 3	Ex. 11	Booklet E: E4	•/•	•	•	•	•

KEY:
SAT 9 Stanford Achievement Test
SAT 10 Stanford Achievement Test
ITBS Iowa Test of Basic Skills
CAT California Achievement Test
CTBS Comprehensive Test of Basic Skills (TerraNova)
MAT Metropolitan Achievement Test

Intervention and Test Prep Resources

INTERVENTION

During Instruction Helpful "If… then…" suggestions in the Teacher's Edition in Ongoing Assessment and Error Intervention

Math Diagnosis and Intervention System Diagnostic tests, individual and class record forms, two-page Intervention Lessons (example, practice, test prep), and one-page Intervention Practice (multiple choice), all in cross-grade strand booklets (Booklets A–E for Grades K–3, Booklets F–M for Grades 4–6).

Online Intervention Diagnostic tests; individual, class, school, and district reports; remediation including tutorials, video, games, practice exercises

TEST PREP

Test Talk before the Chapter Test, p. 151

Cumulative Review and Test Prep end of sections, pp. 136, 148 and end of Chapter 4, pp. 154A–154B

Test-Taking Practice Transparencies for every lesson

Spiral Review and Test Prep for every lesson

SAT 9, SAT 10, TerraNova Practice and Test Prep section quizzes, practice tests

Correlation to NCTM Standards and Grades Pre-K through 2 Expectations

Number and Operations

Understand numbers, ways of representing numbers, relationships among numbers, and number systems.

Grades Pre-K through 2 Expectations

- Count with understanding and recognize "how many" in sets of objects. *Lessons 4-2, 4-3, 4-5, 4-6, 4-7, 4-8*
- Develop understanding of the relative position and magnitude of whole numbers and of ordinal and cardinal numbers and their connections. *Lesson 4-1*
- Develop a sense of whole numbers and represent and use them in flexible ways, including relating, composing, and decomposing numbers. *Lessons 4-1, 4-2, 4-3, 4-4, 4-5, 4-6, 4-7, 4-8*
- Connect number words and numerals to the quantities they represent, using various physical models and representations. *Lessons 4-1, 4-2, 4-3, 4-4, 4-5, 4-6, 4-7, 4-8*

Understand meanings of operations and how they relate to one another.

Grades Pre-K through 2 Expectations

- Understand various meanings of addition and subtraction of whole numbers and the relationship between the two operations. *Lessons 4-1, 4-2, 4-3, 4-4, 4-5, 4-6, 4-7, 4-8*
- Understand the effects of adding and subtracting whole numbers. *Lessons 4-1, 4-2, 4-3, 4-4, 4-5, 4-6, 4-7, 4-8*

Compute fluently and make reasonable estimates.

Grades Pre-K through 2 Expectations

- Develop and use strategies for whole-number computations, with a focus on addition and subtraction. *Lessons 4-1, 4-2, 4-3, 4-4, 4-5, 4-6, 4-7, 4-8*
- Develop fluency with basic number combinations for addition and subtraction. *Lessons 4-1, 4-2, 4-3*
- Use a variety of methods and tools to compute, including objects, mental computation, estimation, paper and pencil, and calculators. *Lessons 4-1, 4-2, 4-3, 4-4, 4-5, 4-6, 4-7, 4-8*

Algebra

Represent and analyze mathematical situations and structures using algebraic symbols.

Grades Pre-K through 2 Expectations

- Illustrate general principles and properties of operations, such as commutativity, using specific numbers. *Lessons 4-5, 4-6, 4-7*
- Use concrete, pictorial, and verbal representations to develop an understanding of invented and conventional symbolic notations. *Lessons 4-4, 4-5, 4-6, 4-7*

Use mathematical models to represent and understand quantitative relationships.

Grades Pre-K through 2 Expectations

- Model situations that involve the addition and subtraction of whole numbers, using objects, pictures, and symbols. *Lessons 4-4, 4-5, 4-6, 4-7*

The NCTM 2000 Pre-K through Grade 12 Content Standards are Number and Operations, Algebra, Geometry, Measurement, and Data Analysis and Probability. The Process Standards (Problem Solving, Reasoning and Proof, Communication, Connections, and Representation) are incorporated throughout lessons.

Strategies for Subtraction Facts to 12

Activity 1

Use in place of the Investigating the Concept activity in Lesson 4-1.

Using Strategies to Solve Facts

Overview Children investigate ways to act out subtraction problems and solve basic subtraction facts and draw pictures to represent their thinking processes before learning specific subtraction techniques in Lesson 4-1.

Materials *(per group)* 10 red connecting cubes; 10 blue connecting cubes

The Task

- Create a train with 2 red cubes and 4 blue cubes. Display the cubes so that all children in the group can see the cubes.
- Have one child separate the red cubes from the blue cubes and then remove the red cubes from sight. **How many cubes are left? How can we draw pictures to represent this subtraction problem?** *(4; answers will vary.)*
- Have other children in the group create a train, using red and blue cubes.
- One group member separates the colors, removes one set of cubes, and represents the strategy, by drawing pictures.

Observing and Questioning

- Observe whether children are removing one group of cubes from sight to represent subtraction. If needed, ask the following questions to spur further thinking.
- **How many cubes did you begin with? How many cubes are left?** *(6; 4)*
- **How does counting the cubes help you to solve the subtraction problem?** *(Sample answer: If I know how many cubes I started with and how many were taken away, I can find how many are left.)*

Sharing and Summarizing

- After children show their work, summarize the different methods used.
- If no children suggest counting up or counting back, ask: **How can you find the answer by counting back? Does counting up help you solve the problem?**
- **Key Idea** Point out that there are many ways to solve a subtraction problem. Children can use counting or related facts to solve subtraction problems. Assure children that they should use the method that is most comfortable for them.

Follow-Up

- Show a train with 5 red cubes and 5 blue cubes. Remove 5 red cubes and discuss ways of solving the problem. For example, children may count the total number of cubes and then count only the blue cubes to find the answer.

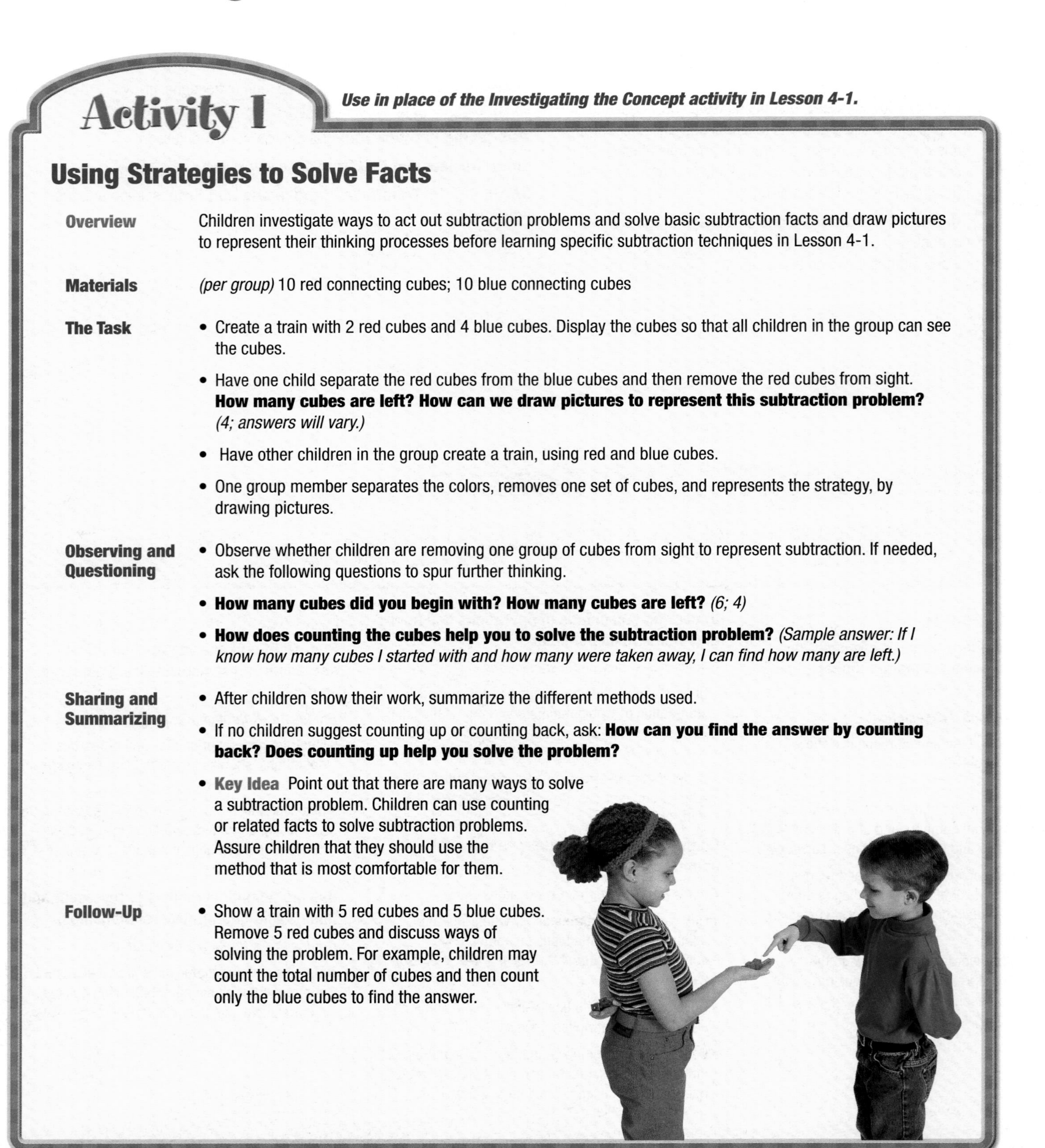

Link to ***Investigations in Number, Data, and Space®*** See the **Joint-Usage Plan** available from Pearson Scott Foresman.

Activity 2

Use in place of the Investigating the Concept activity in Lesson 4-5.

Related Fact Stories

Overview

Children will investigate methods for finding a missing number by counting the total number of cubes and the remaining cubes before learning specific techniques, using related facts in Lesson 4-5.

Materials

(per pair) 12 counters; cup

The Task

- One child writes a number between 1 and 12 on paper and counts out this many counters. The child then hides some of the cubes under the cup.
- A partner uses the number on the paper and the number of visible cubes to determine the number of cubes hidden under the cup. The child then describes how he or she found the missing number.
- Both children then check the counters under the cup.

Observing and Questioning

- As children are working on the problem, observe whether they are subtracting cubes from the total or using related addition facts to find the number of counters hidden under the cup.
- **How did you find the number of counters hidden under the cup?**
- **How did knowing the total number of counters help you to solve the problem?**

Sharing and Summarizing

- After children show their work, summarize the methods used. Children can count back from the total number of cubes to the amount that is not hidden under the cup. Another method is to subtract the counters that can be seen from the total. Children also may count on from the counters they can see to the total number of counters. Each of these methods will tell how many counters are hidden under the cup.
- **Key Idea** As children share their methods for finding the missing number, point out that there are a number of ways, including using related facts, counting back from the total, and counting on. For each of these techniques, it is important to know basic addition and subtraction facts.

Follow-Up

- Have children repeat the activity, using the same number of counters, but placing a different number under the cup.
- **Extension** Have children repeat the activity using 15 counters.

CHAPTER 4

Math Story

Count Back, Jack **(Genre: Realistic fiction)**

In this subtraction story, Jenny helps Jack subtract different numbers of toy cars by using a number line to count back.

Introducing the Story

Ask how many children have ever played with toy cars. Ask children to name a specific number of toy cars and then tell how many cars they would have left if they lost 1 and then 2 cars. Tell them that this story is about two children and how they subtract.

Reading the Story

Read the story through once without stopping. Encourage children to listen carefully and to enjoy the story's repetition and art along with you.

Explain to children that you will read the story again and then ask them what this story is all about, or what the main idea is for the story. Children should be able to tell that the main idea is about two children subtracting by using a number line. Explain to children that they can ask what the main idea is whenever they read stories or solve math problems. (For more on *Identify the Main Idea,* see Reading for Math Success, pp. 131–132.)

Page 4A

Page 4B **Page 4C**

Page 4D **Page 4E**

Page 4F

Follow-up Activities

- **Create Subtraction Stories** Have children look at each page of the story and count the number of toy cars. Then reread the text, having children use the number lines to find the answer after Jack has counted back. When finished, ask children: **What is 4 – 1?** *(3);* **6 – 2?** *(4);* **7 – 2?** *(5);* **8 – 1?** *(7);* **10 – 2?** *(8)*
- **Visualize** Point out the frog on the number line and have children picture in their minds the frog jumping back from one number to the next. Explain that the frog in the story always starts on the number of toy cars and jumps back the number that is being subtracted. Tell children that they can picture in their minds a frog jumping back one number at a time whenever they use a number line to subtract.
- **Extend the Story** Ask: **What is a different subtraction problem that Jack and Jenny can do?** Have children write their problems as subtraction sentences and use a number line to solve them.

Home-School Connection

Purpose Provide families with a quick overview of the material that will be covered in Chapter 4. Included on this page: a family letter, a math activity, references to literature related to the chapter, and new math vocabulary words.

Using Student Page 123

You may wish to read and discuss the family letter with children prior to having them sign it and sending the page home.

The Home-School Connection booklet includes:

- Chapter 4 Family Letter in English and Spanish
- Study Buddies 7
- Study Buddies 8

Study Buddies pages provide reinforcement activities for children to work on with a partner. Each Study Buddy has a page for the child and a page of prompts to help the partner guide the child's learning.

Vocabulary

count back *(pp. 125–126)*

related facts *(pp. 137–138)*

fact family *(pp. 139–140)*

Home-School Connection

Dear Family,

Today my class started chapter 4, **Strategies for Subtraction Facts to 12.** I will learn ways to subtract from the numbers 1 through 12. Here are some of the new math words I will be learning and some things we can do to help me with my math.

Love,

____

Math Activity to Do at Home

Make a group of pennies and a group of nickels, each with fewer than 12 coins. Ask your child to write subtraction sentences to compare the coins. For example, if you give your child 8 pennies and 3 nickels, your child should write $8 - 3 = 5$ to show that there are 5 more pennies.

Books to Read Together

Reading math stories reinforces concepts. Look for these books in your local library:

Turtle Splash
by Cathryn Falwell
(Greenwillow, 2001)

Subtraction Action
by Loreen Leedy
(Holiday House, 2000)

Take It to the NET
More Activities
www.scottforesman.com

My New Math Words

count back Use this strategy to subtract 1 or 2 from a number.

$6 - 2 = 4$

Start at 6.
Count back 5, 4.

related facts Addition and subtraction facts are related if they use the same numbers.

$4 + 3 = 7$
so $7 - 4 = 3$

fact family A fact family is a group of related addition and subtraction facts.

$4 + 5 = 9$
$5 + 4 = 9$
$9 - 5 = 4$
$9 - 4 = 5$

one hundred twenty-three 123

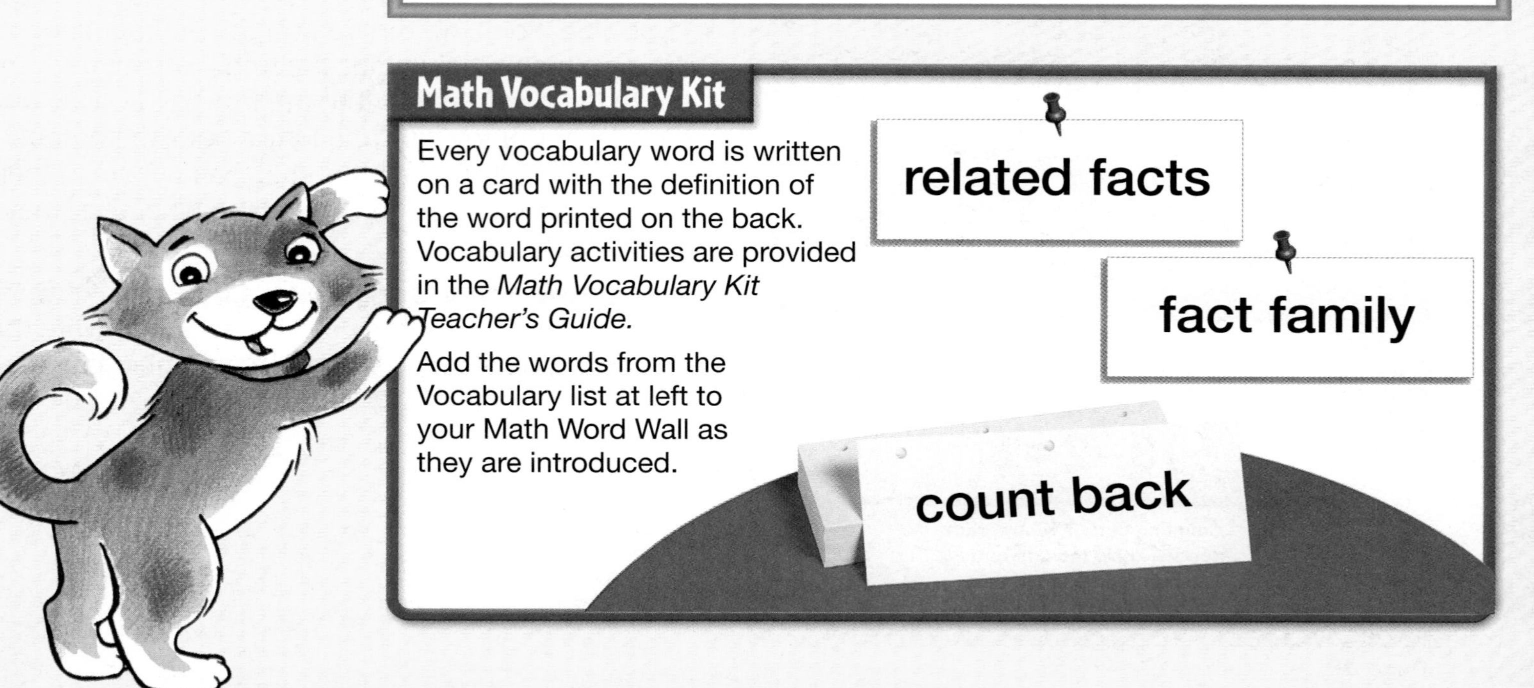

Math Vocabulary Kit
Every vocabulary word is written on a card with the definition of the word printed on the back. Vocabulary activities are provided in the *Math Vocabulary Kit Teacher's Guide.*
Add the words from the Vocabulary list at left to your Math Word Wall as they are introduced.
related facts
fact family
count back

 EC NTL 12 11 10 9 8 7 6 5

Name____________________ Practice Game

Counting Back

What You Need
- paper clip
- pencil
- 2 kinds of game markers

How to Play

1. Take turns spinning the spinner. Name the number you land on. Then count back 1.
2. Place a marker on the answer on the number line.
3. Play until every number is covered.
4. Play again and count back 2. If the spinner lands on 1, skip a turn.

124 one hundred twenty-four

Practice Game

for School or Home

Purpose Provide children with an opportunity to practice skills they have previously learned.

Using Student Page 124

You may choose to discuss these questions with your children before they play "Counting Back."

- **What are some ways to count back?**
- **How can you use a number line to find 8 – 1 by counting back?**
- **What is the answer if you count back to find 5 – 2?**

Give children the materials for the game.

Describe the game, explaining how the children will follow the directions. Lead children through the process of spinning, naming the number, counting back 1, and placing a marker on the resulting difference. Allow children to complete the game.

Describe another way to play: Have children take turns spinning. The child who spins counts back 1 from the number the spinner lands on and places a marker on the result. The child's partner counts back 2 and places a marker on the result. Play continues until every number is covered. The person who covers the most numbers is the winner.

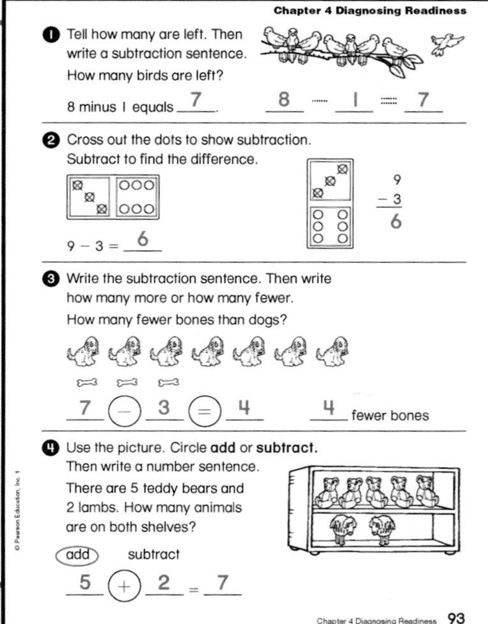

Chapter 4 Diagnosing Readiness

1. Tell how many are left. Then write a subtraction sentence. How many birds are left?
   8 minus 1 equals 7. 8 – 1 = 7
2. Cross out the dots to show subtraction. Subtract to find the difference.
   9 – 3 = 6
   9 – 3 = 6
3. Write the subtraction sentence. Then write how many more or how many fewer. How many fewer bones than dogs?
   7 – 3 = 4   4 fewer bones
4. Use the picture. Circle **add** or **subtract**. Then write a number sentence. There are 5 teddy bears and 2 lambs. How many animals are on both shelves?
   (add) subtract
   5 + 2 = 7

Chapter 4 Diagnosing Readiness 93

Item Analysis for Diagnosis and Intervention

Objective	Items	Student Book Pages*	Intervention System
Write a subtraction sentence to find the difference in a separating situation.	1	65–66	B12
Write the differences for horizontal and vertical forms of subtraction.	2	69–70	B14
Write subtraction sentences to compare and tell how many more or how many fewer.	3	77–78	B15
Solve problems by choosing addition or subtraction.	4	71–72	E4

*For each lesson, there is a *Reteaching* activity in *Reaching All Learners* and a *Reteaching* master.

4-1 Counting Back Using a Number Line

Lesson Organizer

Quick Lesson Overview

Objective Use a number line to count back 1 or 2.

Math Understanding Moving to the left on a number line is one way to show subtraction.

Vocabulary Count back

Professional Development Note

Research Base

During early work with subtraction, counting techniques help children find differences (Folsom, 1975). Number lines are used in this lesson to help children count back to find differences.

NCTM Standards

- Number and Operations

(For a complete correlation to the NCTM Standards and Grades Pre-K through 2 Expectations, see Pages 123G and 123H.)

Getting Started

Spiral Review

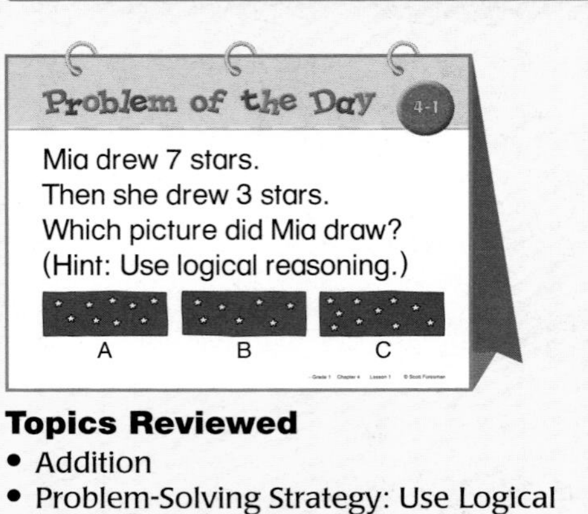

Problem of the Day
4-1
Mia drew 7 stars.
Then she drew 3 stars.
Which picture did Mia draw?
(Hint: Use logical reasoning.)
A
B
C

Topics Reviewed

- Addition
- Problem-Solving Strategy: Use Logical Reasoning

Answer Mia drew picture C. She drew a total of 10 stars.

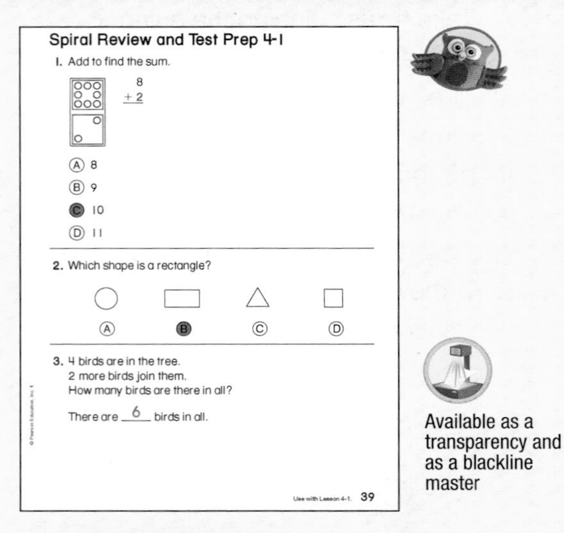

Spiral Review and Test Prep 4-1

1. Add to find the sum.

8
+ 2

Ⓐ 8
Ⓑ 9
Ⓒ 10
Ⓓ 11

2. Which shape is a rectangle?

Ⓐ Ⓑ Ⓒ Ⓓ

3. 4 birds are in the tree.
2 more birds join them.
How many birds are there in all?

There are 6 birds in all.

39

Available as a transparency and as a blackline master

Topics Reviewed

1. Vertical Addition
2. Squares and Other Rectangles
3. Stories about Joining

Investigating the Concept

Using a Number Line to Count Back

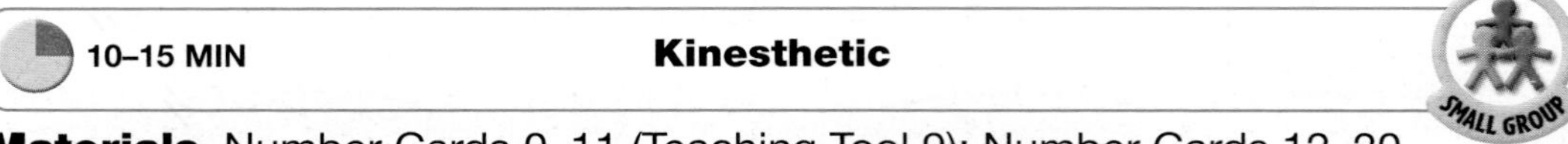

Materials Number Cards 0–11 (Teaching Tool 9); Number Cards 12–20 (Teaching Tool 11); masking tape

What to Do

- Use masking tape and the number cards to create a number line from 0–12 on the floor. Write 6 – 2 on the board. Ask a volunteer to stand on 6.

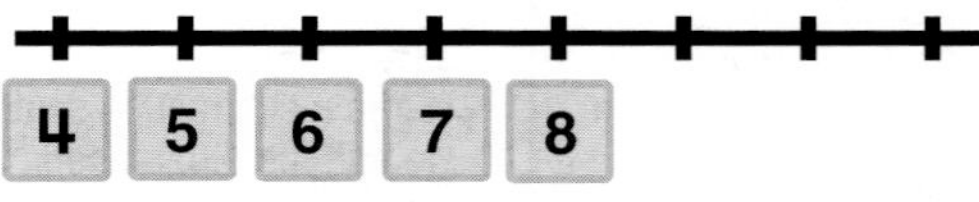

- Introduce the term count back. Have the group count back as the child walks 2 steps toward zero. Say the number the child starts on: **6** – and each number he or she steps on: **5, 4.** Complete the subtraction sentence on the board. *(6 – 2 = 4)*
- Repeat by starting on other numbers and counting back 1 and 2.

Ongoing Assessment

- **Number Sense Which way do you move on a number line to subtract? Why?** *(Sample response: You go toward zero because the numbers get smaller.)*
- **How can you use a number line to show 8 – 1?** *(Start on 8 and count back 1.)*

Reaching All Learners

Math Vocabulary

Understanding *Count Back*

10–15 MIN **Auditory/Linguistic** WHOLE CLASS

- Draw a number line from 0–12 on the board. Review counting on as you count on three from 8. Emphasize the movement from left to right. Write $8 + 3 = 11$ on the board.
- Introduce the phrase *counting back.* Help children recognize that to count back, they must move from right to left. Have a volunteer count back two from 11. Write $11 - 2 = 9$ on the board. Then have children count back one or two from different numbers less than 13.
- Add *count back* to the Math Word Wall.

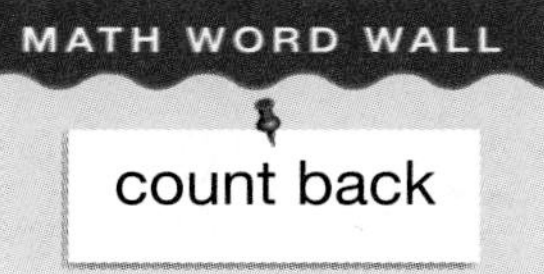

Access Content

English Language Learners

Moving on a Number Line

10–15 MIN **Kinesthetic**

Materials Number Cards 0–11 (Teaching Tool 9); Number Cards 12–20 (Teaching Tool 11); masking tape

- Place a long strip of tape on the floor. Label one-foot intervals with the numbers 0–12 using the number cards.
- Step on 9 and say: **9.** Demonstrate walking two steps toward 0 as you count back: **8, 7.** Write the number sentence that tells what you did: $9 - 2 = 7$.
- Have children count back by walking toward zero on the number line 1 or 2 spaces from a given number. As they walk, have them say the numbers that they walk on in English and in their primary languages. You may wish to have children write and say number sentences to tell what they did.

Reteaching

Practicing on a Number Line

10–15 MIN **Kinesthetic**

Materials *(per child)* Number Lines (Teaching Tool 10)

- Have each child place a finger on the number 10. Then have them move one step toward 0. **What number are you on now?** *(9)* Write the number sentence $10 - 1 = 9$ on the board. Explain that they began on 10 and moved back one to arrive at 9.
- Have children count back two steps from 8. Ask children to write number sentences that tell what they did.
- Repeat, having children count back 1 or 2 from numbers less than 12.

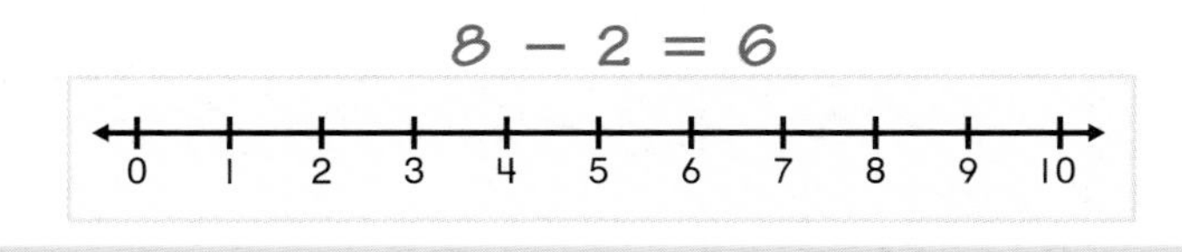

Students with Special Needs

Wooden Number Line

10–15 MIN

Materials *(per pair)* 13 wooden blocks labeled with the numbers 0–12

- Write $8 - 2 =$ ___ on the board. Have the children line up the blocks labeled 0–8 in order to create a number line. Have children point to the 8 block and together say: **8.** As children remove two blocks, one by one, count back: **7, 6.** Invite a child to fill in the answer to the problem on the board.
- Have children work in pairs. One child writes a problem. The other child uses the blocks to find the answer.

Objective Use a number line to count back 1 or 2.

1 Warm Up

Activate Prior Knowledge Review counting on using a number line. Draw a number line on the board leaving out various numbers. Have children fill in the missing numbers. Ask a volunteer to tell how to use the number line to find 4 + 2. *(Start at 4, move away from zero, and count on two.)*

2 Teach

Learn!

Direct children's attention to the number line at the top of the student page. Explain that you move toward zero and count back when you subtract on a number line. **Why do we move toward zero?** *(The numbers get smaller.)* Discuss where to start to find 8 – 2. Have children follow with their fingers as you start on 8 and say: **8** – and count back aloud: **7, 6.**

Ongoing Assessment

Talk About It

- **Why do we count back?** *(It is a way to subtract; we can show how many are left.)*
- **How can you use a number line to find 5 – 2?** *(Start on 5 and count back 4, 3.)*

If children move in the wrong direction,
then have them draw an arrow pointing toward zero below the number line as a reminder.

Error Intervention

If children start on the wrong number,
then have them first circle the starting number. *(Also see* Reteaching, *Page 125B.)*

Think About It Have children demonstrate finding 8 + 2 and 8 – 2 on a number line. **What did you do differently to subtract than you did to add?**

Name ____________

Counting Back Using a Number Line

Learn!

You can use a number line to **count back**.
Count back to subtract.

Start on 8. Count back 2: 7, 6.

8 – 2 = 6

0 1 2 3 4 5 6 7 8 9 10 11 12

Word Bank
count back

Check

Use the number line.
Count back to find each difference.

0 1 2 3 4 5 6 7 8 9 10 11 12

1. 7 – 2 = 5 10 – 1 = 9 4 – 1 = 3
2. 6 – 1 = 5 5 – 2 = 3 11 – 2 = 9
3. 9 – 2 = 7 7 – 1 = 6 3 – 2 = 1
4. 8 – 1 = 7 10 – 2 = 8 2 – 1 = 1
5. 4 – 2 = 2 9 – 1 = 8 6 – 2 = 4

Think About It Reasoning
How is adding on a number line different from subtracting on a number line?
Move right to add on a number line; move left to subtract on a number line.

Reteaching Below Level

Counting Back Using a Number Line R 4-1

To find 7 – 2, start at 7. Circle 7.

0 1 2 3 4 5 6 (7) 8 9 10 11 12

Now count back 2.

0 1 2 3 4 5 6 (7) 8 9 10 11 12

7 – 2 = 5

Count back to subtract.
Show your work on the number line.

1. 0 1 2 3 (4) 5 6 7 8 9 10 11 12

4 – 1 = 3

2. 0 1 2 3 4 5 6 7 8 (9) 10 11 12

9 – 2 = 7

Practice On Level

Counting Back Using a Number Line P 4-1

Count back to subtract.
Use a number line if you like.

0 1 2 3 4 5 6 7 8 9 10 11 12

1. 6 – 2 = 4; 4 – 1 = 3; 7 – 1 = 6; 3 – 2 = 1; 4 – 2 = 2; 5 – 1 = 4
2. 7 – 2 = 5; 6 – 1 = 5; 5 – 2 = 3; 3 – 1 = 2; 8 – 2 = 6; 9 – 1 = 8
3. 10 – 1 = 9; 9 – 2 = 7; 2 – 2 = 0; 12 – 1 = 11; 12 – 2 = 10; 11 – 2 = 9

Problem Solving *Number Sense*
Use the number line to subtract.
Write the missing numbers. Look for a pattern.

4. 0 1 2 3 4 5 6 7 8 9 10 11 12

3	4	5	6	7	8
– 2	– 2	– 2	– 2	– 2	– 2
1	2	3	4	5	6

Practice

Count back to subtract.
Use the number line if you like.

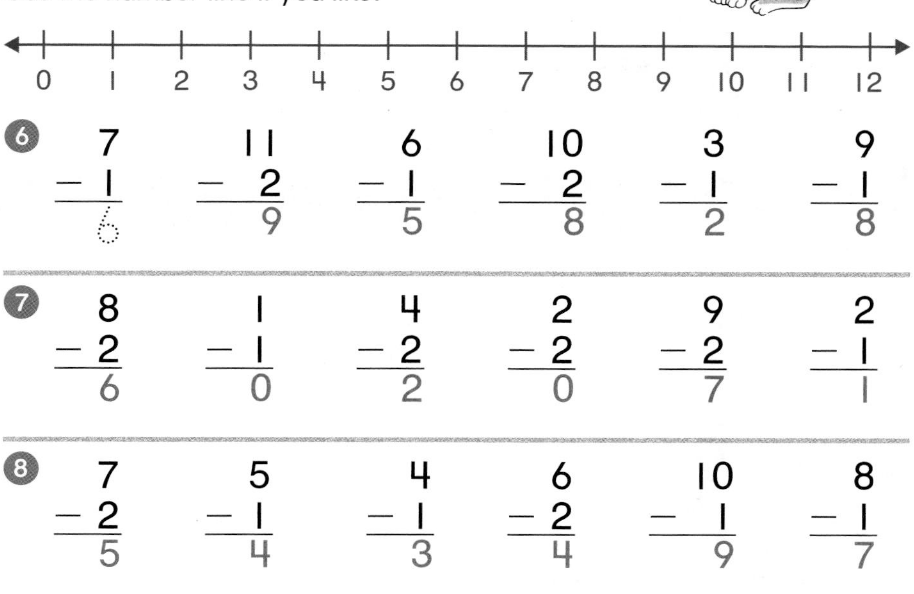

0 1 2 3 4 5 6 7 8 9 10 11 12

6. $7 - 1 = 6$ | $11 - 2 = 9$ | $6 - 1 = 5$ | $10 - 2 = 8$ | $3 - 1 = 2$ | $9 - 1 = 8$

7. $8 - 2 = 6$ | $1 - 1 = 0$ | $4 - 2 = 2$ | $2 - 2 = 0$ | $9 - 2 = 7$ | $2 - 1 = 1$

8. $7 - 2 = 5$ | $5 - 1 = 4$ | $4 - 1 = 3$ | $6 - 2 = 4$ | $10 - 1 = 9$ | $8 - 1 = 7$

Problem Solving **Algebra**

Use the number line to subtract.
Write the missing numbers. Then look for a pattern.

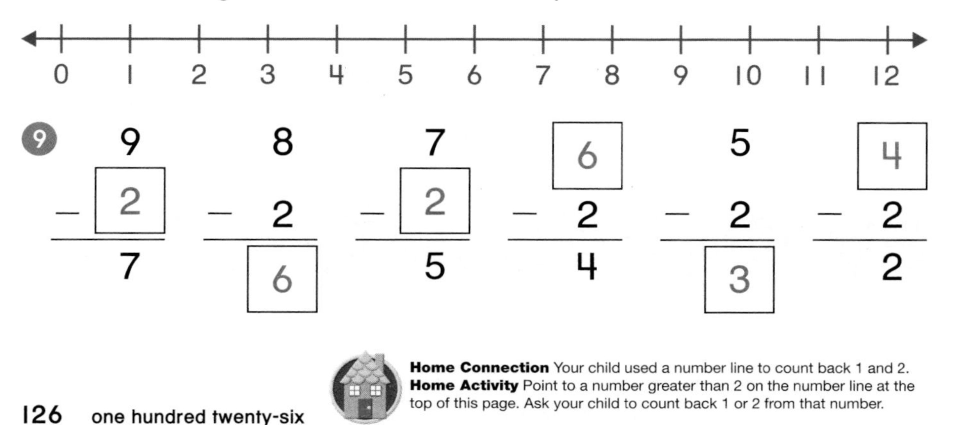

0 1 2 3 4 5 6 7 8 9 10 11 12

9. $9 - \boxed{2} = 7$ | $8 - 2 = \boxed{6}$ | $7 - \boxed{2} = 5$ | $\boxed{6} - 2 = 4$ | $5 - 2 = \boxed{3}$ | $\boxed{4} - 2 = 2$

Home Connection Your child used a number line to count back 1 and 2.
Home Activity Point to a number greater than 2 on the number line at the top of this page. Ask your child to count back 1 or 2 from that number.

3 Practice

After children do Exercise 9, discuss the pattern in the starting numbers and the differences.

Reading Assist: Compare and Contrast How is *counting on* using the number line different from *counting back?* *(For counting on you move right; for counting back you move left.)* **How are they the same?** *(You start, count, and say the answer.)*

Leveled Practice

Below Level Use number lines for all exercises.

On Level Use number lines as needed.

Above Level Do exercises without number lines.

Early Finishers Have children find 5 – 4. **What do you notice about these numbers?** *(Sample answer: They are next to each other on the number line.)* **You are subtracting all but one.** Have children write subtraction problems with a difference of one.

4 Assess

Journal Idea Have children write and answer number riddles. Show them the following model: "I start on 9. I count back 2. Where am I now?" *(7)*

Enrichment Above Level

Count Back E 4-1 ALGEBRA

Count back to subtract.
Use the number line if you like.

0 1 2 3 4 5 6 7 8 9 10 11 12

1. 9 – 2 = 7 I counted back 2.
2. 6 – 2 = 4 I counted back 2.
3. 5 – 1 = 4 I counted back 1.
4. 2 – 2 = 0 I counted back 2.
5. 11 – 2 = 9 I counted back 2.
6. 10 – 1 = 9 I counted back 1.
7. 12 – 2 = 10 I counted back 2.
8. 8 – 1 = 7 I counted back 1.
9. 7 – 1 = 6 I counted back 1.
10. 4 – 2 = 2 I counted back 2.
11. 9 – 1 = 8 I counted back 1.
12. 3 – 1 = 2 I counted back 1.

Use with Lesson 4-1. 39

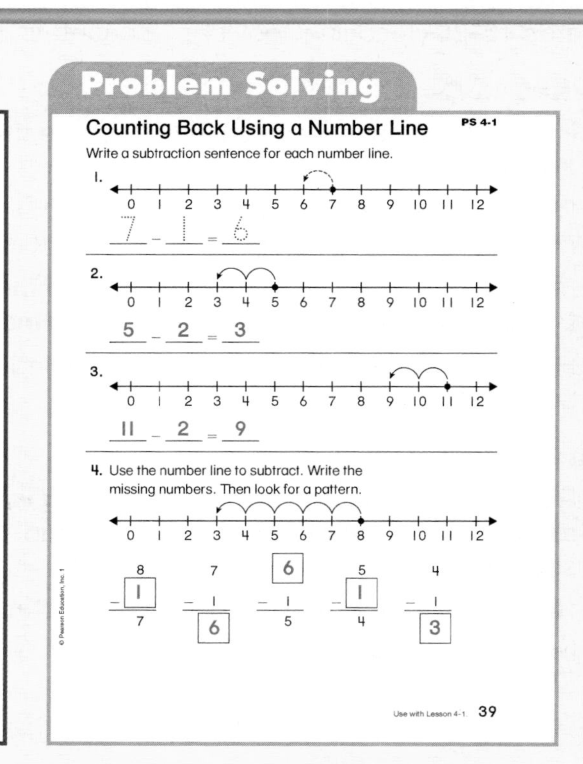

Problem Solving

Counting Back Using a Number Line PS 4-1

Write a subtraction sentence for each number line.

1. 7 – 1 = 6
2. 5 – 2 = 3
3. 11 – 2 = 9
4. Use the number line to subtract. Write the missing numbers. Then look for a pattern.

8 – [1] = 7 | 7 – 1 = [6] | [6] – 1 = 5 | 5 – [1] = 4 | 4 – 1 = [3]

Use with Lesson 4-1. 39

Test-Taking Practice 4-1

1. Count back to find the difference.
Use the number line.

10
– 1

Ⓐ 11
Ⓑ 10
● 9
Ⓓ 8

2. What is the missing number?
Use the number line to subtract.

7
– [ ]
6

Ⓐ 7
Ⓑ 6
Ⓒ 2
● 1

Use with Lesson 4-1. 39

Available as a transparency

4-2 Counting Back

Lesson Organizer

Quick Lesson Overview 

Objective Find differences by counting back 1 or 2.

Math Understanding When counting back, the last number said tells how many are left.

Materials for Student Pages *(per child)* 12 counters

How Children Learn Math
Children will build upon the skill of counting back on the number line. In this lesson they will be simply counting back from a given number. As they count back, some children may need to use manipulatives to touch and count, while others may be ready to say the numbers aloud or to themselves.

NCTM Standards

- Number and Operations

(For a complete correlation to the NCTM Standards and Grades Pre-K through 2 Expectations, see Pages 123G and 123H.)

Getting Started

Spiral Review

Problem of the Day 4-2

1 2 3 4 5
6 7 8 9 10

Read Aloud The Kamba people of Kenya, East Africa, show numbers with their fingers. How could you use your fingers to show the number 4? The number 7? The number 9? (Hint: Use Logical Reasoning)

Topics Reviewed

- Number sense
- Problem-Solving Strategy: Use Logical Reasoning

Answer Check children's fingers.

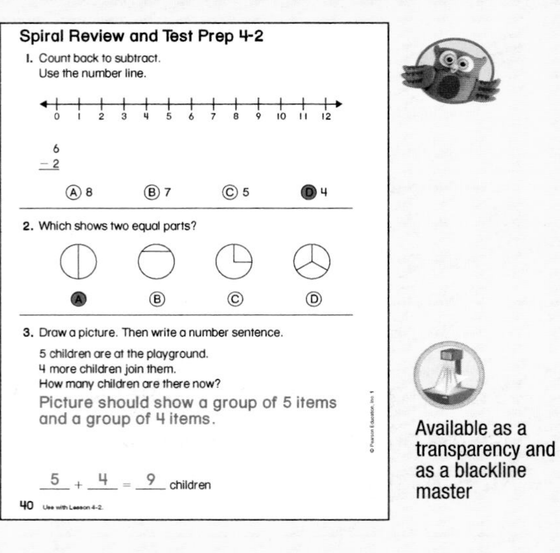
Spiral Review and Test Prep 4-2

1. Count back to subtract. Use the number line.

0 1 2 3 4 5 6 7 8 9 10 11 12

6
− 2

Ⓐ 8 Ⓑ 7 Ⓒ 5 Ⓓ 4

2. Which shows two equal parts?

Ⓐ Ⓑ Ⓒ Ⓓ

3. Draw a picture. Then write a number sentence.

5 children are at the playground.
4 more children join them.
How many children are there now?

Picture should show a group of 5 items and a group of 4 items.

5 + 4 = 9 children

40 Use with Lesson 4-2

Available as a transparency and as a blackline master

Topics Reviewed

1. Counting Back Using a Number Line
2. Equal Parts
3. Draw a Picture

Investigating the Concept

Counting Back

Materials *(per pair)* Number Cards 0–11 (Teaching Tool 9); Number Cards 12–20 (Teaching Tool 11); 12 counters; empty box

What to Do

- Prior to the lesson, have children prepare the number cards for 0 through 12 from the teaching tools.
- Place 5 counters in a box and label the box with the "5" card. Write 5 − 2 on the board and tell children that counting back is one way to subtract.
- Demonstrate counting back two. Point to the number card, and say: **5.** Remove 2 counters as you count back: **4, 3. How many counters are left in the box?** *(3)*
- Have pairs of children work together to find 4 − 2, 8 − 1, and 7 − 2.

5 − 2 = 3

Ongoing Assessment

- **Reasoning Should you start counting with 1 when you are counting back to find 7 − 2? Explain.** *(No, you should start by saying 7 and then count back.)*
- **How can you find how many are left after you take 2 away?** *(Say the starting number and count back 2. The last number that you say is your answer.)*

Reaching All Learners

Math and Literature

Subtracting Roses

10–15 MIN **Auditory/Linguistic**

Materials *Ten Rosy Roses* by Eve Merriam (HarperCollins, 1999)

- Read the story aloud one time without stopping to allow children to enjoy its rhythm and rhyme. After you finish reading, ask children to discuss the pattern that is seen on each consecutive page of the story. *(On each page, the number of roses decreases by one.)*
- Read the story aloud again. Stop after each page and invite a child to write the subtraction sentence on the board that is illustrated on the page.

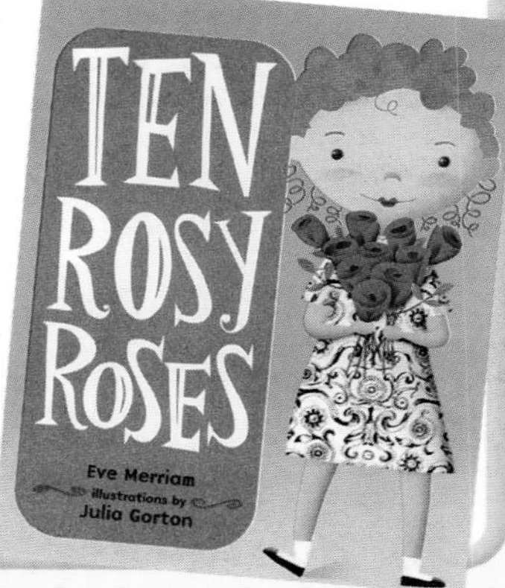

Extend Language

English Language Learners

Countdown

10–15 MIN **Auditory/Kinesthetic**

SMALL GROUP

Materials *(per child)* 10 counters

- Have children line up their counters. Read the following poem aloud:

  Ten little ducks went swimming one day,
  Over the hills and far away,
  Mother Duck said, "Quack, quack, quack,"
  But only nine little ducks came back.

- Have children remove 1 counter from their row. Write 10 − 1 = 9 on the board.
- Repeat the poem. Begin with *Nine little ducks.* Each time, have children remove a counter and write the next subtraction sentence on the board.

Reteaching

Count Back to Subtract

10–15 MIN **Visual/Spatial/Linguistic**

- On the board, write the subtraction sentence 6 − 2 = ___. Draw 6 objects and number them from 1 to 6.
- Point to the group and say: **6.** Erase one object and say: **5.** Erase a second object and say: **4. We started with 6. We counted back two. What is our answer?** *(4)*
- Repeat subtracting 1 or 2 from other numbers. Challenge children to create their own subtraction sentences to solve by drawing and erasing pictures.

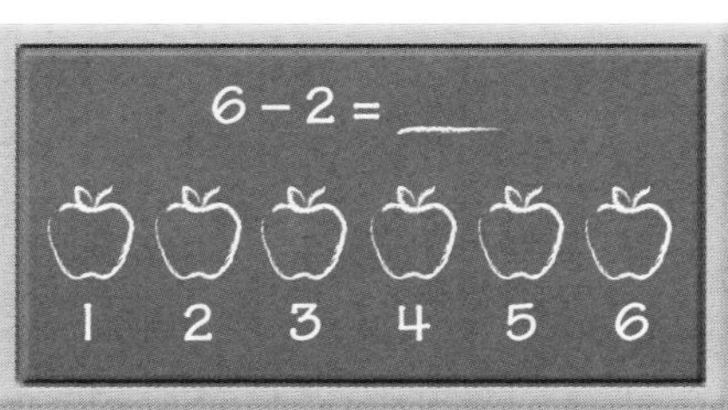

Math and Social Studies

Counting Down the Days Until …

5–10 MIN **Logical/Mathematical**

WHOLE CLASS

Materials Large calendar

- 10 or 12 days prior to a holiday or other special event, show a large calendar to children. On the calendar indicate both the current day and the day of the special event. Have children count how many days before the special occasion.
- Post the total number on the board. Each day, mark off the day on the calendar and count down the number of days that are left.

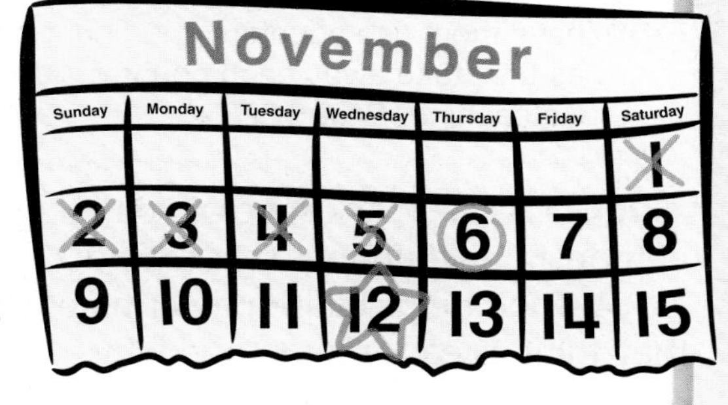

Objective Find differences by counting back 1 or 2.

1 Warm Up

Activate Prior Knowledge Review counting back on the number line. Draw a number line from 0–12 on the board. **Imagine my dinosaur is on 6 and he jumps back 1. Where does he land?** Repeat starting on different numbers. Then have the dinosaur jump back 2.

2 Teach

Learn!

Call attention to the label that tells there were 4 kittens in the bucket. Ask children how they can find out how many kittens are left in the bucket after 1 jumps out. Remind children that counting back is one way to subtract. Say: **4.** Count back aloud: **3.** Then ask how many kittens are left in the bucket. *(3)*

Ongoing Assessment

Talk About It

- **Why do we count back?** *(To find out how many are left)*
- **How would you count back to find 9 – 2?** *(Start at 9 and count back 8, 7.)*

If children have trouble counting back mentally,

then have them use a ruler or a number line to help them count back.

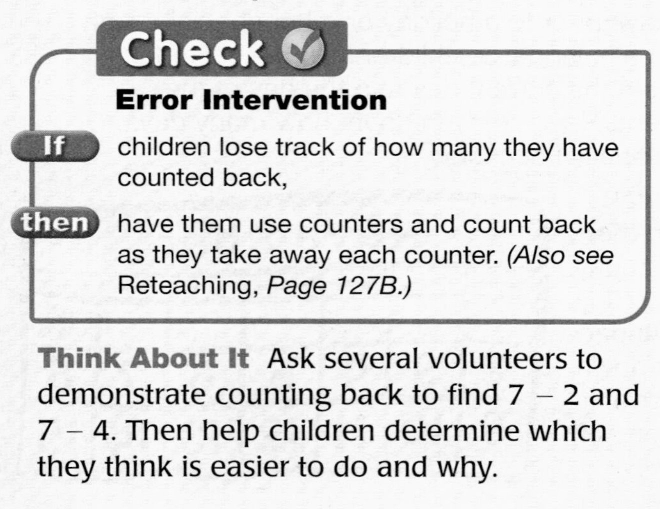

Check

Error Intervention

If children lose track of how many they have counted back,

then have them use counters and count back as they take away each counter. *(Also see Reteaching, Page 127B.)*

Think About It Ask several volunteers to demonstrate counting back to find 7 – 2 and 7 – 4. Then help children determine which they think is easier to do and why.

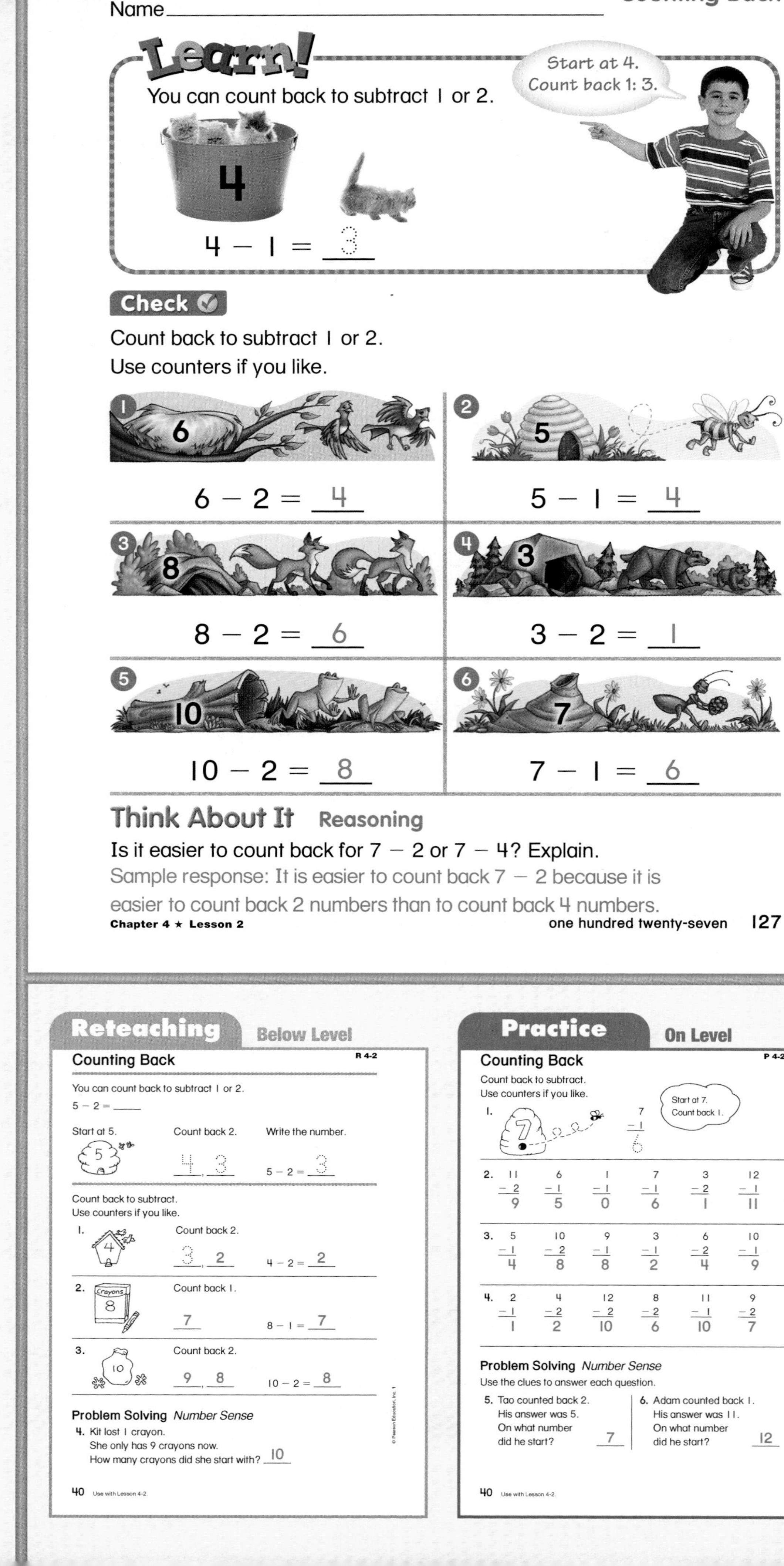

Name__________

Counting Back

Learn!

You can count back to subtract 1 or 2.

Start at 4.
Count back 1: 3.
4

$4 - 1 = 3$

Check

Count back to subtract 1 or 2.
Use counters if you like.

1. $6 - 2 = 4$
2. $5 - 1 = 4$
3. $8 - 2 = 6$
4. $3 - 2 = 1$
5. $10 - 2 = 8$
6. $7 - 1 = 6$

Think About It Reasoning

Is it easier to count back for 7 − 2 or 7 − 4? Explain.

Sample response: It is easier to count back 7 − 2 because it is easier to count back 2 numbers than to count back 4 numbers.

Reteaching Below Level

Counting Back R 4-2

You can count back to subtract 1 or 2.

5 − 2 = ____

Start at 5. Count back 2. 4, 3 Write the number. 5 − 2 = 3

Count back to subtract.
Use counters if you like.

1. Count back 2. 3, 2 4 − 2 = 2
2. Count back 1. 7 8 − 1 = 7
3. Count back 2. 9, 8 10 − 2 = 8

Problem Solving *Number Sense*

4. Kit lost 1 crayon. She only has 9 crayons now. How many crayons did she start with? 10

Practice On Level

Counting Back P 4-2

Count back to subtract.
Use counters if you like.

1. $7 - 1 = 6$ (Start at 7. Count back 1.)

2. $11 - 2 = 9$, $6 - 1 = 5$, $1 - 1 = 0$, $7 - 1 = 6$, $3 - 2 = 1$, $12 - 1 = 11$

3. $5 - 1 = 4$, $10 - 2 = 8$, $9 - 1 = 8$, $3 - 1 = 2$, $6 - 2 = 4$, $10 - 1 = 9$

4. $2 - 1 = 1$, $4 - 2 = 2$, $12 - 2 = 10$, $8 - 2 = 6$, $11 - 1 = 10$, $9 - 2 = 7$

Problem Solving *Number Sense*

Use the clues to answer each question.

5. Tao counted back 2. His answer was 5. On what number did he start? 7

6. Adam counted back 1. His answer was 11. On what number did he start? 12

Practice

Count back to subtract.
Use counters if you like.

Start at 9.
Count back 1: 8.

7.

9
− 1
8

8.

6	5	2	8	4	1
− 2	− 1	− 2	− 1	− 2	− 1
4	4	0	7	2	0

9.

6	11	10	3	7	7
− 1	− 2	− 1	− 1	− 2	− 1
5	9	9	2	5	6

10.

2	5	8	9	4	10
− 1	− 2	− 2	− 2	− 1	− 2
1	3	6	7	3	8

Problem Solving Number Sense

Use the clues to answer each question.

11. Joy counted back 2.
Her answer was 7.
On what number did Joy start?
9

12. Mick counted back 1.
His answer was 9.
On what number did Mick start?
10

Home Connection Your child counted back to subtract 1 or 2.
Home Activity Ask your child to explain how to count back to show 8 − 2.

3 Practice

For Exercise 7, check children's understanding by having them count back aloud.

Reading Assist: Use Picture Clues
Before doing Exercise 7, ask children to look at the picture and tell what is happening. This will help clarify on which number to begin.

Leveled Practice

Below Level Use counters for each exercise.

On Level Use counters as needed.

Above Level Do all exercises without counters.

Early Finishers Invite children to make up riddles, such as: **I started with 5 and counted back to 3. How many did I count back?** Have them exchange and solve each other's riddles.

4 Assess

Journal Idea Have children write how old they are and count back to tell how old they were two years ago. Ask children to write a subtraction sentence that shows how old they were. Have children draw pictures of how they looked then.

Test-Taking Practice 4-2

1. Count back to subtract.
Use counters if you like.

11
− 2

● 9 Ⓒ 12
Ⓑ 10 Ⓓ 13

2. Andy counted back 1.
His answer was 6.
On what number did he start?

Ⓐ 4 Ⓒ 6
Ⓑ 5 ● 7

3. Jessica counted back 3.
Her answer was 5.
On what number did she start?

Ⓐ 9
● 8
Ⓒ 7
Ⓓ 6

Use with Lesson 4-2. 40

Available as a transparency

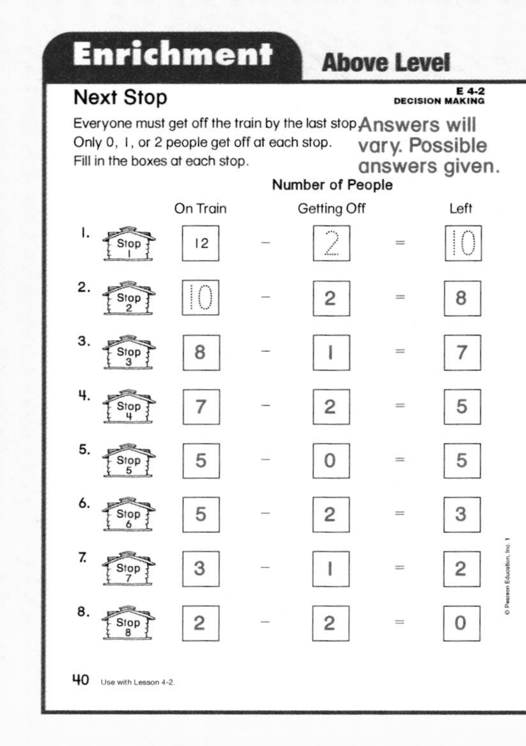

Enrichment Above Level

Next Stop E 4-2 DECISION MAKING

Everyone must get off the train by the last stop.
Only 0, 1, or 2 people get off at each stop.
Fill in the boxes at each stop.

Answers will vary. Possible answers given.

Number of People

	On Train		Getting Off		Left
1. Stop 1	12	−	2	=	10
2. Stop 2	10	−	2	=	8
3. Stop 3	8	−	1	=	7
4. Stop 4	7	−	2	=	5
5. Stop 5	5	−	0	=	5
6. Stop 6	5	−	2	=	3
7. Stop 7	3	−	1	=	2
8. Stop 8	2	−	2	=	0

© Pearson Education, Inc. 1

40 Use with Lesson 4-2.

Problem Solving

Counting Back PS 4-2

The children are playing a counting game.
Use the clues to answer each question.

1. You count back 2.
Your answer is 2.
On what number did you start?
4

2. You count back 1.
Your answer is 6.
On what number did you start?
7

3. You count back 2.
Your answer is 10.
On what number did you start?
12

4. You count back 1.
Your answer is 7.
On what number did you start?
8

5. You started at 10.
Your answer is 8.
By what number did you count back?
2

6. You started at 4.
Your answer is 3.
By what number did you count back?
1

7. You started at 4.
Your answer is 1.
By what number did you count back?
3

8. You started at 2.
Your answer is 0.
By what number did you count back?
2

© Pearson Education, Inc. 1

40 Use with Lesson 4-2.

4-3 Using Doubles to Subtract

Lesson Organizer

Quick Lesson Overview

Objective Find differences by using doubles facts.

Math Understanding Doubles facts can be used to find differences for their related subtraction facts.

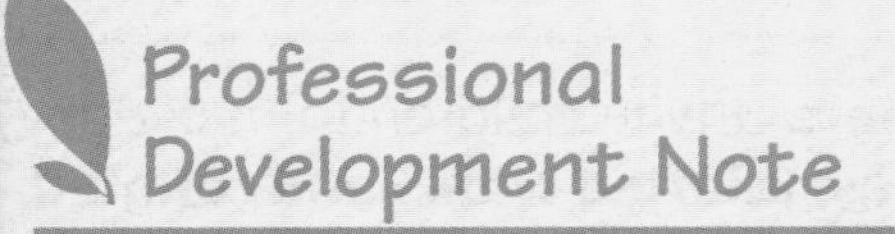

How Children Learn Math
Memorizing doubles facts is important. They should be mastered before children can use them to subtract. Provide more practice for those who are still unsure. Using doubles will help children begin to understand the inverse relationship between addition and subtraction.

NCTM Standards

- Number and Operations

(For a complete correlation to the NCTM Standards and Grades Pre-K through 2 Expectations, see Pages 123G and 123H.)

Getting Started

Spiral Review

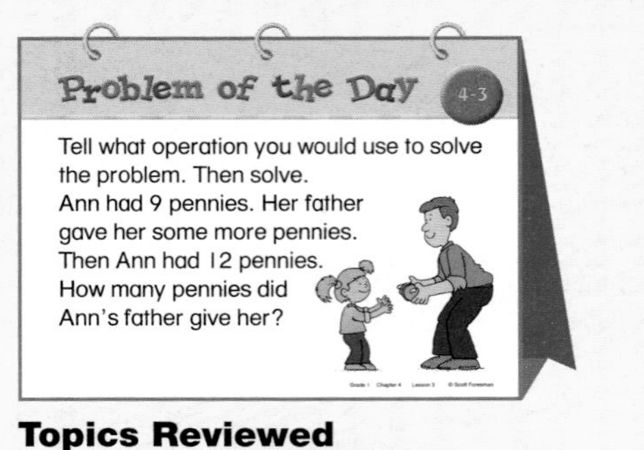

Topics Reviewed
- Addition and subtraction
- Problem-Solving Skill: Choose an Operation

Answer Sample: Use subtraction to solve the problem; 12 – 9 = 3. Ann's father gave her 3 pennies.

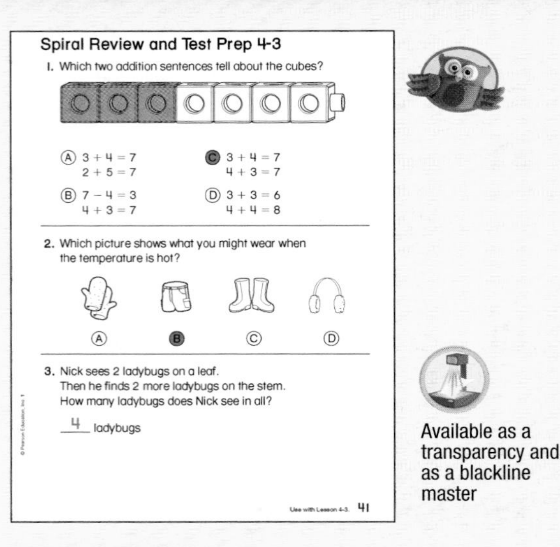

Spiral Review and Test Prep 4-3

1. Which two addition sentences tell about the cubes?

Ⓐ 3 + 4 = 7, 2 + 5 = 7
Ⓒ 3 + 4 = 7, 4 + 3 = 7
Ⓑ 7 – 4 = 3, 4 + 3 = 7
Ⓓ 3 + 3 = 6, 4 + 4 = 8

2. Which picture shows what you might wear when the temperature is hot?

Ⓐ Ⓑ Ⓒ Ⓓ

3. Nick sees 2 ladybugs on a leaf. Then he finds 2 more ladybugs on the stem. How many ladybugs does Nick see in all?

4 ladybugs

Use with Lesson 4-3. 41

Available as a transparency and as a blackline master

Topics Reviewed
1. Adding in Any Order
2. Temperature
3. Stories about Joining

Investigating the Concept

Using Doubles to Subtract

Materials *(per pair)* 12 connecting cubes (6 of one color and 6 of a second color)

What to Do

- Have children work in pairs. Give each child 6 cubes of one color. Have each partner make a cube train using 3 cubes. Then connect the trains. Have one partner write the addition sentence that goes with the cubes. *(3 + 3 = 6)*
- Have children break apart the train into its two different colors and write the subtraction sentence that shows what they did. *(6 – 3 = 3)* Help children understand why knowing 3 + 3 can help you subtract 6 – 3.
- Have pairs repeat the procedure for 2 + 2, 4 + 4, 5 + 5, and 6 + 6.

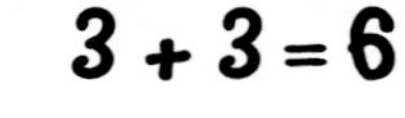

6 – 3 = 3

Ongoing Assessment

- **Number Sense How does knowing 3 + 3 = 6 help you to subtract 6 – 3?** *(Both number sentences have the same parts and whole.)*
- **Which doubles fact would help you find the difference for 10 – 5?** *(5 + 5 = 10)*

Reaching All Learners

Oral Language in Math

Shout It Out!

5–10 MIN **Linguistic**

Materials Subtraction fact cards

- Hold up a subtraction fact card for the group. If the fact can be solved by using doubles, children should shout out, "Doubles!" If it cannot be solved using doubles, children should shout out, "Not doubles!"
- Then invite one child to solve the subtraction problem. He or she should state the complete number sentence, including the answer, and tell which doubles fact helped to solve it.

Doubles!
$3 + 3 = 6$ so $6 - 3 = 3$.

Access Content

English Language Learners

Can Doubles Help You?

10–15 MIN **Linguistic**

Materials Subtraction fact cards; chart paper

- Divide a piece of chart paper into two columns. Label the first column *Doubles Can Help* and the second column *Doubles Can't Help.*
- From a stack of fact cards, show the group a card. Ask children to decide whether or not it can be solved using doubles. Then have a child write the subtraction fact with an answer in the correct column of the chart.

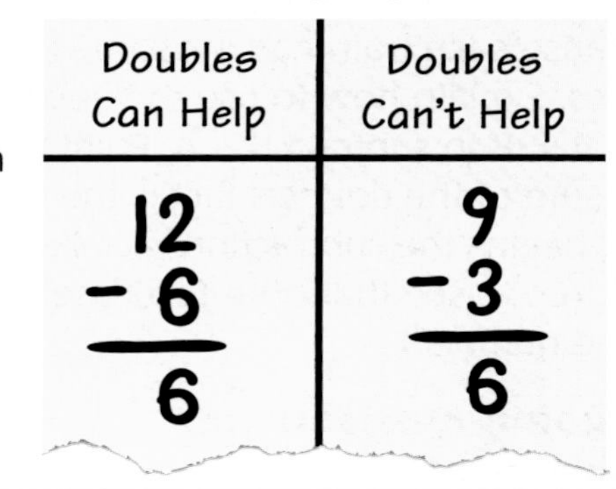

Reteaching

Subtracting with Doubles

10–15 MIN **Logical/Mathematical**

Materials Counters

- On the board write $8 - 4 =$ ___. Have children separate 4 counters from a row of 8 counters. Have children write an addition sentence that tells what is shown by the counters. *(4 + 4 = 8)*
- **How is 4 + 4 = 8 related to 8 − 4 = ___? What is the answer to the subtraction sentence?** *(4)* Help children recognize that the facts have the same parts and wholes. Knowing doubles facts can help with subtracting doubles.
- Repeat with other subtraction sentences that can be solved using doubles facts.

$4 + 4 = 8$
$8 - 4 = 4$

Students with Special Needs

Bags of Cubes

5–10 MIN **Logical/Mathematical**

PAIRS

Materials *(per pair)* Paper bag; green and blue connecting cubes

- Prepare bags with equal numbers of green and blue connecting cubes, such as 5 green cubes and 5 blue cubes.
- Invite each pair of children to select a bag. They should remove all of the cubes from the bag and write an addition sentence and a subtraction sentence about the cubes in the bag, such as $5 + 5 = 10$ and $10 - 5 = 5$.
- Allow pairs to share their sentences with the group.

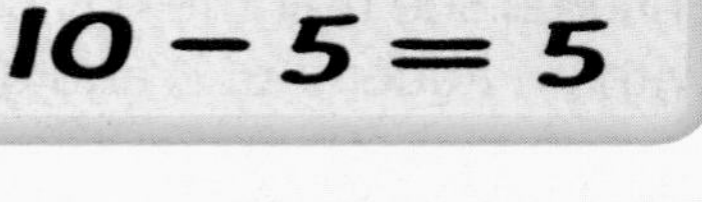

Objective Find differences by using doubles facts.

1 Warm Up

Activate Prior Knowledge Review adding doubles to 12. Write the doubles facts with sums to 12 on the board. Have children work in pairs, using their fingers to show the doubles.

2 Teach

Learn!

Discuss the cubes at the top of the student page. Emphasize that they show doubles because each train has the same number of cubes. Explain how to use the doubles fact $4 + 4 = 8$ to subtract $8 - 4$. Point out that the sum of the doubles fact is the number that begins the subtraction fact. Lead children to see that both facts use the same numbers.

Ongoing Assessment

Talk About It

- **What doubles fact would you use to help you find 4 – 2?** *(2 + 2 = 4)*
- **Which number in the doubles fact gives the difference in the subtraction sentence?** *(Either of the addends)*

If children have difficulty seeing the relationship between the addition and subtraction,

then have them act out the facts using cubes.

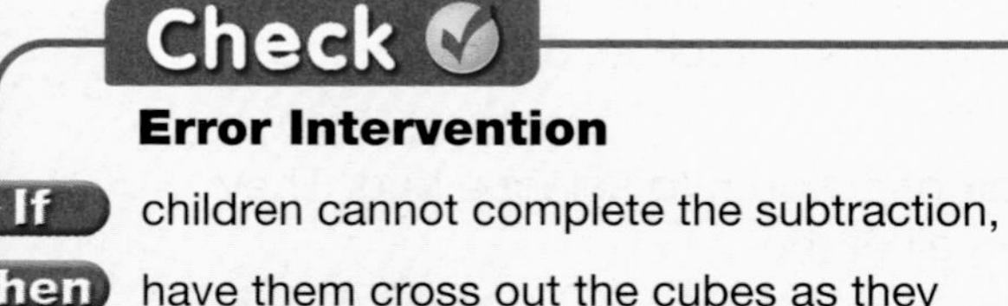

Check

Error Intervention

If children cannot complete the subtraction,

then have them cross out the cubes as they are subtracted. *(Also see* Reteaching, *Page 129B.)*

Think About It Ask: **Which double can you make using two 5s?** *(5 + 5 = 10)* **Which double has a sum of 12?** *(6 + 6 = 12)* Help children see that there is no doubles facts with an addend of 5 and a sum of 12.

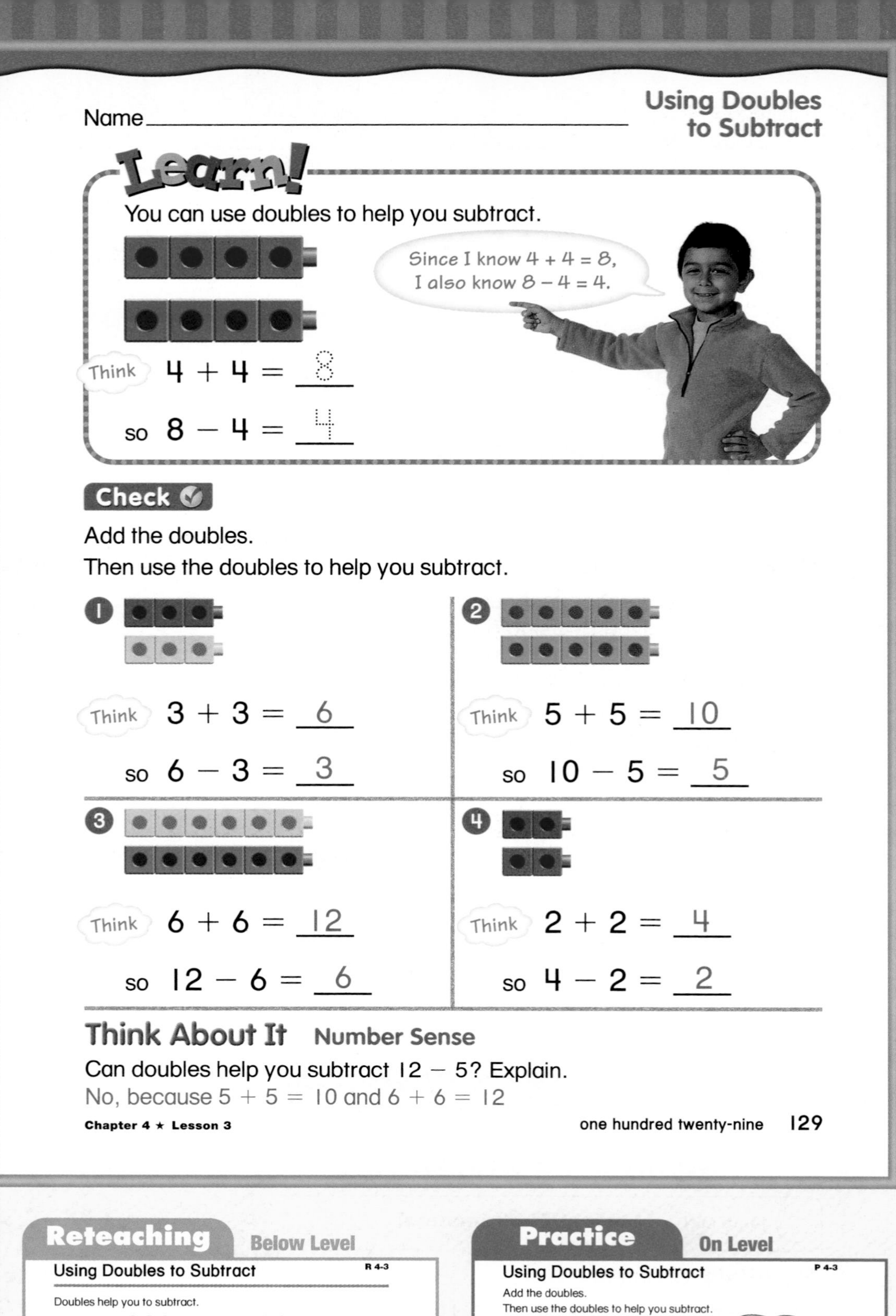

Name ________________

Using Doubles to Subtract

Learn!

You can use doubles to help you subtract.

Since I know 4 + 4 = 8,
I also know 8 – 4 = 4.

Think $4 + 4 = 8$

so $8 - 4 = 4$

Check

Add the doubles.
Then use the doubles to help you subtract.

1. Think $3 + 3 = 6$ so $6 - 3 = 3$
2. Think $5 + 5 = 10$ so $10 - 5 = 5$
3. Think $6 + 6 = 12$ so $12 - 6 = 6$
4. Think $2 + 2 = 4$ so $4 - 2 = 2$

Think About It Number Sense

Can doubles help you subtract $12 - 5$? Explain.

No, because $5 + 5 = 10$ and $6 + 6 = 12$

Chapter 4 ★ Lesson 3 — one hundred twenty-nine 129

Reteaching Below Level

Using Doubles to Subtract R 4-3

Doubles help you to subtract.

Think: $3 + 3 = 6$ so $6 - 3 = 3$

Add the doubles.
Then use the doubles to help you subtract.

1. $1 + 1 = 2$ so $2 - 1 = 1$
2. $4 + 4 = 8$ so $8 - 4 = 4$

Problem Solving *Visual Thinking*

Complete the addition and subtraction sentences.

3. $2 + 2 = 4$
$4 - 2 = 2$

Use with Lesson 4-3. 41

Practice On Level

Using Doubles to Subtract P 4-3

Add the doubles.
Then use the doubles to help you subtract.

1. $3 + 3 = 6$, $6 - 3 = 3$ (If 3 + 3 = 6, then 6 – 3 = 3.)
2. $4 + 4 = 8$, $8 - 4 = 4$
3. $6 + 6 = 12$, $12 - 6 = 6$
4. $2 + 2 = 4$, $4 - 2 = 2$
5. $5 + 5 = 10$, $10 - 5 = 5$

Problem Solving *Visual Thinking*

Write an addition sentence and a subtraction sentence for the picture.

6. $3 + 3 = 6$
$6 - 3 = 3$

Use with Lesson 4-3. 41

Practice

Add the doubles.
Then use the doubles to help you subtract.

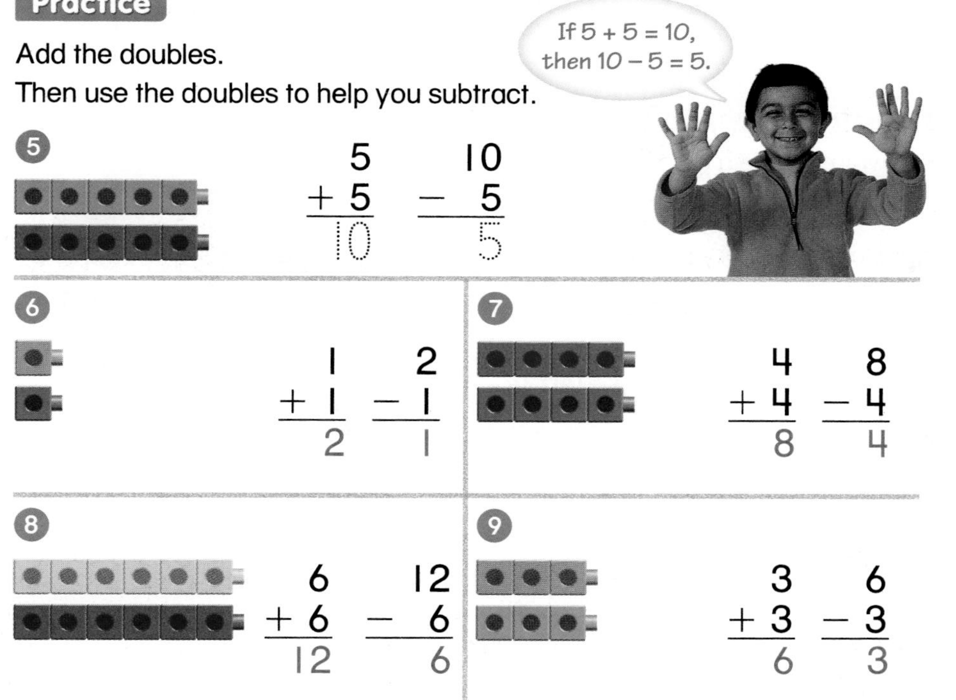

5. $5 + 5 = 10$; $10 - 5 = 5$

6. $1 + 1 = 2$; $2 - 1 = 1$

7. $4 + 4 = 8$; $8 - 4 = 4$

8. $6 + 6 = 12$; $12 - 6 = 6$

9. $3 + 3 = 6$; $6 - 3 = 3$

Problem Solving Visual Thinking

Write an addition sentence and a subtraction sentence for the picture.

10.

4 + 4 = 8

8 − 4 = 4

Home Connection Your child used doubles to subtract. **Home Activity** Ask your child to use buttons or other small objects to show a doubles fact. Then have him or her name the subtraction problem that can be solved using the doubles fact.

3 Practice

Remind children to first complete the doubles fact and then do the subtraction.

For Exercise 10, remind children to count all of the ducks before writing the number sentences.

Leveled Practice

Below Level Use cubes to model each exercise and show the doubles fact.

On Level Complete the exercises as written, using cubes if needed.

Above Level Do all exercises without using cubes.

Early Finishers Invite children to draw a picture of cars to show 3 + 3 = 6 and then write the subtraction sentence that it can help them solve.

4 Assess

Journal Idea Write the following pair of facts on the board: 5 + 5 = 10 and 10 − 5 = 5. Have each child illustrate the pair with one illustration, such as 5 stars and 5 moons.

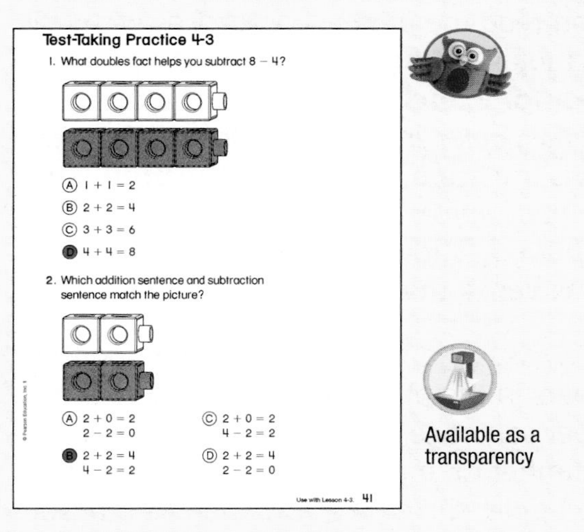

Test-Taking Practice 4-3

1. What doubles fact helps you subtract 8 − 4?

Ⓐ 1 + 1 = 2
Ⓑ 2 + 2 = 4
Ⓒ 3 + 3 = 6
Ⓓ 4 + 4 = 8

2. Which addition sentence and subtraction sentence match the picture?

Ⓐ 2 + 0 = 2, 2 − 2 = 0
Ⓑ 2 + 2 = 4, 4 − 2 = 2
Ⓒ 2 + 0 = 2, 4 − 2 = 2
Ⓓ 2 + 2 = 4, 2 − 2 = 0

Use with Lesson 4-3. 41

Available as a transparency

Enrichment Above Level

Sailing with Doubles E 4-3 ALGEBRA

Use the numbers on the flags to write an addition sentence and a subtraction sentence.

1. 4 + 4 = 8 ; 8 − 4 = 4
2. 5 + 5 = 10 ; 10 − 5 = 5
3. 3 + 3 = 6 ; 6 − 3 = 3
4. 1 + 1 = 2 ; 2 − 1 = 1
5. 2 + 2 = 4 ; 4 − 2 = 2
6. 6 + 6 = 12 ; 12 − 6 = 6

Use with Lesson 4-3. 41

Problem Solving

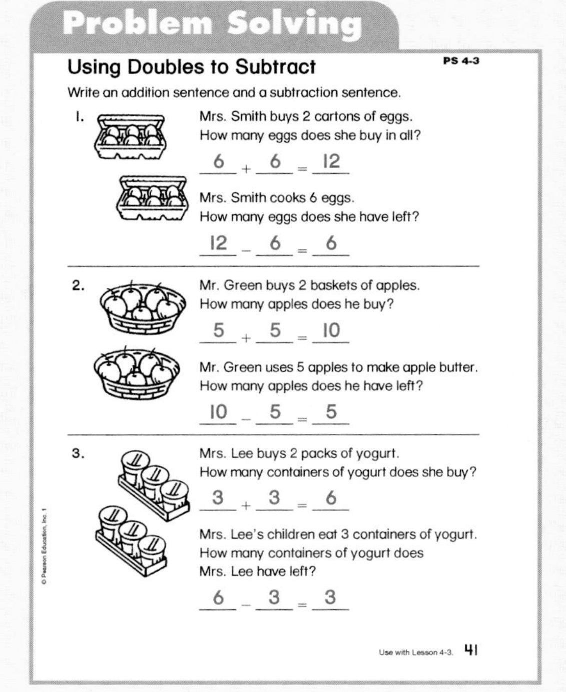

Using Doubles to Subtract PS 4-3

Write an addition sentence and a subtraction sentence.

1. Mrs. Smith buys 2 cartons of eggs. How many eggs does she buy in all? 6 + 6 = 12
Mrs. Smith cooks 6 eggs. How many eggs does she have left? 12 − 6 = 6

2. Mr. Green buys 2 baskets of apples. How many apples does he buy? 5 + 5 = 10
Mr. Green uses 5 apples to make apple butter. How many apples does he have left? 10 − 5 = 5

3. Mrs. Lee buys 2 packs of yogurt. How many containers of yogurt does she buy? 3 + 3 = 6
Mrs. Lee's children eat 3 containers of yogurt. How many containers of yogurt does Mrs. Lee have left? 6 − 3 = 3

Use with Lesson 4-3. 41

Reading for Math Success

Purpose Show children how to apply the reading skill, *Identify the Main Idea,* to their math work. Help prepare children for the problem-solving strategy lesson, *Write a Number Sentence,* which follows.

Using Student Page 131

Reading Skills and Math Understanding Knowing how to identify the main idea of a story is an essential reading skill. If children understand the main idea of a story problem, they will be able to write a number sentence that represents the problem and the solution.

Model the Process Tell children that they will read a story problem. Story problems have an important idea that they need to identify in order to solve the problem. Model the following for children: **When I read a story problem, I ask myself these questions: What is this problem about? What is the most important idea? Do I need to add or subtract to solve this story problem? What numbers in the problem tell me more about the important idea?**

Guide the Activity Have children look at the picture and read the problem in Exercise 1. Then read the next two exercises with children and ask: **Why is "a bowl" not a good answer for Exercise 2?** *(Because the story is all about the apples and what happens to them)* **What is the important idea in the problem?** *(How many apples are left?)* **Does this idea tell you that you should add or subtract to find the answer to the problem?** *(Subtract)*

For Exercises 4 and 5, help children find the numbers in the problem and complete the number sentence. Direct children to count the number of apples in the bowl, recall how many apples Mike eats, and then use these numbers to complete the number sentence.

Think About It Ask for volunteers to answer the question. Guide children to understand that since Mike ate 2 apples, 2 of the apples were taken away. Children needed to subtract to find how many apples were left.

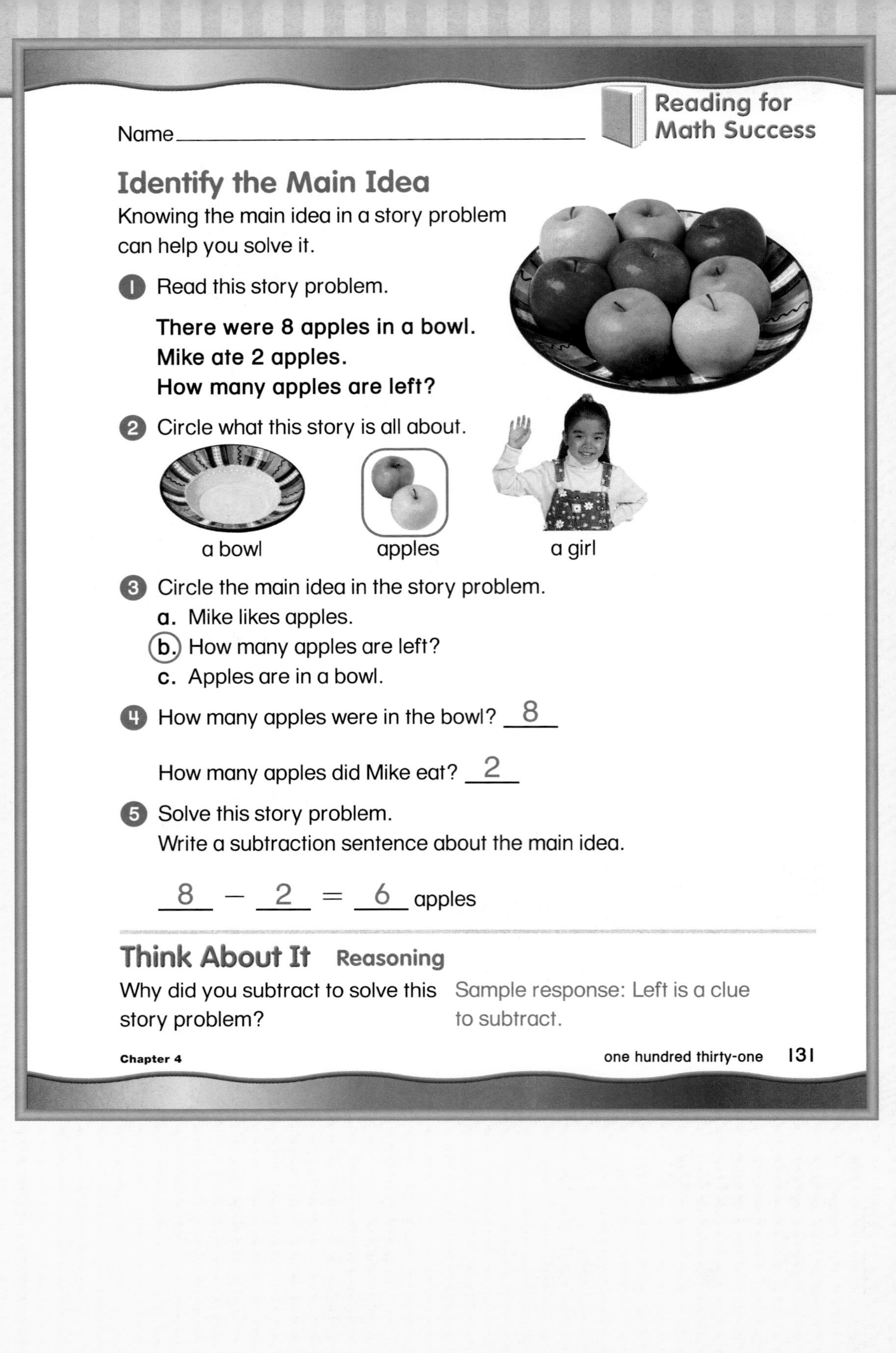

Name ____________________

Reading for Math Success

Identify the Main Idea

Knowing the main idea in a story problem can help you solve it.

1. Read this story problem.

   There were 8 apples in a bowl.
   Mike ate 2 apples.
   How many apples are left?

2. Circle what this story is all about.

   a bowl — (apples) — a girl

3. Circle the main idea in the story problem.
   a. Mike likes apples.
   (b.) How many apples are left?
   c. Apples are in a bowl.

4. How many apples were in the bowl? __8__

   How many apples did Mike eat? __2__

5. Solve this story problem.
   Write a subtraction sentence about the main idea.

   __8__ − __2__ = __6__ apples

Think About It Reasoning

Why did you subtract to solve this story problem?

Sample response: Left is a clue to subtract.

Chapter 4 — one hundred thirty-one 131

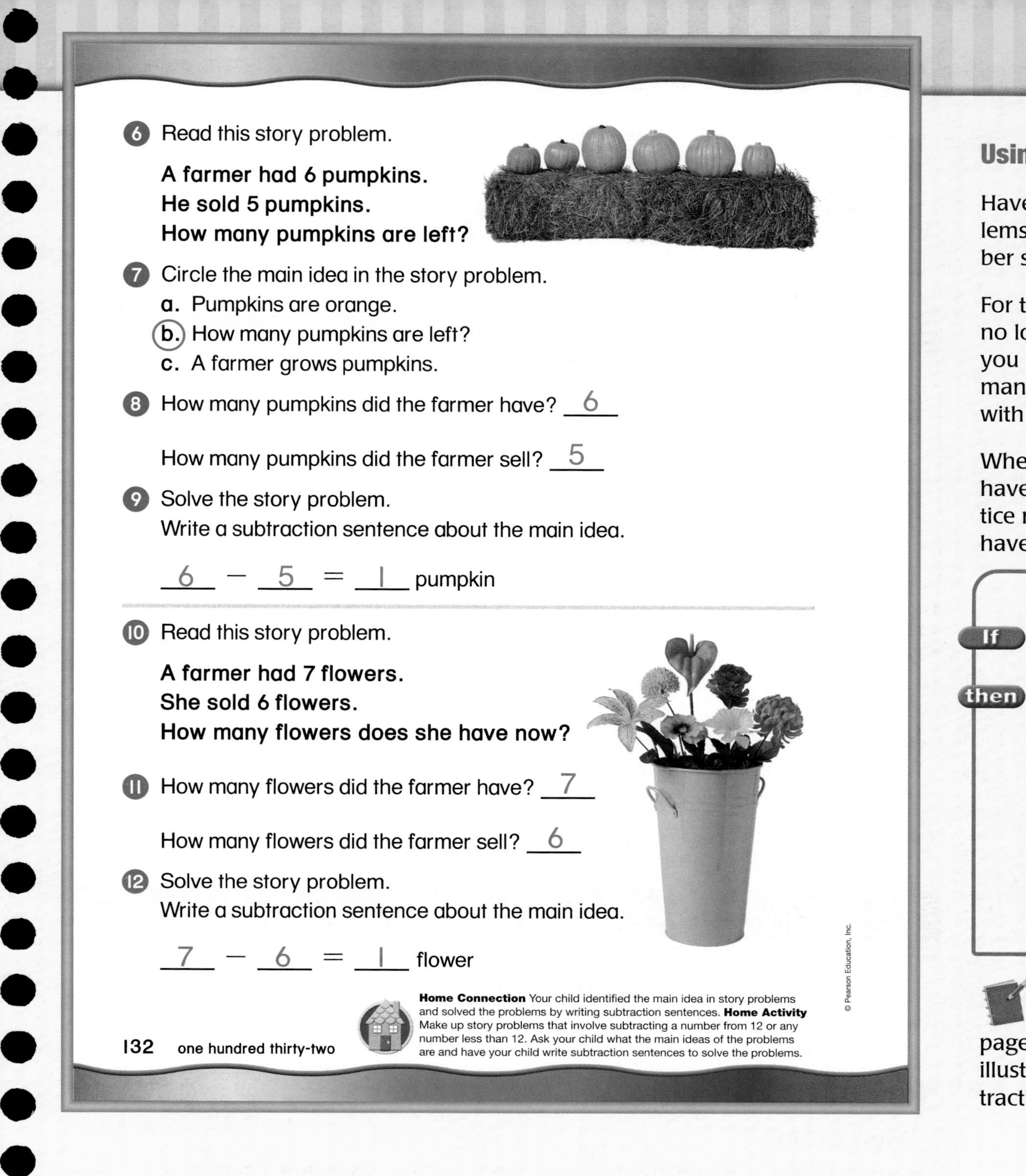

6 Read this story problem.

A farmer had 6 pumpkins.
He sold 5 pumpkins.
How many pumpkins are left?

7 Circle the main idea in the story problem.

a. Pumpkins are orange.
(b.) How many pumpkins are left?
c. A farmer grows pumpkins.

8 How many pumpkins did the farmer have? 6

How many pumpkins did the farmer sell? 5

9 Solve the story problem.
Write a subtraction sentence about the main idea.

6 − 5 = 1 pumpkin

10 Read this story problem.

A farmer had 7 flowers.
She sold 6 flowers.
How many flowers does she have now?

11 How many flowers did the farmer have? 7

How many flowers did the farmer sell? 6

12 Solve the story problem.
Write a subtraction sentence about the main idea.

7 − 6 = 1 flower

Home Connection Your child identified the main idea in story problems and solved the problems by writing subtraction sentences. **Home Activity** Make up story problems that involve subtracting a number from 12 or any number less than 12. Ask your child what the main ideas of the problems are and have your child write subtraction sentences to solve the problems.

Using Student Page 132

Have children independently read the problems, answer the questions, and write number sentences to solve the problems.

For the story problem in Exercise 10, children no longer identify the main idea. However, you may wish to discuss the main idea (How many flowers does the farmer have now?) with children.

When children have completed the page, have them compare their answers and practice reading the number sentences that they have written.

Error Intervention

If children are having difficulty identifying the main idea,

then explain that you will tell them a simple story and you want them to listen for the main idea: **A farmer has 6 cats. The cats like to play in the barn. 3 of the cats are black.** Then explain that whenever they are asked for a story's main idea, they can think about the question, "What is the story all about?" Say: **Tell what this story is all about using only 1 word.** *(cats)* You may wish to tell a similar story about another animal for further practice.

Journal Idea Have children copy one of the problems from the student pages, change the numbers in the problem, illustrate the problem, and write a new subtraction sentence to solve it.

Write a Number Sentence

Lesson Organizer

Quick Lesson Overview

Objective Solve problems by writing subtraction sentences.

Math Understanding Writing a number sentence is one strategy that can be used to solve a problem.

Professional Development Note

Effective Questioning Techniques
As you read a story problem, point out that each number represents a group. Ask questions that help children identify the numbers, such as: **How many were there? How many were taken away? How many are left?**

NCTM Standards

- Number and Operations
- Algebra

(For a complete correlation to the NCTM Standards and Grades Pre-K through 2 Expectations, see Pages 123G and 123H.)

Getting Started

Spiral Review

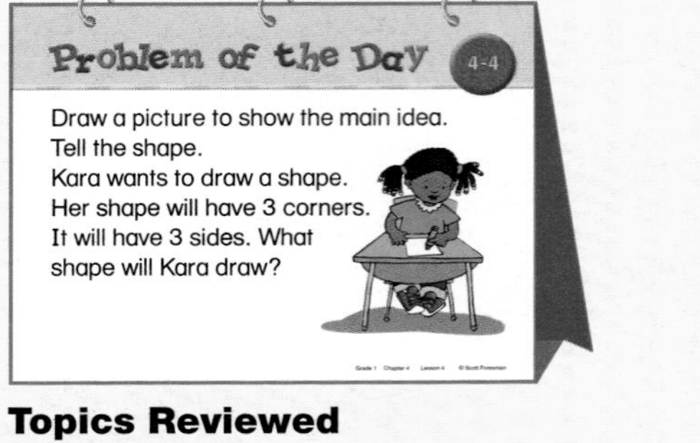

Problem of the Day 4-4

Draw a picture to show the main idea.
Tell the shape.
Kara wants to draw a shape.
Her shape will have 3 corners.
It will have 3 sides. What shape will Kara draw?

Topics Reviewed

- Plane shapes
- Problem-Solving Skill: Use Data from a Picture

Answer Kara will draw a triangle.

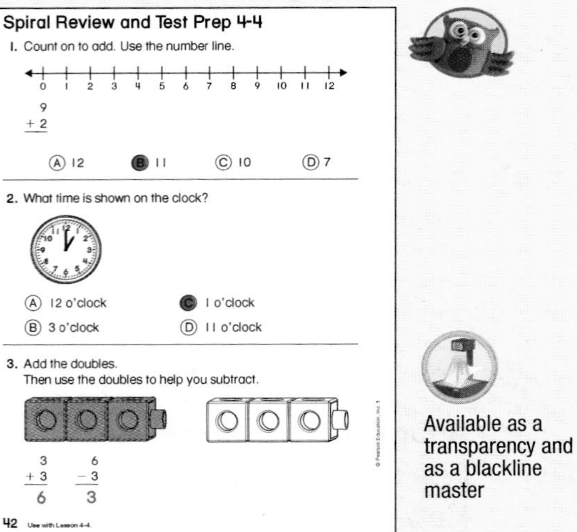

Spiral Review and Test Prep 4-4

1. Count on to add. Use the number line.

0 1 2 3 4 5 6 7 8 9 10 11 12

$9 + 2$

Ⓐ 12 ● 11 Ⓒ 10 Ⓓ 7

2. What time is shown on the clock?

Ⓐ 12 o'clock ● 1 o'clock
Ⓑ 3 o'clock Ⓓ 11 o'clock

3. Add the doubles.
Then use the doubles to help you subtract.

$3 + 3 = 6$ $6 - 3 = 3$

42 Use with Lesson 4-4.

Available as a transparency and as a blackline master

Topics Reviewed

1. Adding Using a Number Line
2. Telling Time on an Analog Clock
3. Using Doubles to Subtract

Investigating the Concept

Finding Out

10–15 MIN **Auditory/Linguistic**

Materials 6 small toy cars; *(per child)* 12 counters

What to Do

- Invite a child to act out this problem using toy cars. **There are 4 cars in front of Melissa's house. 2 cars leave. How many cars are left?** Ask children what they need to find out. *(How many cars are left)*
- Then ask what numbers are in the story problem. *(4, 2)* Help children say the subtraction sentence they should use to find the difference. *(4 − 2 = 2)*
- Have children use counters to act out other subtraction story problems.

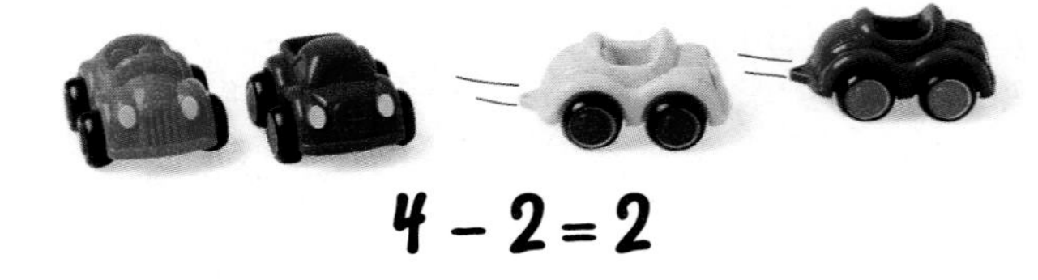

$4 - 2 = 2$

Ongoing Assessment

For each story problem, ask:

- **Reasoning What do you need to find out?** *(Answers will vary.)*
- **What can you do to solve the problem?** *(Write a number sentence.)*

Reaching All Learners

Reading in Math

Word Clues for Problem Solving

5–10 MIN **Linguistic** WHOLE CLASS

- Write subtraction stories on the board. Include these word clues: *How many are left? How many fewer?* and *How many more?*
- Underline the words *left, how many more,* and *how many fewer* as you read each story.
- Explain that these words are clues indicating that the problem should be solved using subtraction. Help children write number sentences to solve each problem.

Sara has 3 crackers.
Jamal has 4 crackers.
How many more crackers does Jamal have than Sara?

Access Content

English Language Learners

Acting Out Number Stories

5–10 MIN **Auditory**

- Help children act out and solve this problem about children in the group:

  Raul has 8 pencils.
  He gave 3 pencils to Luz.
  How many pencils does Raul have left?

- Read a similar story problem, keeping only the general language of the story the same.
- Continue to vary the problems until each child has had an opportunity to participate.

Reteaching

Act Out a Story!

15–20 MIN **Logical/Mathematical** WHOLE CLASS

Materials Number Cards 0–11 (Teaching Tool 9); Number Cards 12–20 (Teaching Tool 11); *(per child)* 12 counters

- Divide the class into small groups. Allow each group several minutes to create and practice a subtraction story that can be acted out.
- As each group acts out its subtraction story for the class, the other children can use counters to re-enact the story. Then one child from the class can be selected to build the subtraction sentence with number and symbol cards. The small group can verify the accuracy of the number sentence.

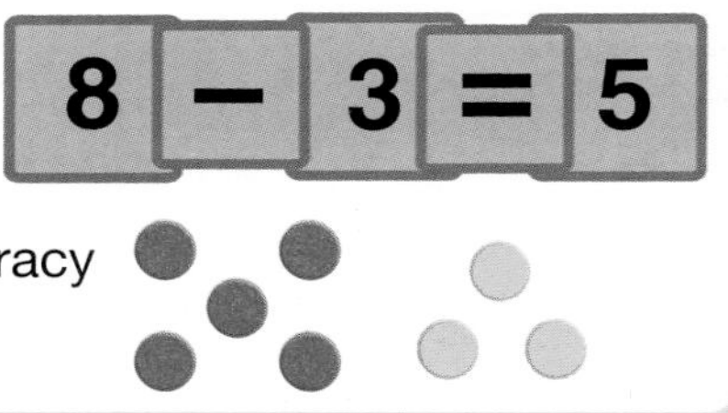

Math and Social Studies

Community Workers

15–20 MIN **Logical/Mathematical**

Materials Construction paper; crayons or markers; subtraction fact cards

- Work as a group to create a list of the people who work in communities. The list might include mail carriers, librarians, firefighters, and police officers.
- Pass out one subtraction fact card to each child. Have children write the subtraction sentences at the bottom of their papers. Have children illustrate their number sentences with community workers doing their jobs. Post the children's work around the classroom.

Objective Solve problems by writing subtraction sentences.

1 Warm Up

Activate Prior Knowledge Review story problems. Have a volunteer act out this problem using books. **I have 5 books. I get 2 more books. How many books do I have in all?** Have another volunteer tell how many in all. Repeat with other addition story problems.

2 Teach

Learn!

Read aloud the problem at the top of the student page. Ask children what they need to find out. *(How many children are left on the bus)* Assist children in writing a number sentence using the numbers found in the story problem.

Ongoing Assessment

Talk About It

- **How can a number sentence help you solve the problem?** *(The number sentence helps me see what subtraction problem to solve.)*
- **How can you check your answer?** *(Sample response: I can use counters to act out the problem.)*

If children cannot tell how many children are left,

then have them draw pictures of 8 children, cross out 2 of them, and count how many are left.

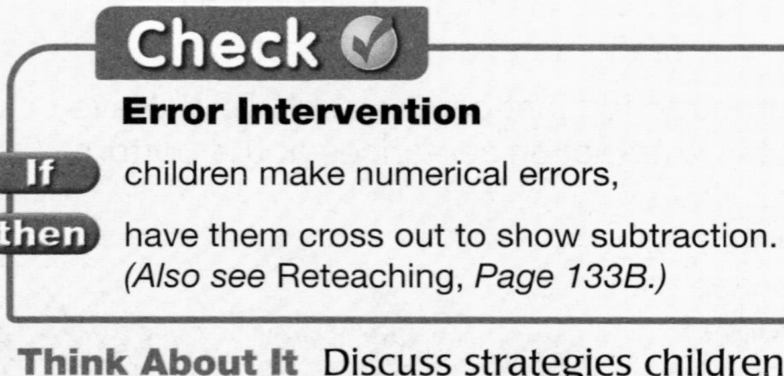

Check

Error Intervention

If children make numerical errors,

then have them cross out to show subtraction. *(Also see* Reteaching, *Page 133B.)*

Think About It Discuss strategies children can use when they subtract. Remind them that they have learned to count back on a number line, count back in their heads, and use doubles.

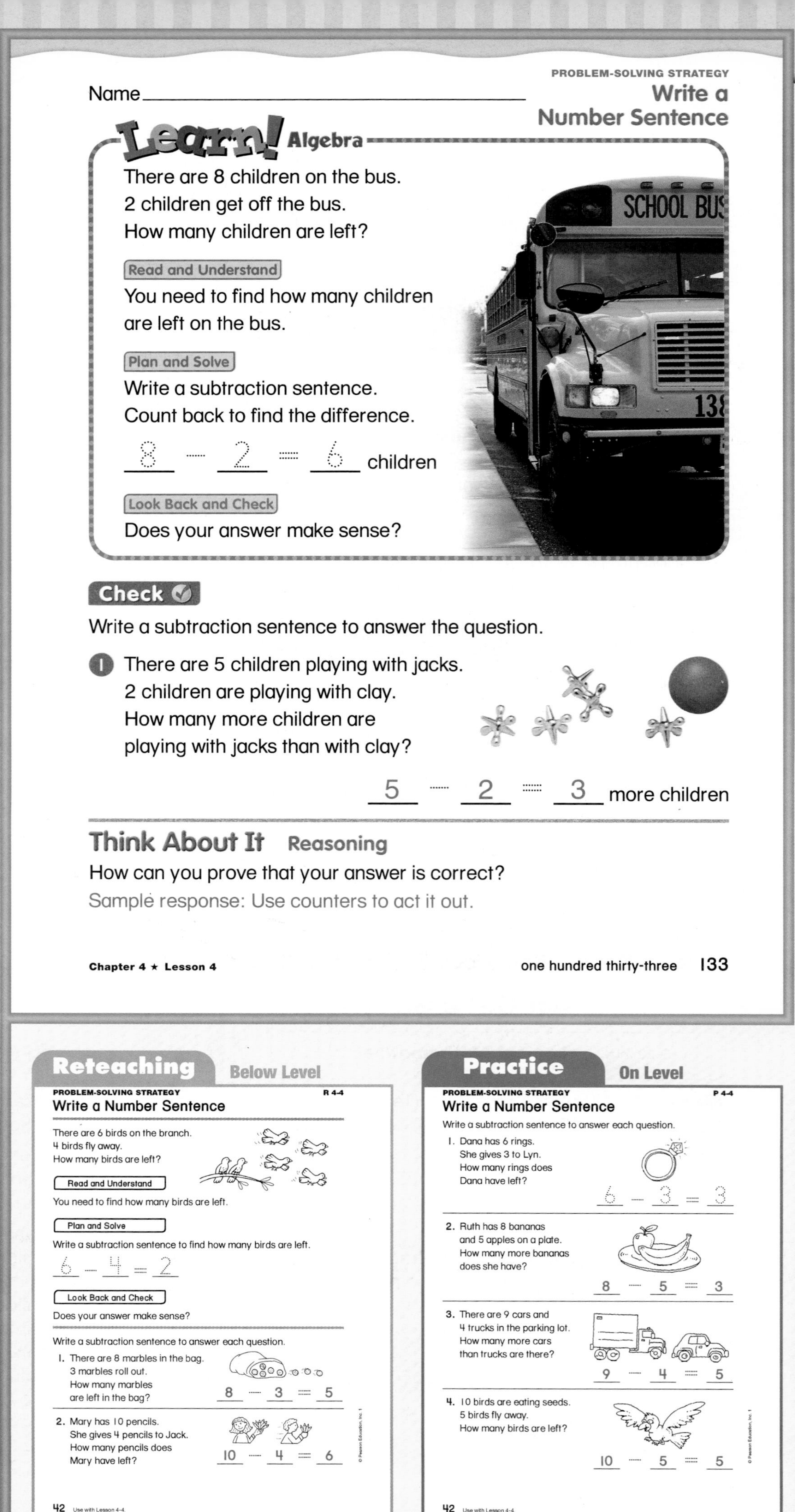

Name ______________________

PROBLEM-SOLVING STRATEGY
Write a Number Sentence

Learn! Algebra

There are 8 children on the bus.
2 children get off the bus.
How many children are left?

Read and Understand

You need to find how many children are left on the bus.

Plan and Solve

Write a subtraction sentence.
Count back to find the difference.

8 − 2 = 6 children

Look Back and Check

Does your answer make sense?

Check

Write a subtraction sentence to answer the question.

1. There are 5 children playing with jacks.
2 children are playing with clay.
How many more children are playing with jacks than with clay?

5 − 2 = 3 more children

Think About It Reasoning

How can you prove that your answer is correct?

Sample response: Use counters to act it out.

Chapter 4 ★ Lesson 4 one hundred thirty-three 133

Reteaching Below Level

PROBLEM-SOLVING STRATEGY R 4-4
Write a Number Sentence

There are 6 birds on the branch.
4 birds fly away.
How many birds are left?

Read and Understand

You need to find how many birds are left.

Plan and Solve

Write a subtraction sentence to find how many birds are left.

6 − 4 = 2

Look Back and Check

Does your answer make sense?

Write a subtraction sentence to answer each question.

1. There are 8 marbles in the bag.
3 marbles roll out.
How many marbles are left in the bag?
8 − 3 = 5

2. Mary has 10 pencils.
She gives 4 pencils to Jack.
How many pencils does Mary have left?
10 − 4 = 6

© Pearson Education, Inc. 1

42 Use with Lesson 4-4.

Practice On Level

PROBLEM-SOLVING STRATEGY P 4-4
Write a Number Sentence

Write a subtraction sentence to answer each question.

1. Dana has 6 rings.
She gives 3 to Lyn.
How many rings does Dana have left?
6 − 3 = 3

2. Ruth has 8 bananas and 5 apples on a plate.
How many more bananas does she have?
8 − 5 = 3

3. There are 9 cars and 4 trucks in the parking lot.
How many more cars than trucks are there?
9 − 4 = 5

4. 10 birds are eating seeds.
5 birds fly away.
How many birds are left?
10 − 5 = 5

© Pearson Education, Inc. 1

42 Use with Lesson 4-4.

Practice

Write a subtraction sentence to answer each question.

2. Rita had 10 crayons.
   She gave 5 crayons to Luz.
   How many crayons
   does Rita have left?

   10 – 5 = 5 crayons

3. Ben has 8 pencils
   and 4 erasers.
   How many more pencils than
   erasers does he have?

   8 – 4 = 4 more pencils

4. There are 7 boys and
   2 girls painting pictures.
   How many more boys
   than girls are painting pictures?

   7 – 2 = 5 more boys

5. 12 children are playing with the blocks.
   6 children move to the art table.
   How many children are left playing
   with blocks?

   12 – 6 = 6 children

Home Connection Your child wrote subtraction sentences to solve problems. **Home Activity** When you are eating with your child, ask questions such as, "How many crackers did you have? How many did you eat? How many do you have left?" Have your child write subtraction sentences for each problem.

3 Practice

For Exercises 2–5, remind children to use numbers from the story problems to write their number sentences.

Reading Assist: Sequence After children complete Exercise 2, ask them to explain the problem-solving steps that they followed.

Leveled Practice

Below Level Listen as the teacher reads each problem. Use counters for all exercises.

On Level Use counters if needed.

Above Level Do exercises without using counters.

Early Finishers Invite children to work in pairs to act out a subtraction story using counters. The first child shows the counters. The second child takes away some counters. The first child writes the number sentence.

4 Assess

Journal Idea Have children choose problems from the page and rewrite them using different numbers. Then have them write the number sentences that solve them.

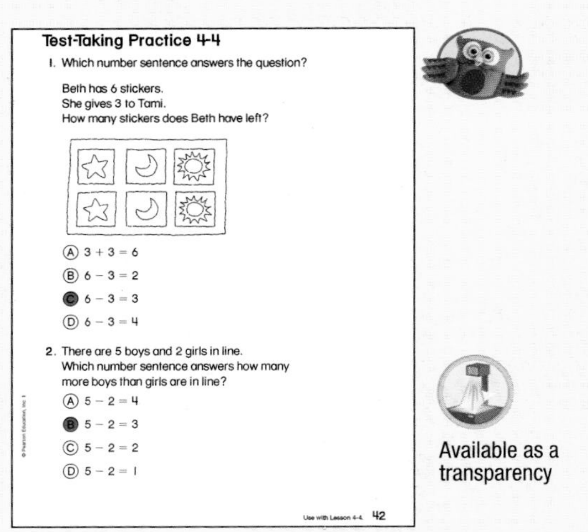

Test-Taking Practice 4-4

1. Which number sentence answers the question?

   Beth has 6 stickers.
   She gives 3 to Tami.
   How many stickers does Beth have left?

   Ⓐ 3 + 3 = 6
   Ⓑ 6 – 3 = 2
   Ⓒ 6 – 3 = 3 (marked)
   Ⓓ 6 – 3 = 4

2. There are 5 boys and 2 girls in line.
   Which number sentence answers how many more boys than girls are in line?

   Ⓐ 5 – 2 = 4
   Ⓑ 5 – 2 = 3 (marked)
   Ⓒ 5 – 2 = 2
   Ⓓ 5 – 2 = 1

Use with Lesson 4-4. 42

Available as a transparency

Enrichment Above Level

Animal Cards E 4-4 NUMBER SENSE

At school the children earn points.
They trade the points for animal cards at the school store.

Dinosaur 8 points
Polar Bear 7 points
Elephant 6 points
Shark 5 points
Lion 4 points
Monkey 3 points

Write a number sentence. Solve.

1. Dan has 10 points.
   He picks a lion card.
   How many points does Dan have left?
   10 ⊖ 4 = 6
   Circle the other card Dan can get.

2. Lina has 12 points.
   She picks a polar bear card.
   How many points does Lina have left?
   12 ⊖ 7 = 5
   Circle the other card Lina can get.

3. Chris has 11 points.
   She picks a dinosaur card.
   How many points does Chris have left?
   11 ⊖ 8 = 3
   Circle the other card Chris can get.

42 Use with Lesson 4-4.

Problem Solving

PROBLEM-SOLVING STRATEGY PS 4-4

Write a Number Sentence

6 girls are drawing on the chalkboard.
2 girls sit down.
How many girls are left at the chalkboard?

Write how many girls are at the chalkboard.	Write how many girls sit down.	Write the difference.
6 –	2 =	4

Write a subtraction sentence to answer the question.

1. There are 7 boys and 5 girls playing kickball.
   How many more boys than girls are playing?
   7 – 5 = 2

2. There are 10 children eating snacks and 4 children playing.
   How many more children are eating snacks?
   10 – 4 = 6

3. There are 7 bikes and 3 scooters.
   How many more bikes are there than scooters?
   7 – 3 = 4

Using the page To help children *plan*, have them first read each exercise and discuss what it is asking them to find. Then have them write down the number sentence that will *solve* the problem.

42 Use with Lesson 4-4.

Diagnostic Checkpoint

Purpose Provide assessment of children's progress to date by checking their understanding of key content covered in the previous section.

Vocabulary Review

You may wish to review this vocabulary term before assigning the page:

count back To subtract by counting backward from the higher number *(pp. 125–126)*

Activities for this section are available in the Math Vocabulary Kit.

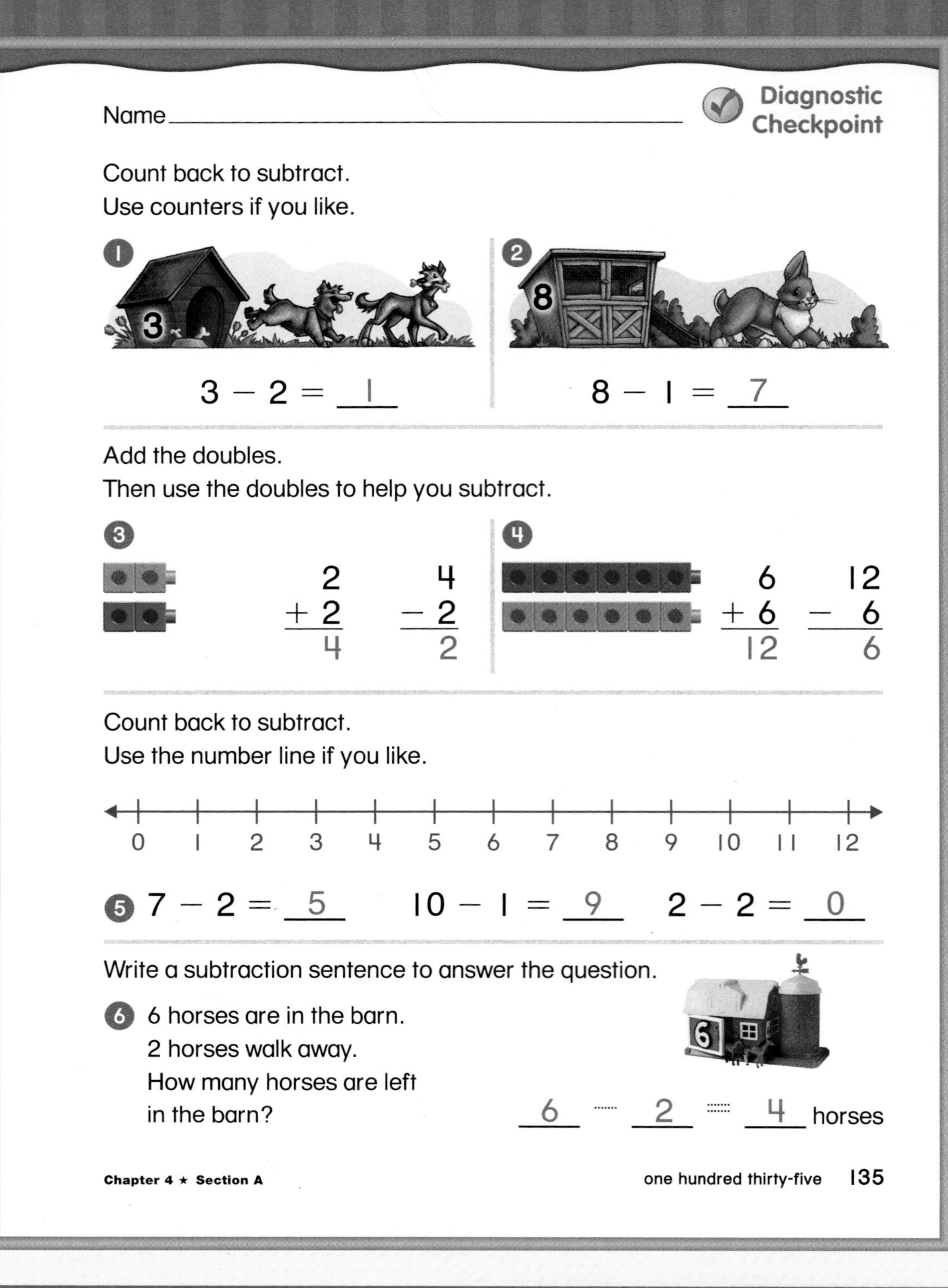

Name ____________________

Diagnostic Checkpoint

Count back to subtract.
Use counters if you like.

1. $3 - 2 = $ 1

2. $8 - 1 = $ 7

Add the doubles.
Then use the doubles to help you subtract.

3. $2 + 2 = 4$ $4 - 2 = 2$

4. $6 + 6 = 12$ $12 - 6 = 6$

Count back to subtract.
Use the number line if you like.

0 1 2 3 4 5 6 7 8 9 10 11 12

5. $7 - 2 = $ 5 $10 - 1 = $ 9 $2 - 2 = $ 0

Write a subtraction sentence to answer the question.

6. 6 horses are in the barn.
2 horses walk away.
How many horses are left in the barn?

6 − 2 = 4 horses

Chapter 4 ★ Section A

one hundred thirty-five 135

Item Analysis for Diagnosis and Intervention

Objective	Items	Student Book Pages*	Intervention System
Find differences by counting back 1 or 2.	1–2	127–128	B25
Find differences by using doubles facts.	3–4	129–130	B26
Use a number line to count back 1 or 2.	5	125–126	B24
Solve problems by writing subtraction sentences.	6	133–134	E36

*For each lesson, there is a *Reteaching* activity in *Reaching All Learners* and a *Reteaching* master.

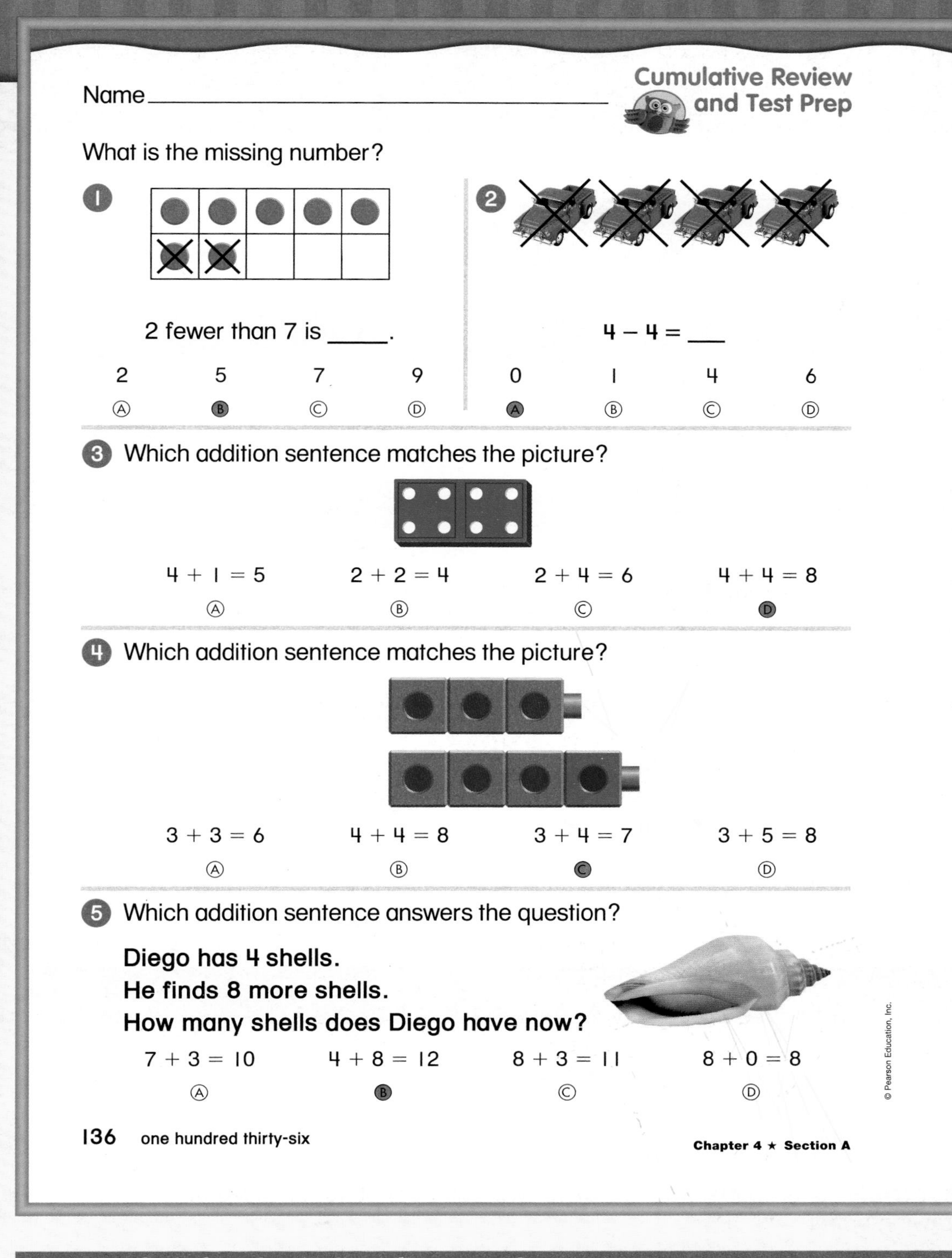

Name ______________________

Cumulative Review and Test Prep

What is the missing number?

1. 2 fewer than 7 is ____.

2 Ⓐ   5 Ⓑ   7 Ⓒ   9 Ⓓ

2. 4 − 4 = ___

0 Ⓐ   1 Ⓑ   4 Ⓒ   6 Ⓓ

3. Which addition sentence matches the picture?

4 + 1 = 5 Ⓐ   2 + 2 = 4 Ⓑ   2 + 4 = 6 Ⓒ   4 + 4 = 8 Ⓓ

4. Which addition sentence matches the picture?

3 + 3 = 6 Ⓐ   4 + 4 = 8 Ⓑ   3 + 4 = 7 Ⓒ   3 + 5 = 8 Ⓓ

5. Which addition sentence answers the question?

Diego has 4 shells.
He finds 8 more shells.
How many shells does Diego have now?

7 + 3 = 10 Ⓐ   4 + 8 = 12 Ⓑ   8 + 3 = 11 Ⓒ   8 + 0 = 8 Ⓓ

Cumulative Review and Test Prep

Purpose Provide children with a review of math concepts. Items appear as they would on a standardized test so children become familiar with that format.

Item Analysis for Diagnosis and Intervention

Objective	Items	Student Book Pages*	Intervention System
Find the numbers that are 1 and 2 fewer than a given number.	1	27–28 or 19–20	A7
Write subtraction sentences using zero.	2	67–68	B13
Recognize doubles as a strategy for remembering sums.	3	103–104	B21
Use doubles facts to learn doubles-plus-1 facts.	4	105–106	B22
Solve problems by writing addition sentences.	5	57–58	E36

*For each lesson, there is a *Reteaching* activity in *Reaching All Learners* and a *Reteaching* master.

4-5 Using Related Facts

Lesson Organizer

Quick Lesson Overview

Objective Write related addition and subtraction facts.

Math Understanding Every addition fact has at least one related subtraction fact.

Vocabulary Related facts

Professional Development Note

Research Base

Activities that emphasize part-part-whole relations help children see how addition and subtraction are related (National Research Council, 2001). In this lesson children work with two-color counters to represent two parts and the whole quantity and write the related addition and subtraction sentences.

NCTM Standards

- Number and Operations
- Algebra

(For a complete correlation to the NCTM Standards and Grades Pre-K through 2 Expectations, see Pages 123G and 123H.)

Getting Started

Spiral Review

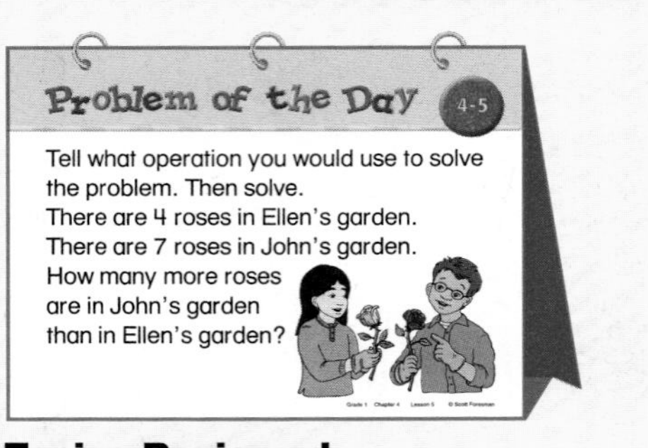

Problem of the Day 4-5

Tell what operation you would use to solve the problem. Then solve.
There are 4 roses in Ellen's garden.
There are 7 roses in John's garden.
How many more roses are in John's garden than in Ellen's garden?

Topics Reviewed

- Subtraction
- Problem-Solving Skill: Choose an Operation

Answer Subtraction; $7 - 4 = 3$; There are 3 more roses in John's garden than in Ellen's garden.

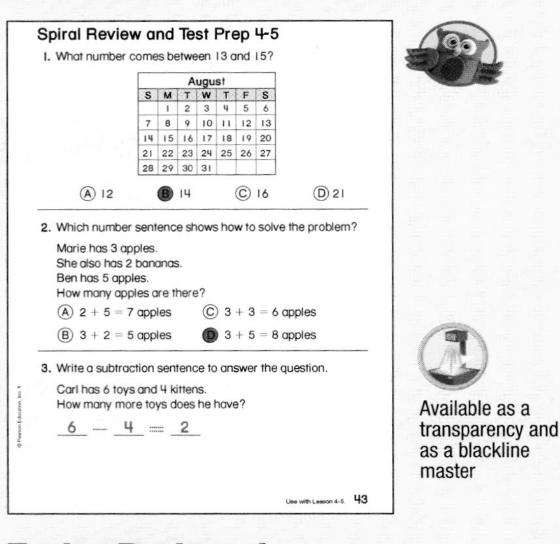

Spiral Review and Test Prep 4-5

1. What number comes between 13 and 15?

August						
S	M	T	W	T	F	S
	1	2	3	4	5	6
7	8	9	10	11	12	13
14	15	16	17	18	19	20
21	22	23	24	25	26	27
28	29	30	31			

Ⓐ 12 Ⓑ 14 Ⓒ 16 Ⓓ 21

2. Which number sentence shows how to solve the problem?

Marie has 3 apples.
She also has 2 bananas.
Ben has 5 apples.
How many apples are there?

Ⓐ $2 + 5 = 7$ apples Ⓒ $3 + 3 = 6$ apples
Ⓑ $3 + 2 = 5$ apples Ⓓ $3 + 5 = 8$ apples

3. Write a subtraction sentence to answer the question.

Carl has 6 toys and 4 kittens.
How many more toys does he have?

6 − 4 = 2

Use with Lesson 4-5. 43

Available as a transparency and as a blackline master

Topics Reviewed

1. Numbers on a Calendar
2. Extra Information
3. Write a Number Sentence

Investigating the Concept

Using Related Facts

10–15 MIN **Visual/Spatial** WHOLE CLASS

Materials Chart paper; *(per child)* 12 two-color counters; 5 pieces of drawing paper

What to Do

- Have children join 3 counters with the red side up and 4 counters with the yellow side up. **What addition fact tells what happened?** Write $3 + 4 = 7$.
- Ask children to separate the groups into red and yellow. **What subtraction fact tells what happened?** Write $7 - 4 = 3$.
- Discuss related facts. Tell children that every addition fact has at least one related subtraction fact. Show that these facts use the same numbers.

Ongoing Assessment

- **Reasoning** **How is subtracting different from adding?** *(In adding you join groups; in subtracting you separate a group.)*
- **How are related addition and subtraction facts alike?** *(They contain the same parts and wholes.)*

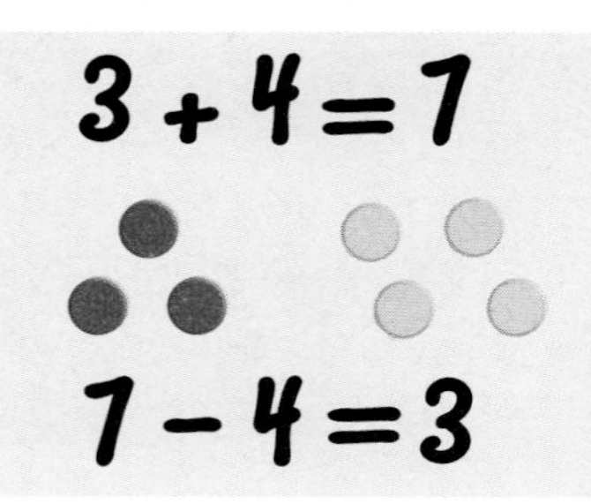

Reaching All Learners

Math Vocabulary

Related Facts

5–10 MIN **Linguistic**

- Write the following number sentences on the board:

  $5 + 4 = 9$ $4 + 3 = 7$

  $9 - 4 = 5$ $8 - 2 = 6$

- Explain to the children that *related facts* use the same numbers. **Which two facts in this group are *related?*** After children have chosen $5 + 4 = 9$ and $9 - 4 = 5$, have children write related facts for $4 + 3 = 7$ and $8 - 2 = 6$. **How can you tell that two facts are related?** *(The parts and the wholes are the same.)*

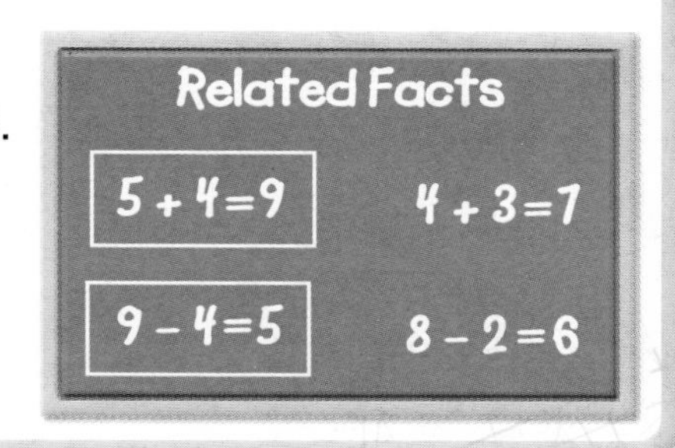

Activate Prior Knowledge/Build Background

English Language Learners

Handfuls of Cubes

10–15 MIN **Linguistic**

Materials *(per pair)* Connecting cubes

- Each child in the pair grabs a handful of cubes. The pair then works together to write an addition sentence and a related subtraction sentence about the cubes. Challenge children to write all of the related facts about the cubes.
- After each of the pairs has finished, invite them to share their number sentences and explain why they are related facts.

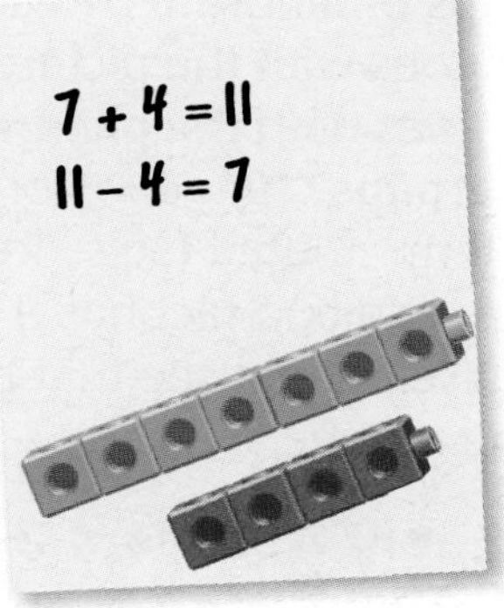

Reteaching

Making Related Facts

5–10 MIN **Logical/Mathematical**

Materials *(per child)* 2 sets of Number Cards 0–11 (Teaching Tool 9); 2 sets of Number Cards 12–20 (Teaching Tool 11); counters

- Have each child take a few counters in each hand and place them in two groups on the table.
- Invite each child to use the number and symbol cards to make a fact about his or her counters. Demonstrate how to make the related fact by switching around the number cards and replacing the + with the −.
- Have children use counters and cards to make other related facts.

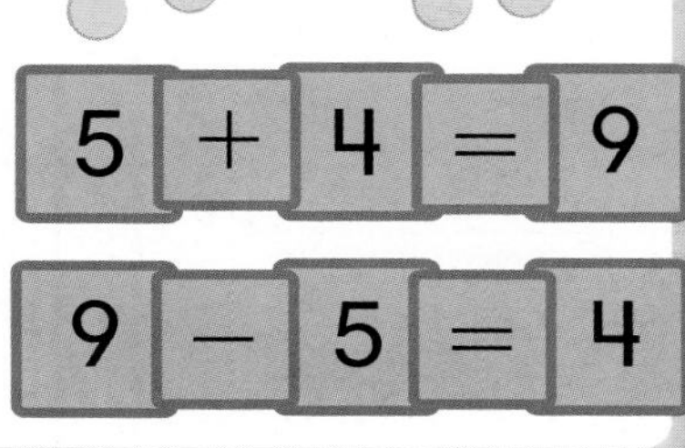

Advanced Learners

Cube Toss

10–15 MIN **Logical/Mathematical**

Materials *(per pair)* 2 number cubes (numbers 1–6)

- Partners take turns tossing the number cubes to make related facts. After the cubes are tossed, one partner writes and completes an addition fact using the two numbers that are face up on the cubes. The other partner must use the addition fact to write a related subtraction fact.
- Children then switch roles so that both players have a chance to toss the number cubes.

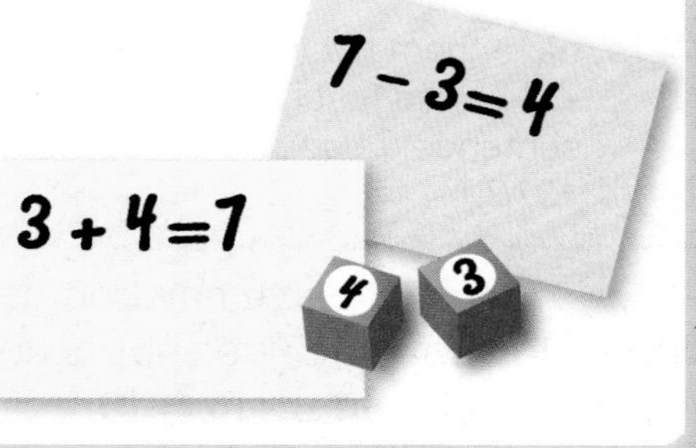

Objective Write related addition and subtraction facts.

1 Warm Up

Activate Prior Knowledge Review using doubles to subtract. Ask children to use counters to show $5 + 5 = 10$. Then ask what subtraction fact the double can help them solve. *(10 – 5 = 5)* Repeat with other doubles.

2 Teach

Learn!

Have children use counters to show the groups of dinosaurs. Read the addition fact that goes with the picture. **What subtraction fact goes with the picture if you separate the groups?** *(9 – 4 = 5 or 9 – 5 = 4)* Introduce the term related facts. Tell children that every addition fact has a related subtraction fact. Help them see that both facts use the same numbers.

Ongoing Assessment

Talk About It

- **How are the two related facts alike?** *(Both use the numbers 5, 4, and 9.)*
- **How can an addition fact help you to write a subtraction fact?** *(The sum in an addition sentence is the largest number in the subtraction sentence.)*

If children do not understand that the facts are related because they have the same parts and wholes,

then have them use counters to act out the facts.

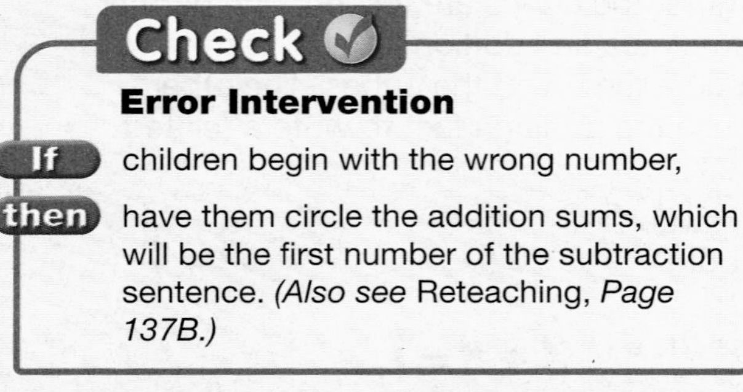

Check

Error Intervention

If children begin with the wrong number,

then have them circle the addition sums, which will be the first number of the subtraction sentence. *(Also see* Reteaching, *Page 137B.)*

Think About It Have children use their fingers to show the two subtraction facts that are related to $6 + 4 = 10$.

EC NTL 12 11 10 9

Name ____________________

Using Related Facts

Learn! Algebra

Addition and subtraction facts are related if they use the same numbers.

These are related facts.

5 + 4 = 9

9 – 4 = 5

Word Bank

related facts

Check

Add.

Then write a related subtraction fact. Sample subtraction facts are given.

1. 1 + 6 = 7
   7 – 6 = 1
2. 5 + 6 = 11
   11 – 6 = 5
3. 3 + 6 = 9
   9 – 6 = 3

Think About It Reasoning

What two subtraction facts are related to $6 + 4 = 10$?

10 – 4 = 6 and 10 – 6 = 4

Reteaching Below Level

Using Related Facts R 4-5

4 + 3 = 7

7 – 3 = 4

The addition fact and the subtraction fact use the same numbers.

6 + 4 = 10

10 – 4 = 6

The sum of the addition sentence is the first number in the subtraction sentence.

Write a related addition and subtraction sentence for each picture.

1. 7 + 4 = 11
   11 – 4 = 7
2. 8 + 2 = 10
   10 – 2 = 8
3. 8 + 3 = 11
   11 – 3 = 8
4. 4 + 6 = 10
   10 – 6 = 4

Practice On Level

Using Related Facts P 4-5

Write an addition sentence and a subtraction sentence for each picture.

1. 3 + 7 = 10
   10 – 3 = 7

The first number in the subtraction sentence is the sum of the numbers in the addition sentence.

2. 9 + 1 = 10
   10 – 9 = 1
3. 2 + 7 = 9
   9 – 2 = 7
4. 4 + 5 = 9
   9 – 4 = 5
5. 8 + 3 = 11
   11 – 8 = 3

Problem Solving *Writing in Math*

Draw a picture to show these related facts.

6. 6 + 3 = 9 9 – 3 = 6

Drawing should show a group of 6 objects and a group of 3 objects.

Practice

Write related addition and subtraction facts for each picture.

The sum of the addition fact is the first number in the subtraction fact.

4 6 + 5 = 11
11 − 5 = 6

Sample answers are given.

5 3 + 7 = 10
10 − 3 = 7

6 5 + 2 = 7
7 − 5 = 2

7 3 + 5 = 8
8 − 3 = 5

8 2 + 4 = 6
6 − 2 = 4

Problem Solving — Writing in Math

Draw a picture to show these related facts.

9 4 + 5 = 9 9 − 5 = 4

Children's drawings should show a group of 4 objects and a group of 5 objects.

Home Connection Your child wrote related addition and subtraction facts. **Home Activity** Set out two groups of small objects. Ask your child to write an addition fact and a subtraction fact for the groups. Then switch roles and repeat.

Enrichment — Above Level

Related Fact Fun E 4-5 NUMBER SENSE

Complete the addition and subtraction facts.
Then circle the two facts in each row that are related.

1. 6 − 3 = 3	2 + 4 = 6	6 − 4 = 2
2. 12 − 5 = 7	7 + 5 = 12	6 + 5 = 11
3. 6 + 2 = 8	6 − 2 = 4	8 − 2 = 6
4. 3 + 5 = 8	2 + 3 = 5	5 − 3 = 2
5. 10 − 3 = 7	10 − 6 = 4	3 + 7 = 10
6. 5 + 2 = 7	6 + 1 = 7	7 − 2 = 5
7. 9 − 4 = 5	6 + 3 = 9	9 − 6 = 3
8. 1 + 5 = 6	6 − 1 = 5	11 − 2 = 9
9. 10 − 5 = 5	4 + 6 = 10	10 − 4 = 6
10. 2 + 7 = 9	9 − 8 = 1	9 − 7 = 2
11. 2 + 5 = 7	3 + 4 = 7	7 − 3 = 4
12. 11 − 5 = 6	11 − 1 = 10	6 + 5 = 11

Problem Solving

Using Related Facts PS 4-5

Fill in the missing numbers.
Then draw lines to match the related addition and subtraction facts.

1. 3 + 7 = 10	7 + 5 = 12
2. 3 + 4 = 7	10 − 7 = 3
3. 12 − 5 = 7	12 − 4 = 8
4. 12 − 3 = 9	8 + 3 = 11
5. 8 + 4 = 12	7 − 4 = 3
6. 11 − 3 = 8	9 + 3 = 12

Writing In Math

7. Draw a picture to show the related facts.

3 + 4 = 7 7 − 4 = 3

Drawings will vary. Drawings should be a group of 3 and a group of 4.

3 Practice

For Exercises 4–8, remind children to check that each pair of facts uses the same numbers.

Reading Assist: Main Idea Ask children to look at Exercise 4. Tell children that the main idea is that every addition fact has a related subtraction fact.

Leveled Practice

Below Level Work in pairs and use counters.

On Level Work individually and use counters.

Above Level Complete all exercises without using counters.

Early Finishers Give children pennies to use to make two groups. Have them write pairs of related addition and subtraction sentences about the pennies.

4 Assess

Journal Idea Ask each child to draw and cut out 6 squares and paste the squares in two groups on the page. Have children write related addition and subtraction facts for their pictures.

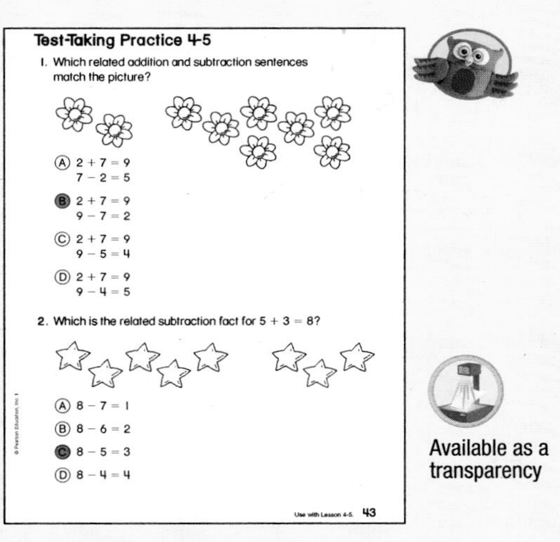
Test-Taking Practice 4-5

1. Which related addition and subtraction sentences match the picture?

Ⓐ 2 + 7 = 9
7 − 2 = 5

Ⓑ 2 + 7 = 9
9 − 7 = 2

Ⓒ 2 + 7 = 9
9 − 5 = 4

Ⓓ 2 + 7 = 9
9 − 4 = 5

2. Which is the related subtraction fact for 5 + 3 = 8?

Ⓐ 8 − 7 = 1

Ⓑ 8 − 6 = 2

Ⓒ 8 − 5 = 3

Ⓓ 8 − 4 = 4

© Pearson Education, Inc. 1

Use with Lesson 4-5. 43

Available as a transparency

4-6 Fact Families

Lesson Organizer

Quick Lesson Overview

Objective Write the addition and subtraction sentences that make up a fact family.

Math Understanding Fact families use the same three numbers and can be used to show how addition and subtraction are related.

Vocabulary Fact family

Materials for Student Pages
(per child) 16 connecting cubes (8 of one color and 8 of another color)

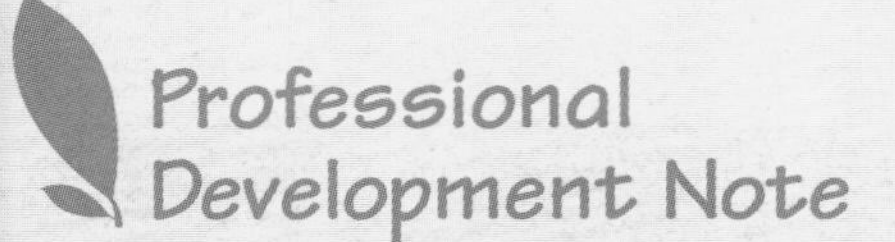

Professional Development Note

Managing Instruction Consider allowing children to work in pairs as they complete these pages. Pair students who show an understanding of related facts with those who still need more practice.

NCTM Standards

- Number and Operations
- Algebra

(For a complete correlation to the NCTM Standards and Grades Pre-K through 2 Expectations, see Pages 123G and 123H.)

Getting Started

Spiral Review

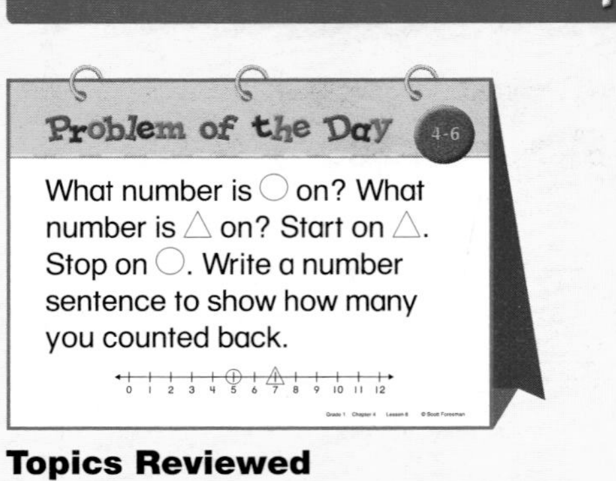
Problem of the Day
4-6
What number is ◯ on? What number is △ on? Start on △. Stop on ◯. Write a number sentence to show how many you counted back.
0 1 2 3 4 5 6 7 8 9 10 11 12

Topics Reviewed

- Subtraction
- Problem-Solving Strategy: Write a Number Sentence

Answer $7 - 2 = 5$. The circle is on 5. The triangle is on 7. Count back 2 from the triangle to the circle.

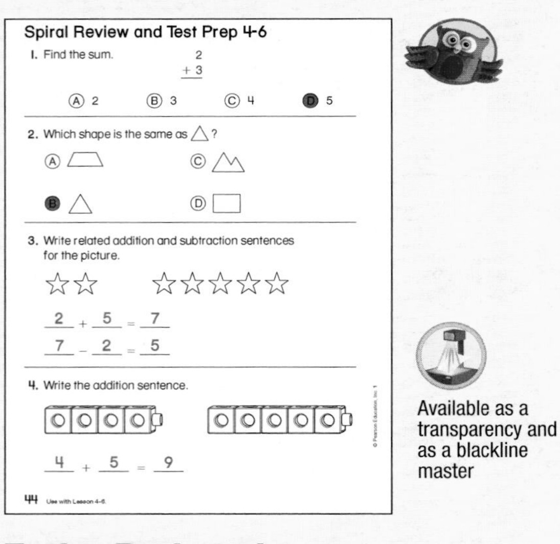

Spiral Review and Test Prep 4-6

1. Find the sum. $2 + 3$
   Ⓐ 2 Ⓑ 3 Ⓒ 4 Ⓓ 5
2. Which shape is the same as △?
   Ⓐ ▱ Ⓒ △△ Ⓑ △ Ⓓ ▭
3. Write related addition and subtraction sentences for the picture.
   $2 + 5 = 7$
   $7 - 2 = 5$
4. Write the addition sentence.
   $4 + 5 = 9$

44 Use with Lesson 4-6.

Available as a transparency and as a blackline master

Topics Reviewed

1. Doubles Plus 1
2. Same and Different
3. Using Related Facts

Investigating the Concept

Writing Fact Families

10–15 MIN | **Visual/Spatial** | WHOLE CLASS

Materials 12 connecting cubes (6 of one color and 6 of a second color)

What to Do

- Have a volunteer make a cube train showing 6 of one color and 4 of another color. Write $6 + 4 = 10$ on the board.
- **What other addition fact tells about the train?** *($4 + 6 = 10$)* Separate the train. **What related subtraction facts can we write for each addition fact?** *($10 - 4 = 6$ and $10 - 6 = 4$)*
- Explain that the facts are a fact family. Point out that this fact family has two addition facts and two subtraction facts, and that each of the facts has the numbers 4, 6, and 10 in it.

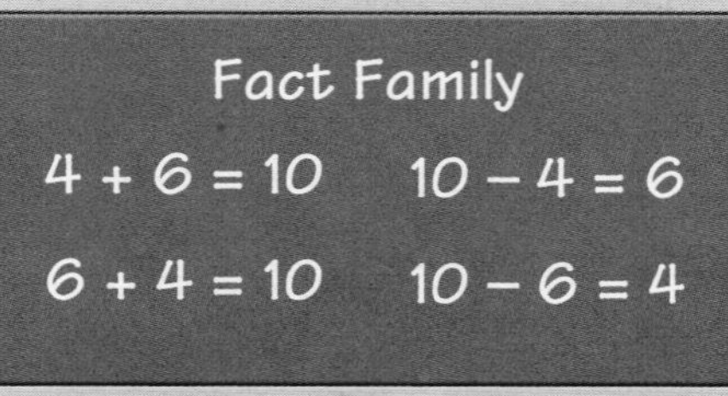
Fact Family
4 + 6 = 10
10 − 4 = 6
6 + 4 = 10
10 − 6 = 4

Ongoing Assessment

- **In what way are the number sentences in the fact family the same?** *(They all contain the same numbers.)*
- **Reasoning How many facts are in the fact family with $5 + 5 = 10$? Explain.** *(Only two facts, because two of the numbers are the same.)*

Reaching All Learners

Math Vocabulary

Fact Families

5–10 MIN **Linguistic**

- Discuss how everyone in a family is *related.* Give some examples about how family members are related.
- Write these facts on the board:

  $4 + 3 = 7$ $\quad$ $7 - 4 = 3$

  $3 + 4 = 7$ $\quad$ $7 - 3 = 4$
- **Number facts also come in families. How are the number sentences on the board related?** Help children understand that a fact family includes all of the related addition and subtraction facts that contain the same numbers.
- Add *fact family* and an example to the Math Word Wall.

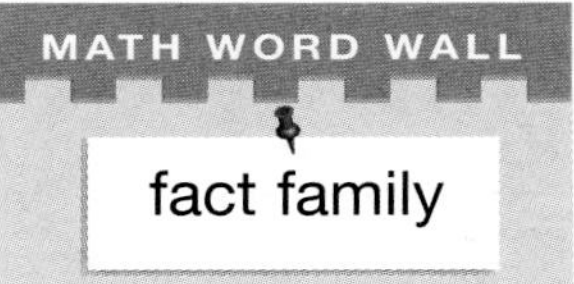

Activate Prior Knowledge/Build Background

English Language Learners

My Fact Family

15–20 MIN **Visual/Spatial**

Materials *(per child)* Construction paper; crayons or markers

- Each child draws a picture of his or her family, drawing the boys on one side of the page and the girls on the other side. The numbers of boys and girls can be used to create the facts in a fact family.
- Invite children to share their work with the class. For those children who have equal numbers of boys and girls, discuss why their fact families have only two facts.

Reteaching

Making Fact Families

10–15 MIN **Logical/Mathematical**

Materials 12 two-color counters

- Have children line up 7 counters red-side-up and 3 counters yellow-side-up. Have children write the facts to show the sum of yellow plus red: $3 + 7 = 10$ and red plus yellow: $7 + 3 = 10$. Next have children take away the yellow to make $10 - 3 = 7$ and take away the red to make $10 - 7 = 3$.
- Point out that all of the facts include 7, 3, and 10. **These facts are called a *fact family.***

Advanced Learners

Sorting Out Fact Families

10–15 MIN **Logical/Mathematical**

Materials Number Cards 0–11 (Teaching Tool 9); Number Cards 12–20 (Teaching Tool 11); envelopes

- Fill each envelope with number and symbol cards to create one fact family. An envelope might include four 4s, four 5s, four 9s, four = signs, two + signs, and two – signs. Fill enough envelopes for each child to have one.
- After giving each child an envelope, say: **Go!** Have the children see who can be the first to assemble an accurate fact family. Allow children to trade envelopes to play repeatedly.

Objective Write the addition and subtraction sentences that make up a fact family.

1 Warm Up

Activate Prior Knowledge Review adding in any order. Join a group of 4 children and a group of 3 children. **What addition fact tells what happened?** *(3 + 4 = 7)* Have children change places and name the new fact. *(4 + 3 = 7)*

2 Teach

Learn!

Ask children to use their cubes to replicate the cube train at the top of the student page and write the two addition sentences that go with the train. Then ask children to separate their trains and write the subtraction sentences that go with the separated trains. Explain that in a fact family all of the facts use the same numbers.

Ongoing Assessment

Talk About It

- **What numbers are used in this fact family?** *(3, 7, and 10)*
- **What kinds of facts are in this fact family?** *(Two addition facts and two subtraction facts)*

If children do not see the differences in the facts,

then model each fact with cubes after you read it.

Check

Error Intervention

If children repeat facts in the fact families,

then remind them that all of the facts must be different. *(Also see* Reteaching, *Page 139B.)*

Think About It Discuss why fact families for doubles only have two facts. Point out that because the addends in a doubles fact are the same, their order can not be changed.

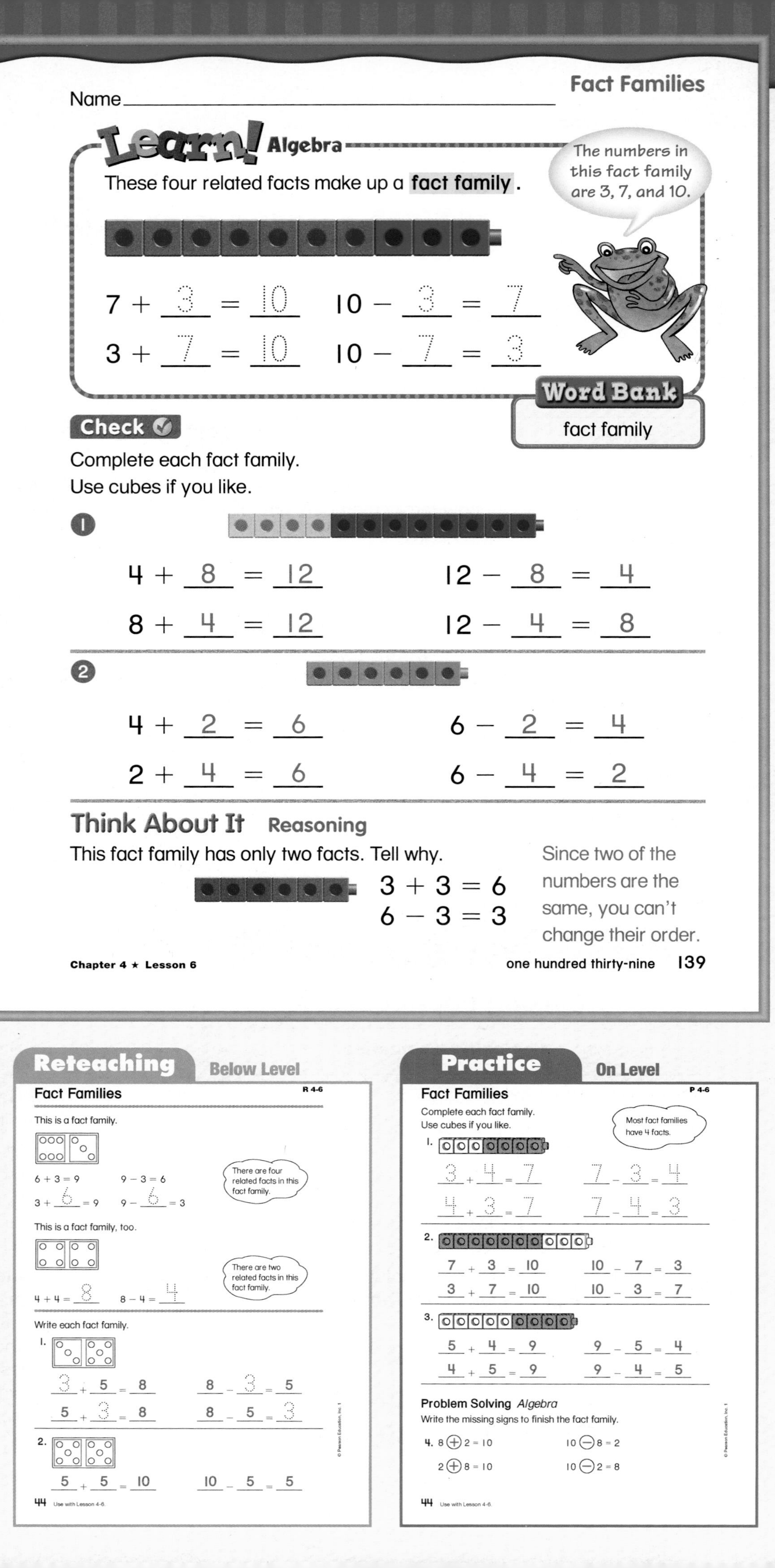

Name ______________________ **Fact Families**

Learn! Algebra

These four related facts make up a **fact family**.

The numbers in this fact family are 3, 7, and 10.

7 + 3 = 10   10 − 3 = 7

3 + 7 = 10   10 − 7 = 3

Word Bank

fact family

Check

Complete each fact family.
Use cubes if you like.

1.

4 + 8 = 12   12 − 8 = 4

8 + 4 = 12   12 − 4 = 8

2.

4 + 2 = 6   6 − 2 = 4

2 + 4 = 6   6 − 4 = 2

Think About It Reasoning

This fact family has only two facts. Tell why.

3 + 3 = 6

6 − 3 = 3

Since two of the numbers are the same, you can't change their order.

Chapter 4 ★ Lesson 6   one hundred thirty-nine 139

Reteaching Below Level

Fact Families R 4-6

This is a fact family.

6 + 3 = 9   9 − 3 = 6

3 + 6 = 9   9 − 6 = 3

There are four related facts in this fact family.

This is a fact family, too.

4 + 4 = 8   8 − 4 = 4

There are two related facts in this fact family.

Write each fact family.

1. 3 + 5 = 8   8 − 3 = 5

5 + 3 = 8   8 − 5 = 3

2. 5 + 5 = 10   10 − 5 = 5

44 Use with Lesson 4-6.

Practice On Level

Fact Families P 4-6

Complete each fact family.
Use cubes if you like.

Most fact families have 4 facts.

1. 3 + 4 = 7   7 − 3 = 4

4 + 3 = 7   7 − 4 = 3

2. 7 + 3 = 10   10 − 7 = 3

3 + 7 = 10   10 − 3 = 7

3. 5 + 4 = 9   9 − 5 = 4

4 + 5 = 9   9 − 4 = 5

Problem Solving *Algebra*

Write the missing signs to finish the fact family.

4. 8 + 2 = 10   10 − 8 = 2

2 + 8 = 10   10 − 2 = 8

44 Use with Lesson 4-6.

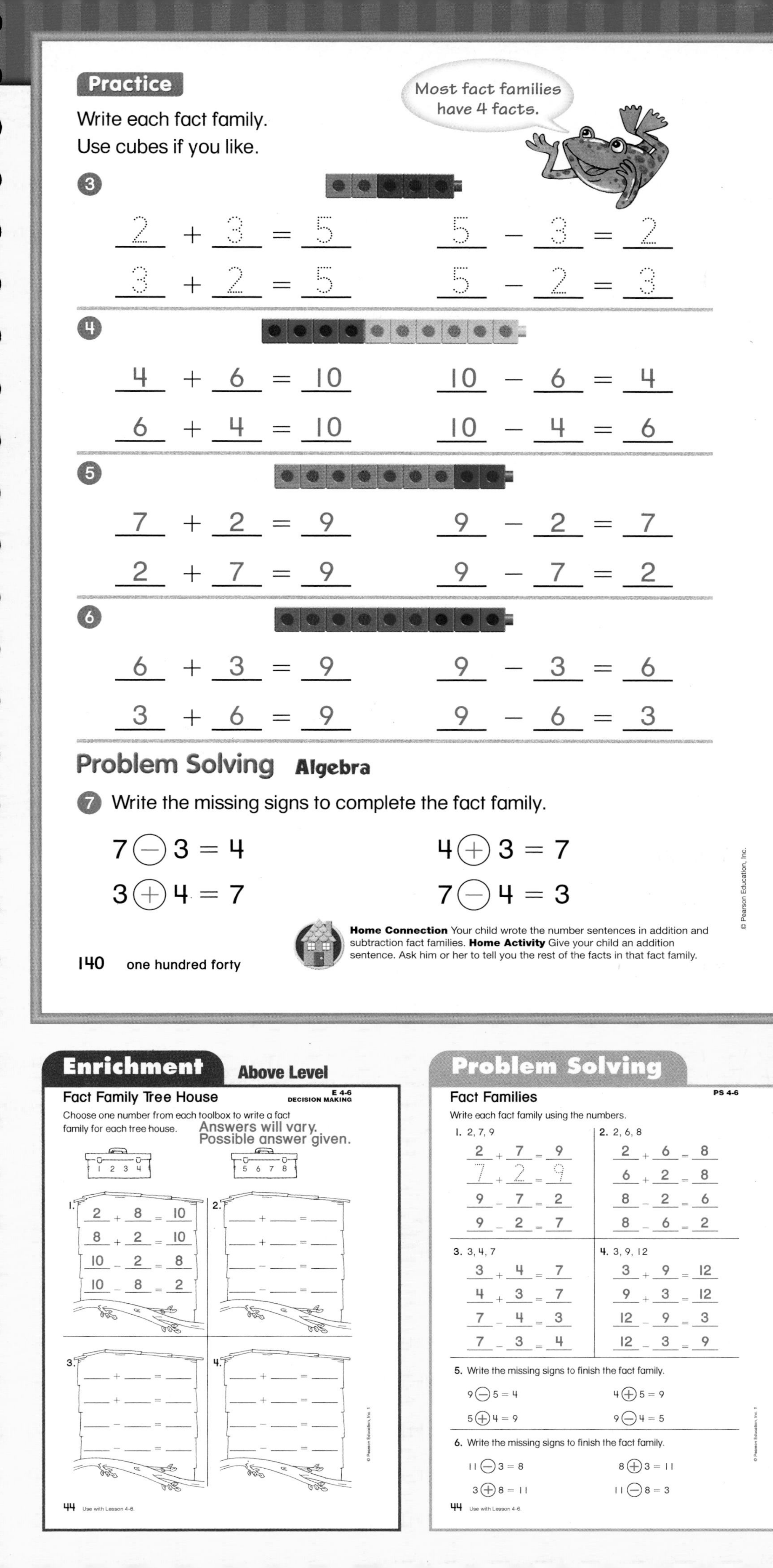

Practice

Write each fact family.
Use cubes if you like.

Most fact families have 4 facts.

3. 2 + 3 = 5 5 − 3 = 2
3 + 2 = 5 5 − 2 = 3

4. 4 + 6 = 10 10 − 6 = 4
6 + 4 = 10 10 − 4 = 6

5. 7 + 2 = 9 9 − 2 = 7
2 + 7 = 9 9 − 7 = 2

6. 6 + 3 = 9 9 − 3 = 6
3 + 6 = 9 9 − 6 = 3

Problem Solving **Algebra**

7. Write the missing signs to complete the fact family.

7 (−) 3 = 4 4 (+) 3 = 7
3 (+) 4 = 7 7 (−) 4 = 3

Home Connection Your child wrote the number sentences in addition and subtraction fact families. **Home Activity** Give your child an addition sentence. Ask him or her to tell you the rest of the facts in that fact family.

Enrichment Above Level

Fact Family Tree House — E 4-6 DECISION MAKING

Choose one number from each toolbox to write a fact family for each tree house.

Answers will vary. Possible answer given.

1. 2 + 8 = 10
8 + 2 = 10
10 − 2 = 8
10 − 8 = 2

2. ___ + ___ = ___
___ + ___ = ___
___ − ___ = ___
___ − ___ = ___

3. ___ + ___ = ___
___ + ___ = ___
___ − ___ = ___
___ − ___ = ___

4. ___ + ___ = ___
___ + ___ = ___
___ − ___ = ___
___ − ___ = ___

Problem Solving

Fact Families — PS 4-6

Write each fact family using the numbers.

1. 2, 7, 9
2 + 7 = 9
7 + 2 = 9
9 − 7 = 2
9 − 2 = 7

2. 2, 6, 8
2 + 6 = 8
6 + 2 = 8
8 − 2 = 6
8 − 6 = 2

3. 3, 4, 7
3 + 4 = 7
4 + 3 = 7
7 − 4 = 3
7 − 3 = 4

4. 3, 9, 12
3 + 9 = 12
9 + 3 = 12
12 − 9 = 3
12 − 3 = 9

5. Write the missing signs to finish the fact family.
9 (−) 5 = 4 4 (+) 5 = 9
5 (+) 4 = 9 9 (−) 4 = 5

6. Write the missing signs to finish the fact family.
11 (−) 3 = 8 8 (+) 3 = 11
3 (+) 8 = 11 11 (−) 8 = 3

3 Practice

For Exercise 7, have children check that they have written two addition signs and two subtraction signs.

Reading Assist: Draw Conclusions Look at Exercise 3 together and ask children to draw a conclusion about how they can figure out the facts in the family.

Leveled Practice

Below Level Use cubes to model each exercise.

On Level Use cubes if needed.

Above Level Complete all exercises without using cubes.

Early Finishers Have each child toss two number cubes, name the numbers for a fact family, and write the facts in that family.

4 Assess

Journal Idea Invite children to cut out pictures from magazines and make joining pictures and separating pictures for any of the fact families on the page. Have them write the fact families that they are illustrating.

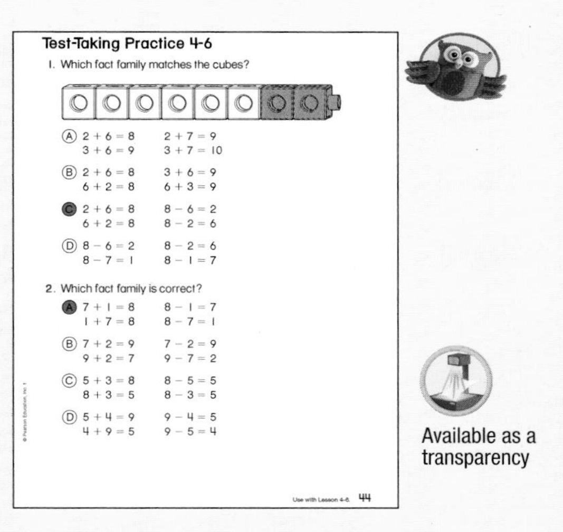

Test-Taking Practice 4-6

1. Which fact family matches the cubes?

(A) 2 + 6 = 8, 3 + 6 = 9, 2 + 7 = 9, 3 + 7 = 10
(B) 2 + 6 = 8, 6 + 2 = 8, 3 + 6 = 9, 6 + 3 = 9
(C) 2 + 6 = 8, 6 + 2 = 8, 8 − 6 = 2, 8 − 2 = 6
(D) 8 − 6 = 2, 8 − 7 = 1, 8 − 2 = 6, 8 − 1 = 7

2. Which fact family is correct?

(A) 7 + 1 = 8, 1 + 7 = 8, 8 − 1 = 7, 8 − 7 = 1
(B) 7 + 2 = 9, 9 + 2 = 7, 7 − 2 = 9, 9 − 7 = 2
(C) 5 + 3 = 8, 8 + 3 = 5, 8 − 5 = 3, 8 − 3 = 5
(D) 5 + 4 = 9, 4 + 9 = 5, 9 − 4 = 5, 9 − 5 = 4

Available as a transparency

4-7 Using Addition Facts to Subtract

Lesson Organizer

Quick Lesson Overview

Objective Find differences by using known addition facts.

Math Understanding An addition fact can be used to find the difference in a related subtraction fact.

Professional Development Note

Math Background Children have had experiences with the inverse relationship between addition and subtraction when writing fact families. Encourage them to use addition facts that they know to solve related subtraction problems.

NCTM Standards

- Number and Operations
- Algebra

(For a complete correlation to the NCTM Standards and Grades Pre-K through 2 Expectations, see Pages 123G and 123H.)

Getting Started

Spiral Review

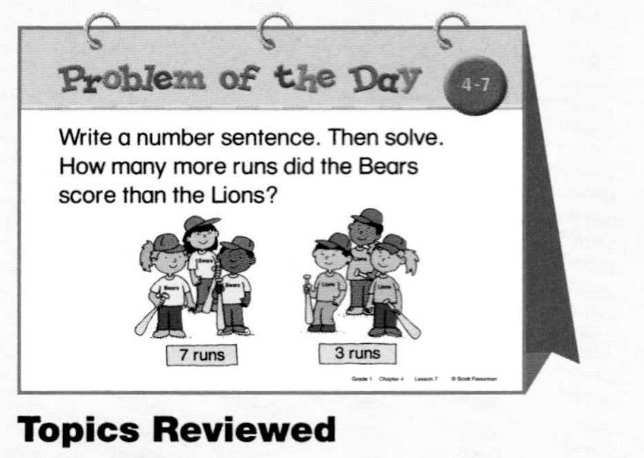

Problem of the Day
4-7
Write a number sentence. Then solve.
How many more runs did the Bears score than the Lions?
7 runs
3 runs

Topics Reviewed

- Subtraction
- Problem-Solving Strategy: Write a Number Sentence

Answer 7 − 3 = 4. The Bears scored 4 more runs than the Lions.

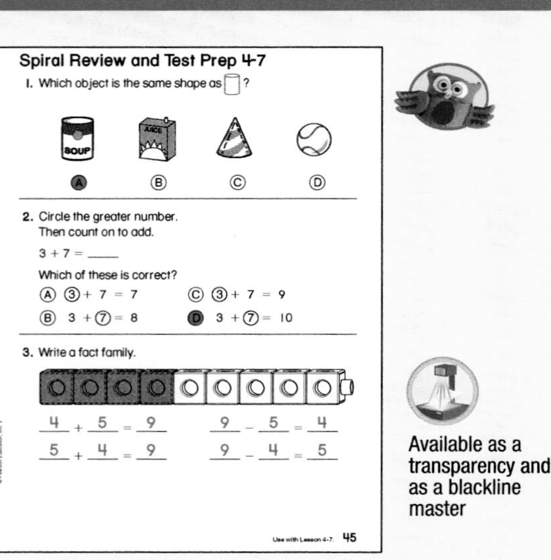

Spiral Review and Test Prep 4-7

1. Which object is the same shape as ▯?

Ⓐ Ⓑ Ⓒ Ⓓ

2. Circle the greater number. Then count on to add.

3 + 7 = ____

Which of these is correct?

Ⓐ ③ + 7 = 7 Ⓒ ③ + 7 = 9

Ⓑ 3 + ⑦ = 8 Ⓓ 3 + ⑦ = 10

3. Write a fact family.

4 + 5 = 9 9 − 5 = 4

5 + 4 = 9 9 − 4 = 5

Use with Lesson 4-7. 45

Available as a transparency and as a blackline master

Topics Reviewed

1. Solid Figures
2. Adding 1, 2, or 3
3. Fact Families

Investigating the Concept

Using Addition to Subtract

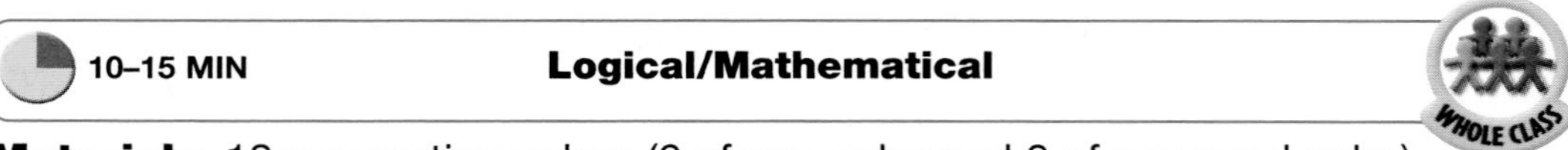

Materials 12 connecting cubes (6 of one color and 6 of a second color)

What to Do

- Display a cube train showing 6 cubes of one color and 3 cubes of another color. Ask what addition fact the cubes show. *(6 + 3 = 9)*
- Ask children how they could use the same train to find the difference for 9 − 3. *(Separate the train.)* Write 9 − 3 = 6 on the board. Discuss how knowing an addition fact can help children subtract.
- Ask children to tell which fact will help them find the difference for 10 − 6.

Ongoing Assessment

- **Number Sense What addition fact could you use to find 9 − 2?** *(7 + 2 = 9 or 2 + 7 = 9)*
- **How do you know which addition fact to use?** *(Sample response: Use the one that has the same numbers as the subtraction sentence.)*

Reaching All Learners

Oral Language in Math

Related Riddles

5–10 MIN **Linguistic** PAIRS

- Read this riddle to the children:

  I am in the 8, 3, 5 fact family.
  You can use me to answer 8 – 3.
  I begin with a 3.
  What number sentence am I? *(3 + 5 = 8)*

- Reread the riddle. After you read the first clue, have children list all of the possible answers. As you read each subsequent clue, have children cross out any incorrect answers until they are left with one correct answer.

★ 3 + 5 = 8 ~~8 – 3 = 5~~
~~5 + 3 = 8~~ ~~8 – 5 = 3~~

Activate Prior Knowledge/Build Background

What's Missing

5–10 MIN **Visual/Spatial/Linguistic** SMALL GROUP

Materials Index cards

- On each index card, write two of the three numbers in a fact family. One number should be the sum. Underline the sum. For example, a card might have 7 and 12.
- Pass out one card to each child in the group. One at a time, invite children to share their cards with the group in English and in their primary languages. They should tell what number is missing from the fact family. They should also name an addition fact and a related subtraction fact from the fact family.

Reteaching

Find Your Match

10–15 MIN **Visual/Spatial** WHOLE CLASS

Materials Addition fact cards; subtraction fact cards

- Pass out an addition or a subtraction fact card to each child. After looking at their cards, have those children holding subtraction cards walk around the room, looking for the child who has the addition fact card that can be used to solve their problems.
- Children then work together to explain to the rest of the class why the subtraction fact can be solved using the related addition fact.

Students with Special Needs

Matching Related Facts

5–10 MIN **Visual/Spatial** SMALL GROUP

Materials Index cards

- On one set of index cards, write subtraction sentences *without* the differences. On another set of index cards, write addition sentences *with* the sums.
- Place all of the addition cards face up. Hold up a subtraction card. Invite a child to find the addition fact card that will help them solve the subtraction problem and give the difference.
- Continue showing subtraction cards until each child has solved a problem.

Objective Find differences by using known addition facts.

1 Warm Up

Activate Prior Knowledge Review addition facts. Divide the class into two teams. Have them take turns telling sums for addition facts to 12, just as you would in a spelling bee.

2 Teach

Learn!

Discuss the picture and ask children to name the addition fact that the picture shows. *(1 + 7 = 8)* Tell children that when they are trying to do subtraction, it is helpful to think of related addition facts. Ask children to name a subtraction problem they could solve that is related to 1 + 7 = 8. *(8 − 7 = 1 or 8 − 1 = 7)* Discuss what is alike about the facts.

Ongoing Assessment

Talk About It

- **What numbers are the same in these two sentences?** *(8, 1, 7)*
- **How can an addition fact help you subtract?** *(You can use the numbers from the addition fact to solve the subtraction fact.)*

If children cannot tell how the addition fact is related to the subtraction fact,

then have children compare the numbers in a pair of related facts.

Check

Error Intervention

If children cannot complete the subtraction fact,

then have them circle the numbers that are the same in the related addition fact. *(Also see* Reteaching, *Page 141B.)*

Think About It On the board, write 4 + ___ = 7 and ___ + 4 = 7 to help the children answer the question.

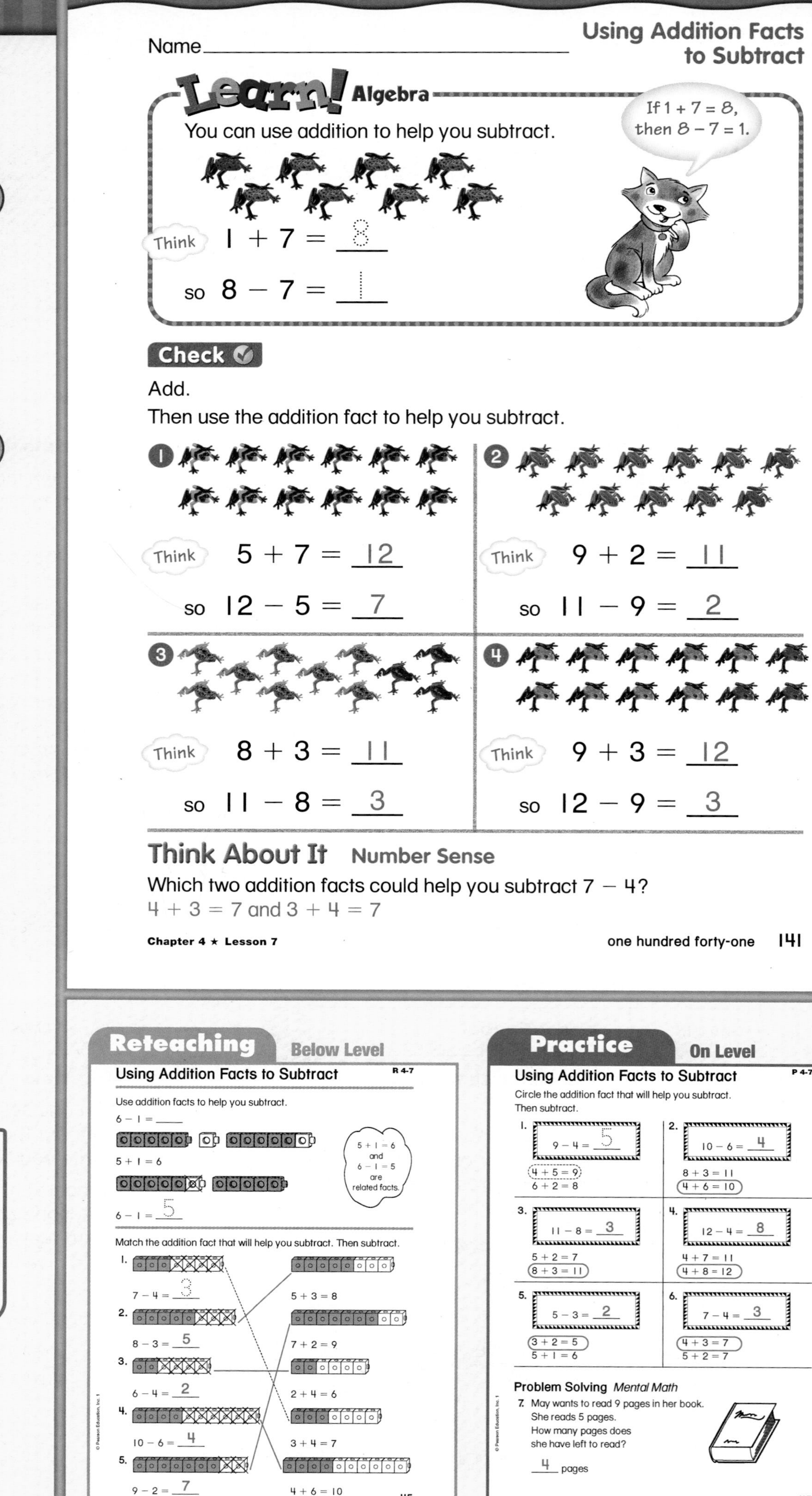

Name ______________________

Using Addition Facts to Subtract

Learn! Algebra

You can use addition to help you subtract.

Think 1 + 7 = 8

so 8 − 7 = 1

Check

Add.
Then use the addition fact to help you subtract.

1. Think 5 + 7 = 12
   so 12 − 5 = 7

2. Think 9 + 2 = 11
   so 11 − 9 = 2

3. Think 8 + 3 = 11
   so 11 − 8 = 3

4. Think 9 + 3 = 12
   so 12 − 9 = 3

Think About It Number Sense

Which two addition facts could help you subtract 7 − 4?

4 + 3 = 7 and 3 + 4 = 7

Chapter 4 ★ Lesson 7 — one hundred forty-one 141

Reteaching Below Level

Using Addition Facts to Subtract R 4-7

Use addition facts to help you subtract.

6 − 1 = ___

5 + 1 = 6

6 − 1 = 5

Match the addition fact that will help you subtract. Then subtract.

1. 7 − 4 = 3
2. 8 − 3 = 5
3. 6 − 4 = 2
4. 10 − 6 = 4
5. 9 − 2 = 7

5 + 3 = 8
7 + 2 = 9
2 + 4 = 6
3 + 4 = 7
4 + 6 = 10

© Pearson Education, Inc. 1 — Use with Lesson 4-7. 45

Practice On Level

Using Addition Facts to Subtract P 4-7

Circle the addition fact that will help you subtract.
Then subtract.

1. 9 − 4 = 5 — (4 + 5 = 9), 6 + 2 = 8
2. 10 − 6 = 4 — 8 + 3 = 11, (4 + 6 = 10)
3. 11 − 8 = 3 — 5 + 2 = 7, (8 + 3 = 11)
4. 12 − 4 = 8 — 4 + 7 = 11, (4 + 8 = 12)
5. 5 − 3 = 2 — (3 + 2 = 5), 5 + 1 = 6
6. 7 − 4 = 3 — (4 + 3 = 7), 5 + 2 = 7

Problem Solving *Mental Math*

7. May wants to read 9 pages in her book. She reads 5 pages. How many pages does she have left to read?

4 pages

© Pearson Education, Inc. 1 — Use with Lesson 4-7. 45

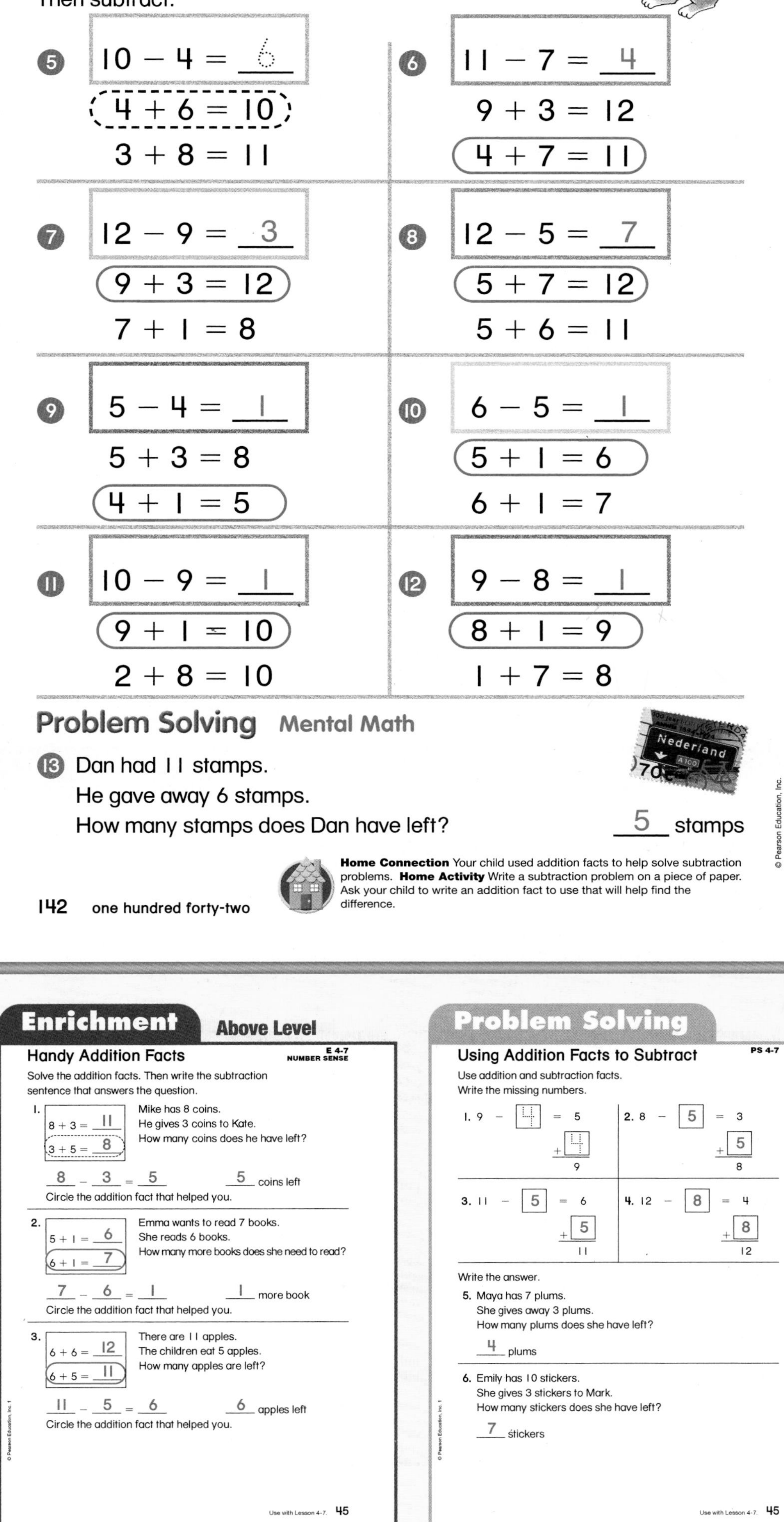

Practice

Circle the addition fact that will help you subtract.
Then subtract.

5. $10 - 4 = 6$
   - (circled) $4 + 6 = 10$
   - $3 + 8 = 11$

6. $11 - 7 = 4$
   - $9 + 3 = 12$
   - (circled) $4 + 7 = 11$

7. $12 - 9 = 3$
   - (circled) $9 + 3 = 12$
   - $7 + 1 = 8$

8. $12 - 5 = 7$
   - (circled) $5 + 7 = 12$
   - $5 + 6 = 11$

9. $5 - 4 = 1$
   - $5 + 3 = 8$
   - (circled) $4 + 1 = 5$

10. $6 - 5 = 1$
    - (circled) $5 + 1 = 6$
    - $6 + 1 = 7$

11. $10 - 9 = 1$
    - (circled) $9 + 1 = 10$
    - $2 + 8 = 10$

12. $9 - 8 = 1$
    - (circled) $8 + 1 = 9$
    - $1 + 7 = 8$

Problem Solving Mental Math

13. Dan had 11 stamps.
    He gave away 6 stamps.
    How many stamps does Dan have left? 5 stamps

Home Connection Your child used addition facts to help solve subtraction problems. **Home Activity** Write a subtraction problem on a piece of paper. Ask your child to write an addition fact to use that will help find the difference.

Enrichment Above Level

Handy Addition Facts

E 4-7 NUMBER SENSE

Solve the addition facts. Then write the subtraction sentence that answers the question.

1. $8 + 3 = 11$; (circled) $3 + 5 = 8$
   Mike has 8 coins.
   He gives 3 coins to Kate.
   How many coins does he have left?
   $8 - 3 = 5$ 5 coins left
   Circle the addition fact that helped you.

2. $5 + 1 = 6$; (circled) $6 + 1 = 7$
   Emma wants to read 7 books.
   She reads 6 books.
   How many more books does she need to read?
   $7 - 6 = 1$ 1 more book
   Circle the addition fact that helped you.

3. $6 + 6 = 12$; (circled) $6 + 5 = 11$
   There are 11 apples.
   The children eat 5 apples.
   How many apples are left?
   $11 - 5 = 6$ 6 apples left
   Circle the addition fact that helped you.

Use with Lesson 4-7. 45

Problem Solving

Using Addition Facts to Subtract

PS 4-7

Use addition and subtraction facts.
Write the missing numbers.

1. $9 - 4 = 5$; $5 + 4 = 9$
2. $8 - 5 = 3$; $3 + 5 = 8$
3. $11 - 5 = 6$; $6 + 5 = 11$
4. $12 - 8 = 4$; $4 + 8 = 12$

Write the answer.

5. Maya has 7 plums.
   She gives away 3 plums.
   How many plums does she have left?
   4 plums

6. Emily has 10 stickers.
   She gives 3 stickers to Mark.
   How many stickers does she have left?
   7 stickers

Use with Lesson 4-7. 45

3 Practice

For Exercises 5–12, remind children to circle the addition fact before doing the subtraction.

Leveled Practice

Below Level Use cubes to show each addition fact before choosing which to use.

On Level Complete all exercises as written, using cubes if needed.

Above Level Do all exercises without using cubes.

Early Finishers Invite partners to use subtraction fact cards. For each card, in addition to saying the difference, have them name the addition fact that helped them solve the problem.

4 Assess

Journal Idea Invite children to choose related addition and subtraction facts from this page and draw pictures to go with them.

Test-Taking Practice 4-7

1. Which addition fact helps you subtract $11 - 5$?
   - Ⓐ $9 + 2 = 11$
   - Ⓑ $8 + 3 = 11$
   - Ⓒ $6 + 5 = 11$ (filled)
   - Ⓓ $4 + 7 = 11$

2. Ann has 8 pencils.
   She gives away 2 pencils.
   How many pencils does Ann have left?
   - Ⓐ 10 pencils
   - Ⓑ 8 pencils
   - Ⓒ 7 pencils
   - Ⓓ 6 pencils (filled)

3. Which addition fact helps you subtract $12 - 7$?
   - Ⓐ $9 + 3 = 12$
   - Ⓑ $8 + 4 = 12$
   - Ⓒ $7 + 5 = 12$ (filled)
   - Ⓓ $6 + 6 = 12$

Use with Lesson 4-7. 45

Available as a transparency

Choose an Operation

Lesson Organizer

Quick Lesson Overview

Objective Solve problems by choosing addition or subtraction.

Math Understanding Addition and subtraction can both be useful in answering joining, separating, and comparing problems.

Professional Development Note

Effective Questioning Techniques Children may be comfortable with *How many in all?* and *How many are left?* questions, but may not know what to do for comparisons. Ask questions such as: **Which words let you know that you are looking for the difference and should subtract?** *(How many more? How many fewer?)*

NCTM Standards

- Number and Operations

(For a complete correlation to the NCTM Standards and Grades Pre-K through 2 Expectations, see Pages 123G and 123H.)

Getting Started

Spiral Review

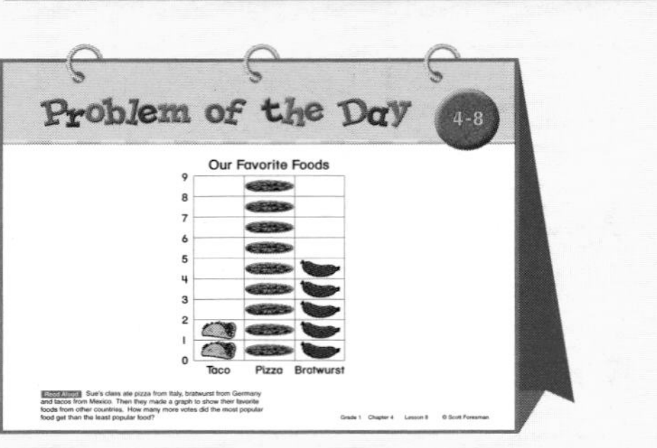

Read Aloud Sue's class ate pizza from Italy, bratwurst from Germany, and tacos from Mexico. Then they made a graph to show their favorite foods from other countries. How many more votes did the most popular food get than the least popular food?

Topics Reviewed

- Subtraction
- Problem-Solving Skill: Use Data from a Graph

Answer Pizza, the most popular food, got 7 more votes than tacos, the least popular food.

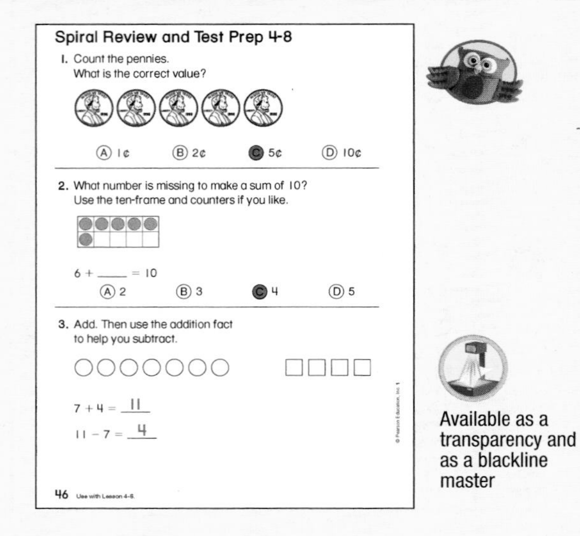

Spiral Review and Test Prep 4-8

1. Count the pennies.
What is the correct value?

Ⓐ 1¢ Ⓑ 2¢ Ⓒ 5¢ Ⓓ 10¢

2. What number is missing to make a sum of 10?
Use the ten-frame and counters if you like.

6 + ___ = 10

Ⓐ 2 Ⓑ 3 Ⓒ 4 Ⓓ 5

3. Add. Then use the addition fact to help you subtract.

7 + 4 = 11
11 − 7 = 4

46 Use with Lesson 4-8

Available as a transparency and as a blackline master

Topics Reviewed

1. Penny
2. Sums of 10
3. Using Addition Facts to Subtract

Investigating the Concept

Choose an Operation

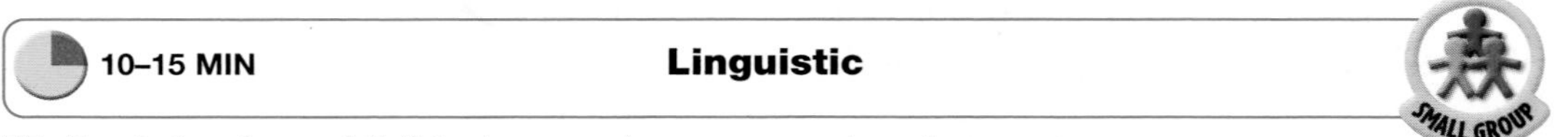

Materials *(per child)* Index card; crayons; drawing paper

What to Do

- Have each child write a plus sign (+) on one side of an index card and minus sign (−) on the other side.
- Then tell simple joining or separating stories that children can draw, such as: **5 red birds are in a tree. 2 bluebirds fly to the tree. How many fewer bluebirds are there than red birds?** Then, ask children to hold up their index cards to show the sign that names the operation they would use to find the answer.
- Have children discuss why they chose the operation and then solve the problem by writing the number sentence.
- Repeat for various addition and subtraction stories.

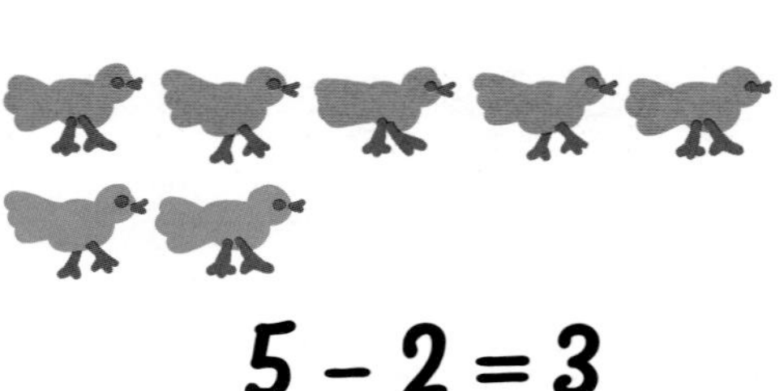

Ongoing Assessment

- **Do you add or subtract to find how many more or how many fewer?** *(Subtract)*
- **Reasoning How do you know when to add?** *(Add to join two groups.)*

Reaching All Learners

Reading in Math

Looking for the Main Idea

10–15 MIN **Linguistic**

- Write these stories on a chart or on the board.

  Juan has 3 fish.
  He buys 2 more fish.
  How many fish does Juan have in all?

  Robin has 6 fish.
  She gives 2 fish to Max.
  How many fish are left?

- Discuss each story problem with the children. **Should I add or subtract? How do you know?**

  Should I add or subtract?

- Then have children write and solve number sentences for the stories.

Extend Language

English Language Learners

Rebus Stories

10–15 MIN **Visual/Spatial/Linguistic**

SMALL GROUP

Materials Magazines; glue

- Provide an outline for children, such as the following:

  I have __ _______.
  I get __ more ________.
  How many ______ do I have in all?

- Invite children to cut pictures from magazines and add numbers to complete the stories. They can then read their stories aloud with friends who can write number sentences to solve the problems.

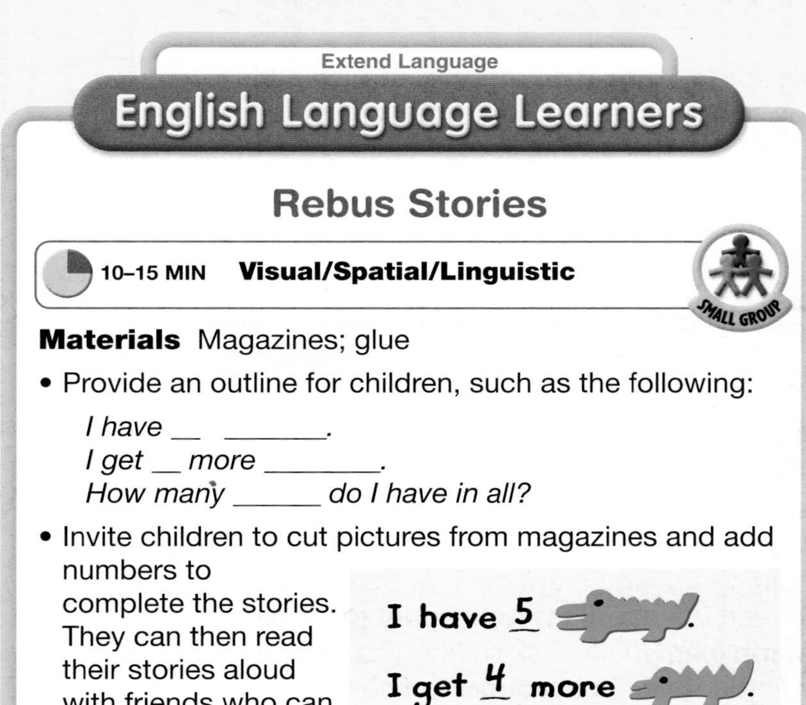

I have 5
I get 4 more
How many
do I have in all?

Reteaching

Add or Subtract?

10–15 MIN **Logical/Mathematical/Kinesthetic**

WHOLE CLASS

Materials 12 counters

- Put a number of counters on a table. Begin telling a story problem about the counters, such as: **7 children are at the zoo.** Invite a child to finish the story, deciding whether it will be an addition or a subtraction story. The child either adds or removes counters.
- Each child in the class writes the number sentence that solves the problem. Children can then compare answers and discuss why addition or subtraction was used.

Math and Science

Math Habitats

15–20 MIN **Visual/Spatial/Linguistic**

Materials *(per group)* Posterboard; markers or other art supplies

- Assign each group a habitat, such as the desert, and give them a piece of posterboard.
- The group selects one addition sentence and one subtraction sentence. They then draw groups of animals or plants native to the habitat to illustrate both number sentences.
- Have groups share their work by telling addition or subtraction stories.

Objective Solve problems by choosing addition or subtraction.

1 Warm Up

Activate Prior Knowledge Review adding and subtracting. Using a set of Number Cards 0–11 (Teaching Tool 9), select two cards. Hold them up and allow children to compute their sum and their difference.

2 Teach

Learn!

Read the word problem aloud to the children and ask what they are trying to find out. *(How many seeds in all)* Help children determine that 7 and 3 are the numbers to use. Reread the question: **How many seeds did Maria plant in all?** Ask children to choose whether to add or subtract to find the answer. Then discuss why they need to add.

Ongoing Assessment

Talk About It

- **Where do you find the numbers you need to solve a problem?** *(In the problem)*
- **How do you decide whether to add or subtract?** *(By deciding if the story is joining, separating, or comparing groups)*

If children cannot explain their choices of operations,

then have them act out the situation with counters.

Check

Error Intervention

If children have difficulty writing the number sentences,

then have them circle the numbers in the story problem before writing the number sentence. *(Also see* Reteaching, *Page 143B.)*

Think About It You may wish to have children pantomime the story to help them decide whether to add or subtract.

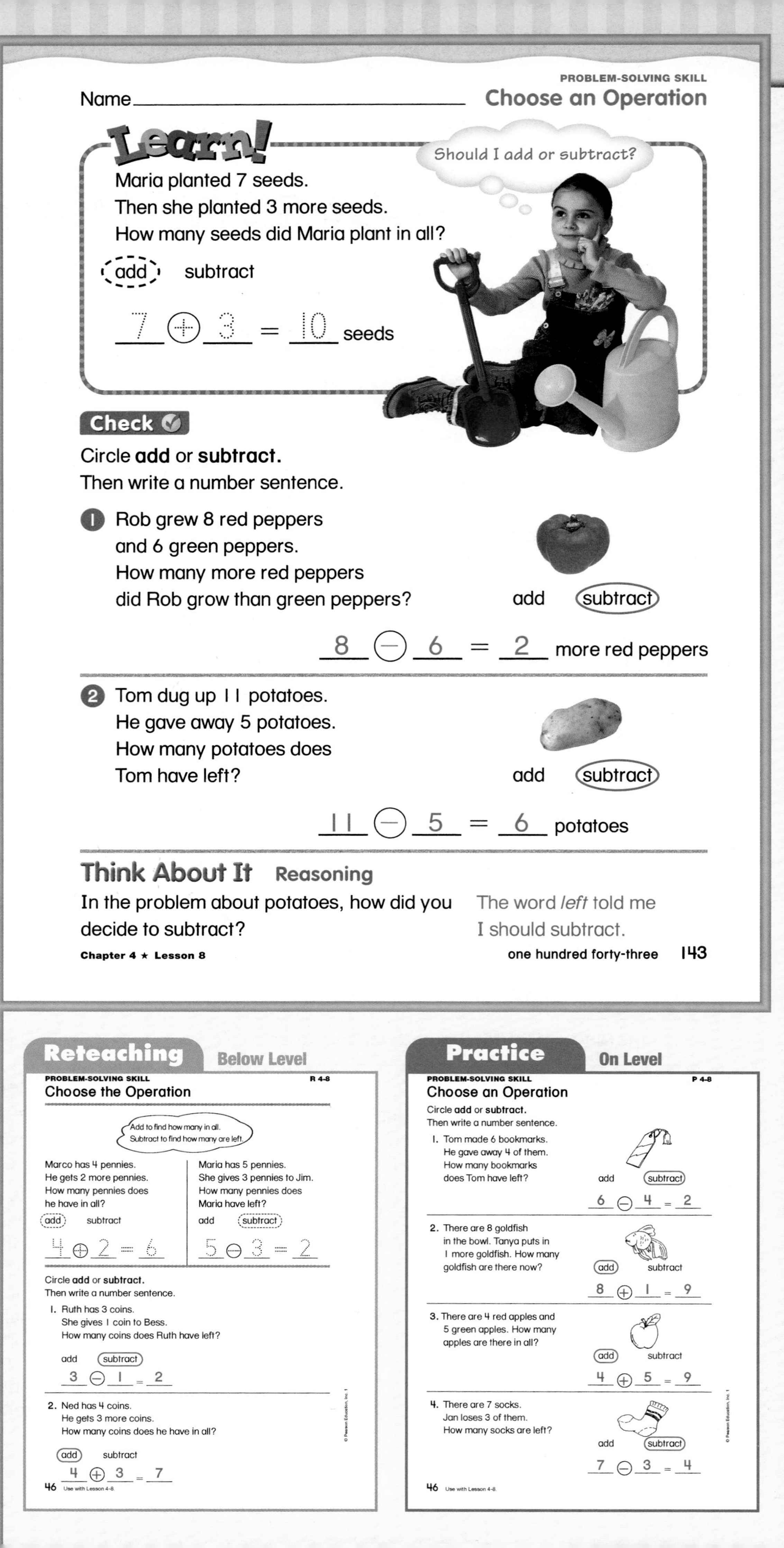

PROBLEM-SOLVING SKILL

Name ____________

Choose an Operation

Learn!

Maria planted 7 seeds.
Then she planted 3 more seeds.
How many seeds did Maria plant in all?

(add) subtract

7 ⊕ 3 = 10 seeds

Check

Circle **add** or **subtract.**
Then write a number sentence.

1. Rob grew 8 red peppers and 6 green peppers. How many more red peppers did Rob grow than green peppers? add (subtract)

8 ⊖ 6 = 2 more red peppers

2. Tom dug up 11 potatoes. He gave away 5 potatoes. How many potatoes does Tom have left? add (subtract)

11 ⊖ 5 = 6 potatoes

Think About It Reasoning

In the problem about potatoes, how did you decide to subtract?

The word *left* told me I should subtract.

Chapter 4 ★ Lesson 8 one hundred forty-three 143

Reteaching Below Level

PROBLEM-SOLVING SKILL R 4-8

Choose the Operation

Add to find how many in all.
Subtract to find how many are left.

Marco has 4 pennies. He gets 2 more pennies. How many pennies does he have in all? (add) subtract

4 ⊕ 2 = 6

Maria has 5 pennies. She gives 3 pennies to Jim. How many pennies does Maria have left? add (subtract)

5 ⊖ 3 = 2

Circle **add** or **subtract.**
Then write a number sentence.

1. Ruth has 3 coins. She gives 1 coin to Bess. How many coins does Ruth have left? add (subtract)

3 ⊖ 1 = 2

2. Ned has 4 coins. He gets 3 more coins. How many coins does he have in all? (add) subtract

4 ⊕ 3 = 7

46 Use with Lesson 4-8

Practice On Level

PROBLEM-SOLVING SKILL P 4-8

Choose an Operation

Circle **add** or **subtract.**
Then write a number sentence.

1. Tom made 6 bookmarks. He gave away 4 of them. How many bookmarks does Tom have left? add (subtract)

6 ⊖ 4 = 2

2. There are 8 goldfish in the bowl. Tanya puts in 1 more goldfish. How many goldfish are there now? (add) subtract

8 ⊕ 1 = 9

3. There are 4 red apples and 5 green apples. How many apples are there in all? (add) subtract

4 ⊕ 5 = 9

4. There are 7 socks. Jan loses 3 of them. How many socks are left? add (subtract)

7 ⊖ 3 = 4

46 Use with Lesson 4-8

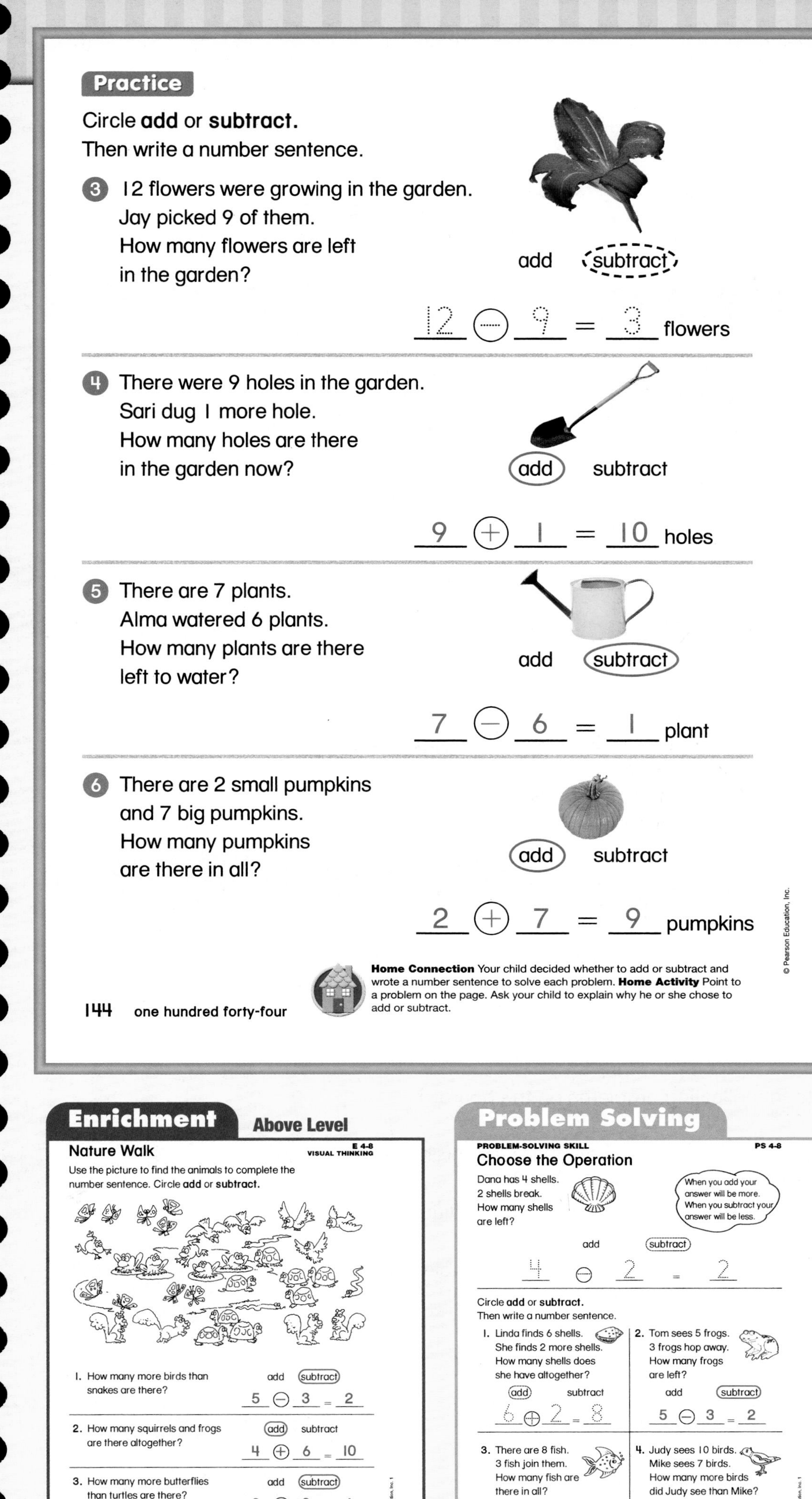

Practice

Circle **add** or **subtract.**
Then write a number sentence.

3. 12 flowers were growing in the garden. Jay picked 9 of them. How many flowers are left in the garden?

add (subtract)

12 ⊖ 9 = 3 flowers

4. There were 9 holes in the garden. Sari dug 1 more hole. How many holes are there in the garden now?

(add) subtract

9 ⊕ 1 = 10 holes

5. There are 7 plants. Alma watered 6 plants. How many plants are there left to water?

add (subtract)

7 ⊖ 6 = 1 plant

6. There are 2 small pumpkins and 7 big pumpkins. How many pumpkins are there in all?

(add) subtract

2 ⊕ 7 = 9 pumpkins

Home Connection Your child decided whether to add or subtract and wrote a number sentence to solve each problem. **Home Activity** Point to a problem on the page. Ask your child to explain why he or she chose to add or subtract.

Enrichment Above Level

Nature Walk E 4-8 VISUAL THINKING

Use the picture to find the animals to complete the number sentence. Circle **add** or **subtract**.

1. How many more birds than snakes are there? add (subtract) 5 ⊖ 3 = 2
2. How many squirrels and frogs are there altogether? (add) subtract 4 ⊕ 6 = 10
3. How many more butterflies than turtles are there? add (subtract) 9 ⊖ 8 = 1
4. How many turtles and snakes are there in all? (add) subtract 8 ⊕ 3 = 11

46 Use with Lesson 4-8.

Problem Solving

PROBLEM-SOLVING SKILL PS 4-8

Choose the Operation

Dana has 4 shells. 2 shells break. How many shells are left?

When you add your answer will be more. When you subtract your answer will be less.

add (subtract)

4 ⊖ 2 = 2

Circle **add** or **subtract**.
Then write a number sentence.

1. Linda finds 6 shells. She finds 2 more shells. How many shells does she have altogether? (add) subtract 6 ⊕ 2 = 8
2. Tom sees 5 frogs. 3 frogs hop away. How many frogs are left? add (subtract) 5 ⊖ 3 = 2
3. There are 8 fish. 3 fish join them. How many fish are there in all? (add) subtract 8 ⊕ 3 = 11
4. Judy sees 10 birds. Mike sees 7 birds. How many more birds did Judy see than Mike? add (subtract) 10 ⊖ 7 = 3

Using the page Encourage children to **look back** and **check** that their answer is less than the number they subtracted from or more than the numbers they added.

46 Use with Lesson 4-8.

3 Practice

Tell children to use both the numbers and the question in the problem to decide whether to add or subtract.

Reading Assist: Draw Conclusions Read the questions at the end of each problem in Exercises 3 and 4. Help children draw the conclusion that the question in a problem gives a hint about whether to add or subtract to solve it.

Leveled Practice

Below Level Listen as the teacher reads each problem. Use counters to solve the problems.

On Level Use counters if needed.

Above Level Do exercises without counters.

Early Finishers Have each child draw pictures to justify their answers to Exercises 5 and 6.

4 Assess

Journal Idea Have each child rewrite a story problem by changing the numbers. Then have them write number sentences to solve the problems.

Test-Taking Practice 4-8

1. Which number sentence answers the question?
   Fran has 6 gel pens and 2 markers. How many more gel pens does Fran have?
   Ⓐ 6 + 2 = 8 Ⓑ 6 − 2 = 4 Ⓒ 6 + 6 = 12 Ⓓ 2 − 2 = 0
2. Which number sentence answers the question?
   Dom has 3 football cards and 9 baseball cards. How many cards does Dom have in all?
   Ⓐ 3 + 9 = 12 Ⓑ 9 − 3 = 6 Ⓒ 3 + 3 = 6 Ⓓ 9 − 9 = 0
3. Which number sentence answers the question?
   David has 6 toy cars and 5 toy trucks. How many toy cars and trucks does David have in all?
   Ⓐ 5 − 1 = 4 Ⓑ 6 + 1 = 7 Ⓒ 6 − 5 = 1 Ⓓ 6 + 5 = 11

Use with Lesson 4-8. 46

Available as a transparency

PROBLEM-SOLVING APPLICATIONS 4-9

Playful Puppies

Lesson Organizer

Quick Lesson Overview

Objective Review and apply concepts, skills, and strategies learned in this and previous chapters.

Math Understanding Some real-world problems can be solved using known concepts, skills, and strategies.

Professional Development Note

Math Background Children have had experience finding differences by counting back, using a number line, and using related facts. Children can apply what they know to solve new problems. Remind children of methods they can use to find a difference.

NCTM Standards

- Number and Operations
- Algebra

(For a complete correlation to the NCTM Standards and Grades Pre-K through 2 Expectations, see Pages 123G and 123H.)

Getting Started

Spiral Review

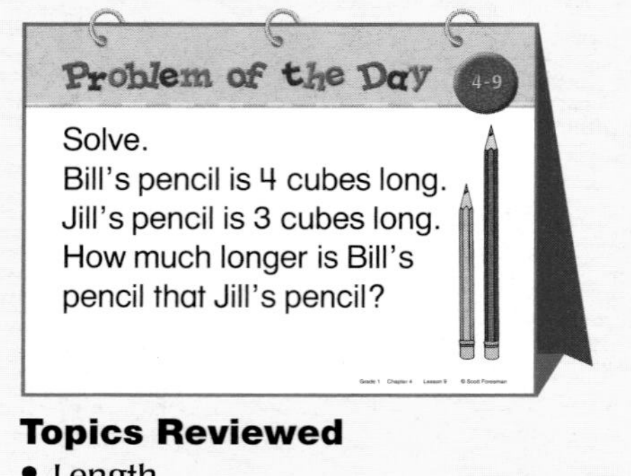

Problem of the Day
4-9
Solve.
Bill's pencil is 4 cubes long.
Jill's pencil is 3 cubes long.
How much longer is Bill's pencil that Jill's pencil?

Topics Reviewed

- Length
- Problem-Solving: One-Step Problem

Answer Bill's pencil is 1 cube longer than Jill's pencil

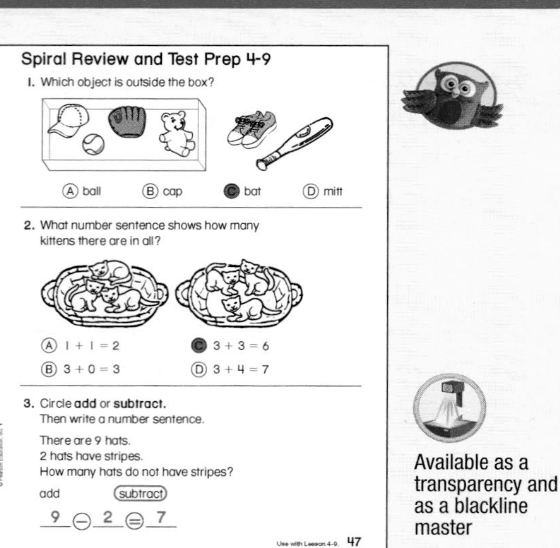

Spiral Review and Test Prep 4-9

1. Which object is outside the box?

Ⓐ ball Ⓑ cap Ⓒ bat Ⓓ mitt

2. What number sentence shows how many kittens there are in all?

Ⓐ 1 + 1 = 2 Ⓑ 3 + 0 = 3 Ⓒ 3 + 3 = 6 Ⓓ 3 + 4 = 7

3. Circle **add** or **subtract**.
Then write a number sentence.
There are 9 hats.
2 hats have stripes.
How many hats do not have stripes?

add (subtract)

9 − 2 = 7

47

Available as a transparency and as a blackline master

Topics Reviewed

1. Inside and Outside
2. Doubles
3. Choose an Operation

Investigating the Concept

Reviewing Subtraction

10–15 MIN **Logical/Mathematical** WHOLE CLASS

What to Do

- Write the following problems on the board: 7 − 1 = ___; 9 − 2 = ___; 11 − 8 = ___; 12 − 5 = ___.
- Invite children to circle two subtraction problems that might be solved by counting back. *(7 − 1, 9 − 2)*
- Invite another child to write a related addition fact that might be used to find the difference for 11 − 8. *(8 + 3 = 11)*
- Have another child write an addition doubles fact that might be used to find the difference for 12 − 5. *(6 + 6 = 12)*
- Then have children solve each of the problems.

Ongoing Assessment

- **Reasoning When is counting back helpful?** *(When you are subtracting 1 or 2)*
- **What addition doubles fact would help you find the answer to 8 − 4?** *(4 + 4 = 8)*

7 − 1 = ___ 11 − 8 = ___
9 − 2 = ___ 12 − 5 = ___

Reaching All Learners

Oral Language in Math

Fewer and Fewer

5–10 MIN **Auditory/Logical/Mathematical**

Materials *(per child)* Counters

- Tell this math story to children: **There were 3 puppies at the animal shelter. A girl took 1 puppy home. Now how many puppies still need a home?** Children act out the story with their counters to answer the question.
- Tell another story: **There were 2 puppies at the animal shelter. A boy took 1 puppy home. Now how many puppies still need homes?**
- Continue until all of the puppies have found homes.

Extend Language

English Language Learners

Word Web Subtraction Stories

10–15 MIN **Linguistic**

Materials *(per child)* Construction paper

- Write the following story on the board: "5 kittens are in a basket. 2 jump out. How many are left?"
- Underline key words that make the story a subtraction problem.
- Have each child create a word web by writing *Subtraction* on construction paper and circling it. Then have the child copy key words from the story and connect them to the circle with lines.
- As you write other similar subtraction stories, children can add new words to their word webs.

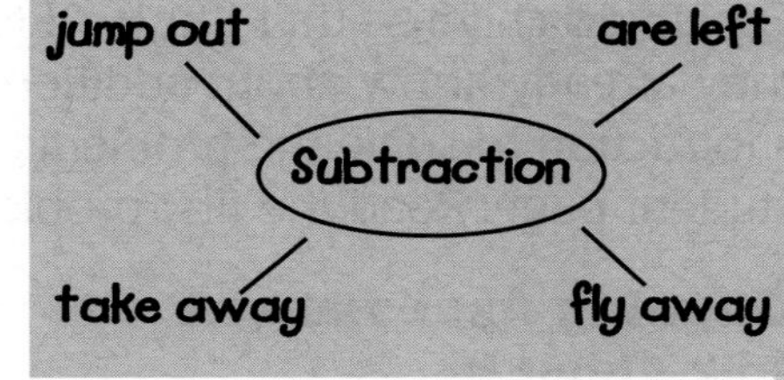

Reteaching

Counting Back

10–15 MIN **Linguistic/Kinesthetic**

Materials Number Cards 0–11 (Teaching Tool 9); masking tape

- Use masking tape to mark a number line with 10 spaces on the floor. Place number cards face down.
- Begin subtraction problems with 10. Have a child choose a card to determine which number to subtract. For example, if a child chooses a 5, the problem is $10 - 5 = \_\_\_$.
- Write the problem on the board. Have a child act out the problem by standing at 10 on the number line and stepping toward zero the appropriate number of spaces to subtract. Write the answer on the board.
- Continue with other subtraction problems.

Math and Technology

Subtracting on a Calculator

5–10 MIN **Logical/Mathematical**

INDIVIDUAL

Materials *(per child)* Calculator

- Provide children with a number of subtraction problems for them to solve using a calculator.
- You may wish to have them first complete the problems by using counters, counting back on a number line, or drawing pictures, and then use the calculator to check their answers.
- Before children begin, review the buttons on the calculator and locate the minus sign.
- You may wish to review how to count back by repeatedly pressing **−1.**

Objective Review and apply concepts, skills, and strategies learned in this and previous chapters.

1 Warm Up

Activate Prior Knowledge Review using subtraction to compare. Draw a row of 10 fishbowls on the board. Draw 1 goldfish under 7 of the bowls. **What subtraction sentence tells about the picture?** *(10 – 7 = 3)* Repeat with other similar problems.

2 Teach

Explain to children that they will use what they already know about addition and subtraction to solve the problems on the student page. Read the first problem aloud.

Ongoing Assessment

Talk About It

- **What do we need to find out?** *(How many more puppies are needed to have 10 in all)*
- **What do we know?** *(There are 4 puppies in the picture.)*
- **How can we solve this problem?** *(Sample response: Act it out; use counters; draw a picture; or use numbers.)*
- **What related subtraction fact could help you solve this problem?** *(10 – 4 = 6)*

If children cannot complete the number sentence,

then have them draw an X for every puppy added until they reach 10.

Error Intervention

If children do not recognize this as a sum of 10,

then have them use a ten-frame. *(Also see Reteaching, Page 145B.)*

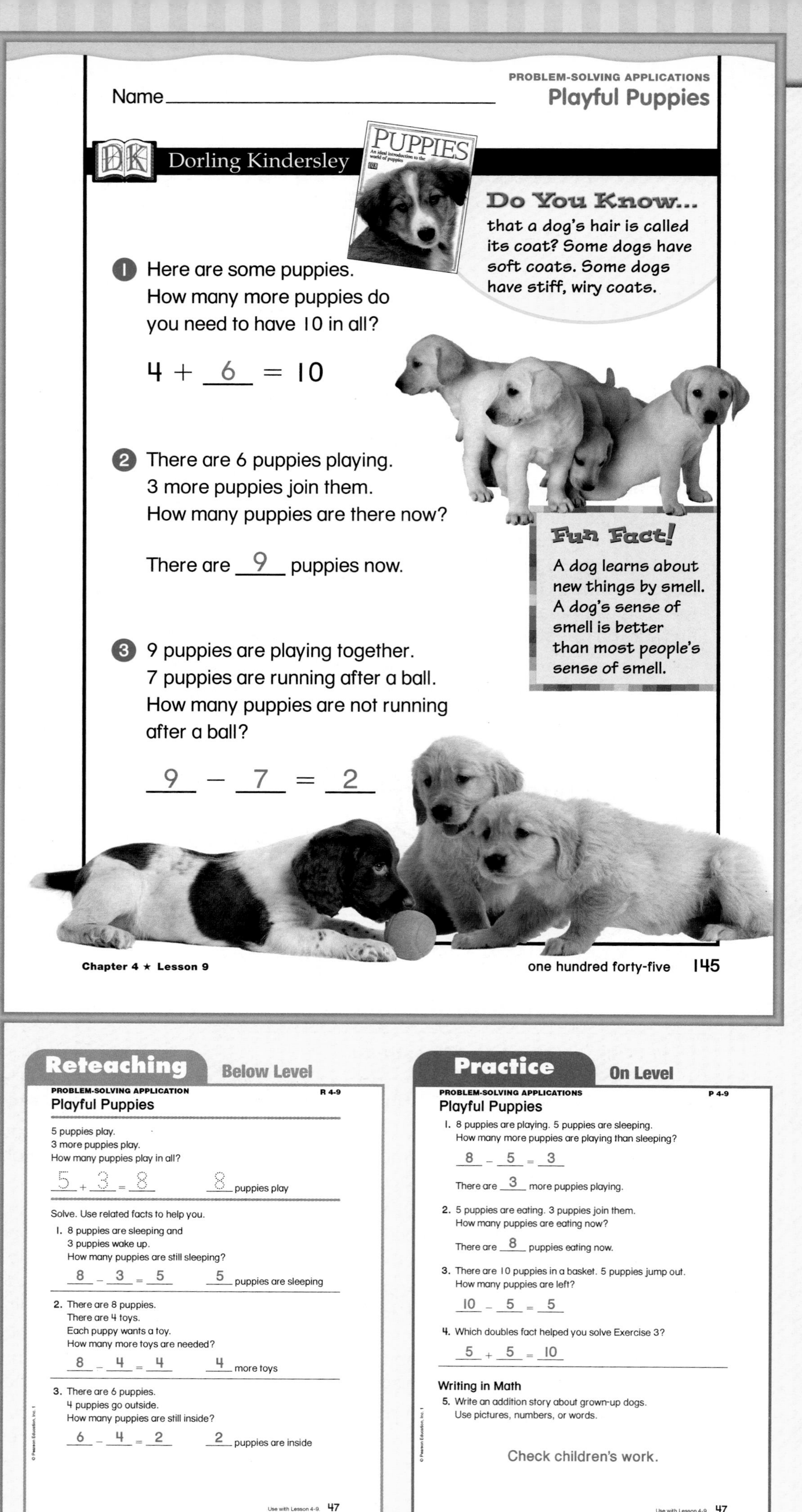
Name ______________________

PROBLEM-SOLVING APPLICATIONS
Playful Puppies

Dorling Kindersley

PUPPIES

Do You Know...
that a dog's hair is called its coat? Some dogs have soft coats. Some dogs have stiff, wiry coats.

1. Here are some puppies. How many more puppies do you need to have 10 in all?

4 + 6 = 10

2. There are 6 puppies playing. 3 more puppies join them. How many puppies are there now?

There are 9 puppies now.

Fun Fact!
A dog learns about new things by smell. A dog's sense of smell is better than most people's sense of smell.

3. 9 puppies are playing together. 7 puppies are running after a ball. How many puppies are not running after a ball?

9 – 7 = 2

Chapter 4 ★ Lesson 9 one hundred forty-five 145

Reteaching Below Level

PROBLEM-SOLVING APPLICATION R 4-9
Playful Puppies

5 puppies play.
3 more puppies play.
How many puppies play in all?

5 + 3 = 8 8 puppies play

Solve. Use related facts to help you.

1. 8 puppies are sleeping and 3 puppies wake up. How many puppies are still sleeping?
8 – 3 = 5 5 puppies are sleeping

2. There are 8 puppies. There are 4 toys. Each puppy wants a toy. How many more toys are needed?
8 – 4 = 4 4 more toys

3. There are 6 puppies. 4 puppies go outside. How many puppies are still inside?
6 – 4 = 2 2 puppies are inside

Use with Lesson 4-9. 47

Practice On Level

PROBLEM-SOLVING APPLICATIONS P 4-9
Playful Puppies

1. 8 puppies are playing. 5 puppies are sleeping. How many more puppies are playing than sleeping?
8 – 5 = 3
There are 3 more puppies playing.

2. 5 puppies are eating. 3 puppies join them. How many puppies are eating now?
There are 8 puppies eating now.

3. There are 10 puppies in a basket. 5 puppies jump out. How many puppies are left?
10 – 5 = 5

4. Which doubles fact helped you solve Exercise 3?
5 + 5 = 10

Writing in Math

5. Write an addition story about grown-up dogs. Use pictures, numbers, or words.

Check children's work.

Use with Lesson 4-9. 47

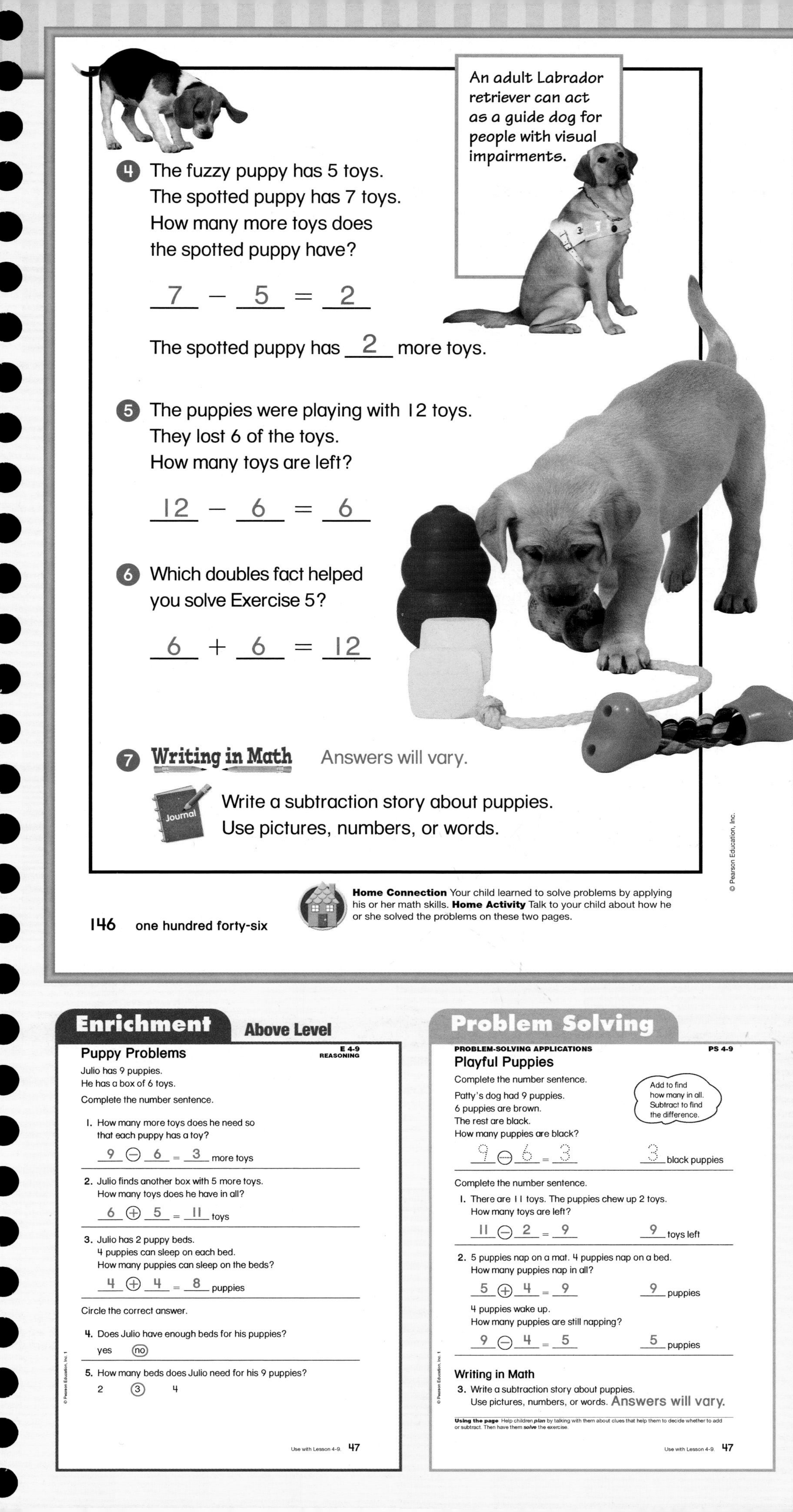

An adult Labrador retriever can act as a guide dog for people with visual impairments.

4 The fuzzy puppy has 5 toys.
The spotted puppy has 7 toys.
How many more toys does the spotted puppy have?

7 − 5 = 2

The spotted puppy has 2 more toys.

5 The puppies were playing with 12 toys.
They lost 6 of the toys.
How many toys are left?

12 − 6 = 6

6 Which doubles fact helped you solve Exercise 5?

6 + 6 = 12

7 **Writing in Math** Answers will vary.

Write a subtraction story about puppies.
Use pictures, numbers, or words.

Home Connection Your child learned to solve problems by applying his or her math skills. **Home Activity** Talk to your child about how he or she solved the problems on these two pages.

Enrichment Above Level

E 4-9 REASONING

Puppy Problems

Julio has 9 puppies.
He has a box of 6 toys.
Complete the number sentence.

1. How many more toys does he need so that each puppy has a toy?
9 ⊖ 6 = 3 more toys
2. Julio finds another box with 5 more toys. How many toys does he have in all?
6 ⊕ 5 = 11 toys
3. Julio has 2 puppy beds. 4 puppies can sleep on each bed. How many puppies can sleep on the beds?
4 ⊕ 4 = 8 puppies

Circle the correct answer.

4. Does Julio have enough beds for his puppies?
yes (no)
5. How many beds does Julio need for his 9 puppies?
2 (3) 4

Problem Solving

PROBLEM-SOLVING APPLICATIONS PS 4-9

Playful Puppies

Complete the number sentence.

Add to find how many in all. Subtract to find the difference.

Patty's dog had 9 puppies.
6 puppies are brown.
The rest are black.
How many puppies are black?

9 ⊖ 6 = 3 3 black puppies

Complete the number sentence.

1. There are 11 toys. The puppies chew up 2 toys. How many toys are left?
11 ⊖ 2 = 9 9 toys left
2. 5 puppies nap on a mat. 4 puppies nap on a bed. How many puppies nap in all?
5 ⊕ 4 = 9 9 puppies
4 puppies wake up. How many puppies are still napping?
9 ⊖ 4 = 5 5 puppies

Writing in Math

3. Write a subtraction story about puppies. Use pictures, numbers, or words. Answers will vary.

Using the page Help children *plan* by talking with them about clues that help them to decide whether to add or subtract. Then have them *solve* the exercise.

3 Practice

Tell children that they will have to refer to Exercise 5 in order to answer Exercise 6.

Reading Assist: Compare and Contrast Ask children to tell how Exercises 4 and 5 are alike and different.

Leveled Practice

Below Level Work with a partner.

On Level Work with a partner to solve only the problem in Exercise 7.

Above Level Solve all problems independently.

Early Finishers Have children draw 12 puppies, 7 brown and 5 tan. Ask children to write a fact family about the picture.

4 Assess

Journal Idea Read the following problem aloud: **There are 6 puppies. The mother dog carries in 3 more. What number sentence tells how many puppies there are in all?** Have children draw a picture, write the sum, and complete the fact family.

Test-Taking Practice 4-9

1. Wendy picked 7 apples. How many more apples must she pick to have 10 apples in all?
What is the missing number?
7 + ____ = 10
Ⓐ 4
Ⓑ 3 (filled)
Ⓒ 2
Ⓓ 1
2. Which number sentence answers the question?
Ken's team scored 9 points in the first game. They scored 2 points in the second game. How many more points did the team score in the first game?
Ⓐ 9 − 2 = 5 points
Ⓑ 9 − 2 = 6 points
Ⓒ 9 − 2 = 7 points (filled)
Ⓓ 9 + 2 = 11 points

Available as a transparency

Diagnostic Checkpoint

Purpose Provide assessment of children's progress to date by checking their understanding of key content covered in the previous section.

Vocabulary Review

You may wish to review these terms before assigning the page:

fact family A group of related facts using the same set of numbers *(pp. 139–140)*

related facts An addition fact and a subtraction fact that use the same numbers *(pp. 137–138)*

Activities for this section are available in the Math Vocabulary Kit.

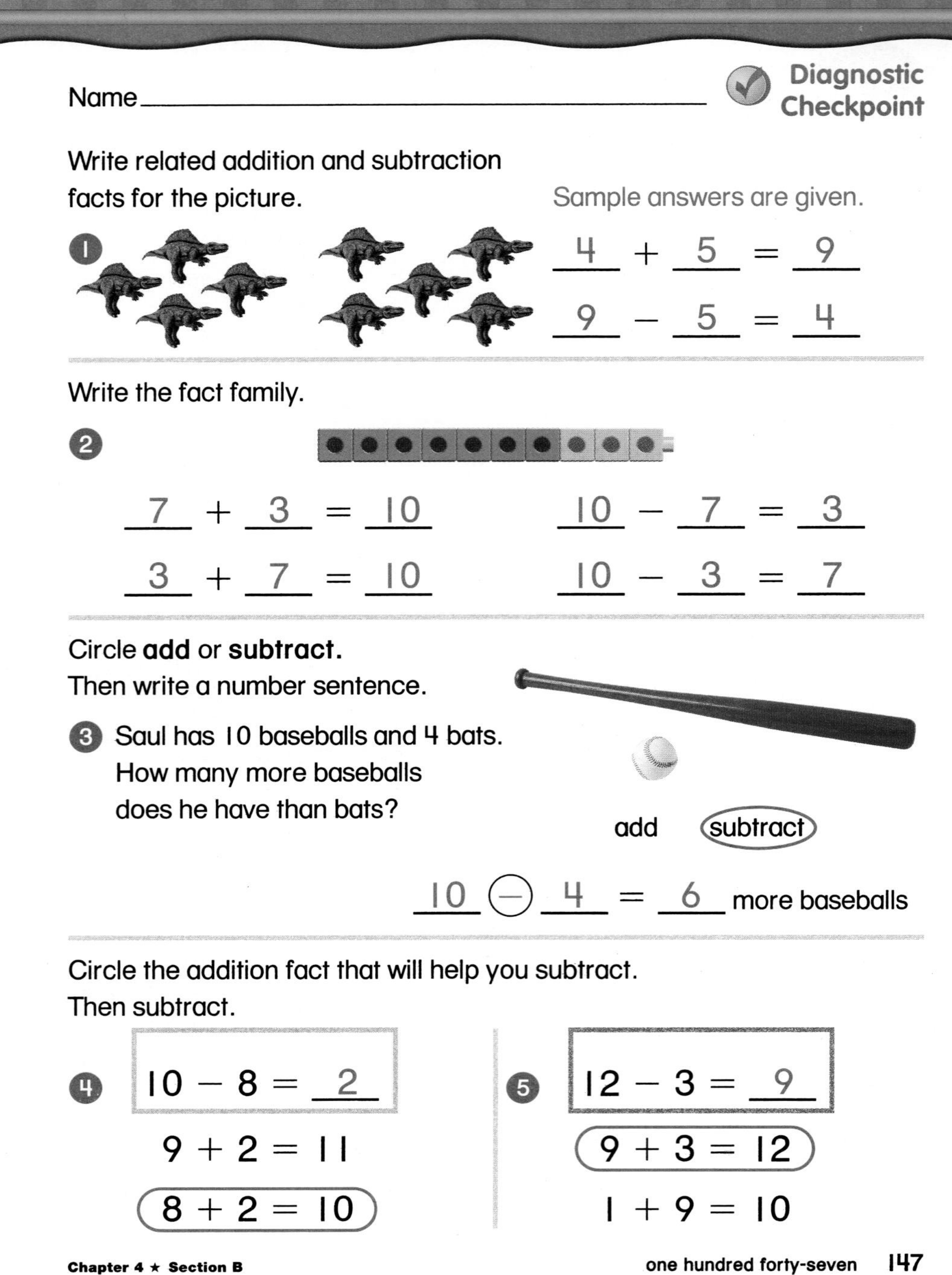

Name ____________________ Diagnostic Checkpoint

Write related addition and subtraction facts for the picture. Sample answers are given.

1. 4 + 5 = 9
   9 − 5 = 4

Write the fact family.

2. 7 + 3 = 10 10 − 7 = 3
   3 + 7 = 10 10 − 3 = 7

Circle **add** or **subtract.** Then write a number sentence.

3. Saul has 10 baseballs and 4 bats. How many more baseballs does he have than bats?

   add (subtract)

   10 (−) 4 = 6 more baseballs

Circle the addition fact that will help you subtract. Then subtract.

4. 10 − 8 = 2
   9 + 2 = 11
   (8 + 2 = 10)

5. 12 − 3 = 9
   (9 + 3 = 12)
   1 + 9 = 10

Chapter 4 ★ Section B one hundred forty-seven 147

Item Analysis for Diagnosis and Intervention

Objective	Items	Student Book Pages*	Intervention System
Write related addition and subtraction facts.	1	137–138	B27
Write the addition and subtraction sentences that make up a fact family.	2	139–140	B28
Solve problems by choosing addition or subtraction.	3	143–144	E4
Find differences by using known addition facts.	4–5	141–142	B29

*For each lesson, there is a *Reteaching* activity in *Reaching All Learners* and a *Reteaching* master.

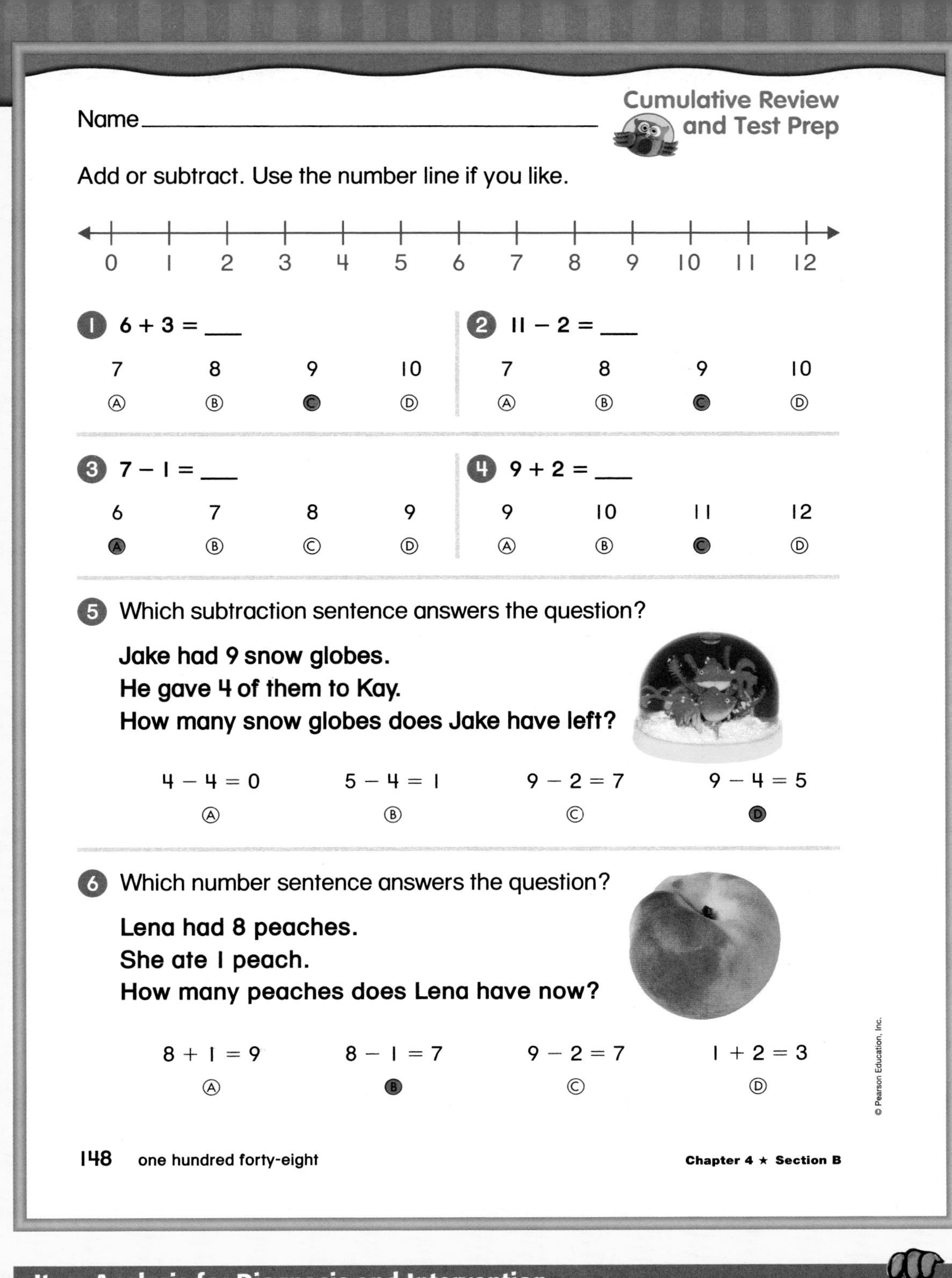

Name ____________________

Cumulative Review and Test Prep

Add or subtract. Use the number line if you like.

0 1 2 3 4 5 6 7 8 9 10 11 12

1. $6 + 3 =$ ___

7 Ⓐ 8 Ⓑ 9 Ⓒ 10 Ⓓ

2. $11 - 2 =$ ___

7 Ⓐ 8 Ⓑ 9 Ⓒ 10 Ⓓ

3. $7 - 1 =$ ___

6 Ⓐ 7 Ⓑ 8 Ⓒ 9 Ⓓ

4. $9 + 2 =$ ___

9 Ⓐ 10 Ⓑ 11 Ⓒ 12 Ⓓ

5. Which subtraction sentence answers the question?

Jake had 9 snow globes.
He gave 4 of them to Kay.
How many snow globes does Jake have left?

$4 - 4 = 0$ Ⓐ $5 - 4 = 1$ Ⓑ $9 - 2 = 7$ Ⓒ $9 - 4 = 5$ Ⓓ

6. Which number sentence answers the question?

Lena had 8 peaches.
She ate 1 peach.
How many peaches does Lena have now?

$8 + 1 = 9$ Ⓐ $8 - 1 = 7$ Ⓑ $9 - 2 = 7$ Ⓒ $1 + 2 = 3$ Ⓓ

Cumulative Review and Test Prep

Purpose Provide children with a review of math concepts. Items appear as they would on a standardized test so children become familiar with that format.

Item Analysis for Diagnosis and Intervention

Objective	Items	Student Book Pages*	Intervention System
Use a number line to count on 1, 2, or 3.	1, 4	97–98	B20
Use a number line to count back 1 or 2.	2, 3	125–126	B24
Solve problems by writing subtraction sentences.	5	133–134	E36
Solve problems by choosing addition or subtraction.	6	71–72	E4

*For each lesson, there is a *Reteaching* activity in *Reaching All Learners* and a *Reteaching* master.

Enrichment

Purpose Provide children with related mathematical topics and applications beyond the basic chapter content.

Using Student Page 149

Remind children that they have already learned many strategies for both addition and subtraction. Tell them that this page will help them apply those strategies as they find many names for one number.

Before having children work through the page, you may want to use a Number Line (Teaching Tool 10) to show how one number can be named using addition or subtraction. Begin by having children find number pairs with a sum of 6. For example, children might start on the 4 and count on 2, for 4 + 2. List the addition expressions on the board. To model subtraction, have children place their finger on the 8 of the number line, count back to 6, and tell how many they counted back. *(2)* Record "8 − 2" on the board. Repeat the process, having children begin at 7, 9, and 11. Point out that each expression on the board is a name for 6.

When children are comfortable with the process, read the directions on the page and make sure children understand how to complete the exercises.

When finding names for a number, children should think about addition and subtraction names. They may wish to use a number line, cubes, or other strategies to help them find names for a given number. For the Writing in Math feature, encourage children to think about sums and differences that name 10. As children share names, make a master list on the board.

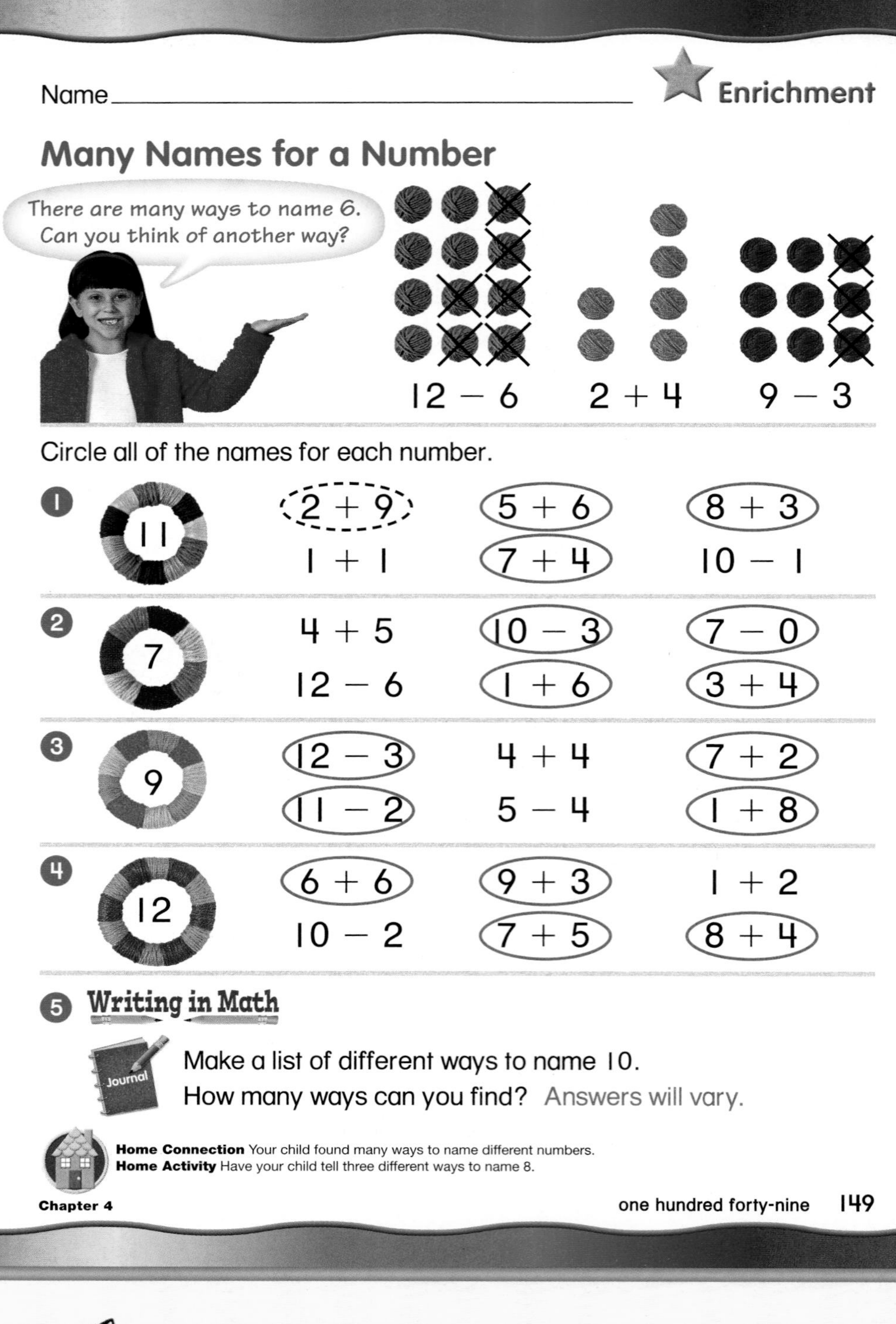

Name ______________________ Enrichment

Many Names for a Number

There are many ways to name 6. Can you think of another way?

12 − 6 2 + 4 9 − 3

Circle all of the names for each number.

1. 11: (2 + 9) (5 + 6) (8 + 3) 1 + 1 (7 + 4) 10 − 1
2. 7: 4 + 5 (10 − 3) (7 − 0) 12 − 6 (1 + 6) (3 + 4)
3. 9: (12 − 3) 4 + 4 (7 + 2) (11 − 2) 5 − 4 (1 + 8)
4. 12: (6 + 6) (9 + 3) 1 + 2 10 − 2 (7 + 5) (8 + 4)
5. Writing in Math
Make a list of different ways to name 10.
How many ways can you find? Answers will vary.

Home Connection Your child found many ways to name different numbers.
Home Activity Have your child tell three different ways to name 8.

Chapter 4 one hundred forty-nine 149

Name ____________________

Learning with Technology

Subtract Using a Calculator

You can use a calculator to subtract.
Press ON/C. Press the keys that you see below.
Write the number you see in the display after you press =.

1. 8 − 2 = 6
2. 5 − 1 = 4
3. 4 − 3 = 1
4. 9 − 5 = 4

Press ON/C each time you begin.
Write what the display shows each time you press =.

5. 6 − 1 = = = Display: 5 4 3
6. 1 0 − 2 = = = Display: 8 6 4
7. 2 0 − 4 = = = Display: 16 12 8
8. 3 0 − 5 = = = Display: 25 20 15

Think About It Number Sense

In Exercise 6, how many more times would you need to press = before the display would show 0?

If I pressed = two more times, the display would show 0.

Home Connection Your child used a calculator to learn how to subtract the same amount over and over again. **Home Activity** Ask your child to explain how many times he or she would need to subtract 10 to get from 50 back to 0. *(5 times)* 40? *(4 times)* 30? *(3 times)* 20? *(2 times)* 10? *(1 time)*

Learning with Technology

Purpose Subtract using a calculator.

Using Student Page 150

Distribute calculators to children. Briefly review what they know about the calculator, identifying specific keys: the ON/C key, the + symbol key, the − symbol key, and the ten digits 0–9.

Explain to children that they will use their calculators to subtract. Ask children to explain how they might do this. Then read the directions on the page and lead children through the first exercise. Check that children have 6 showing on their calculator displays. Have children complete Exercises 2–4 independently. Remind them to clear the screen, or press the ON/C key, before they begin a new exercise.

Read the directions before Exercises 5–8 and lead children through Exercise 5. Have them stop each time they press the equal-sign key to record the next number in the sequence. Have children work in pairs to complete the page.

Think About It In Exercise 6, help children understand that each time they press the equal-sign key, they are subtracting 2. Since the last number displayed was 4, they would need to press the equal-sign key two more times before the display would show 0. Ask children what number they are subtracting each time they press the equal-sign key in Exercise 7. *(4)* How many times would they have to press the equal-sign key in Exercise 7 before the display would show 0? *(2)* Repeat the questions for Exercise 8.

Test Talk

Purpose Teach children a particular test-taking strategy and help them become more comfortable with the language and format used on standardized tests.

Using Student Page 151

This page is designed to give children practice in understanding test questions.

Children often have difficulty on standardized tests not because they haven't been introduced to the concept or skill being tested, but because they fail to understand what they are being asked to do or how they are being asked to do it. This page can help with both the what and the how.

Discuss the question in Exercise 1. Ask children to explain how they would use the number line to find the answer. Point out to children that the answer bubble is completely filled in by the correct answer choice. Stress the importance of filling in the bubble completely and not coloring or making any marks outside of the bubble.

Have children complete Exercise 2 independently. When they have finished, ask them to explain how they used the number line to find the answer. Then have children check that they completely filled in the bubble before the answer choice of 4 and that they did not color or make any marks outside of the bubble.

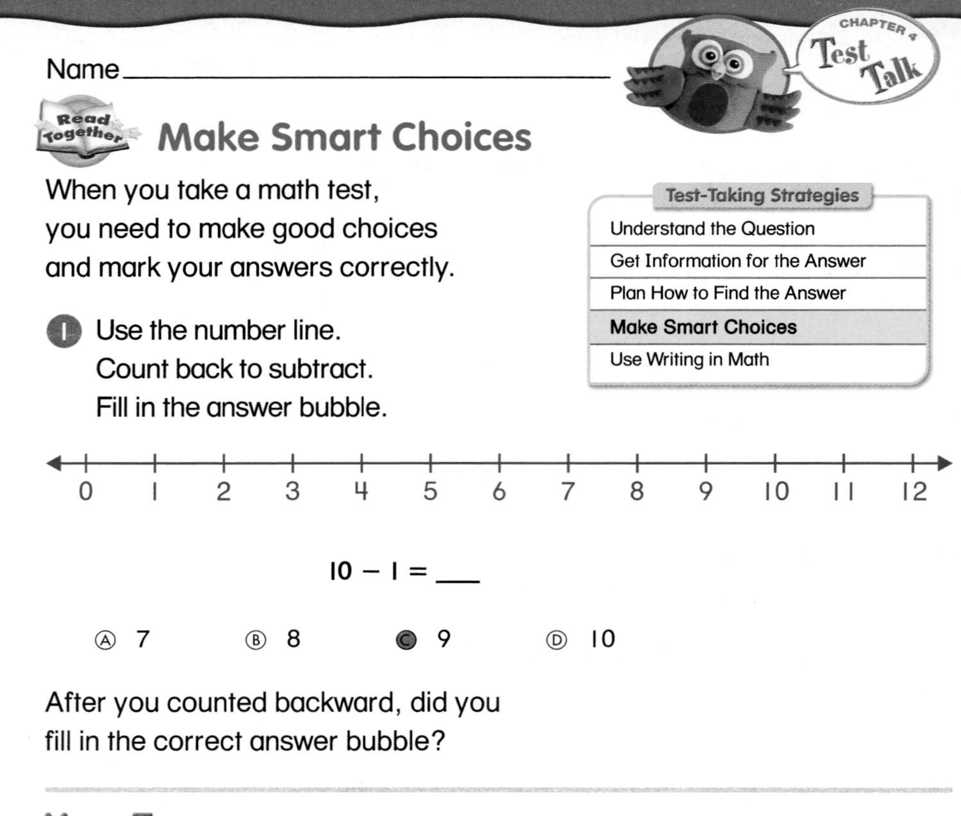

Name ______________________

Chapter 4 Test Talk

Read Together

Make Smart Choices

When you take a math test, you need to make good choices and mark your answers correctly.

Test-Taking Strategies
Understand the Question
Get Information for the Answer
Plan How to Find the Answer
Make Smart Choices
Use Writing in Math

1. Use the number line. Count back to subtract. Fill in the answer bubble.

0 1 2 3 4 5 6 7 8 9 10 11 12

10 − 1 = ___

Ⓐ 7 Ⓑ 8 ● 9 Ⓓ 10

After you counted backward, did you fill in the correct answer bubble?

Your Turn

Solve the problem and fill in the answer bubble.

2. Use the number line. Count back to subtract.

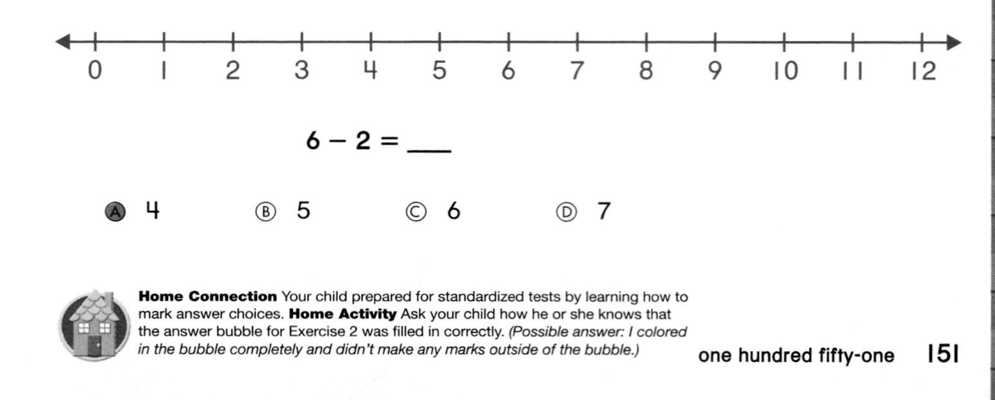

0 1 2 3 4 5 6 7 8 9 10 11 12

6 − 2 = ___

● 4 Ⓑ 5 Ⓒ 6 Ⓓ 7

Home Connection Your child prepared for standardized tests by learning how to mark answer choices. **Home Activity** Ask your child how he or she knows that the answer bubble for Exercise 2 was filled in correctly. *(Possible answer: I colored in the bubble completely and didn't make any marks outside of the bubble.)*

one hundred fifty-one 151

Test-Taking Strategies

Understand the Question

- Look for important words.
- Turn the question into a statement: "I need to find out…"

Get Information for the Answer

- Get information from text.
- Get information from pictures, maps, diagrams, tables, graphs.

Plan How to Find the Answer

- Think about problem-solving skills and strategies.
- Choose computation methods.

Make Smart Choices

- Eliminate wrong answers.
- Try working backward from an answer.
- Check answers for reasonableness; estimate.

Use Writing in Math

- Make your answer brief but complete.
- Use words from the problem and use math terms accurately.
- Describe steps in order.
- Draw pictures to explain your thinking.

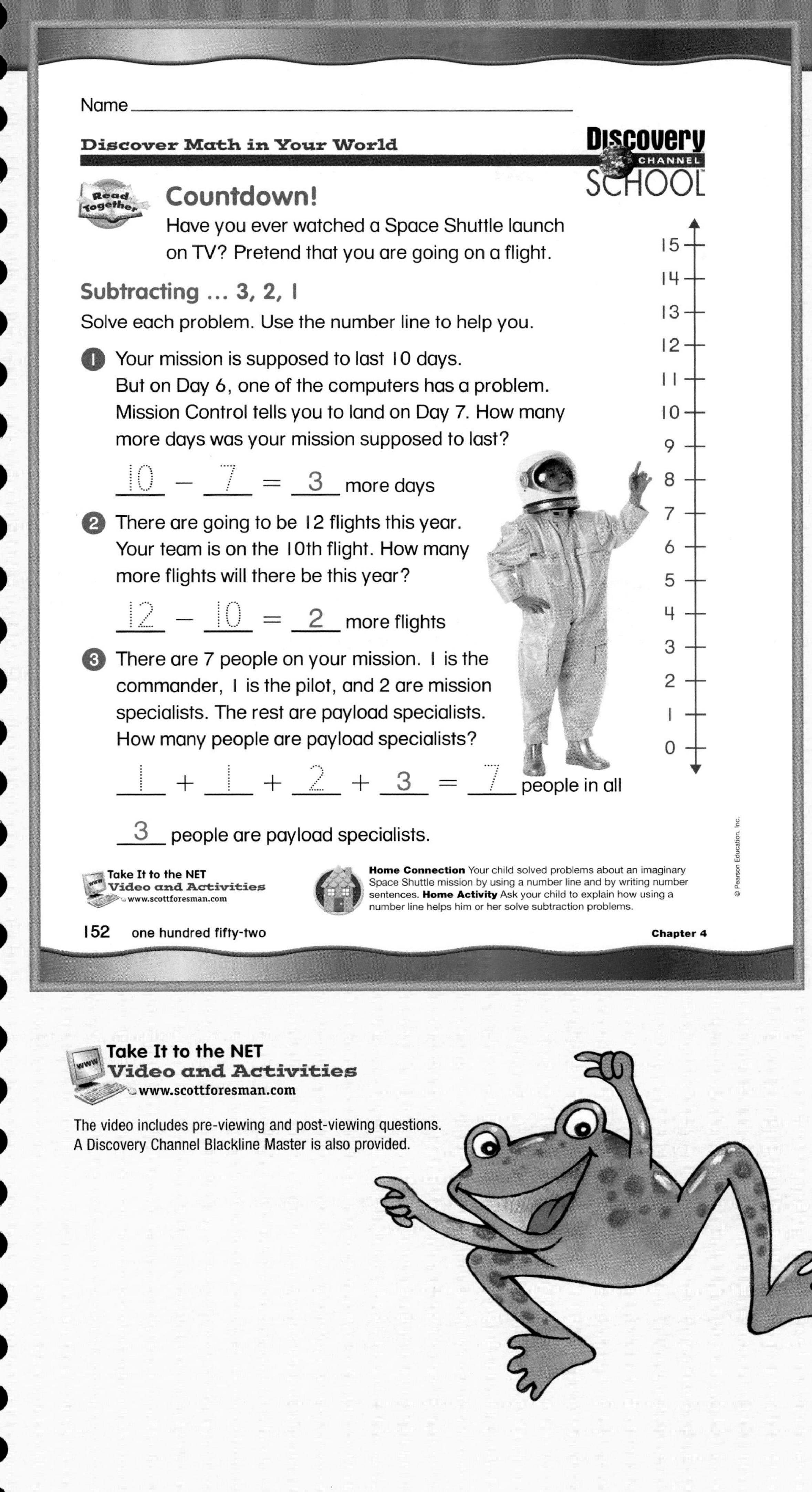

Name ________________________________

Discover Math in Your World

Discovery Channel School

Countdown!

Read Together

Have you ever watched a Space Shuttle launch on TV? Pretend that you are going on a flight.

Subtracting ... 3, 2, 1

Solve each problem. Use the number line to help you.

1. Your mission is supposed to last 10 days. But on Day 6, one of the computers has a problem. Mission Control tells you to land on Day 7. How many more days was your mission supposed to last?

   10 − 7 = 3 more days

2. There are going to be 12 flights this year. Your team is on the 10th flight. How many more flights will there be this year?

   12 − 10 = 2 more flights

3. There are 7 people on your mission. 1 is the commander, 1 is the pilot, and 2 are mission specialists. The rest are payload specialists. How many people are payload specialists?

   1 + 1 + 2 + 3 = 7 people in all

   3 people are payload specialists.

15, 14, 13, 12, 11, 10, 9, 8, 7, 6, 5, 4, 3, 2, 1, 0

Take It to the NET Video and Activities www.scottforesman.com

Home Connection Your child solved problems about an imaginary Space Shuttle mission by using a number line and by writing number sentences. **Home Activity** Ask your child to explain how using a number line helps him or her solve subtraction problems.

Take It to the NET
Video and Activities
www.scottforesman.com

The video includes pre-viewing and post-viewing questions. A Discovery Channel Blackline Master is also provided.

Discover Math in Your World

Purpose Help children connect math content to everyday applications.

Using Student Page 152

On this page, children will use real-life data and a number line to write number sentences and answer questions.

Discuss space shuttle launches with children, helping them understand the vocabulary: **_Teams_ of _astronauts_ are groups of persons who travel in space. Astronauts can travel in _space shuttles,_ which are reusable spacecraft that can land like an airplane. Sometimes spacecraft _orbit,_ or go around, Earth. Each trip has a _mission,_ or job, such as studying space or repairing a _space station. Mission control_ consists of the people on Earth who direct the mission. The _commander_ is in charge of the shuttle. A _pilot_ flies the shuttle. _Mission specialists_ know a lot of information about the work that their mission is going to do. _Payload specialists_ have other important jobs; they might be doctors or computer specialists. Space shuttles travel for about 10 days.**

Read the first paragraph with children and draw their attention to the pictures and the number line. Make sure children understand how to add and subtract on the vertical number line; point out that they will move *up* the number line if they are adding and that they will move *down* the number line if they are subtracting. Then help children read the directions and the problems. Make sure they understand how to complete the exercises.

Note: In Exercise 3, children might first add to get the number of people who are not payload specialists. *(1 + 1 + 3 = 5)* Children can then think of the number sentence 5 + ? = 8 to determine the number of people on the mission who are payload specialists.

Even though first graders will not be formally introduced to adding 3 numbers until Chapter 11, this page may be used to lay the groundwork for future instruction.

Chapter Test

Purpose Assess children's progress by checking their understanding of the concepts and skills covered in Chapter 4. Use as a review, practice test, or chapter test.

MindPoint Quiz Show CD-ROM Use *MindPoint Quiz Show* for additional practice on Chapter 4.

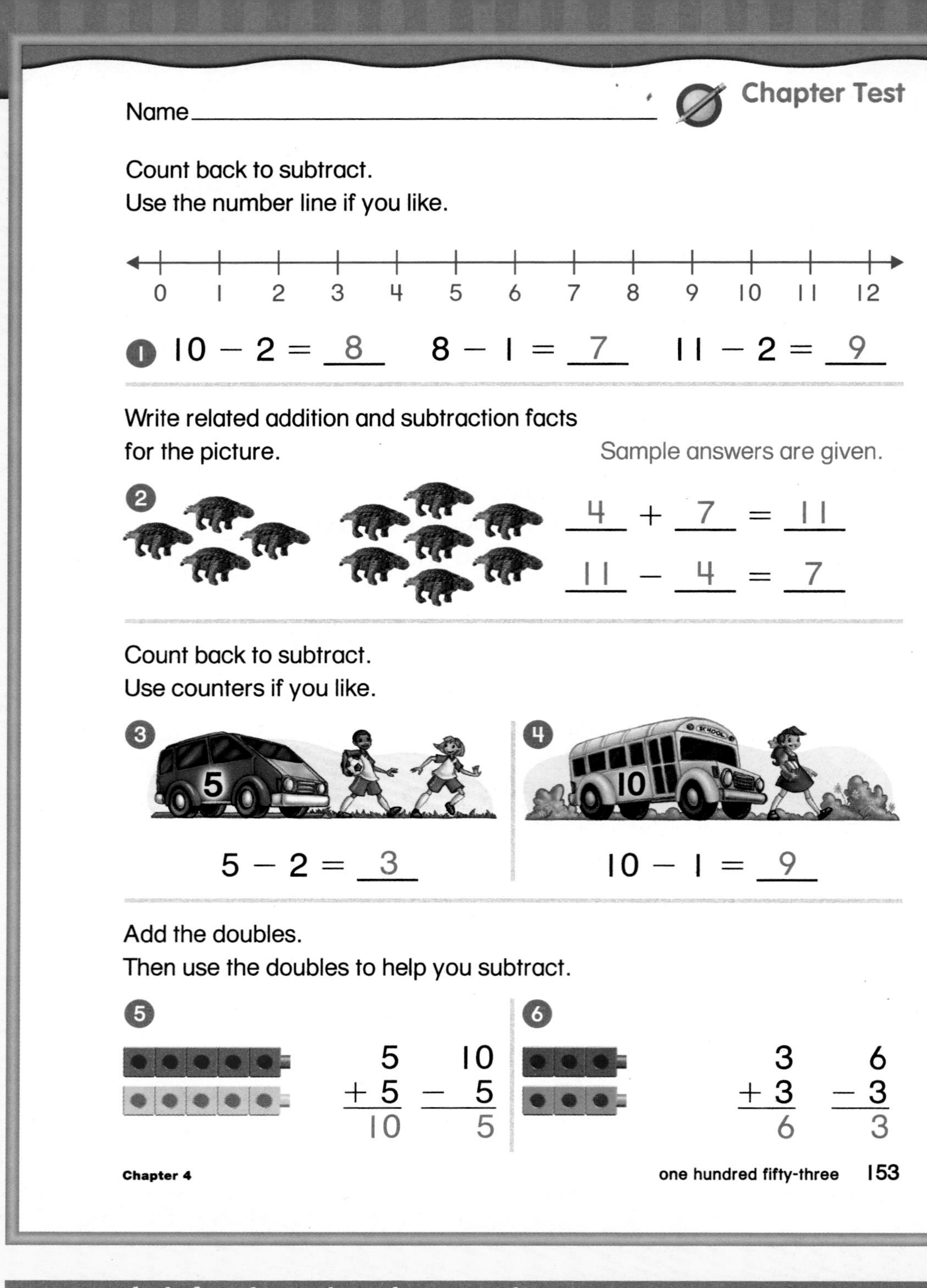
Name________________________ Chapter Test

Count back to subtract.
Use the number line if you like.

0 1 2 3 4 5 6 7 8 9 10 11 12

1. 10 − 2 = 8 8 − 1 = 7 11 − 2 = 9

Write related addition and subtraction facts for the picture. Sample answers are given.

2. 4 + 7 = 11
11 − 4 = 7

Count back to subtract.
Use counters if you like.

3. 5 − 2 = 3

4. 10 − 1 = 9

Add the doubles.
Then use the doubles to help you subtract.

5. 5 + 5 = 10 10 − 5 = 5

6. 3 + 3 = 6 6 − 3 = 3

Chapter 4 one hundred fifty-three 153

Item Analysis for Diagnosis and Intervention

Objective	Items	Student Book Pages*	Intervention System
Use a number line to count back 1 or 2.	1	125–126	B24
Write related addition and subtraction facts.	2	137–138	B27
Find differences by counting back 1 or 2.	3–4	127–128	B25
Find differences by using doubles facts.	5–6	129–130	B26

*For each lesson, there is a *Reteaching* activity in *Reaching All Learners* and a *Reteaching* master.

 EC NTL 12 11 10 9

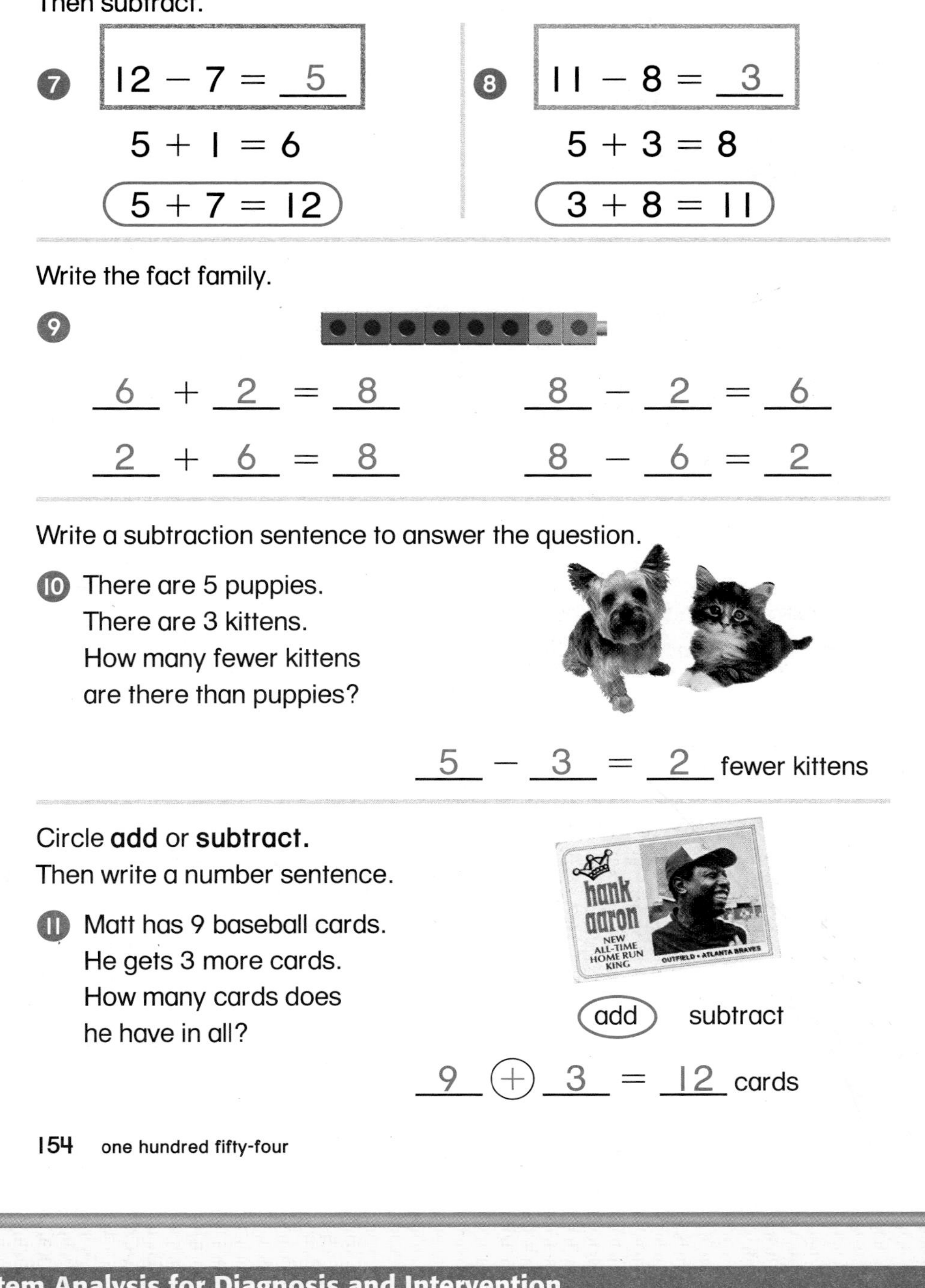

Circle the addition fact that will help you subtract.
Then subtract.

7. 12 − 7 = 5
5 + 1 = 6
(5 + 7 = 12)

8. 11 − 8 = 3
5 + 3 = 8
(3 + 8 = 11)

Write the fact family.

9. 6 + 2 = 8   8 − 2 = 6
2 + 6 = 8   8 − 6 = 2

Write a subtraction sentence to answer the question.

10. There are 5 puppies.
There are 3 kittens.
How many fewer kittens are there than puppies?

5 − 3 = 2 fewer kittens

Circle **add** or **subtract.**
Then write a number sentence.

11. Matt has 9 baseball cards.
He gets 3 more cards.
How many cards does he have in all?

(add) subtract

9 (+) 3 = 12 cards

Item Analysis for Diagnosis and Intervention

Objective	Items	Student Book Pages*	Intervention System
Find differences by using known addition facts.	7–8	141–142	B29
Write the addition and subtraction sentences that make up a fact family.	9	139–140	B28
Solve problems by writing subtraction sentences.	10	133–134	E36
Solve problems by choosing addition or subtraction.	11	143–144	E4

*For each lesson, there is a *Reteaching* activity in *Reaching All Learners* and a *Reteaching* master.

Assessment Sourcebook

These additional assessment options may be found in the *Assessment Sourcebook:*

- Chapter 4 Free-Response Test (Forms A and B)
- Chapter 4 Multiple-Choice Test (Forms C and D)
- Chapter 4 Performance Assessment

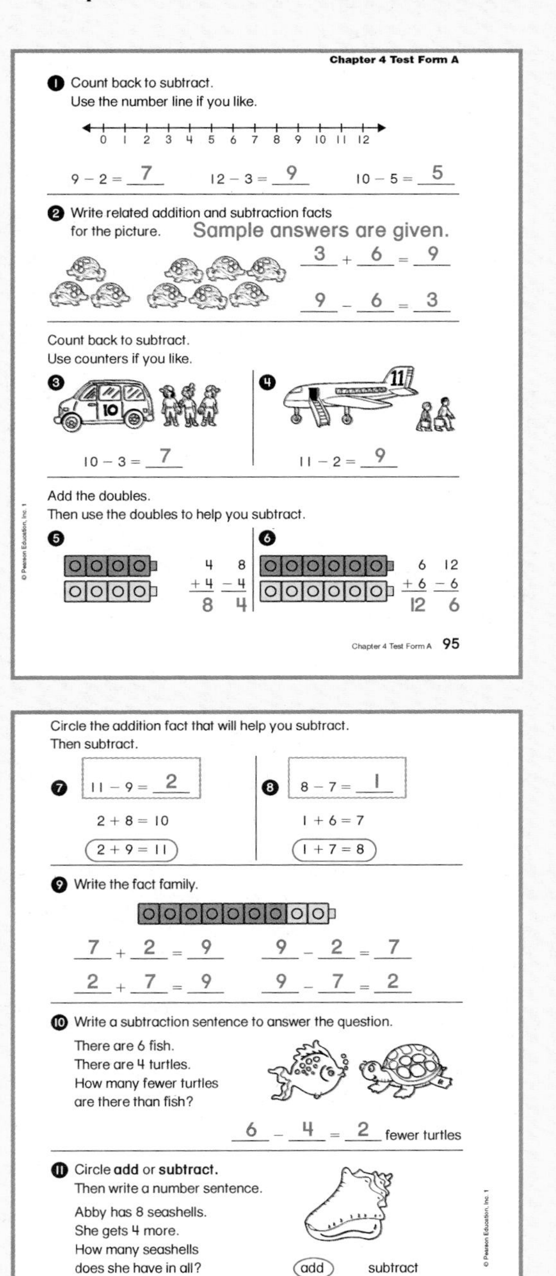

Chapter 4 Test Form A

1. Count back to subtract.
Use the number line if you like.

0 1 2 3 4 5 6 7 8 9 10 11 12

9 − 2 = 7   12 − 3 = 9   10 − 5 = 5

2. Write related addition and subtraction facts for the picture. Sample answers are given.

3 + 6 = 9
9 − 6 = 3

Count back to subtract.
Use counters if you like.

3. 10 − 3 = 7

4. 11 − 2 = 9

Add the doubles.
Then use the doubles to help you subtract.

5. 4 + 4 = 8   8 − 4 = 4

6. 6 + 6 = 12   12 − 6 = 6

Circle the addition fact that will help you subtract.
Then subtract.

7. 11 − 9 = 2
2 + 8 = 10
(2 + 9 = 11)

8. 8 − 7 = 1
1 + 6 = 7
(1 + 7 = 8)

9. Write the fact family.

7 + 2 = 9   9 − 2 = 7
2 + 7 = 9   9 − 7 = 2

10. Write a subtraction sentence to answer the question.
There are 6 fish.
There are 4 turtles.
How many fewer turtles are there than fish?

6 − 4 = 2 fewer turtles

11. Circle **add** or **subtract.**
Then write a number sentence.
Abby has 8 seashells.
She gets 4 more.
How many seashells does she have in all?

(add) subtract

8 (+) 4 (=) 12 seashells

Cumulative Review and Test Prep

Purpose Provide children with a review of math concepts. Items on page 154A appear as they would on a standardized test so children become familiar with that format.

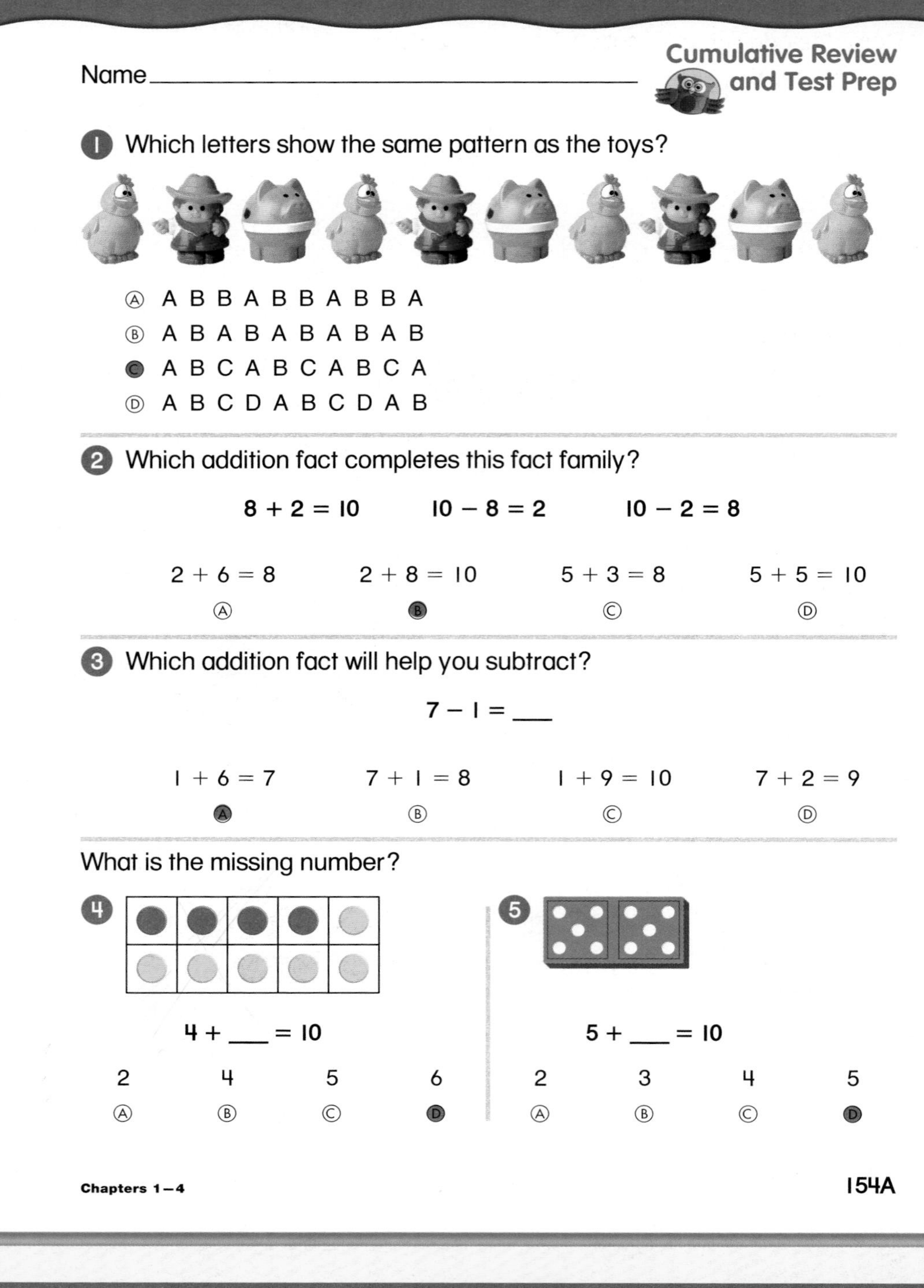

Name ____________________

Cumulative Review and Test Prep

1 Which letters show the same pattern as the toys?

Ⓐ A B B A B B A B B A
Ⓑ A B A B A B A B A B
Ⓒ A B C A B C A B C A
Ⓓ A B C D A B C D A B

2 Which addition fact completes this fact family?

$8 + 2 = 10$ $10 - 8 = 2$ $10 - 2 = 8$

$2 + 6 = 8$	$2 + 8 = 10$	$5 + 3 = 8$	$5 + 5 = 10$
Ⓐ	Ⓑ	Ⓒ	Ⓓ

3 Which addition fact will help you subtract?

$7 - 1 =$ ___

$1 + 6 = 7$	$7 + 1 = 8$	$1 + 9 = 10$	$7 + 2 = 9$
Ⓐ	Ⓑ	Ⓒ	Ⓓ

What is the missing number?

4 $4 +$ ___ $= 10$

2	4	5	6
Ⓐ	Ⓑ	Ⓒ	Ⓓ

5 $5 +$ ___ $= 10$

2	3	4	5
Ⓐ	Ⓑ	Ⓒ	Ⓓ

Chapters 1–4

154A

Item Analysis for Diagnosis and Intervention

Objective	Items	Student Book Pages*	Intervention System
Use shapes to create patterns and then translate the patterns into letters.	1	5–6 or 29–30	D44
Write the addition and subtraction sentences that make up a fact family.	2	139–140	B28
Find differences by using known addition facts.	3	141–142	B29
Recognize facts that have sums of 10.	4	107–108	B23
Recognize doubles as a strategy for remembering sums.	5	103–104	B21

*For each lesson, there is a *Reteaching* activity in *Reaching All Learners* and a *Reteaching* master.

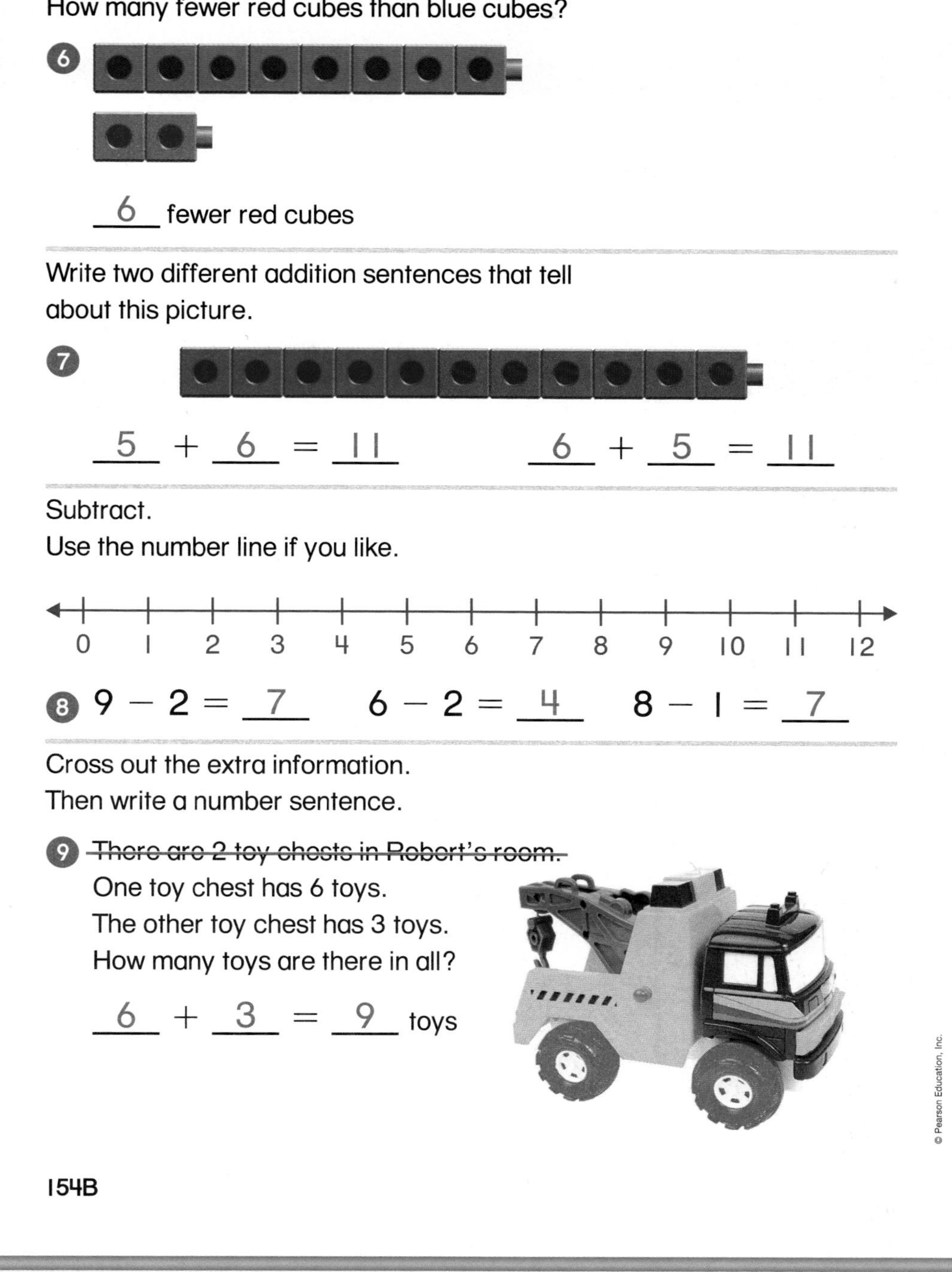

How many fewer red cubes than blue cubes?

6

6 fewer red cubes

Write two different addition sentences that tell about this picture.

7

5 + 6 = 11 6 + 5 = 11

Subtract.
Use the number line if you like.

0 1 2 3 4 5 6 7 8 9 10 11 12

8 9 − 2 = 7 6 − 2 = 4 8 − 1 = 7

Cross out the extra information.
Then write a number sentence.

9 ~~There are 2 toy chests in Robert's room.~~
One toy chest has 6 toys.
The other toy chest has 3 toys.
How many toys are there in all?

6 + 3 = 9 toys

154B

Item Analysis for Diagnosis and Intervention

Objective	Review Items	Student Book Pages*	Intervention System
Compare two groups to find out how many more or how many fewer.	6	75–76	B15
Use the commutative property to find sums.	7	93–94	B18
Use a number line to count back 1 or 2.	8	125–126	B24
Solve problems by identifying unnecessary information and writing number sentences.	9	99–100	E8

*For each lesson, there is a *Reteaching* activity in *Reaching All Learners* and a *Reteaching* master.

Lesson Planner

Geometry and Fractions

Suggested Pacing: 17 to 19 days

Section A Solid Figures

5-1 pp. 157–158	5-2 pp. 159–160	5-3 pp. 161–162
Identifying Solid Figures **Objective** Identify and name standard geometric solids and recognize them in the environment. **Math Understanding** Many everyday objects closely approximate standard geometric solids. **Vocabulary** Cube, rectangular prism, sphere, cone, cylinder	**Flat Surfaces and Vertices** **Objective** Count the number of flat surfaces and vertices on geometric solids. **Math Understanding** Many solids are comprised of flat surfaces and vertices; the flat surfaces on prisms are called faces. **Vocabulary** Solid figure, flat surface, vertex (vertices), face, corner **Materials for Student Pages** *(per group)* Geometric solids	**Relating Plane Shapes to Solid Figures** **Objective** Match a geometric solid to an outline of one of its flat surfaces. **Math Understanding** The flat surfaces of solid figures are plane shapes. **Materials for Student Pages** *(per group)* Geometric solids **Section A Diagnostic Checkpoint, p. 163** **Cumulative Review and Test Prep, p. 164**

Math Story: ***No Problem!*****, pp. 5A–5F** **Home-School Connection, p. 155**
Practice Game: ***Fraction Concentration*****, p. 156**

Resources in the Student Book

Ongoing Assessment and Test Prep *Also see* pp. 155G–155H.

Instant Check System™
- **Check** before Practice
- **Think About It** after examples
- **Diagnostic Checkpoint** end of sections

Test Prep
- **Test Talk** end of chapter
- **Cumulative Review and Test Prep** end of sections

Daily Real-World Problem Solving plus ...

Problem-Solving Applications lesson on pp. 193–194 uses data from Dorling Kindersley literature.

Discover Math in Your World on p. 200 uses data from a topic in the Discovery Channel School Video Library, Segment 5.

Section B Plane Shapes

5-4 pp. 165–166	5-5 pp. 167–168	5-6 pp. 169–170	5-7 pp. 171–172	5-8 pp. 173–174
Identifying Plane Shapes **Objective** Identify and name standard plane shapes and recognize them in the environment. **Math Understanding** Many everyday objects are close approximations of standard plane shapes. **Vocabulary** Plane shape, triangle, rectangle, circle, square	**Properties of Plane Shapes** **Objective** Sort plane shapes and identify their properties. **Math Understanding** Plane shapes have many properties that make them different from one another. **Vocabulary** Side, vertex (vertices)	**Same Size and Same Shape** **Objective** Identify and create figures that are the same size and the same shape. **Math Understanding** Two shapes can have the same shape and the same size even if they do not share the same orientation. **Vocabulary** Same size, same shape	**Symmetry** **Objective** Identify objects that show symmetry and draw lines of symmetry. **Math Understanding** Symmetric figures have two congruent halves. **Vocabulary** Symmetry, line of symmetry	**Slides, Flips, and Turns** **Objective** Perform slide, flip, or turn on an object and identify the resulting position. **Math Understanding** Slides, flips, and turns can be used to change an object's position in space. **Vocabulary** Slide, flip, turn **Materials for Student Pages** *(per child)* Pattern blocks: 1 triangle, 1 diamond, and 1 trapezoid Reading For Math Success pp. 175–176

Reading and Writing in Math *Throughout*

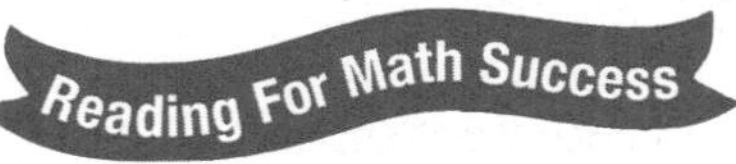

This feature shows how reading skills and strategies can help with problem-solving skills and strategies in math.
Also, **Reading Assists** are in the Teacher's Edition.

Some lessons include **Writing in Math** exercises. Also, daily **Journal Ideas** are in the Teacher's Edition.

Technology Resources for Students *Also see* p. T20.

Take It to the NET
More Activities
www.scottforesman.com

More activities, Discovery Channel School Video Library, and Math eTools

Math eTools: electronic manipulatives online, on CD-ROM, and in the Online Student's Edition

All text pages are available online and on CD-ROM. The Online Student's Edition includes Math eTools plus glossary links for vocabulary.

Geometry and Fractions (continued)

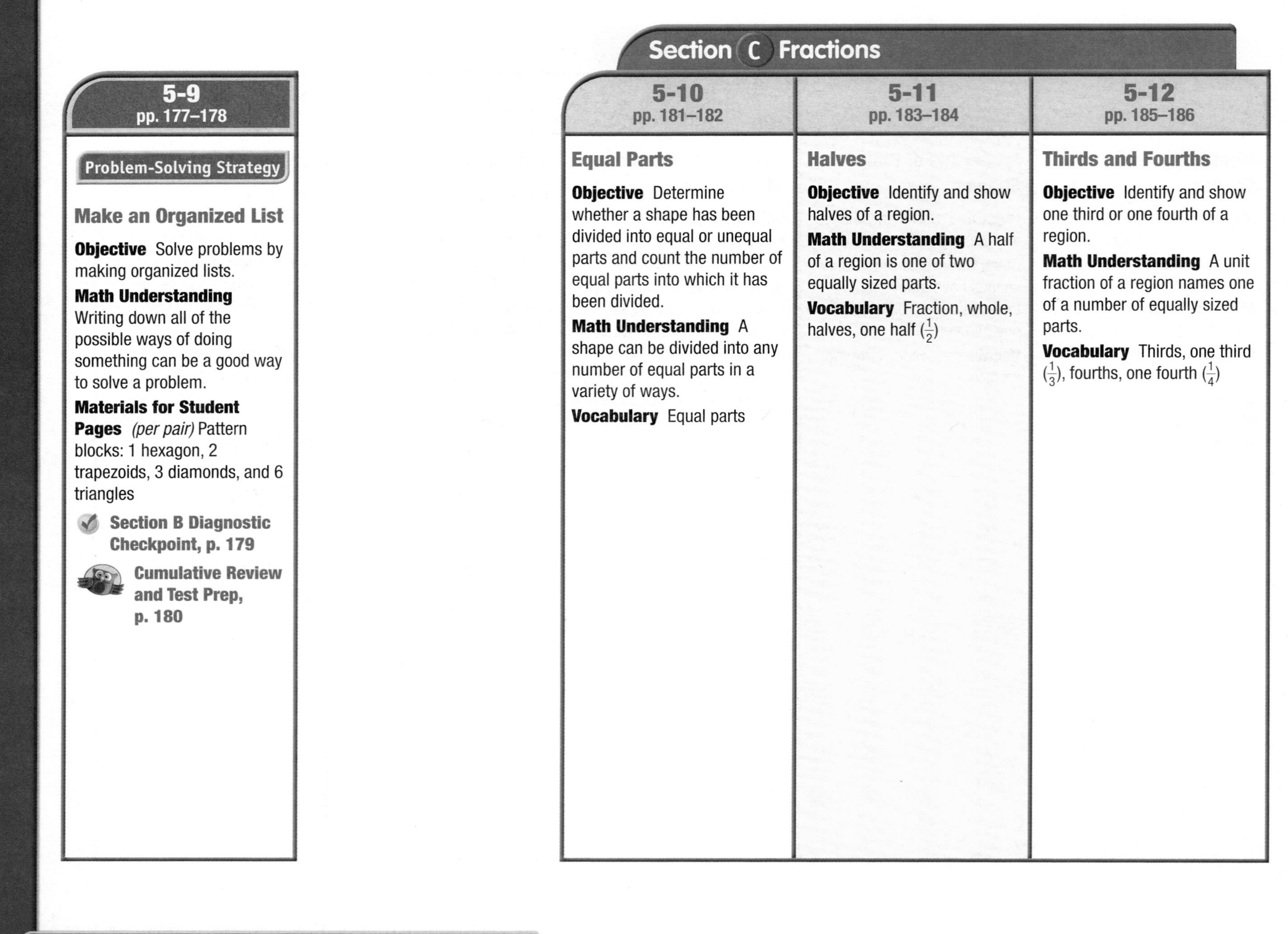

5-9 pp. 177–178	Section C Fractions: 5-10 pp. 181–182	5-11 pp. 183–184	5-12 pp. 185–186
Problem-Solving Strategy **Make an Organized List** **Objective** Solve problems by making organized lists. **Math Understanding** Writing down all of the possible ways of doing something can be a good way to solve a problem. **Materials for Student Pages** *(per pair)* Pattern blocks: 1 hexagon, 2 trapezoids, 3 diamonds, and 6 triangles **Section B Diagnostic Checkpoint, p. 179** **Cumulative Review and Test Prep, p. 180**	**Equal Parts** **Objective** Determine whether a shape has been divided into equal or unequal parts and count the number of equal parts into which it has been divided. **Math Understanding** A shape can be divided into any number of equal parts in a variety of ways. **Vocabulary** Equal parts	**Halves** **Objective** Identify and show halves of a region. **Math Understanding** A half of a region is one of two equally sized parts. **Vocabulary** Fraction, whole, halves, one half ($\frac{1}{2}$)	**Thirds and Fourths** **Objective** Identify and show one third or one fourth of a region. **Math Understanding** A unit fraction of a region names one of a number of equally sized parts. **Vocabulary** Thirds, one third ($\frac{1}{3}$), fourths, one fourth ($\frac{1}{4}$)

Additional Resources for ...

Reaching All Learners

- **Practice** Masters/Workbook, every lesson
- **Reteaching** Masters/Workbook, every lesson
- **Enrichment** Masters/Workbook, every lesson
- **Every Student Learns** A teacher resource with daily suggestions for helping students overcome language barriers to learning math
- **Spiral Review and Test Prep** Transparencies and Masters/Workbook, every lesson
- **Math Games** Use *Name That Shape* anytime after Lesson 5-4. Use *Fraction Fun* anytime after Lesson 5-12.
- **Investigation** See pp. 155I–155J.

Problem Solving

- **Problem Solving** Masters/Workbook, every lesson
- **Problem of the Day** Flipchart/Transparencies, every lesson
- **Discovery Channel School** Masters, follow-up to Segment 5 in the Discovery Channel School Video Library

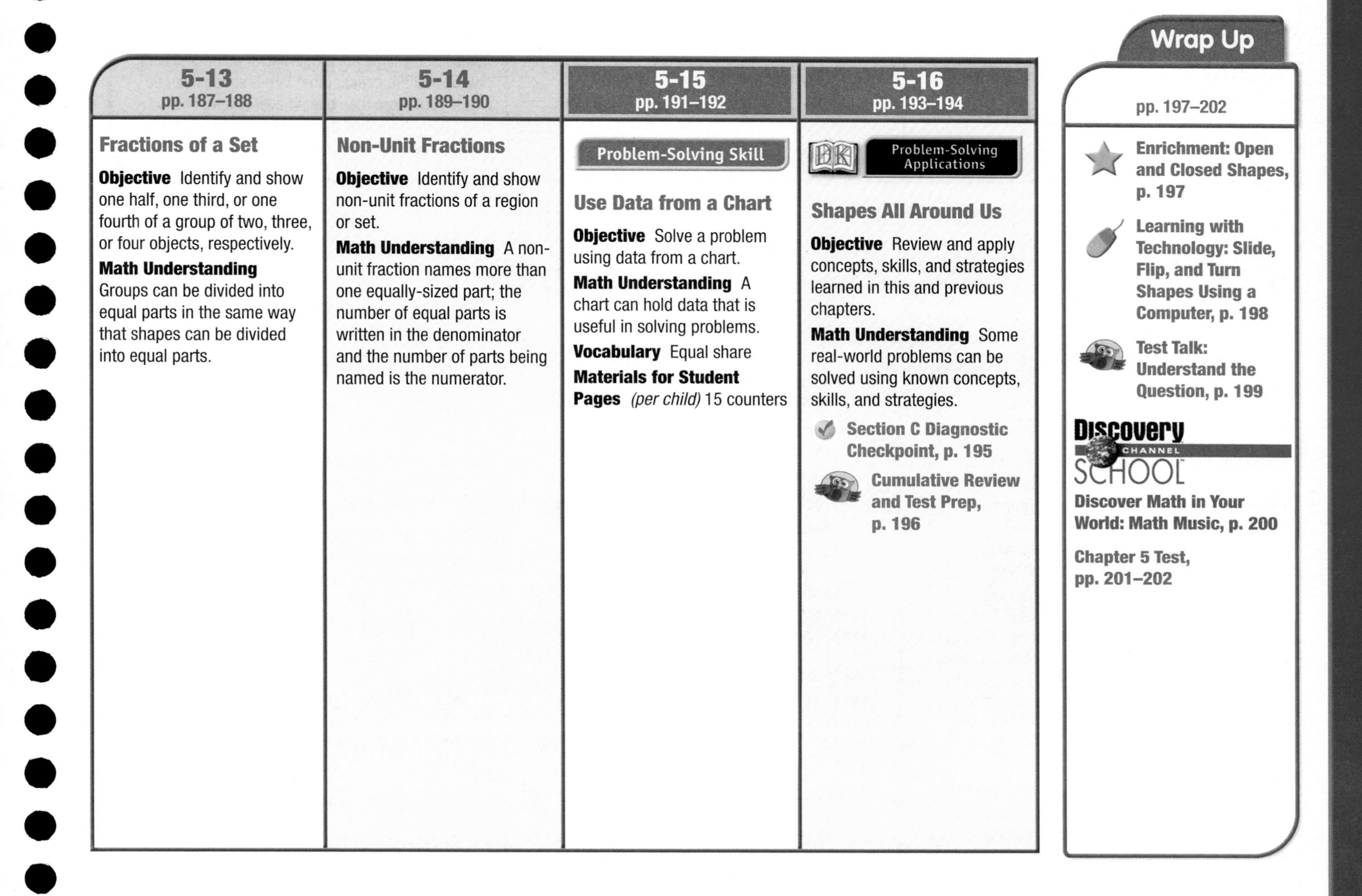

5-13 pp. 187–188	5-14 pp. 189–190	5-15 pp. 191–192	5-16 pp. 193–194
Fractions of a Set **Objective** Identify and show one half, one third, or one fourth of a group of two, three, or four objects, respectively. **Math Understanding** Groups can be divided into equal parts in the same way that shapes can be divided into equal parts.	**Non-Unit Fractions** **Objective** Identify and show non-unit fractions of a region or set. **Math Understanding** A non-unit fraction names more than one equally-sized part; the number of equal parts is written in the denominator and the number of parts being named is the numerator.	Problem-Solving Skill **Use Data from a Chart** **Objective** Solve a problem using data from a chart. **Math Understanding** A chart can hold data that is useful in solving problems. **Vocabulary** Equal share **Materials for Student Pages** *(per child)* 15 counters	DK Problem-Solving Applications **Shapes All Around Us** **Objective** Review and apply concepts, skills, and strategies learned in this and previous chapters. **Math Understanding** Some real-world problems can be solved using known concepts, skills, and strategies. **Section C Diagnostic Checkpoint, p. 195** **Cumulative Review and Test Prep, p. 196**

Wrap Up

pp. 197–202

- **Enrichment: Open and Closed Shapes, p. 197**
- **Learning with Technology: Slide, Flip, and Turn Shapes Using a Computer, p. 198**
- **Test Talk: Understand the Question, p. 199**

Discovery Channel School

Discover Math in Your World: Math Music, p. 200

Chapter 5 Test, pp. 201–202

Reading in Math

- **Vocabulary Kit** Word Cards plus transparencies and activities for instructional word walls and for small groups
- **Dorling Kindersley Literature Library** Books with interesting data

Assessment, Intervention, and Test Prep

- **Assessment Sourcebook** See pp. 155G–155H.
- **Math Diagnosis and Intervention System** See pp. 155G–155H.
- **Test-Taking Practice** Transparencies, every lesson
- **SAT 9, SAT 10, TerraNova Practice and Test Prep** Includes practice tests, correlations, and more

Teacher Support

- **Teaching Tools** Masters: paper manipulatives and more
- **Home-School Connection** Masters, use Chapter 5 Family Letter at the start of the chapter. Use Study Buddies 9 and 10 after Lessons 5-2 and 5-10.
- **Professional Development Resources** See p. T18.
- **Technology Resources** See p. T20.

CHAPTER 5

Professional Development

Skills Trace - Geometry and Fractions

BEFORE Chapter 5	DURING Chapter 5	AFTER Chapter 5
Grade K introduced identifying solid objects shaped like a sphere, cube, cone, or cylinder and identifying plane figures that are flat surfaces of solid figures. Objects that show equal parts, halves, and fourths were also introduced.	**Chapter 5** focuses on identifying and naming plane and solid figures and recognizing them in the environment. Identifying and showing halves, thirds, and fourths is developed.	**Chapter 6 in Grade 1** applies halves to reading time to the half hour. **Grade 2** develops the properties of plane and solid figures and the concept that larger shapes can be made from more than one smaller shape. The meaning of a fraction as part of a whole or part of a group is also developed.

Math Background and Teaching Tips

Section A

Solid Figures

pp. 157–164

Geometry, the study of shapes in space and of spatial relationships, is important because it offers children opportunities to relate mathematics to the real world.

Ball

Sphere

Geometric solids like cones, rectangular prisms, and spheres are "perfect" figures—they only exist as abstractions. They do not exist in the real world. But many real objects are close approximations to their shapes: ice cream cones, cereal boxes, and baseballs, for example.

TIP! For Kinesthetic Learners *The most lasting geometry learning comes from hands-on experiences with three-dimensional objects. Provide physical learning experiences for children.*

Children will first recognize these figures globally without being cognizant of their different properties. A figure will be identified as a cube, for example, "just because it looks like one."

It looks like a cube.

A major goal of this section is to move children from that global recognition to an examination of the properties of the figure.

Math Understandings

- Many everyday objects closely approximate standard geometric solids.
- Many solids are comprised of flat surfaces and vertices; the flat surfaces on prisms are called faces.
- The flat surfaces of solid figures are plane shapes.

TIP! Encourage Communication *Talk about properties of solids using everyday language: Would it roll? Does it have a flat side?*

TIP! Encourage Communication *It is important that children share their observations about figures with each other. By describing what they see, they will be identifying the various properties of the figures.*

The relationship between two-dimensional shapes and three-dimensional figures is one of progression. Two-dimensional shapes have length and width. Three-dimensional figures add depth.

Rectangular Prism

Square

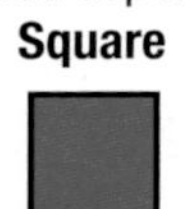

Investigations of three-dimensional figures lead naturally to an exploration of the two-dimensional shapes that comprise them. As children sort and classify solid shapes in a variety of ways, they observe that some solids have all flat parts and others have flat and curved parts. Some may have no flat parts at all. After making these discoveries, children are ready to focus on the flat surfaces of the solid shapes.

Section B

Plane Shapes

pp. 165–180

Following their experience with solids, in this section children study plane shapes that comprise the different flat surfaces of solids.

Again, the shapes studied here are "perfect"—they do not exist in the world, but connections can be made to objects that are close approximations.

TIP! Encourage Flexibility *When providing models of plane shapes for children to see and work with, frequently place them in "non-standard" orientations. Children can develop too narrow a concept of what a triangle is, for instance, expecting the "bottom" of it to always be horizontal.*

Studying the attributes of shapes is a more sophisticated level of the geometric thinking. At this point, children begin to notice properties of shapes such as the numbers of sides, whether it has a flat side or a curve, and so on.

Classifying and sorting focuses attention on individual attributes of shapes. Drawing shapes is a means of internalizing and constructing new concepts for children.

Two shapes are congruent if they have the same size and the same shape.

Math Understandings

- Many everyday objects are close approximations of standard plane shapes.
- Plane shapes have many properties that make them different from one another.
- Two shapes can have the same shape and the same size even if they do not share the same orientation.
- Symmetric figures have two congruent halves.
- Slides, flips, and turns can be used to change an object's position in space.
- Writing down all the possible ways of doing something can be a good way to solve a problem.

Symmetry is a property of some shapes. Shapes have line symmetry if they can be divided by a straight line into two congruent parts. These two parts must match if the shape is "folded" on the line.

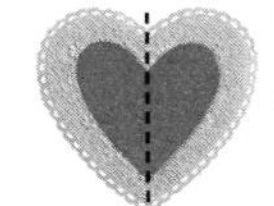

TIP! Use Technology *Computer programs that allow children to create and manipulate shapes are excellent environments for the exploration of geometric properties such as symmetry and congruence.*

Section C

Fractions

pp. 181–196

A fraction describes a relationship between a part and a whole. The initial concepts that children develop are based on partitioning geometric shapes.

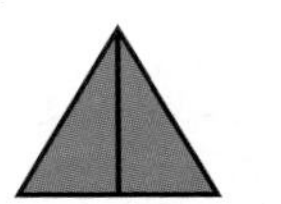

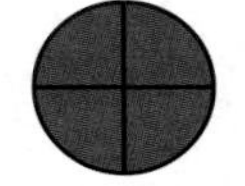

Children learn to associate $\frac{1}{2}$ with 1 of 2 equal parts of a shape. They also see $\frac{1}{3}$ as 1 of 3 equal parts and $\frac{1}{4}$ as 1 of 4 equal parts. Non-unit fractions such as $\frac{2}{3}$—2 of 3 equal parts—are also presented in this section.

However, there are at least two other important meanings of fractions—a part of a set (4 out of 5 students are $\frac{4}{5}$ of the students) and the definition of length (the paper clip is $\frac{7}{8}$ of an inch long).

Fractions name a whole (region or shape) that has been divided in a specified number of equal parts—that number is the denominator of the fraction. Both the number of parts and the fact that they are equal parts are stressed.

TIP! Make Connections *Emphasize the idea of equal parts as "fair shares." Use examples such as sharing a pizza or a cake equally.*

Comparing and ordering fractions is done visually at this level. The fewer number of parts an object is divided into, the larger the parts are. This concept is reflected in the denominator. The smaller the number, the larger the parts.

Math Understandings

- A shape can be divided into any number of equal parts in a variety of ways.
- A half of a region is one of two equally-sized parts.
- A unit fraction of a region names one of a number of equally-sized parts.
- Groups can be divided into equal parts in the same way that shapes can be divided into equal parts.
- A chart can hold data that is useful in solving problems.

Extracting information from a chart, table, or graph is a skill that supports problem solving. The title of the table states the classification of the information. The rows record the individual groupings within that classification.

Favorite Videos

Adventure	15
Drama	7

Assessment, Intervention, Test Prep

Assessment Resources

DIAGNOSING READINESS

Start of Year Diagnosing Readiness for Grade 1, Assessment Sourcebook pp. 43–46 and in Online Intervention

✓ **Start of Chapter** Diagnosing Readiness for Chapter 1, Assessment Sourcebook pp. 107–108 and in Online Intervention

✓ **Start of Lesson** Warm Up, Teacher's Edition pp. 157, 159, 161, 165, 167, 169, 171, 173, 177, 181, 183, 185, 187, 189, 191, 193

✓ Instant Check System™

ONGOING ASSESSMENT

✓ **Before Independent Practice** Check and Think About It, Student Book, every lesson

✓ **After a Section** Diagnostic Checkpoint, pp. 163, 179, 195 and in Online Intervention

Basic-Facts Timed Test 5 Assessment Sourcebook, p. 31

FORMAL EVALUATION

Chapter Tests Chapter 5 Test, Student Book pp. 201–202; Assessment Sourcebook Forms A and B Free Response pp. 109–112, Forms C and D Multiple Choice pp. 113–120, Performance Assessment p. 9; Multiple-Choice Chapter Test in Online Intervention

Cumulative Tests Chapters 1–3, 1–6, 1–9, 1–12, Assessment Sourcebook, pp. 89–92, 135–138, 181–184, 227–230; Online Intervention

Test Generator Computer-generated tests; can be customized

Correlation to Assessments, Intervention, and Standardized Tests

	Assessments		Intervention	Standardized Tests				
Lessons	Diagnostic Checkpoint	Chapter Test	Math Diagnosis and Intervention System	SAT 9/10	ITBS	CTBS	CAT	MAT
5-1 Identifying Solid Figures	p. 163: Ex. 1, 2	Ex. 1, 2	Booklet D: D45	/•	•	•	•	•
5-2 Flat Surfaces and Vertices	p. 163: Ex. 3	Ex. 3	Booklet D: D46	•/•		•	•	•
5-3 Relating Plane Shapes to Solid Figures	p. 163: Ex. 4, 5	Ex. 4	Booklet D: D47, D48	•/•	•	•	•	
5-4 Identifying Plane Shapes	p. 163: Ex. 4, 5	Ex. 5	Booklet D: D49	•/•	•	•	•	•
5-5 Properties of Plane Shapes	p. 179: Ex. 1	Ex. 6	Booklet D: D49, D50	•/•		•	•	•
5-6 Same Size and Same Shape	p. 179: Ex. 2	Ex. 7	Booklet D: D51	•/•	•		•	
5-7 Symmetry	p. 179: Ex. 3	Ex. 8	Booklet D: D52	•/•		•	•	
5-8 Slides, Flips, and Turns	p. 179: Ex. 4	Ex. 7	Booklet D: D53			•		
5-9 Problem-Solving Strategy: Make an Organized List			Booklet E: E23	•/•		•		•
5-10 Equal Parts	p. 195: Ex. 5	Ex. 9, 10	Booklet A: A59	•/•	•			
5-11 Halves	p. 195: Ex. 1	Ex. 8	Booklet A: A60	•/•	•			•
5-12 Thirds and Fourths	p. 195: Ex. 2	Ex. 9, 10	Booklet A: A60	•/•	•			•
5-13 Fractions of a Set	p. 195: Ex. 3	Ex. 11	Booklet A: A61	•/•	•			•
5-14 Non-Unit Fractions	p. 195: Ex. 4		Booklet A: A62	•/•	•			•
5-15 Problem-Solving Skill: Use Data from a Chart	p. 195: Ex. 5		Booklet E: E1	•/•	•	•	•	•

KEY:
SAT 9 Stanford Achievement Test
SAT 10 Stanford Achievement Test
ITBS Iowa Test of Basic Skills
CAT California Achievement Test
CTBS Comprehensive Test of Basic Skills (TerraNova)
MAT Metropolitan Achievement Test

Intervention and Test Prep Resources

INTERVENTION

During Instruction Helpful "If... then..." suggestions in the Teacher's Edition in Ongoing Assessment and Error Intervention

Math Diagnosis and Intervention System Diagnostic tests, individual and class record forms, two-page Intervention Lessons (example, practice, test prep), and one-page Intervention Practice (multiple choice), all in cross-grade strand booklets (Booklets A–E for Grades K–3, Booklets F–M for Grades 4–6).

Online Intervention Diagnostic tests; individual, class, school, and district reports; remediation including tutorials, video, games, practice exercises

TEST PREP

Test Talk before the Chapter Test, p. 199

Cumulative Review and Test Prep end of sections, pp. 164, 180, 196

Test-Taking Practice Transparencies for every lesson

Spiral Review and Test Prep for every lesson

SAT 9, SAT 10, TerraNova Practice and Test Prep section quizzes, practice tests

Correlation to NCTM Standards and Grades Pre-K through 2 Expectations

Number and Operations

Understand numbers, ways of representing numbers, relationships among numbers, and number systems.

Grades Pre-K through 2 Expectations

- Count with understanding and recognize "how many" in sets of objects. *Lessons 5-4, 5-9, 5-10, 5-13, 5-14, 5-15*
- Develop understanding of the relative position and magnitude of whole numbers and of ordinal and cardinal numbers and their connections. *Lesson 5-5*
- Develop a sense of whole numbers and represent and use them in flexible ways, including relating, composing, and decomposing numbers. *Lessons 5-2, 5-5, 5-9, 5-10, 5-15*
- Connect number words and numerals to the quantities they represent, using various physical models and representations. *Lessons 5-2, 5-4, 5-6, 5-9, 5-10, 5-13, 5-14, 5-15*
- Understand and represent commonly used fractions, such as $\frac{1}{4}$, $\frac{1}{3}$, and $\frac{1}{2}$. *Lessons 5-11, 5-12, 5-13, 5-14*

Algebra

Understand patterns, relations, and functions.

Grades Pre-K through 2 Expectations

- Sort, classify, and order objects by size, number, and other properties. *Lesson 5-15*

Use mathematical models to represent and understand quantitative relationships.

Grades Pre-K through 2 Expectations

- Model situations that involve the addition and subtraction of whole numbers, using objects, pictures, and symbols. *Lesson 5-15*

Geometry

Analyze characteristics and properties of two- and three-dimensional geometric shapes and develop mathematical arguments about geometric relationships.

Grades Pre-K through 2 Expectations

- Recognize, name, build, draw, compare, and sort two- and three-dimensional shapes. *Lessons 5-1, 5-2, 5-3, 5-4, 5-5, 5-6, 5-7, 5-9, 5-10, 5-11, 5-12*
- Describe attributes and parts of two- and three-dimensional shapes. *Lessons 5-1, 5-2, 5-3, 5-4, 5-5, 5-6, 5-7, 5-8, 5-9, 5-10, 5-11, 5-12*
- Investigate and predict the results of putting together and taking apart two- and three-dimensional shapes. *Lessons 5-3, 5-4, 5-9*

Specify locations and describe spatial relationships using coordinate geometry and other representational systems.

Grades Pre-K through 2 Expectations

- Describe, name, and interpret relative positions in space and apply ideas about relative position. *Lesson 5-6*

Apply transformations and use symmetry to analyze mathematical situations.

Grades Pre-K through 2 Expectations

- Recognize and apply slides, flips, and turns. *Lessons 5-8, 5-9*
- Recognize and create shapes that have symmetry. *Lesson 5-7*

Use visualization, spatial reasoning, and geometric modeling to solve problems.

Grades Pre-K through 2 Expectations

- Create mental images of geometric shapes using spatial memory and spatial visualization. *Lessons 5-3, 5-9*
- Recognize and represent shapes from different perspectives. *Lessons 5-1, 5-3, 5-6, 5-9*
- Relate ideas in geometry to ideas in number and measurement. *Lessons 5-2, 5-4, 5-5, 5-9, 5-10, 5-12*
- Recognize geometric shapes and structures in the environment and specify their location. *Lesson 5-1*

The NCTM 2000 Pre-K through Grade 12 Content Standards are Number and Operations, Algebra, Geometry, Measurement, and Data Analysis and Probability. The Process Standards (Problem Solving, Reasoning and Proof, Communication, Connections, and Representation) are incorporated throughout lessons.

CHAPTER 5

Investigation

Geometry and Fractions

Activity I

Use in place of the Investigating the Concept activity in Lesson 5-4.

Identifying Plane Shapes

Overview
Children classify plane shapes according to size, color, and shape and draw pictures to record the ways they categorized the shapes.

Materials
(per group) Plane Shape Cards (Teaching Tool 16); More Plane Shape Cards (Teaching Tool 17)

The Task
- Discuss ways to sort different shapes, encouraging children to notice the shape, color, and size of objects.
- Hold up one Plane Shape Card for all children in the group to see. Have volunteers describe the shape, using shape, color, and size of the shape as sorting rules.
- One child sorts the Plane Shape Cards into piles, draws pictures to record the way shapes were classified, and explains which sorting rule was used.
- Children continue to sort the cards according to shape, color, and size, record them by drawing pictures, and explain the rule that was used.

Observing and Questioning
- As children sort the shapes, observe whether they classify them according to specific sorting rules.
- If children have difficulty sorting the shapes, ask the following questions to help spur their thinking.
- **How can you use the color, size, or number of sides of each object to sort them?**
- **What rule did you use to sort the shapes?**

Sharing and Summarizing
- After children explain the rules used to sort the shapes into different groups, summarize the methods they used.
- If children sort shapes using only the color of the objects, ask: **How can we use the number of sides to sort the objects?**
- **Key Idea** Point out that there are many ways to group the shapes. Sorting rules can include the shape of the object, number of sides, the size, and the color of the object.

Follow-Up
- **Extension** Have children tell one object in their home that is an example of a circle and one that is an example of a square. *(Sample answers for circles include dinner plates and round windows. Sample answers for squares include mirrors and computer screens.)*

One group has four sides, and one group has no sides.

Link to *Investigations in Number, Data, and Space*® See the **Joint-Usage Plan** available from Pearson Scott Foresman.

Activity 2

Use in place of the Investigating the Concept activity in Lesson 5-10.

Equal Parts

Overview

Children practice ways of sharing objects and sets of objects to realize the importance of equal shares before learning specific techniques for dividing objects into equal parts in Lesson 5-10.

Materials

(per pair) 12 connecting cubes; 1 piece of paper; string; scissors

The Task

- Have partners place the cubes between them in the workspace.
- **How can you share the cubes between 2 people? Record all of the ways you can think of.** *(One group of 11 and one group of 1; etc.)*
- When children have recorded all of the ways of sharing the cubes, ask: **Which way is the most fair so that both children have the same amount?** *(Each child gets 6 cubes.)*
- Discuss methods that children used to share the cubes and which way is the fairest.
- Repeat with the piece of paper and then the string. **How can you share the paper and the string so that each child has an equal amount?**

Observing and Questioning

- As children are sharing the objects and set of objects, observe whether they divide them into 2 equal groups. To help stimulate thinking, you might ask:
- **How did you decide to share the objects between 2 people?**
- **Who has more cubes, and who has fewer cubes? Is this the fairest way?** *(Both children have the same number; this is the fairest way.)*
- When using the string and paper, ask: **Can you use the scissors to help you share these materials?**

Sharing and Summarizing

- Discuss with children the different ways children used to share objects and sets of objects. For example, each object or set of objects is divided equally.
- If children do not divide objects and groups of objects equally, ask: **How are you making sure that both partners get an equal share?** *(Sample answer: Compare each child's amount.)*
- **Key Idea** Point out the importance of sharing each object or set of objects equally. This makes it easy to find how much of an object each person gets and how many of a set of objects each person gets.

Follow-Up

- Have children take one of the pieces of string and share it equally between 2 people.

CHAPTER 5

Math Story

No Problem! **(Genre: Realistic fiction)**

In this story about fractions, two boys share fruit by dividing it in half until their baby sister comes along and they have to learn to divide fruit into thirds.

Introducing the Story

Ask children if they've ever shared food with a brother, sister, cousin, or friend. Have them tell what type of food and how they shared it. Show them the cover of *No Problem!* and tell them that this story is about two brothers who share different kinds of fruit equally.

Reading the Story

Read the story through once without stopping. Encourage children to listen carefully and to enjoy the story and art along with you.

Read the story again. Then challenge children to recall the different ways the children shared fruit. List the different ways, such as halves, on the board. Explain that a list is a way to organize information. Remind children that they can use this reading strategy, understanding lists, whenever they are reading and solving math problems. (For more on *Understand Graphic Sources: Lists,* see Reading for Math Success, pp. 175–176.)

Page 5A

Page 5B **Page 5C**

Even when their new baby sister was born, no problem.
She was too little to eat fruit.
5D
But then one day, while the two brothers were sharing a dozen grapes, their little sister said,
"Hey! Where's mine?"
Uh-oh! Big problem!
5E

Page 5D

Page 5E

But they solved it. Here's how.

If there was only 1 banana, they did this:

Page 5F

Follow-up Activities

- **Use Picture Clues** Have children check to make sure that the words and the pictures match. **Did each boy get half a banana? How many strawberries did each boy get? How did the children divide the grapes and banana into 3 groups?** Then point to the drawings on the last page that show equal shares. **How do these drawings help you understand how the 3 children shared fruit equally?** Explain that drawings are sometimes better than words at explaining how something is shared.
- **Main Idea** Tell children that you will give them three answer choices for what *No Problem!* is all about, and that you want them to choose the correct answer. Give them these three choices: a joining story, a comparing story, or a sharing story. If children need help, explain that a sharing story is the correct answer because the children share fruit by cutting it into equal-sized pieces or separating it into equal groups. Remind children that thinking about what a story is all about will help them understand a story better.
- **Extend the Story** Ask leading questions: **How could the 3 children share 12 blueberries equally? How could they share an apple equally? What other food might they share?**

Home-School Connection

Purpose Provide families with an overview of Chapter 5 material: a family letter, a math activity, references to literature related to the chapter, and new math vocabulary words.

Using Student Page 155

You may wish to read and discuss the family letter with children prior to having them sign it and sending the page home.

Literature: Dorling Kindersley

Available in the Scott Foresman Dorling Kindersley Literature Library

Play and Learn: Shapes
edited by Lara Tankel Holtz
(Dorling Kindersley Ltd., 1993)

Three fuzzy ducks introduce the geometric shapes of familiar objects. Questions on every page encourage children to learn the names of shapes.

The Home-School Connection booklet:

- Chapter 5 Family Letter, English and Spanish
- Study Buddies 9, 10

Study Buddies pages (one for the child, one for the person guiding the child's learning) provide reinforcement activities.

Vocabulary

cube *(pp. 157–158)*
rectangular prism *(pp. 157–158)*
sphere, cone *(pp. 157–158)*
cylinder *(pp. 157–158)*
solid figure *(pp. 159–160)*
flat surface *(pp. 159–160)*
vertex (vertices) *(pp. 159–160)*
face, corner *(pp. 159–160)*
plane shape *(pp. 165–166)*
triangle, rectangle *(pp. 165–166)*
circle, square *(pp. 165–166)*
side *(pp. 167–168)*
vertex, vertices *(pp. 167–168)*
same size *(pp. 169–170)*
same shape *(pp. 169–170)*
symmetry *(pp. 171–172)*
line of symmetry *(pp. 171–172)*
slide, flip *(pp. 173–174)*
turn *(pp. 173–174)*
equal parts *(pp. 181–182)*
fraction, whole *(pp. 183–184)*
halves, one half ($\frac{1}{2}$) *(pp. 183–184)*
thirds, one third ($\frac{1}{3}$) *(pp. 185–186)*
fourths, one fourth ($\frac{1}{4}$) *(pp. 185–186)*
equal share *(pp. 191–192)*

Home-School Connection

Dear Family,

Today my class started Chapter 5, **Geometry and Fractions.** I will learn about solid figures like a cube and a cone, and also about plane shapes like a triangle and a square. I will learn about fractions and talk about halves, thirds, and fourths. Here are some of the math words I will be learning and some things we can do to help me with my math.

Love,

____

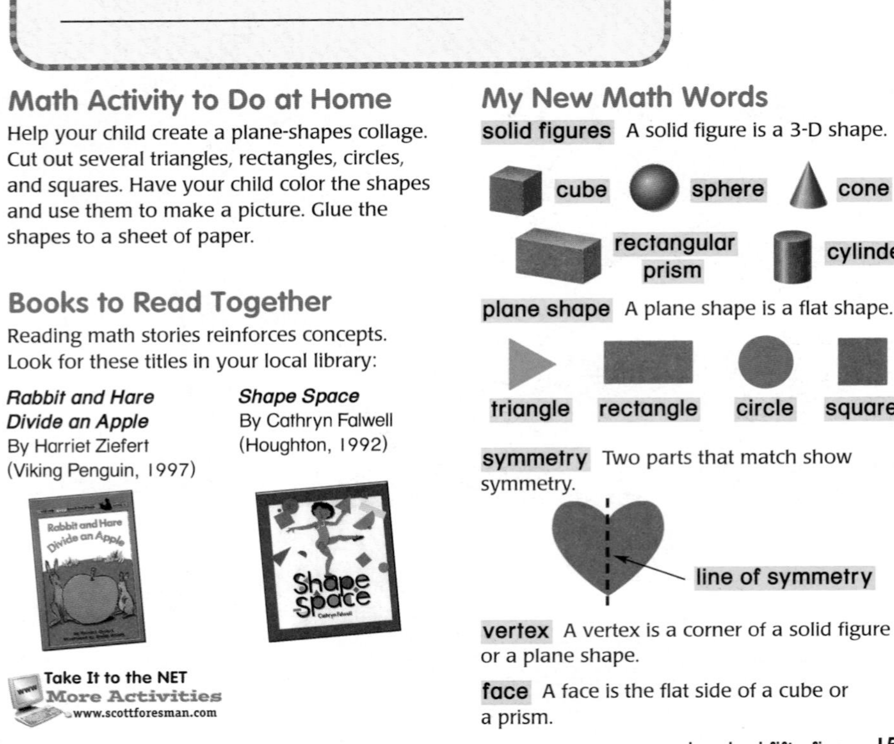

Math Activity to Do at Home

Help your child create a plane-shapes collage. Cut out several triangles, rectangles, circles, and squares. Have your child color the shapes and use them to make a picture. Glue the shapes to a sheet of paper.

Books to Read Together

Reading math stories reinforces concepts. Look for these titles in your local library:

Rabbit and Hare Divide an Apple
By Harriet Ziefert
(Viking Penguin, 1997)

Shape Space
By Cathryn Falwell
(Houghton, 1992)

Take It to the NET
More Activities
www.scottforesman.com

My New Math Words

solid figures A solid figure is a 3-D shape.

cube sphere cone
rectangular prism cylinder

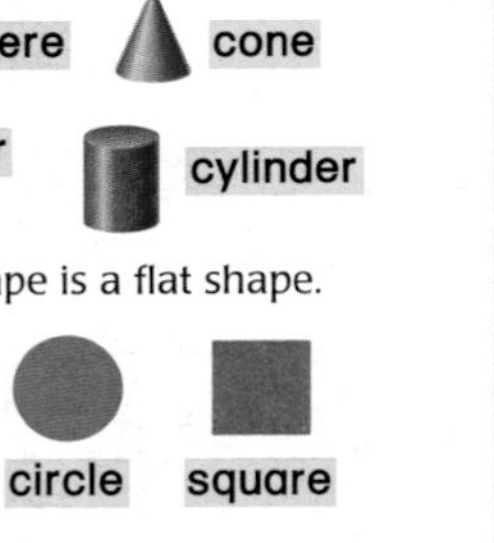

plane shape A plane shape is a flat shape.

triangle rectangle circle square

symmetry Two parts that match show symmetry.

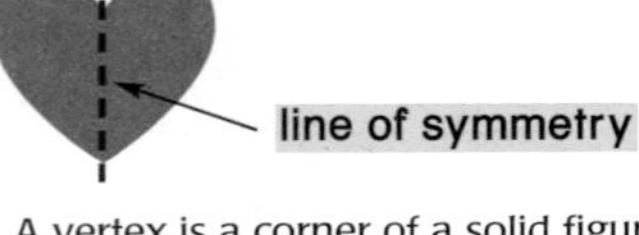

vertex A vertex is a corner of a solid figure or a plane shape.

face A face is the flat side of a cube or a prism.

Math Vocabulary Kit

Every vocabulary word is written on a card with the definition of the word printed on the back. Vocabulary activities are provided in the *Math Vocabulary Kit Teacher's Guide.*

Add the words from the Vocabulary list at left to your Math Word Wall as they are introduced.

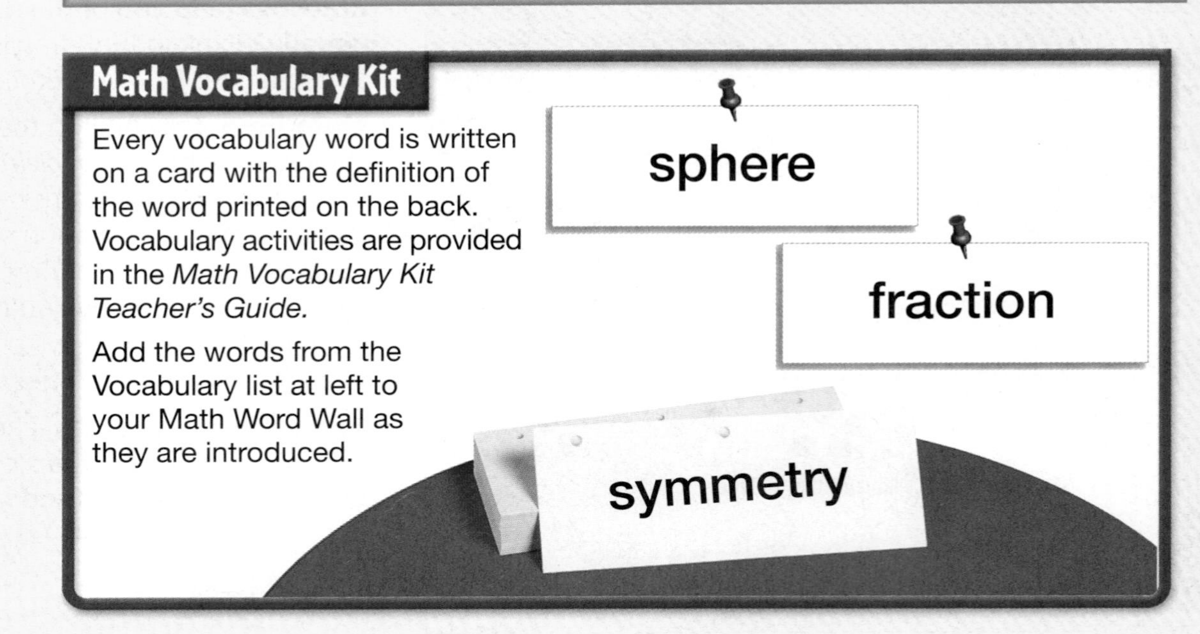

Name________________________ Practice Game

Fraction Concentration

What You Need

12 paper squares

How to Play

1. Place the squares on the gameboard.
2. Take turns. Remove 2 squares.
3. If you find a match, keep both squares.
4. If you do not find a match, put the squares back.
5. Keep playing until you have made all of the matches.
6. Don't forget to concentrate!

Practice Game

for School or Home

Purpose Provide children with an opportunity to practice skills they have previously learned.

Using Student Page 156

You may choose to discuss these questions with your children before they play "Fraction Concentration."

- **A shape is divided into fourths. 3 out of 4 parts are shaded. What fraction of the picture is shaded?**
- **How could you show one-half of a circle?**

Give children the materials for the game.

Describe the game, explaining how the children will follow the directions. Lead children through the process of turning over two paper squares and deciding if the picture and fraction match. Make sure children understand that they take the paper squares if they make a match, but return them to the gameboard if they do not match. Allow children to complete the game.

Describe another way to play: One player places a paper square on a fraction picture. The other player identifies the picture's value and covers the corresponding fraction on the gameboard. Players switch roles and repeat the process. Play continues until the entire gameboard is covered.

Chapter 5 Diagnosing Readiness

1. Circle the objects that have the same shape as the cube.
2. Circle all the rectangles. Mark an X on all the rectangles that are not squares.
3. Circle the larger bear and mark an X on the smaller bear.
4. Circle all the white buttons.
5. Use pattern blocks to cover the larger shape. Draw and color the pattern blocks on the larger shape to show how they fit.

   Sample answer is given. blue green green

6. Circle the objects that are cut into equal parts.

Item Analysis for Diagnosis and Intervention

Objective	Items	Student Book Pages*	Intervention System
Identify cubes, spheres, cones, and cylinders.	1	Kindergarten	D43
Identify and describe circles, triangles, squares, and other rectangles.	2	Kindergarten	D43
Identify *same* and *different* by the attributes of color, shape, size, and kind.	3–4	Kindergarten	D42
Recognize that shapes can be combined to make different shapes.	5	Kindergarten	D43
Identify equal parts of a whole.	6	Kindergarten	D43

*For each lesson, there is a *Reteaching* activity in *Reaching All Learners* and a *Reteaching* master.

Math Leveled Literature Library

Rabbit and Hare Divide an Apple (Challenging) ★
Harriet Ziefert. New York: Puffin Books, 1998.
Rabbit and Hare try to divide their whole food into parts of a set, but can't. What will they do?

Shape Spotters (Easy)
Megan E. Bryant. New York: Grosset & Dunlap, 2002.
Ms. Carey's class looks around the school to identify and classify different shapes.

5-1 Identifying Solid Figures

Lesson Organizer

Quick Lesson Overview

Objective Identify and name standard geometric solids and recognize them in the environment.

Math Understanding Many everyday objects closely approximate standard geometric solids.

Vocabulary Cube, rectangular prism, sphere, cone, cylinder

Math Monster Videos Use Episode 5: *Geometry* with or anytime after Lesson 5-1

Professional Development Note

Research Base

When just beginning their studies of geometry and space, students benefit greatly by seeing connections between the "ideal" geometric shapes and real world objects. Manipulatives and concrete geometric models are important in helping them bridge the gap (Clements & Batista, 1992). The first few lessons in this chapter focus on using such materials to identify different shapes and their parts.

NCTM Standards

- Geometry
- Number and Operations

(For a complete correlation to the NCTM Standards and Grades Pre-K through 2 Expectations, see Pages 155G and 155H.)

Getting Started

Spiral Review

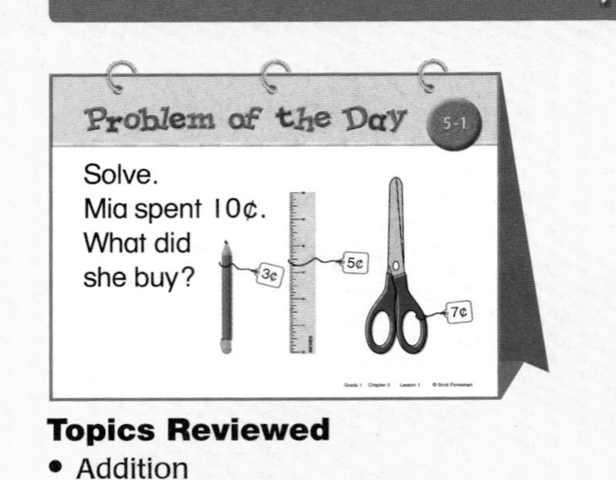

Topics Reviewed

- Addition
- Problem-Solving: One-Step Problem

Answer Mia bought the pencil and the pair of scissors. 3¢ + 7¢ = 10¢

Spiral Review and Test Prep 5-1

1. Add.
Use the number line to help you.
0 1 2 3 4 5 6 7 8 9 10 11 12
8 + 3 = ____
Ⓐ 9 Ⓑ 10 Ⓒ 11 Ⓓ 12

2. Which subtraction sentence matches the picture?
Ⓐ 4 − 1 = 3
Ⓑ 4 − 0 = 4
Ⓒ 4 − 2 = 2
Ⓓ 4 − 4 = 0

3. There are 4 children in the park.
4 more children join them.
How many children are there now?
There are 8 children now.

48 Use with Lesson 5-1.

Available as a transparency and as a blackline master

Topics Reviewed

1. Adding Using a Number Line
2. Zero in Subtraction
3. Choose an Operation

Investigating the Concept

Searching for Solids

Materials Geometric solids; chart paper

What to Do

- Create a chart with each geometric solid listed along the left side of the paper. Leave space beside each solid to record children's responses.
- Present each of the geometric solids. Ask children to describe and name them. Accept informal names, such as *can, box,* and *ball,* but provide the mathematical names (*cone*, *cylinder*, *cube*, *rectangular prism*, and *sphere*).
- Have children find objects in the classroom that match the shape of each solid figure. On the chart, draw pictures of the objects.

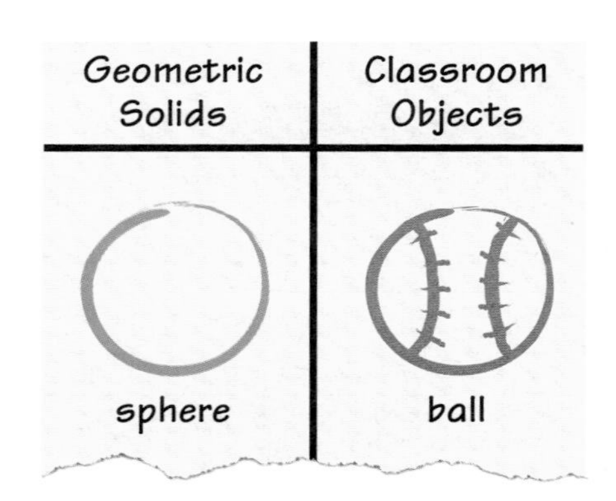

Ongoing Assessment

- **How are a sphere and a ball alike?** *(Sample response: They are both round.)*
- **Reasoning How are a cube and a cylinder different?** *(Sample response: The cube has pointed parts, but the cylinder does not.)*

Reaching All Learners

Math Vocabulary

Using Names for Solid Figures

5–10 MIN **Linguistic**

Materials Math Vocabulary Cards: *cube, sphere, cone, cylinder, rectangular prism;* geometric solids

- Display the geometric solids and allow children to take time exploring them. Invite children to describe each shape.
- Then lay out the cards in random order. Have children match each solid with the correct word card and offer a reason for their choice such as, "It is a cone because it has a pointy top."
- After each of the geometric solids has been named, post the names on the Math Word Wall.

Extend Language

English Language Learners

I Spy ...

10–15 MIN **Visual/Spatial**

Materials Geometric solids

- Use geometric solids to review the names of solid figures: *cube, sphere, cone, cylinder,* and *rectangular prism.*
- Invite children to look around the room to find solid figures. Give each child a turn to "spy" a figure and give clues about the figure. For example, a child who identifies a globe might say "I see a green and blue sphere." The child then calls on others to guess what object he or she is identifying.

Reteaching

Solid Construction

15–20 MIN **Kinesthetic**

Materials Geometric solids; clay

- Hold up the appropriate solid figure as you review the characteristics of a sphere, rectangular prism, cylinder, cube, and cone. Encourage children to offer descriptions of the solid figures, using their own words. Children may be challenged to tell how two solid figures are alike and how they are different.
- Then have children use clay to construct each of the shapes.
- Ask children to tell you the name of each of their constructions.

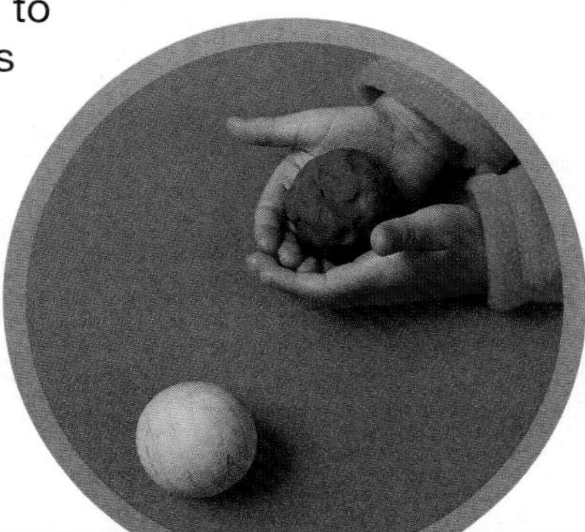

Math and Social Studies

Grocery Lists

15–20 MIN **Visual/Spatial**

INDIVIDUAL

Materials *(per child)* Grocery store advertisements; construction paper; scissors; glue

- Pass out a collection of grocery store advertisements to children. Have children sort through the ads to find items that have the same shapes as geometric solids. Children may find foods, such as oranges, cans of food, and boxes of cereal. Encourage them to also find nonfood items, such as rolls of paper towels and sponges.
- Have them cut out the shapes and glue them to a piece of construction paper labeled "Grocery List."

Objective Identify and name standard geometric solids and recognize them in the environment.

1 Warm Up

Activate Prior Knowledge Review vocabulary. Have children label parts of objects with the terms *flat, round, pointed,* and *curved.*

2 Teach

Learn!

Name each solid figure in the picture: cube, rectangular prism, sphere, cone, and cylinder. Ask children to think of everyday objects that have these shapes. For example, a can of soup is a cylinder and a basketball is a sphere.

Ongoing Assessment

Talk About It

- **What is the same about the cube and the other rectangular prism?** *(They each have flat parts and pointed parts.)*
- **Why do you think we call cubes *special* rectangular prisms?** *(All of the flat parts of a cube are the same size and shape.)*

If children name an everyday object that does not match any of the solid figures,

then display a geometric solid next to the object and have children compare the two.

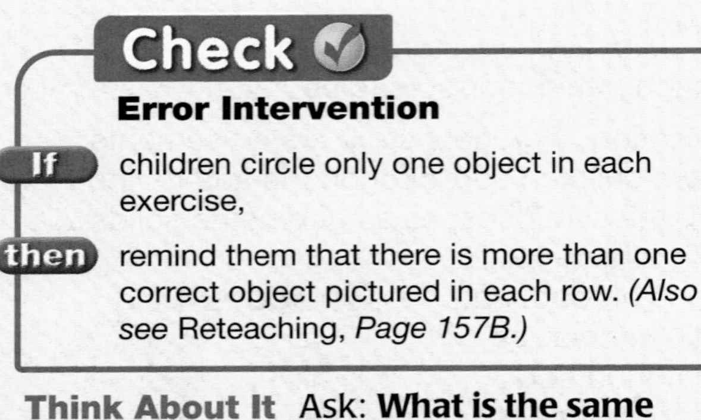

Check
Error Intervention
If children circle only one object in each exercise,
then remind them that there is more than one correct object pictured in each row. (Also see Reteaching, Page 157B.)

Think About It Ask: **What is the same about all four rectangular prisms?** *(Each has six flat parts and eight pointed parts.)* **What is special or different about the cubes?** *(They are cubes. All of the flat parts of each cube are the same size and shape.)*

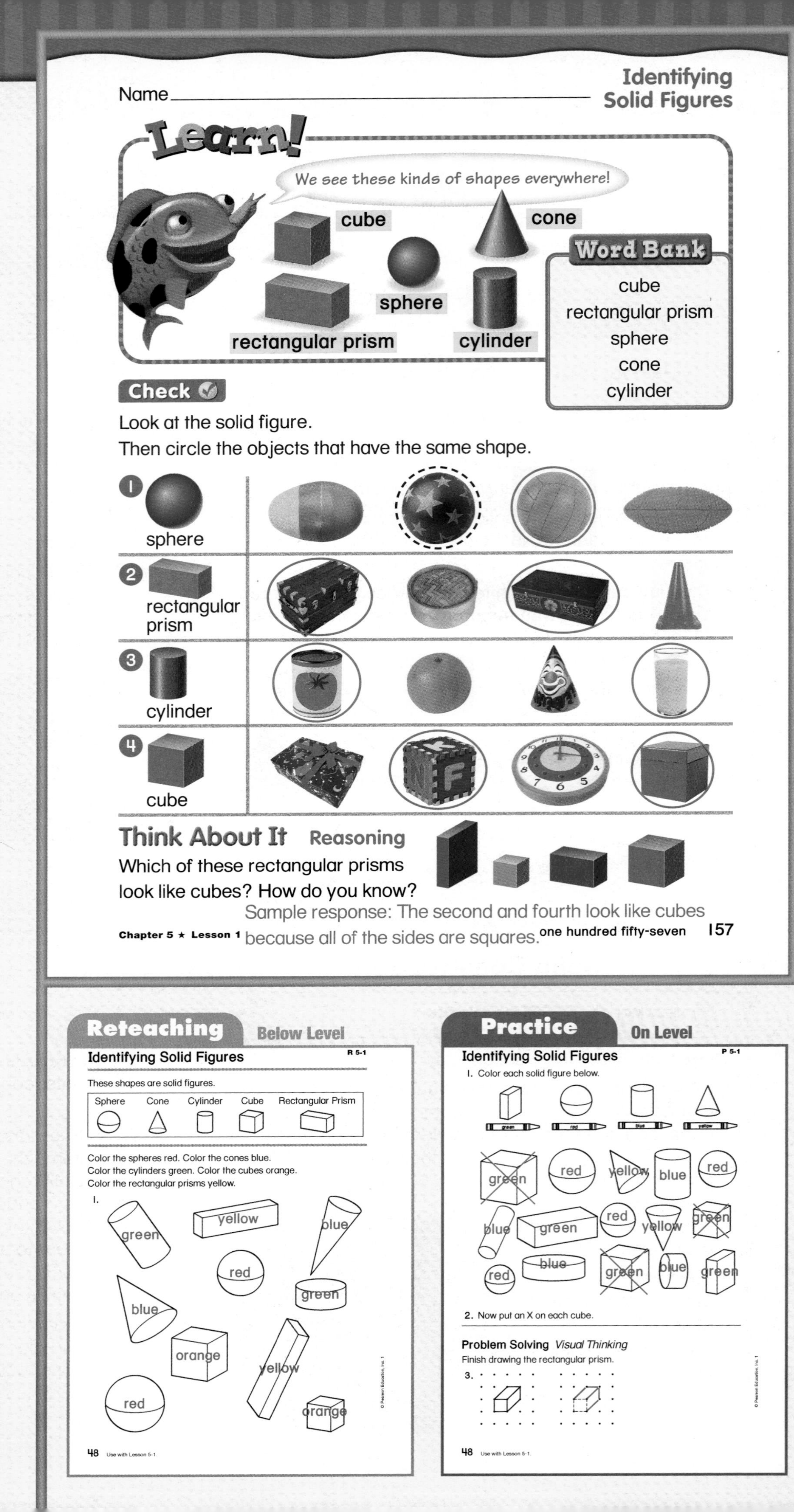

Practice

5 Color each solid figure below.
Now put an **X** on each cube.

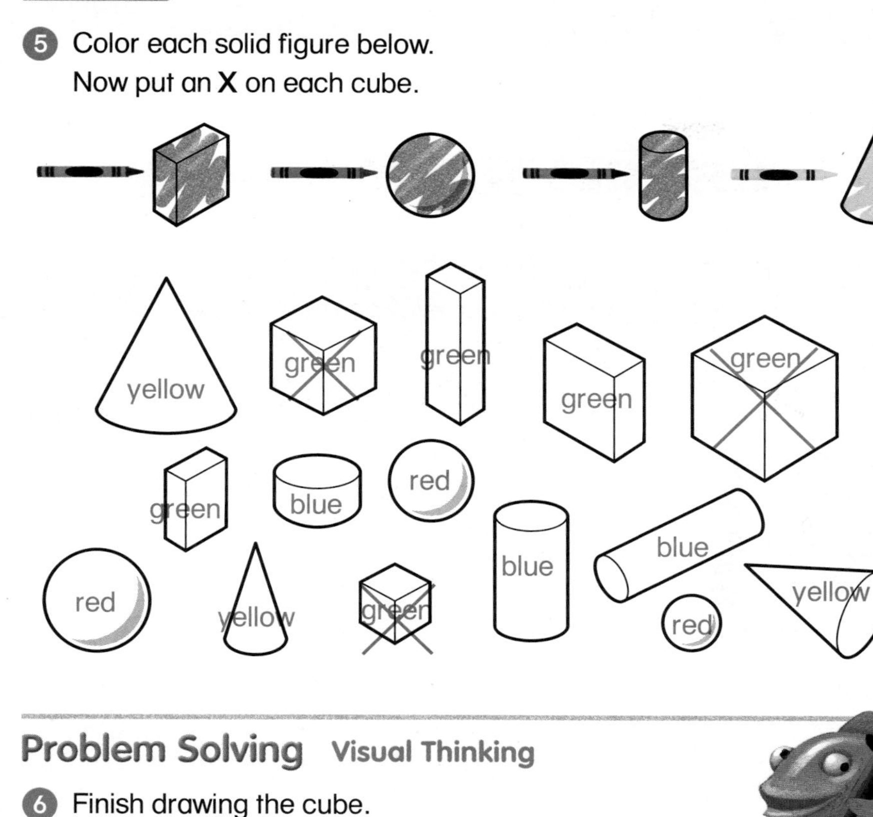

Problem Solving Visual Thinking

6 Finish drawing the cube.

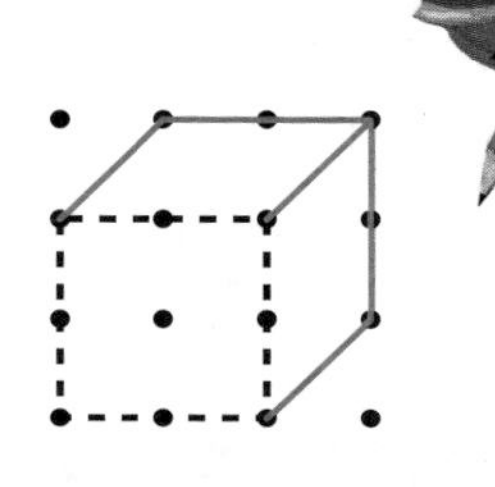

Home Connection Your child identified solid figures. **Home Activity** Be on the lookout for everyday objects that have the same shapes as these solid figures.

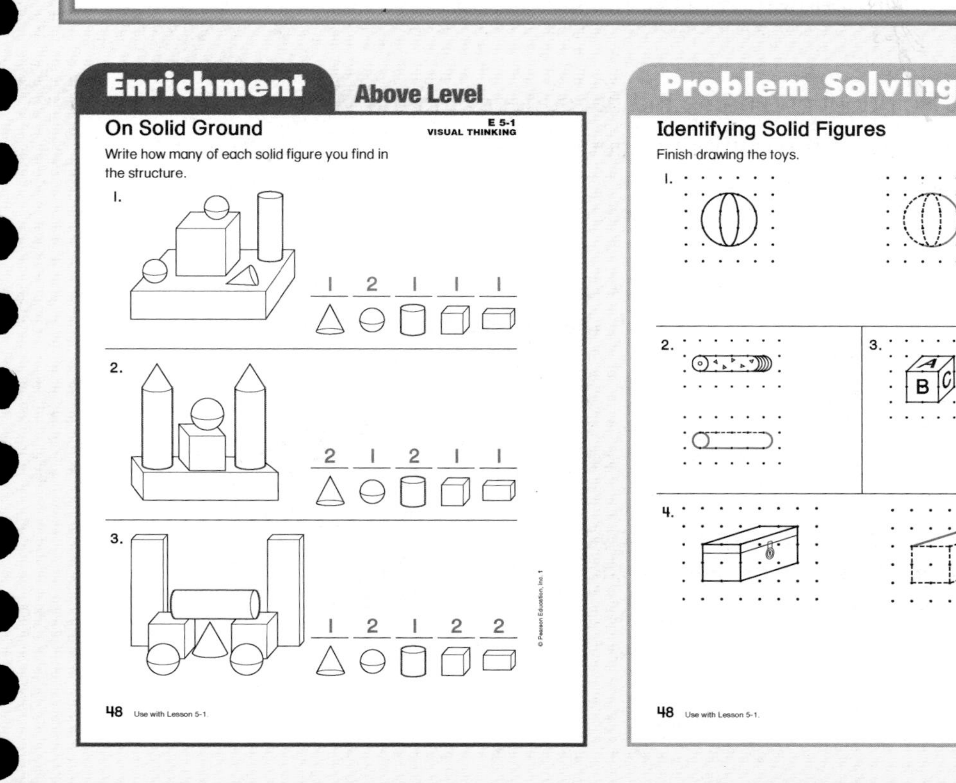

Enrichment Above Level

On Solid Ground — E 5-1 VISUAL THINKING

Write how many of each solid figure you find in the structure.

1. 1 2 1 1 1
2. 2 1 2 1 1
3. 1 2 1 2 2

48 Use with Lesson 5-1

Problem Solving

Identifying Solid Figures — PS 5-1

Finish drawing the toys.

1.
2.
3.
4.

48 Use with Lesson 5-1

3 Practice

Point out that children are to color *all* of the rectangular prisms green, including the *special rectangular prisms* or cubes.

Remind children to go back after coloring the rectangular prisms and mark an X on each cube.

Leveled Practice

Below Level Use geometric solids for all exercises.

On Level Use geometric solids only for Exercise 5.

Above Level Complete all exercises without geometric solids.

Early Finishers Have children look through magazines for pictures of objects that match the solid figures in this lesson. Children may enjoy using the pictures to make shape books.

4 Assess

Journal Idea On the board, write the names of the geometric solids and the terms: *round, pointed,* and *flat.* Have children complete the following sentence for each solid figure. "A ________ has ________ parts."

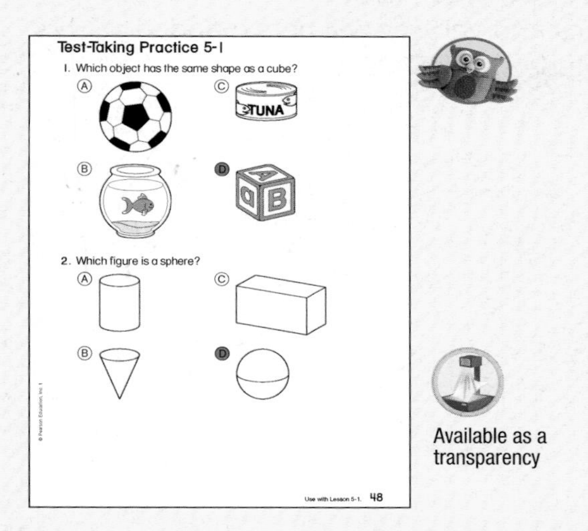

Test-Taking Practice 5-1

1. Which object has the same shape as a cube?
Ⓐ Ⓑ Ⓒ Ⓓ

2. Which figure is a sphere?
Ⓐ Ⓑ Ⓒ Ⓓ

Use with Lesson 5-1. 48

Available as a transparency

5-2 Flat Surfaces and Vertices

Lesson Organizer

Quick Lesson Overview

Objective Count the number of flat surfaces and vertices on geometric solids.

Math Understanding Many solid figures are comprised of flat surfaces and vertices; the flat surfaces on prisms are called *faces.*

Vocabulary Solid figure, flat surface, vertex (vertices), face, corner

Materials for Student Pages *(per group)* Geometric solids

Professional Development Note

Math Background At this level, children should understand only that faces are flat sides of cubes and rectangular prisms, and that vertices are the "pointy parts," or corners, of solid figures. Each year, their understanding of faces and vertices will be expanded to include special cases.

NCTM Standards

- Geometry
- Number and Operations

(For a complete correlation to the NCTM Standards and Grades Pre-K through 2 Expectations, see Pages 155G and 155H.)

Getting Started

Spiral Review

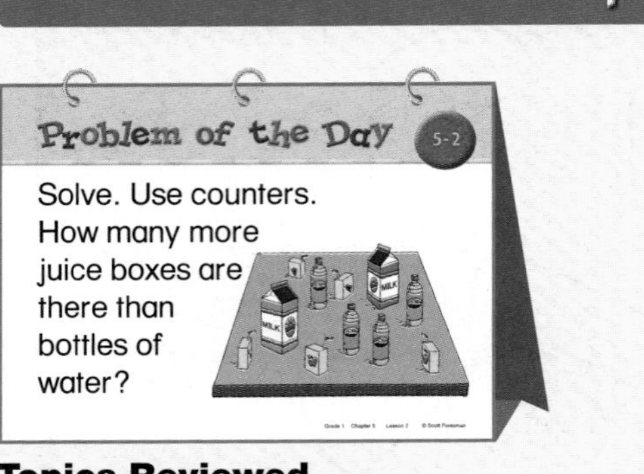

Problem of the Day
5-2
Solve. Use counters.
How many more juice boxes are there than bottles of water?

Topics Reviewed

- Addition and subtraction
- Problem-Solving Strategy: Act It Out or Use Objects

Answer There is 1 more juice box than bottle of water.

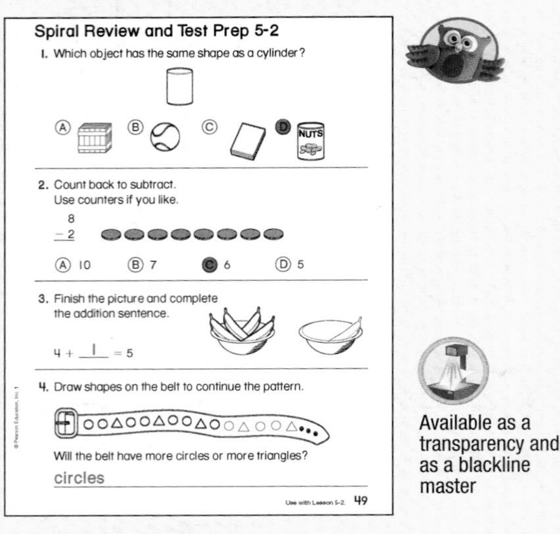

Spiral Review and Test Prep 5-2

1. Which object has the same shape as a cylinder?

Ⓐ Ⓑ Ⓒ Ⓓ NUTS

2. Count back to subtract.
Use counters if you like.

8
− 2

Ⓐ 10 Ⓑ 7 Ⓒ 6 Ⓓ 5

3. Finish the picture and complete the addition sentence.

4 + 1 = 5

4. Draw shapes on the belt to continue the pattern.

Will the belt have more circles or more triangles?
circles

Use with Lesson 5-2. 49

Available as a transparency and as a blackline master

Topics Reviewed
1. Identifying Solid Figures **2.** Counting Back
3. Adding 1, 2, or 3 **4.** Use Data from a Picture

Investigating the Concept

Counting Surfaces

15–20 MIN **Visual/Spatial** SMALL GROUP

Materials *(per group)* Geometric solids; masking tape

What to Do

- Hold up a cone. Point out and name the flat surface and the vertex or corners.
- Have small groups count the number of flat surfaces on the other solid figures. As they count, have them place a small piece of tape on each flat surface. Then, have the groups count the number of vertices on each solid, using tape to keep track of their counting.
- Hold up the cube and the rectangular prism. Explain that the flat surfaces on these solid figures are special. **We call the flat surfaces on cubes and rectangular prisms faces.**

Ongoing Assessment

- **Which solid figure has no flat surfaces or vertices?** *(Sphere)*
- **Reasoning Which two solid figures have the same number of flat surfaces?** *(Cube and other rectangular prism)*

Reaching All Learners

Oral Language in Math

Find It

10–15 MIN **Visual/Spatial**

Materials Geometric solids; classroom objects

- Hold up the cylinder from the classroom set of geometric solids. Invite children to move around the classroom looking for classroom items that have the same shape as the cylinder.
- For each object found, encourage children to say, "It looks like a cylinder." Place all of the cylinders that children find with the geometric solid.
- Repeat with the other solids until children have created a pile of classroom objects matching each geometric solid.

Access Content

English Language Learners

Flat Surfaces and Vertices

5–10 MIN **Linguistic**

- Model identifying the *flat surfaces* and *vertices* of an object in the classroom, such as a book.
- Hold up an object, such as a large box and have children say "flat surface" or "vertex" as you point to each. Repeat with other objects whose shape approximates a geometric solid.
- Invite children to look around the room for additional examples.

vertex

Reteaching

On the Surface

10–15 MIN **Visual/Spatial**

Materials Geometric solids; box or bag

- Have children work in groups of three: One child is the referee and two children are the players. The referee reaches into the box and picks out one solid shape for each player. Each player counts the number of surfaces (or vertices) on his or her figure. The counter who has the greatest number of surfaces (or vertices) earns a point.
- Play continues until one player earns 5 points.

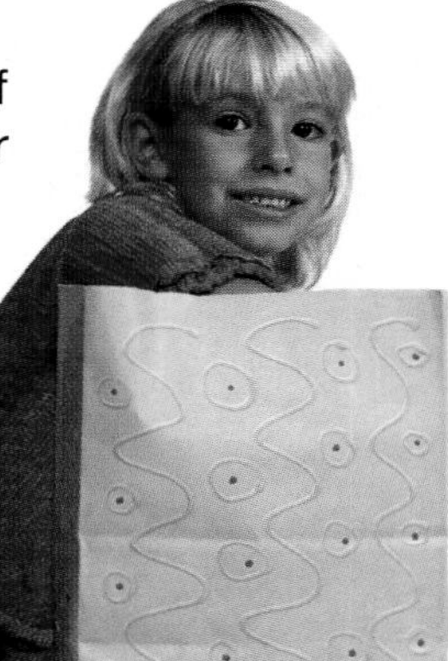

Students with Special Needs

Can You Guess?

10–15 MIN **Kinesthetic**

Materials Geometric solids; box; blindfold

- Pass around each solid figure, allowing children to handle the shapes. Model your thinking as you handle each shape. For example: **I know this is a sphere because it has no flat surfaces or vertices.**
- Place all of the figures in a box. One at a time, blindfold children and allow them to reach into the box and remove a solid figure. Encourage children to guess what they have chosen and tell how they know.

Objective Count the number of flat surfaces and vertices on geometric solids.

1 Warm Up

Activate Prior Knowledge Review geometric solids. Show children a cube and a cone. Ask them to name them and tell how they are alike and how they are different. Continue by having children compare other pairs of solid figures.

2 Teach

Learn!

Display a cube. Describe and name the parts: flat surface and vertex, or corner. Explain that the flat surface of a rectangular prism or a cube is called a face. Discuss the number of flat surfaces and vertices that the children found on the cube. Ask similar questions for the other solid figures. Then introduce the term *edge.* Show children the edges on each of the solid figures.

Ongoing Assessment

Talk About It

- **Why don't we see all six of the flat surfaces in the picture?** *(Three other surfaces are hidden.)*
- **Which solid figure has two flat surfaces and no vertices?** *(Cylinder)*

If children count the curved surfaces,

then have them try to place the surface in question onto the table. Explain that if the solid figure rolls, then the surface is curved, not flat.

Check

Error Intervention

If children have trouble counting,

then have them use tape to identify the parts as they count them. *(Also see* Reteaching, *Page 159B.)*

Think About It Have children look at the chart on the page to help with this question. **Which shapes have the same number in both columns?**

EC NTL 12 11 10 9 8 7 6 5

Name ______________________

Flat Surfaces and Vertices

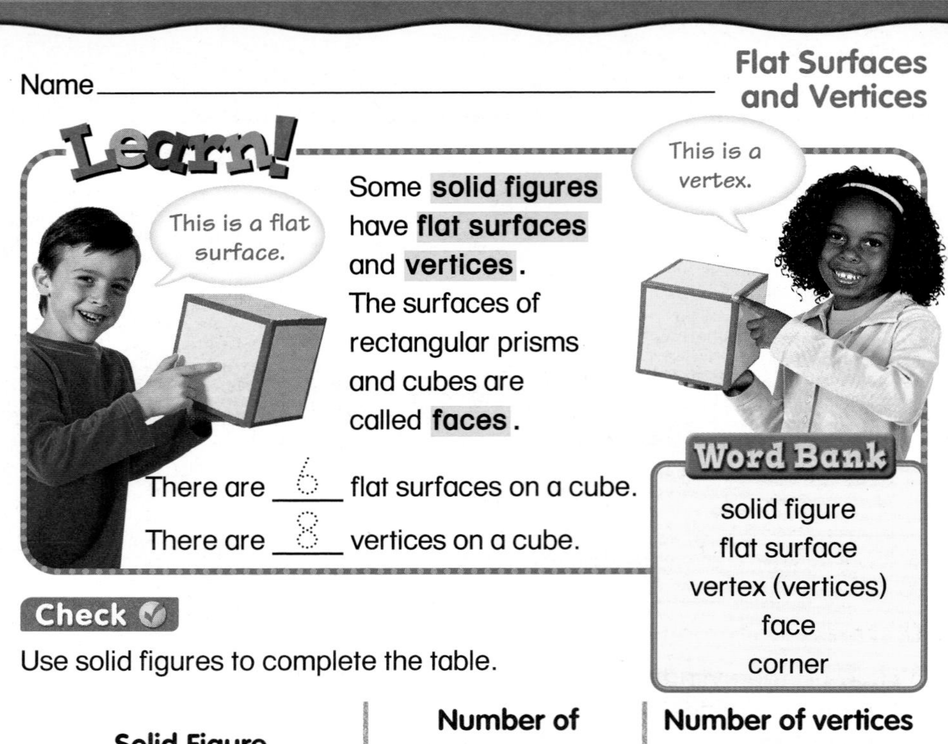

Learn!
This is a flat surface.
This is a vertex.

Some **solid figures** have **flat surfaces** and **vertices**. The surfaces of rectangular prisms and cubes are called **faces**.

There are 6 flat surfaces on a cube.

There are 8 vertices on a cube.

Word Bank
solid figure
flat surface
vertex (vertices)
face
corner

Check

Use solid figures to complete the table.

Solid Figure	Number of flat surfaces:	Number of vertices (corners):
1	6	8
2	2	0
3	1	1
4	0	0

Think About It Number Sense

Which solid figures have the same number of flat surfaces as vertices? Sphere and cone

---

Reteaching Below Level

Flat Surfaces and Vertices R 5-2

These solid figures have flat surfaces.

Cone Cylinder

These solid figures have all flat surfaces called **faces.**

Rectangular Prism Cube

These solid figures have **vertices** or corners.

Use solid figures to complete the table.

Solid Figure	Number of Flat Surfaces	Number of Vertices (Corners)	Number of Faces
1. cube	6	8	6
2. cone	1	1	0
3. rectangular prism	6	8	6
4. cylinder	2	0	0

Practice On Level

Flat Surfaces and Vertices P 5-2

Circle the solid figure that answers each question.

1. Which solid figure has 2 flat surfaces and 0 vertices?
2. Which solid figure has 0 flat surfaces and 0 vertices?
3. Which solid figures have 6 flat surfaces and 8 vertices?

Problem Solving *Reasoning*

Use the clues to answer each question.

4. I have 1 flat surface. I have 1 vertex. Which solid figure am I? cone
5. I have 2 flat surfaces. I have no vertices. Which solid figure am I? cylinder

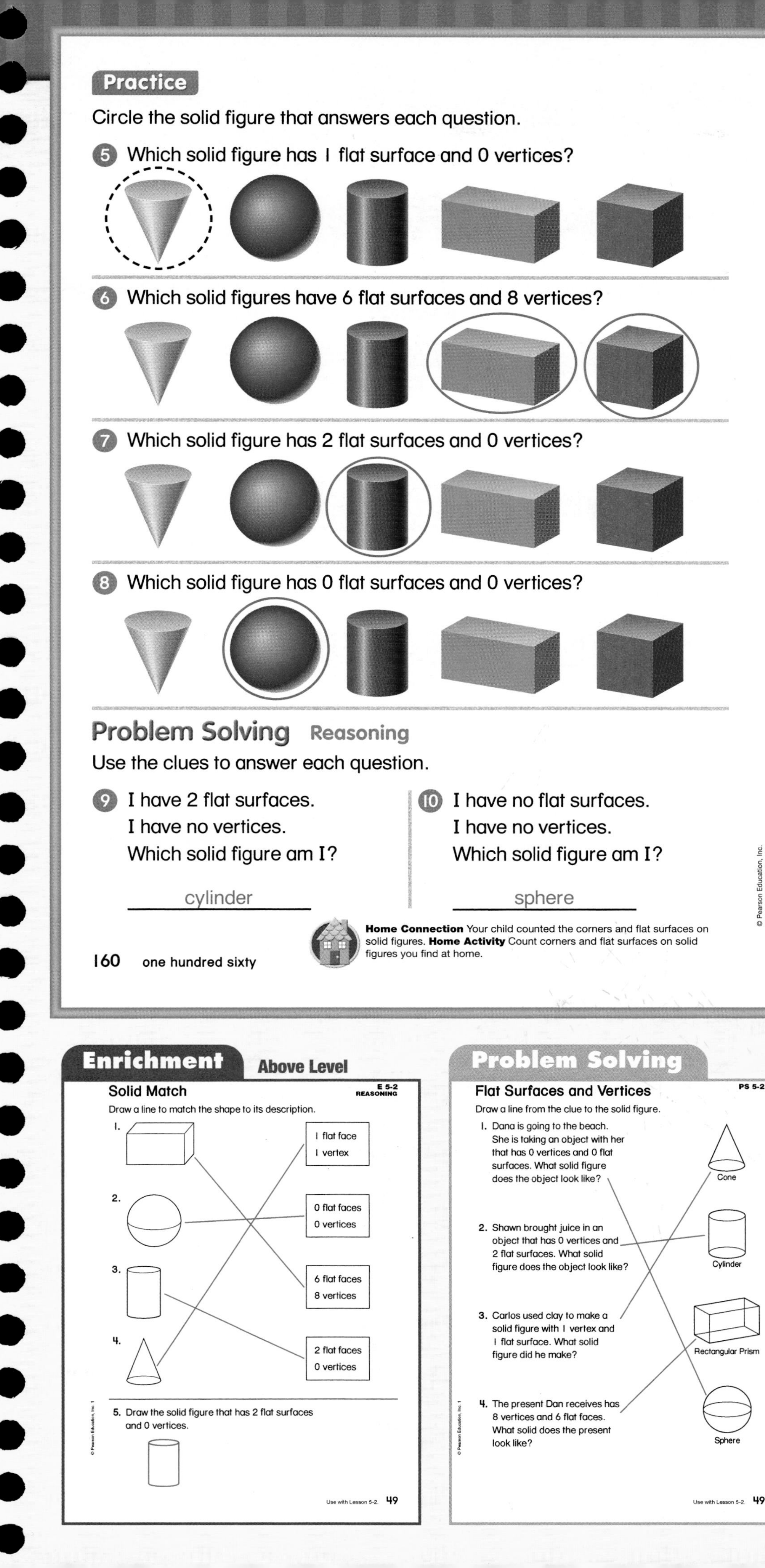

Practice

Circle the solid figure that answers each question.

5. Which solid figure has 1 flat surface and 0 vertices?

6. Which solid figures have 6 flat surfaces and 8 vertices?

7. Which solid figure has 2 flat surfaces and 0 vertices?

8. Which solid figure has 0 flat surfaces and 0 vertices?

Problem Solving Reasoning

Use the clues to answer each question.

9. I have 2 flat surfaces.
I have no vertices.
Which solid figure am I?
cylinder

10. I have no flat surfaces.
I have no vertices.
Which solid figure am I?
sphere

Home Connection Your child counted the corners and flat surfaces on solid figures. **Home Activity** Count corners and flat surfaces on solid figures you find at home.

Enrichment Above Level

Solid Match E 5-2 REASONING

Draw a line to match the shape to its description.

1. 2. 3. 4.

1 flat face 1 vertex

0 flat faces 0 vertices

6 flat faces 8 vertices

2 flat faces 0 vertices

5. Draw the solid figure that has 2 flat surfaces and 0 vertices.

Use with Lesson 5-2. 49

Problem Solving

Flat Surfaces and Vertices PS 5-2

Draw a line from the clue to the solid figure.

1. Dana is going to the beach. She is taking an object with her that has 0 vertices and 0 flat surfaces. What solid figure does the object look like?

2. Shawn brought juice in an object that has 0 vertices and 2 flat surfaces. What solid figure does the object look like?

3. Carlos used clay to make a solid figure with 1 vertex and 1 flat surface. What solid figure did he make?

4. The present Dan receives has 8 vertices and 6 flat faces. What solid does the present look like?

Cone

Cylinder

Rectangular Prism

Sphere

Use with Lesson 5-2. 49

Think About It Have children look at the chart on the page to help with this question. **Which shapes have the same number in both columns?**

3 Practice

Explain that solid figures, like the rectangular prism, may differ in size and sometimes shape but the number of vertices and flat surfaces for each type remains the same.

Reading Assist: Classify Draw two columns labeled "Has Flat Surfaces" and "Has No Flat Surfaces." Have children tell in which category each solid figure belongs.

Leveled Practice

Below Level Use solids to complete all exercises.

On Level Complete Exercises 5–8 without solids.

Above Level Complete exercises without solids.

Early Finishers In the margin of Student Page 159, have children add a column labeled "Edges." Ask children to find and record the number of edges on each solid.

4 Assess

Journal Idea Have children copy the following: "0 vertices, 0 flat surfaces," "0 vertices, 2 flat surfaces," "1 vertex, 1 flat surface," "8 vertices, 6 flat surfaces." Then have them draw a solid(s) for each.

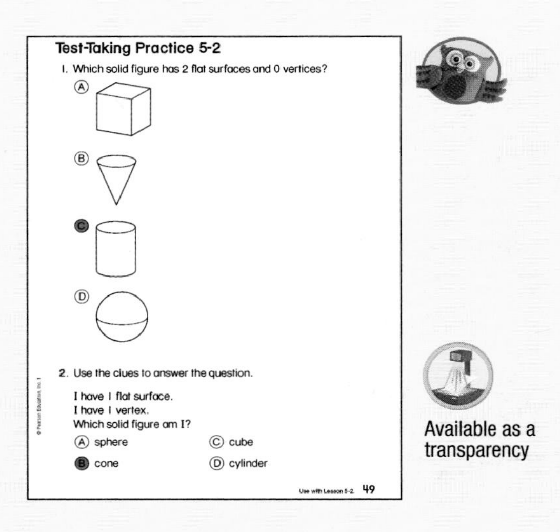

Test-Taking Practice 5-2

1. Which solid figure has 2 flat surfaces and 0 vertices?

Ⓐ Ⓑ Ⓒ Ⓓ

2. Use the clues to answer the question.

I have 1 flat surface.
I have 1 vertex.
Which solid figure am I?

Ⓐ sphere Ⓒ cube
Ⓑ cone Ⓓ cylinder

Use with Lesson 5-2. 49

Available as a transparency

5-3 Relating Plane Shapes to Solid Figures

Lesson Organizer

Quick Lesson Overview

Objective Match a geometric solid to an outline of one of its flat surfaces.

Math Understanding The flat surfaces of solid figures are plane shapes.

Materials for Student Pages *(per group)* Geometric solids

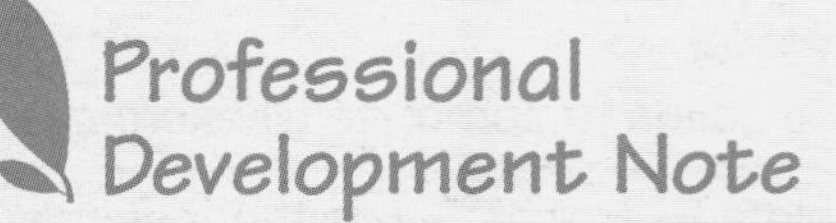

How Children Learn Math Some children may need additional experiences with concrete materials to help them understand the difference between three-dimensional solid figures and two-dimensional plane shapes. Provide ample hands-on practice and opportunities to verbalize conclusions.

NCTM Standards

- Geometry
- Number and Operations

(For a complete correlation to the NCTM Standards and Grades Pre-K through 2 Expectations, see Pages 155G and 155H.)

Getting Started

Spiral Review

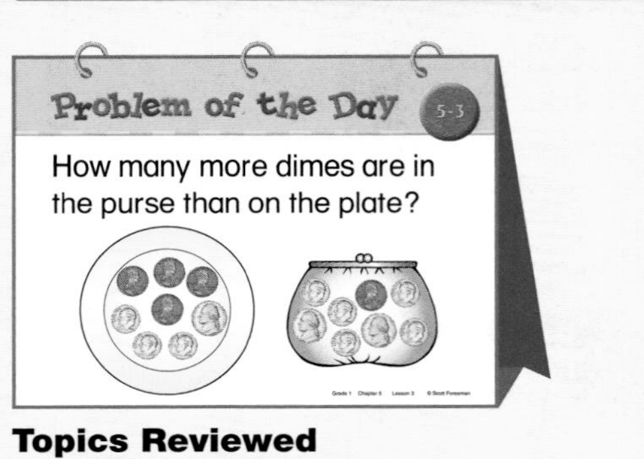

Problem of the Day
5-3
How many more dimes are in the purse than on the plate?

Topics Reviewed
- Money; subtraction
- Problem-Solving Strategy: Act It Out or Use Objects

Answer There are 5 – 3, or 2 more dimes in the purse than on the plate.

Spiral Review and Test Prep 5-3

1. Which solid figure has 1 vertex and 1 flat surface?
Ⓐ Ⓑ Ⓒ Ⓓ

2. What is the missing number?
8 + ____ = 10
Ⓐ 0 Ⓑ 1 Ⓒ 2 Ⓓ 3

3. Write an addition sentence and a subtraction sentence for the picture.

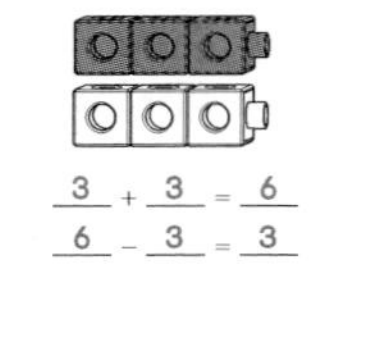

3 + 3 = 6
6 – 3 = 3

50 Use with Lesson 5-3.

Available as a transparency and as a blackline master

Topics Reviewed
1. Flat Surfaces and Vertices
2. Sums of 10
3. Using Doubles to Subtract

Investigating the Concept

Matching Plane Shapes and Solid Figures

Materials *(per group)* Geometric solids; Flat Surfaces of Solid Figures (Teaching Tool 15)

What to Do
- Make two sets of cards for each group of children.
- On the board, trace a flat surface of a solid figure to make a plane shape. Have children name the shape. Then display one card and ask children to name the solid figure that has a flat surface that matches this shape. Check that the shapes are the same.
- Have children work in small groups to sort the cards by matching them to the appropriate solid figures.

Ongoing Assessment
- **Which solid figures have surfaces that are circles?** *(Cylinder and cone)*
- **Reasoning** **What shape would I make if I traced a flat surface of a sphere? Explain.** *(No shape is made from tracing a sphere since a sphere has no flat surfaces.)*

Reaching All Learners

Reading in Math

Vocabulary Labels

10–15 MIN **Linguistic**

WHOLE CLASS

Materials *(per child)* 3 index cards labeled *flat surface, face,* and *vertex;* tape

- Review the meanings of *flat surface, face,* and *vertex* by labeling three things in the classroom. Explain why you selected what you did. Stress that faces are found on rectangular prisms and cubes.
- Give children several minutes to walk quietly around the room labeling items in the room with their index cards. Then call on children one at a time. Allow each child to point out his or her labels and explain why the label is appropriate.

Activate Prior Knowledge/Build Background

English Language Learners

Making Shapes

10–15 MIN **Kinesthetic**

Materials Geometric solids; clay

- Review the names of plane shapes: *circle, square, triangle, rectangle.* Flatten a piece of clay. Ask children to predict what shape they will see if they press the flat surface of the cone into the clay. "I think I will see a circle." Invite a child to press the cone into the clay to check the prediction.
- Repeat the activity by pressing other solid figures into the clay.

Reteaching

A Shape from a Solid

10–15 MIN **Visual/Spatial**

Materials Geometric solids; crayons; construction paper squares

- Give each child in the group a solid figure. Have children secretly trace around their solid onto a square of construction paper.
- Allow each child to share his or her paper with the group. Invite other children in the group to guess what shape was traced to make the shape.
- Encourage children to discuss which solids make the same shape when they are traced.

Math and Art

Shape Stamps

15–20 MIN **Visual/Spatial/Kinesthetic**

INDIVIDUAL

Materials Old blocks; construction paper; paint

- Show children how to make an imprint of a solid figure by dipping the flat surface into the paint and stamping the shape onto paper. Suggest that children create shape patterns.
- Display children's artwork in a classroom Shape Art Gallery. Encourage children to identify the solid figures that were used to create the shapes seen in the artwork.

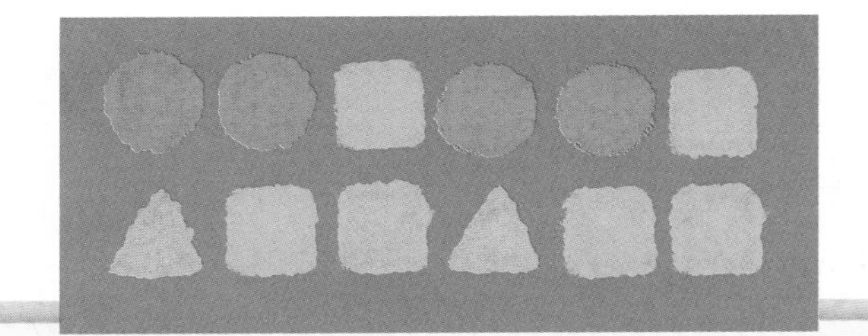

Objective Match a geometric solid to an outline of one of its flat surfaces.

1 Warm Up

Activate Prior Knowledge Review attributes of geometric solids. Ask descriptive riddles about solid figures, such as: **I have only one vertex and only one flat surface. What am I?** *(A cone)*

2 Teach

Learn!

Discuss what the child in the picture is doing. Children should suggest that she is tracing the flat surface of a cylinder. Ask children to name other solid figures that have flat surfaces that can be traced. *(Cube, rectangular prism, cone)*

Ongoing Assessment

Talk About It

- **If you were to trace around a surface of a cube, what shape would you make?** *(Square)*
- **Which shape cannot be traced? Why not?** *(Sphere, because it has no flat surfaces)*

If children are confused by the fact that a sphere has no flat surfaces,

then have them touch a sphere to see that it is completely round without any flat parts.

Check ✓

Error Intervention

If children have difficulty picturing the shape of a flat surface,

then allow them to use geometric solids to help. *(Also see* Reteaching, *Page 161B.)*

Think About It Have children name each of the five solid figures and tell the shape of each flat surface.

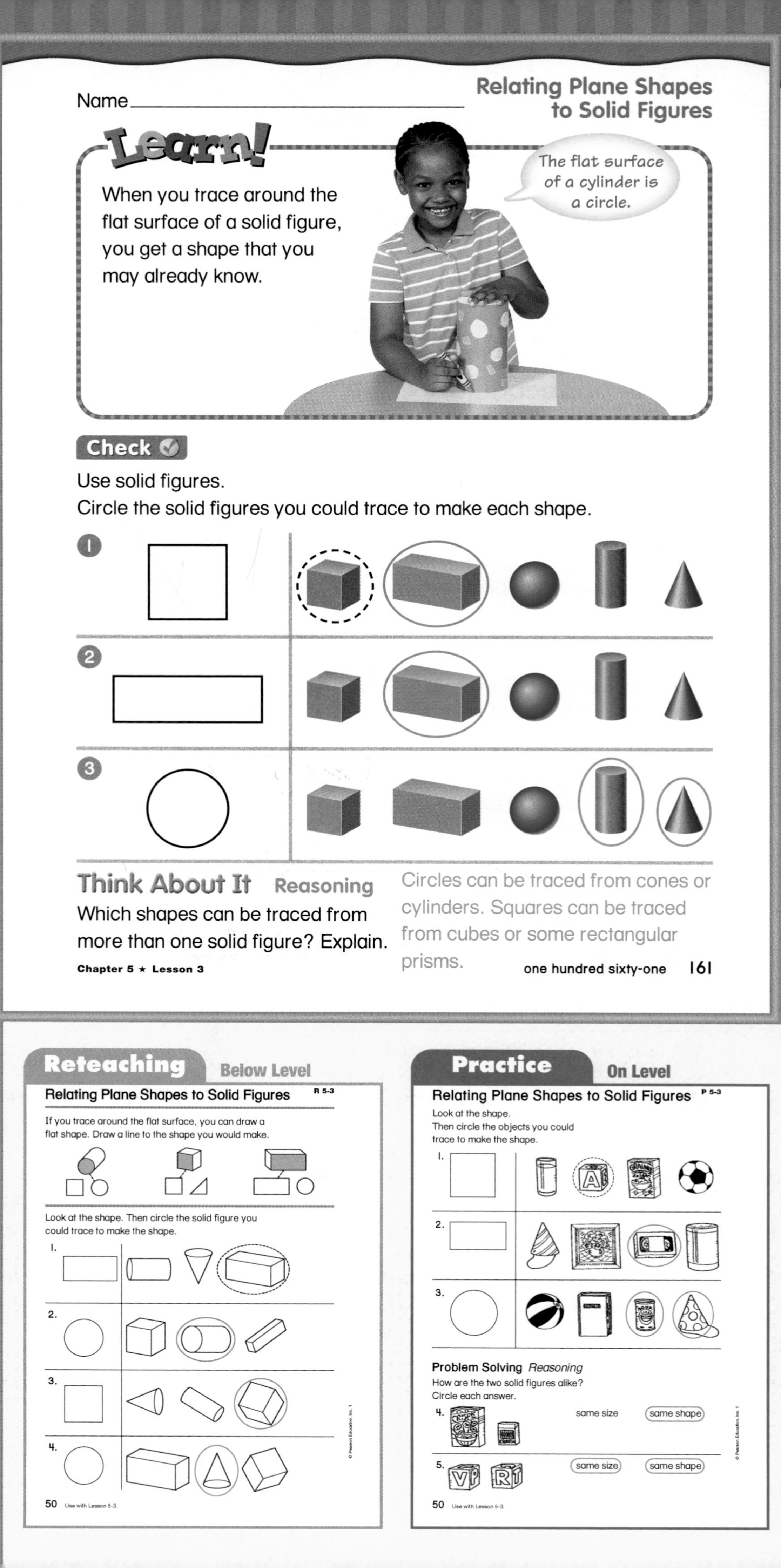

Name ____________

Relating Plane Shapes to Solid Figures

Learn!

When you trace around the flat surface of a solid figure, you get a shape that you may already know.

Check ✓

Use solid figures.

Circle the solid figures you could trace to make each shape.

1. (square)
2. (rectangle)
3. (circle)

Think About It Reasoning

Which shapes can be traced from more than one solid figure? Explain.

Circles can be traced from cones or cylinders. Squares can be traced from cubes or some rectangular prisms.

Chapter 5 ★ Lesson 3 — one hundred sixty-one 161

Reteaching Below Level

Relating Plane Shapes to Solid Figures R 5-3

If you trace around the flat surface, you can draw a flat shape. Draw a line to the shape you would make.

Look at the shape. Then circle the solid figure you could trace to make the shape.

1.
2.
3.
4.

50 Use with Lesson 5-3

Practice On Level

Relating Plane Shapes to Solid Figures P 5-3

Look at the shape.
Then circle the objects you could trace to make the shape.

1.
2.
3.

Problem Solving *Reasoning*

How are the two solid figures alike?
Circle each answer.

4. same size — same shape
5. same size — same shape

50 Use with Lesson 5-3

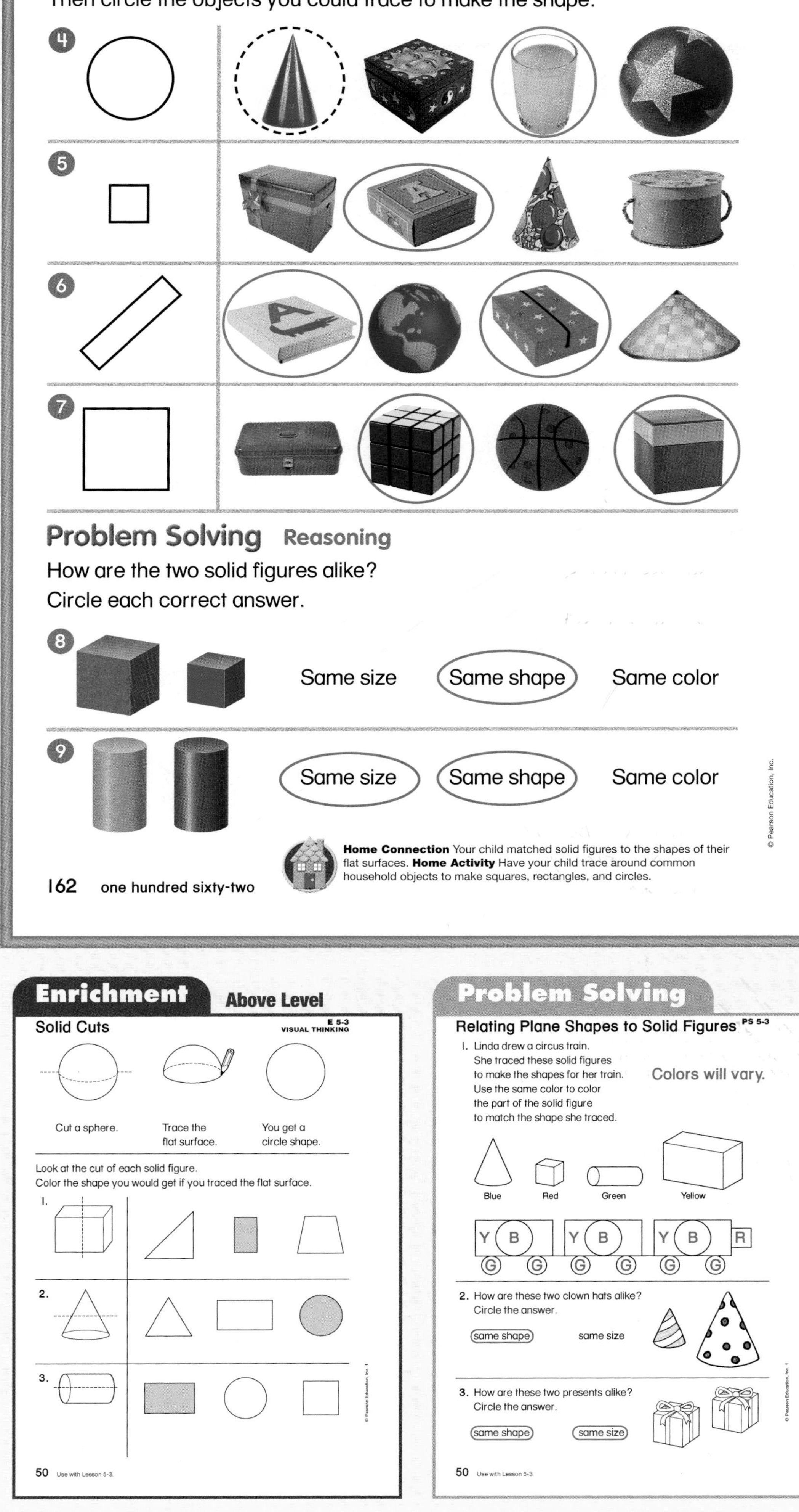

Practice

Look at the shape.
Then circle the objects you could trace to make the shape.

4
5
6
7

Problem Solving Reasoning

How are the two solid figures alike?
Circle each correct answer.

8 Same size Same shape Same color

9 Same size Same shape Same color

Home Connection Your child matched solid figures to the shapes of their flat surfaces. **Home Activity** Have your child trace around common household objects to make squares, rectangles, and circles.

Enrichment Above Level

Solid Cuts E 5-3 VISUAL THINKING

Cut a sphere. Trace the flat surface. You get a circle shape.

Look at the cut of each solid figure.
Color the shape you would get if you traced the flat surface.

1.
2.
3.

50 Use with Lesson 5-3.

Problem Solving

Relating Plane Shapes to Solid Figures PS 5-3

1. Linda drew a circus train.
She traced these solid figures
to make the shapes for her train.
Use the same color to color
the part of the solid figure
to match the shape she traced.

Colors will vary.

Blue Red Green Yellow

2. How are these two clown hats alike?
Circle the answer.

same shape same size

3. How are these two presents alike?
Circle the answer.

same shape same size

50 Use with Lesson 5-3.

3 Practice

Have children name each object and tell which solid figure it resembles.

Reading Assist: Use Picture Clues
Have children cover the direction line for Exercises 4–7 and look only at the pictures. **What do you think you are going to do on this page? Why do you think so?**

Leveled Practice

Below Level Use solids to complete all exercises.

On Level Complete Exercises 4–9 without solids.

Above Level Put an X on each object that does not have any flat surfaces.

Early Finishers Have children work in pairs. One child secretly traces the flat surface of a solid figure, and the other child names the solid figure that was traced.

4 Assess

Journal Idea Have each child choose a solid figure and write all that he or she knows about it. Provide prompts, such as: **Does it have rounded, pointed, or flat parts? How many vertices does it have?**

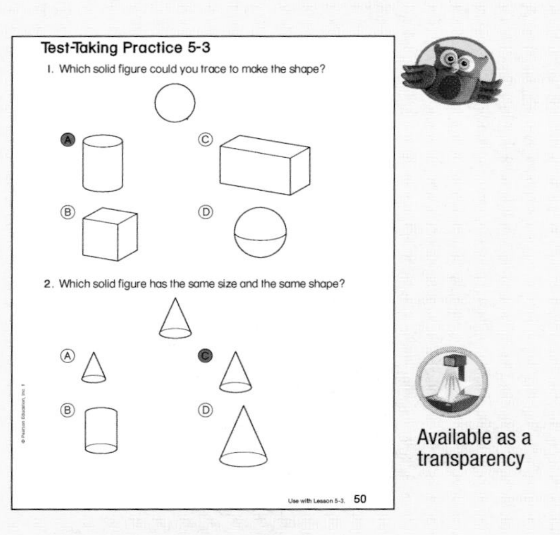

Test-Taking Practice 5-3

1. Which solid figure could you trace to make the shape?

Ⓐ Ⓑ Ⓒ Ⓓ

2. Which solid figure has the same size and the same shape?

Ⓐ Ⓑ Ⓒ Ⓓ

Use with Lesson 5-3. 50

Available as a transparency

Diagnostic Checkpoint

Purpose Provide assessment of children's progress to date by checking their understanding of key content covered in the previous section.

Vocabulary Review

You may wish to review this vocabulary term before assigning the page:

cone A solid figure with one circular base and one vertex *(pp. 157–158)*

corner A point where two sides or two or more edges meet *(pp. 159–160)*

cube A solid figure whose six faces are all squares of the same size *(pp. 157–158)*

cylinder A solid figure with two congruent circular faces *(pp. 157–158)*

face A flat surface of a prism *(pp. 159–160)*

rectangular prism A solid figure whose six faces are all rectangles *(pp. 157–158)*

solid figure A figure that has length, width, height, and volume *(pp. 159–160)*

sphere A solid figure that has the shape of a round ball *(pp. 157–158)*

vertex (vertices) A point where two sides or two or more edges meet *(pp. 159 –160)*

Activities for this section are available in the Math Vocabulary Kit.

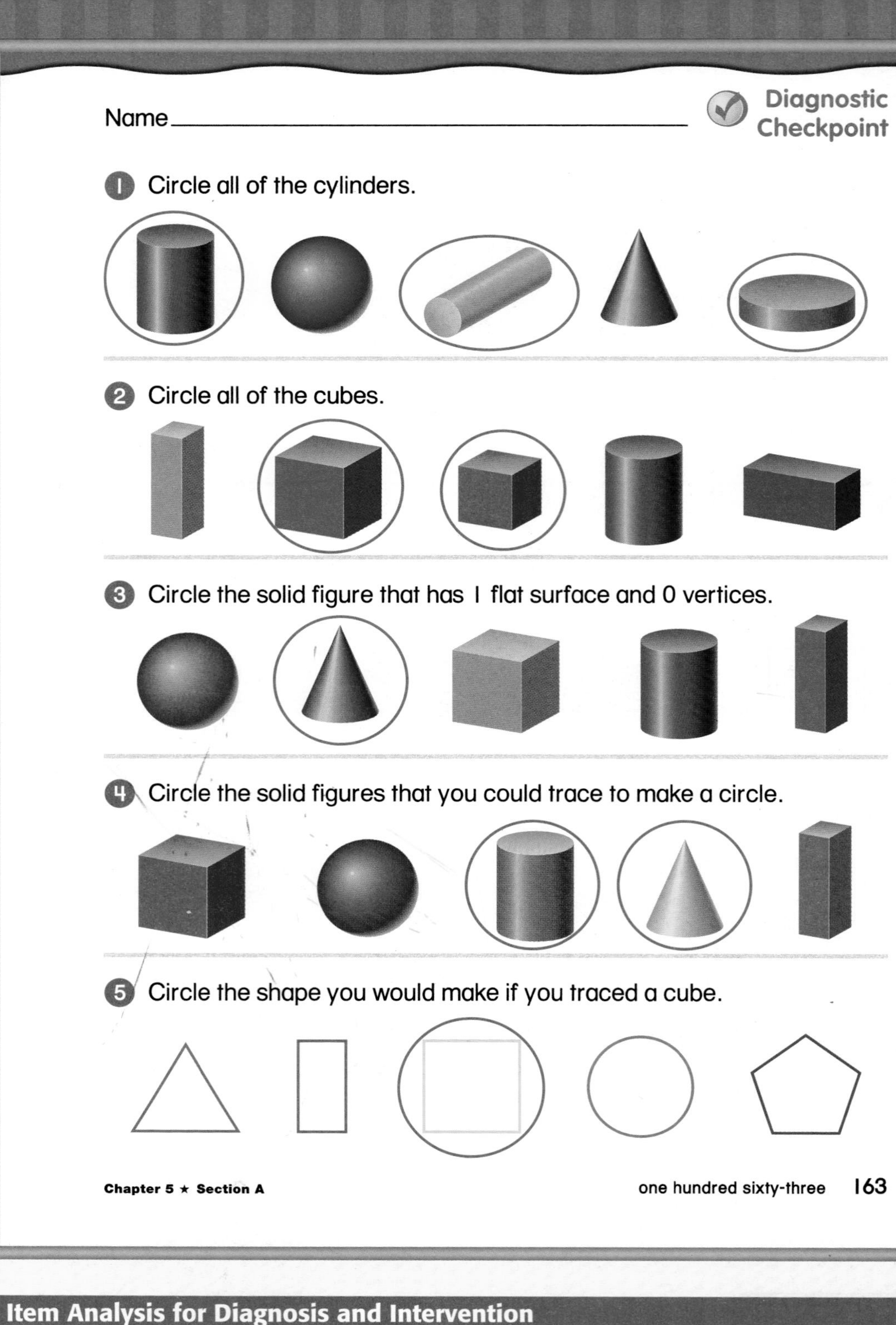

Name______________________

Diagnostic Checkpoint

1. Circle all of the cylinders.

2. Circle all of the cubes.

3. Circle the solid figure that has 1 flat surface and 0 vertices.

4. Circle the solid figures that you could trace to make a circle.

5. Circle the shape you would make if you traced a cube.

Chapter 5 ★ Section A — one hundred sixty-three 163

Item Analysis for Diagnosis and Intervention

Objective	Items	Student Book Pages*	Intervention System
Identify and name standard geometric solids and recognize them in the environment.	1–2	157–158	D45
Count the number of flat surfaces and vertices on geometric solids.	3	159–160	D46
Match a geometric solid to an outline of one of its flat surfaces.	4–5	161–162	D47, D48

*For each lesson, there is a *Reteaching* activity in *Reaching All Learners* and a *Reteaching* master.

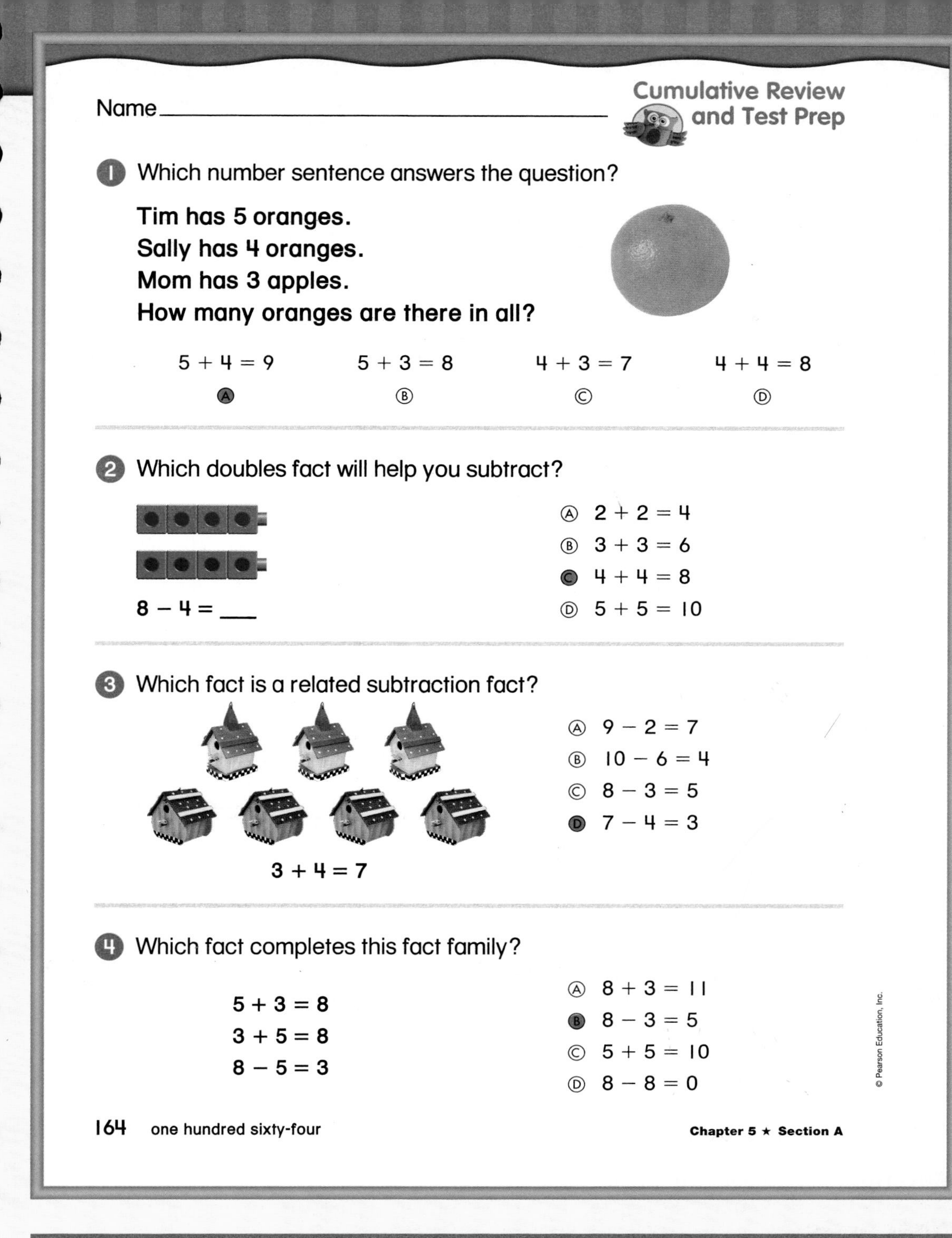

Name ____________________

Cumulative Review and Test Prep

1 Which number sentence answers the question?

Tim has 5 oranges.
Sally has 4 oranges.
Mom has 3 apples.
How many oranges are there in all?

$5 + 4 = 9$	$5 + 3 = 8$	$4 + 3 = 7$	$4 + 4 = 8$
Ⓐ	Ⓑ	Ⓒ	Ⓓ

2 Which doubles fact will help you subtract?

$8 - 4 =$ ___

Ⓐ $2 + 2 = 4$
Ⓑ $3 + 3 = 6$
Ⓒ $4 + 4 = 8$
Ⓓ $5 + 5 = 10$

3 Which fact is a related subtraction fact?

$3 + 4 = 7$

Ⓐ $9 - 2 = 7$
Ⓑ $10 - 6 = 4$
Ⓒ $8 - 3 = 5$
Ⓓ $7 - 4 = 3$

4 Which fact completes this fact family?

$5 + 3 = 8$
$3 + 5 = 8$
$8 - 5 = 3$

Ⓐ $8 + 3 = 11$
Ⓑ $8 - 3 = 5$
Ⓒ $5 + 5 = 10$
Ⓓ $8 - 8 = 0$

Cumulative Review and Test Prep

Purpose Provide children with a review of math concepts. Items appear as they would on a standardized test so children become familiar with that format.

Item Analysis for Diagnosis and Intervention

Objective	Items	Student Book Pages*	Intervention System
Solve problems by identifying unnecessary information and writing number sentences.	1	99–100	E8
Find differences by using doubles facts.	2	129–130	E36
Write related addition and subtraction facts.	3	137–138	B27
Write the addition and subtraction sentences that make up a fact family.	4	139–140	B28

*For each lesson, there is a *Reteaching* activity in *Reaching All Learners* and a *Reteaching* master.

Identifying Plane Shapes

5-4

Lesson Organizer

Quick Lesson Overview 

Objective Identify and name standard plane shapes and recognize them in the environment.

Math Understanding Many every-day objects are close approximations of standard plane shapes.

Vocabulary Plane shape, triangle, rectangle, circle, square

Professional Development Note

Research Base

First grade children are beginning to make a transition from identifying a square as a square "just because it looks like one," and identifying it as a square because it has the properties of a square: four sides, equal sides, four square corners. They are making a similar transition with other simple geometric shapes (van Hiele, 1986). This section explicitly focuses on the properties of the common and most basic plane shapes.

NCTM Standards

- Geometry
- Number and Operations

(For a complete correlation to the NCTM Standards and Grades Pre-K through 2 Expectations, see Pages 155G and 155H.)

Getting Started

Spiral Review

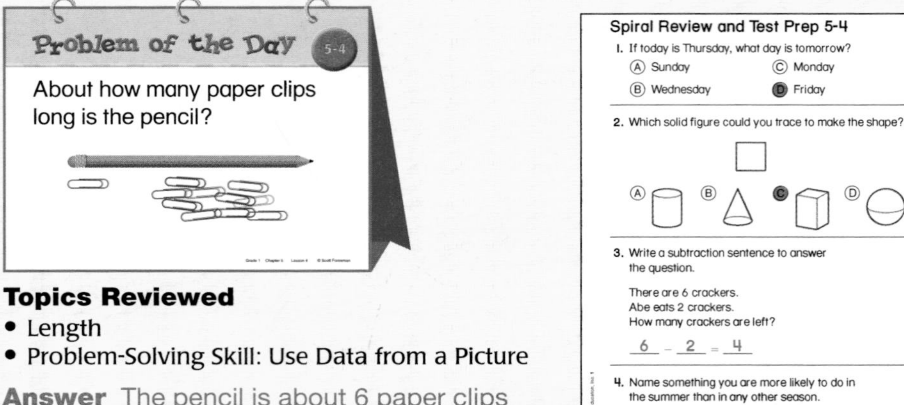

Problem of the Day 5-4

About how many paper clips long is the pencil?

Spiral Review and Test Prep 5-4

1. If today is Thursday, what day is tomorrow?
   (A) Sunday (C) Monday
   (B) Wednesday (D) Friday
2. Which solid figure could you trace to make the shape?
   (A) (B) (C) (D)
3. Write a subtraction sentence to answer the question.
   There are 6 crackers.
   Abe eats 2 crackers.
   How many crackers are left?
   6 − 2 = 4
4. Name something you are more likely to do in the summer than in any other season.
   Answers will vary. Sample answers: swim, work in the garden, go to the beach

Use with Lesson 5-4. 51

Topics Reviewed

- Length
- Problem-Solving Skill: Use Data from a Picture

Answer The pencil is about 6 paper clips long. Accept reasonable answers.

Available as a transparency and as a blackline master

Topics Reviewed

1. Yesterday, Today, and Tomorrow **2.** Relating Plane Shapes to Solid Figures **3.** Write a Number Sentence **4.** Months and Seasons

Investigating the Concept

Shape Search

15–20 MIN | **Visual/Spatial** | WHOLE CLASS

Materials Large paper models of standard plane shapes; chart paper

What to Do

- Create a chart with each plane shape listed along the left side of the paper. Leave space beside each shape to record children's responses.
- Present models of a circle, triangle, rectangle, and square. Have children name and describe them. Ask children to find objects in the classroom that have parts that are the same shape as one of the plane shapes. Draw and label children's suggestions.
- Discuss with children that squares are called *special rectangles* because all four straight parts are the same length.

Ongoing Assessment

- **How is a triangle like a square?** *(They both have straight sides and vertices.)*
- **Reasoning How is a square different from a rectangle?** *(All of a square's sides are the same length.)*

Reaching All Learners

Math and Literature

Shape Zoo

10–15 MIN **Visual/Spatial** SMALL GROUP

Materials *Color Zoo* by Lois Ehlert (HarperCollins, 1989); colored-paper shapes; glue

- Read *Color Zoo* to explore plane shapes. Children can identify and compare the hexagons, ovals, triangles, octagons, and other shapes that form the zoo animal on each page.
- Children may wish to use the animals in the book as models for their own shape animals. Provide children with precut paper shapes to use to make the animals.
- Display children's creations in a Classroom Zoo.

Activate Prior Knowledge/Build Background

English Language Learners

Shapes in Objects

10–15 MIN **Visual/Spatial/Linguistic**

Materials Plane Shape Cards (Teaching Tool 16)

- Display a list of the plane shapes (triangle, rectangle, circle, and square). Read each shape name aloud, and invite volunteers to draw the shape next to the name.
- Give a different Plane Shape Card to each pair of children.
- Have children look for objects in the classroom that have the same shape as their pair's card and list the objects they find. If children have difficulty finding objects with their shape, have them draw and label objects that contain the shape.
- Have a child from each pair read aloud their list.

Reteaching

Shapes in the Air

5–10 MIN **Kinesthetic** WHOLE CLASS

Materials Large models of a black-outlined triangle, rectangle, circle, and square

- Review the names of the shapes as you point to each model. Ask children to draw each shape in the air as you trace the border on the model.
- Next, do an "air drawing" of a shape, and ask children to identify the shape that you have drawn. Invite children to come to the front of the class to do "air drawings" and call on classmates to guess the shapes.

Math and Art

Shape Sculpture

15–20 MIN **Visual/Spatial/Kinesthetic** INDIVIDUAL

Materials Construction paper; clay; toothpicks

- Give each child a triangle, rectangle, and a square made from construction paper.
- Invite children to make a copy of each shape by connecting small balls of clay with toothpicks. Demonstrate as needed.
- When all shapes are completed, have children identify and label them.

Objective Identify and name standard plane shapes and recognize them in the environment.

1 Warm Up

Activate Prior Knowledge Review flat surfaces of geometric solids. On the board, draw a plane shape and have children name all of the solid figures with flat surfaces of the same shape.

2 Teach

Learn!

Direct attention to the plane shapes in the picture and have children name them. *(Triangle, rectangle, circle, square)* Explain that a square is a special rectangle because each of its sides is the same length. Have children compare pairs of shapes.

Ongoing Assessment

Talk About It

- **How is a circle different from the other plane shapes?** *(Circles have no sides and no vertices.)*
- **Which two plane shapes look the most similar?** *(Square and rectangle)*

If children do not identify different-sized rectangles as the same shape,

then explain that shapes can be different sizes and still be the same shape.

Check

Error Intervention

If children do not recognize a rotated shape,

then have them slowly turn their papers to move the shape into a more familiar orientation. *(Also see* Reteaching, *Page 165B.)*

Think About It This shape is a parallelogram. A parallelogram is a four-sided plane figure whose opposite sides are parallel and equal. Ask: **How is this shape (a parallelogram) like a rectangle? How is it different?**

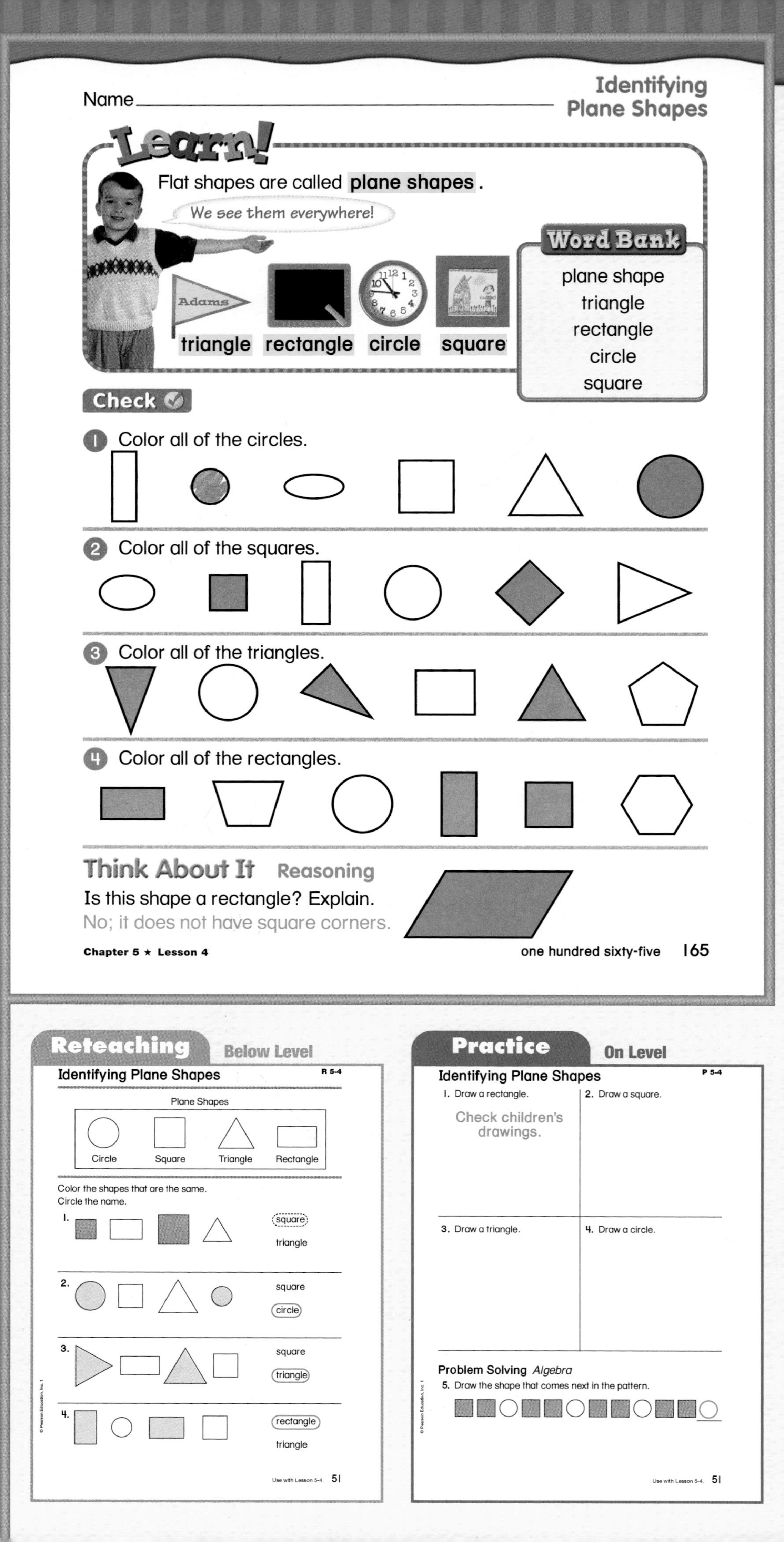

Name ____________________

Identifying Plane Shapes

Learn!

Flat shapes are called **plane shapes**.

We see them everywhere!

triangle rectangle circle square

Word Bank
plane shape
triangle
rectangle
circle
square

Check

1. Color all of the circles.
2. Color all of the squares.
3. Color all of the triangles.
4. Color all of the rectangles.

Think About It Reasoning
Is this shape a rectangle? Explain.
No; it does not have square corners.

Chapter 5 ★ Lesson 4 one hundred sixty-five 165

Reteaching Below Level

Identifying Plane Shapes R 5-4

Plane Shapes

Circle Square Triangle Rectangle

Color the shapes that are the same.
Circle the name.

1. square / triangle (square)
2. square / circle (circle)
3. square / triangle (triangle)
4. rectangle / triangle (rectangle)

Use with Lesson 5-4. 51

Practice On Level

Identifying Plane Shapes P 5-4

1. Draw a rectangle. Check children's drawings.
2. Draw a square.
3. Draw a triangle.
4. Draw a circle.

Problem Solving *Algebra*
5. Draw the shape that comes next in the pattern.

Use with Lesson 5-4. 51

Practice

5 Draw a square.

Check children's drawings.

6 Draw a circle.

Check children's drawings.

7 Draw a rectangle.

Check children's drawings.

8 Draw a triangle.

Check children's drawings.

Problem Solving Algebra

Draw the shape that comes next in the pattern.

9 ▲ ● ● ▲ ● ● ▲ ● ● ▲ red

Home Connection Your child learned to recognize and draw plane shapes. **Home Activity** Take your child on a shapes hunt to look for plane shapes in your home or neighborhood.

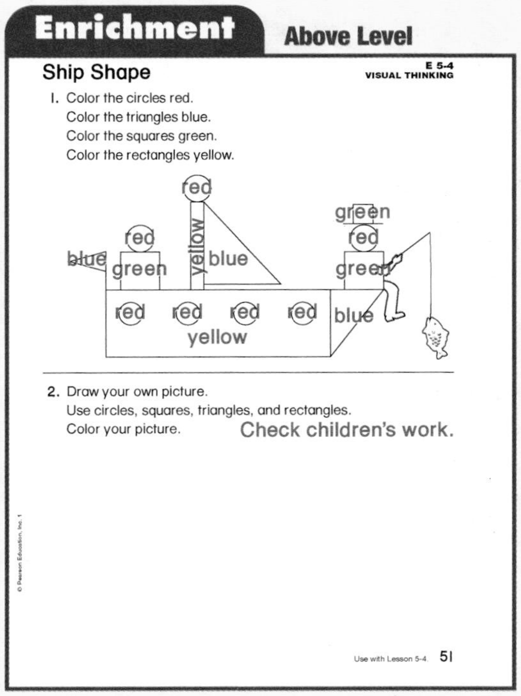

Enrichment Above Level

Ship Shape E 5-4 VISUAL THINKING

1. Color the circles red.
Color the triangles blue.
Color the squares green.
Color the rectangles yellow.

red red green red blue green yellow blue green red red red red blue yellow

2. Draw your own picture.
Use circles, squares, triangles, and rectangles.
Color your picture. Check children's work.

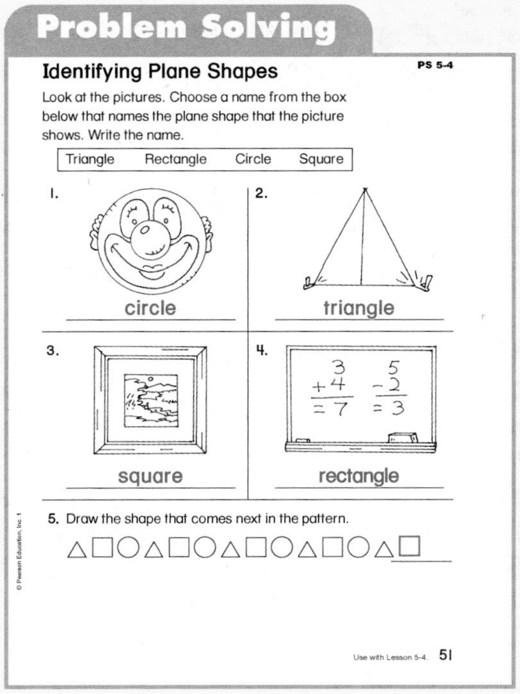

Problem Solving

Identifying Plane Shapes PS 5-4

Look at the pictures. Choose a name from the box below that names the plane shape that the picture shows. Write the name.

Triangle	Rectangle	Circle	Square

1. circle
2. triangle
3. square
4. rectangle ($3 + 4 = 7$, $5 - 2 = 3$)

5. Draw the shape that comes next in the pattern.
△□○△□○△□○△□○△ □

3 Practice

Remind children that shapes can come in many different sizes.

Reading Assist: Vocabulary Have children label objects around the room according to their shapes.

Leveled Practice

Below Level Use pictures of plane shapes to complete all exercises.

On Level Complete all exercises as written.

Above Level Write the names of the shapes in the pattern in Exercise 9.

Early Finishers Have children look through magazines for pictures of objects that match the shapes in this lesson. Invite children to cut out the pictures and make a poster of plane shapes.

4 Assess

Journal Idea Have children fold their papers to make four sections and write the name of a plane shape in each section. Beneath each name, have children draw the shape in different sizes and positions.

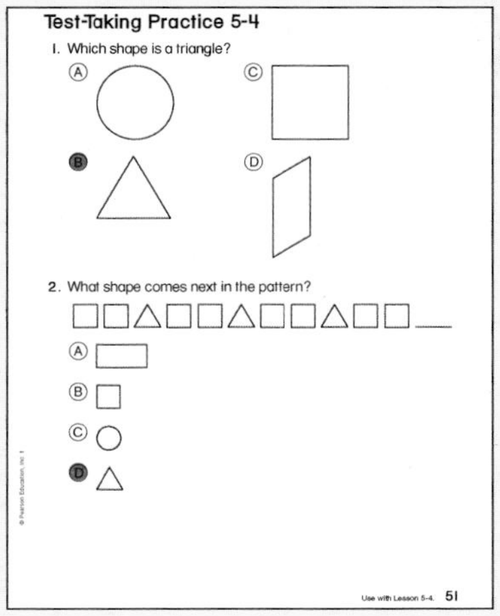

Test-Taking Practice 5-4

1. Which shape is a triangle?
Ⓐ ○ Ⓑ △ Ⓒ □ Ⓓ ▱

2. What shape comes next in the pattern?
□□△□□△□□△□□ ___
Ⓐ ▭ Ⓑ □ Ⓒ ○ Ⓓ △

Available as a transparency

5-5 Properties of Plane Shapes

Lesson Organizer

Quick Lesson Overview

Objective Sort plane shapes and identify their properties.

Math Understanding Plane shapes have many properties that make them different from one another.

Vocabulary Side, vertex (vertices)

Professional Development Note

Effective Questioning Techniques To help children think about the difference between the sides of a plane shape and its vertices, ask open-ended questions, such as: **How is a vertex on a square different from a side?** *(The vertex is pointed. The side is long and straight.)*

NCTM Standards

- Geometry
- Number and Operations

(For a complete correlation to the NCTM Standards and Grades Pre-K through 2 Expectations, see Pages 155G and 155H.)

Getting Started

Spiral Review

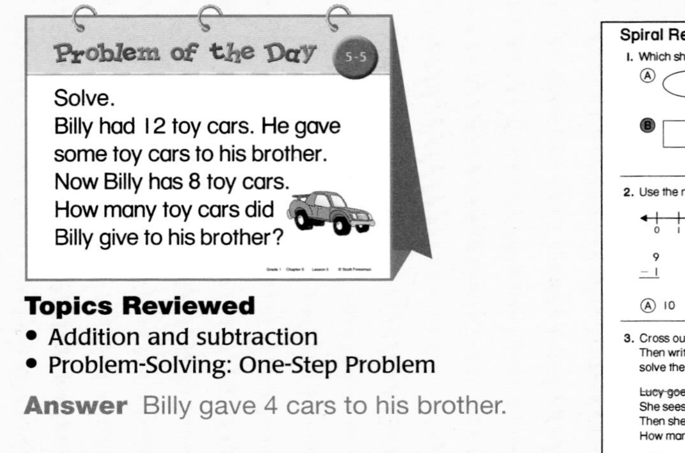

Problem of the Day 5-5

Solve.
Billy had 12 toy cars. He gave some toy cars to his brother.
Now Billy has 8 toy cars.
How many toy cars did Billy give to his brother?

Topics Reviewed

- Addition and subtraction
- Problem-Solving: One-Step Problem

Answer Billy gave 4 cars to his brother.

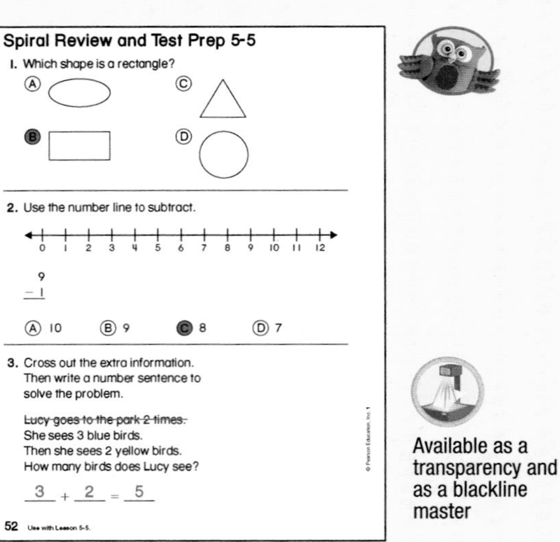

Spiral Review and Test Prep 5-5

1. Which shape is a rectangle?

Ⓐ Ⓑ Ⓒ Ⓓ

2. Use the number line to subtract.

0 1 2 3 4 5 6 7 8 9 10 11 12

9
− 1

Ⓐ 10 Ⓑ 9 Ⓒ 8 Ⓓ 7

3. Cross out the extra information. Then write a number sentence to solve the problem.

~~Lucy goes to the park 2 times.~~
She sees 3 blue birds.
Then she sees 2 yellow birds.
How many birds does Lucy see?

3 + 2 = 5

52 Use with Lesson 5-5.

Available as a transparency and as a blackline master

Topics Reviewed

1. Identifying Plane Shapes
2. Counting Back Using a Number Line
3. Extra Information

Investigating the Concept

Shape Sort

Materials *(per group)* Plane Shape Cards (Teaching Tool 16); More Plane Shape Cards (Teaching Tool 17)

What to Do

- Display the cards and discuss the properties of plane shapes. As children describe each shape, review the meaning of *vertex* and introduce the meaning of *side*.
- Sort the cards into two groups by the rule: *has three sides* and *does not have three sides.* Ask children to figure out how the cards were sorted. Have groups sort plane shape cards in other ways.

straight sides

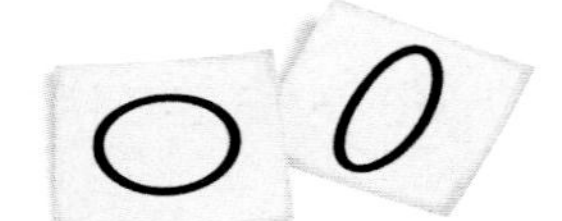

no straight sides

Ongoing Assessment

- **How could you sort the cards so that the circle and the triangle are in the same group?** *(Sample response:* Has four sides *and* does not have four sides*)*
- **Reasoning How could you sort the cards so that only two shapes end up in one of the groups?** *(Sample response:* Has straight sides *and* has no straight sides*)*

Reaching All Learners

Math Vocabulary

Sides and Vertices

5–10 MIN **Linguistic**

Materials *(per child)* Plane Shape Cards (Teaching Tool 16)

- Introduce the words *side* and *vertex* to the children. Draw several plane shapes on the board. Invite children to label the sides and vertices on each of the shapes.
- Pass out a set of cards to each child. Have children work independently to label the sides and vertices of each shape. You may wish to have children write "S" for side and "V" for vertex.

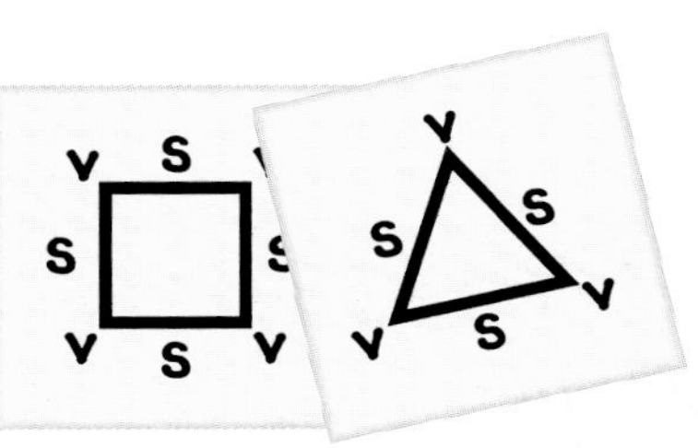

Access Content

English Language Learners

How Did I Sort?

10–15 MIN **Linguistic**

Materials *(per group)* Plane Shape Cards (Teaching Tool 16); More Plane Shape Cards (Teaching Tool 17)

- Review the word *vertex* and introduce the word *side.*
- Demonstrate sorting the cards, saying: **This shape has four sides** or **This shape does not have four sides.** Model determining how the shapes were sorted.
- Invite one child to sort the shapes in another way and ask, "How did I sort these shapes?"

Reteaching

I Do! I Don't!

5–10 MIN **Visual/Spatial**

Materials Plane Shape Cards (Teaching Tool 16); More Plane Shape Cards (Teaching Tool 17)

- Distribute one shape to each child in the group. **I am looking for a shape that has four square corners. Do you have this shape?**
- Children respond with, "I do," or "I don't." Each child in the group who has a shape that you are looking for should share the shape with the class.
- Children can take turns leading the group and saying, "I'm looking for a shape that has …"

Advanced Learners

Sides and Vertices

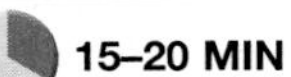

15–20 MIN **Visual/Spatial**

Materials *(per pair)* Plane Shape Cards (Teaching Tool 16); More Plane Shape Cards (Teaching Tool 17); construction paper; crayons

- Have children divide the shapes into groups based on the numbers of sides and vertices. Invite children to glue each group to a different piece of paper. Each page should be given a title based on the number of sides and vertices. Children may wish to color the shapes or otherwise decorate the page.
- Then have children bind the pages together in a shape book.

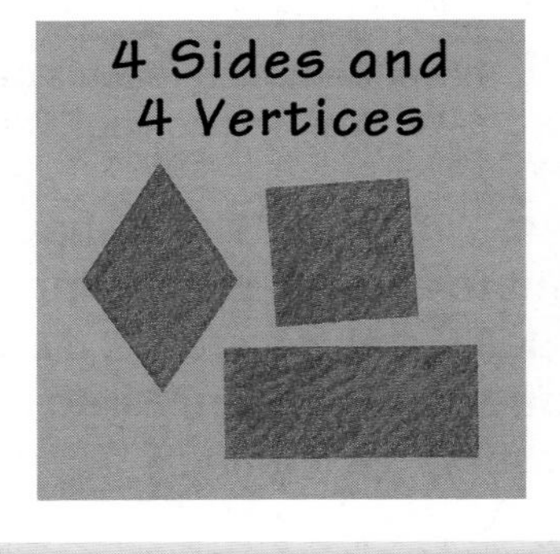

Objective Sort plane shapes and identify their properties.

1 Warm Up

Activate Prior Knowledge Review plane shapes. Think of a plane shape. Invite children to guess your shape by asking questions that require a *Yes* or *No* answer. Continue playing until children guess your shape.

2 Teach

Learn!

Direct attention to the goldfish sorting shapes. Ask children to explain why the square is in the first group. *(It has straight sides and vertices.)* Then ask children to explain why the circle is in the second group. *(It does not have straight sides or vertices. Instead, it has curves.)*

Ongoing Assessment

Talk About It

- **Can you find a shape with a different number of vertices than straight sides?** *(No; each shape with vertices has the same number of straight sides.)*
- **Can you think of another way to sort the shapes?** *(Sample responses: Does it have more than three vertices? Is it curved?)*

If children are confused about the sorting rule,

then focus on the attributes of one shape. **Do other shapes in the group have the same attributes?**

Error Intervention

If children have trouble counting the sides,

then have them mark each side as it is counted. *(Also see* Reteaching, *Page 167B.)*

Think About It Draw shapes on the board. Point to a circle. **What can we say about this circle?** *(Sample response: It is round.)* **Can you change that sentence into a sorting question?** *(Is it round?)*

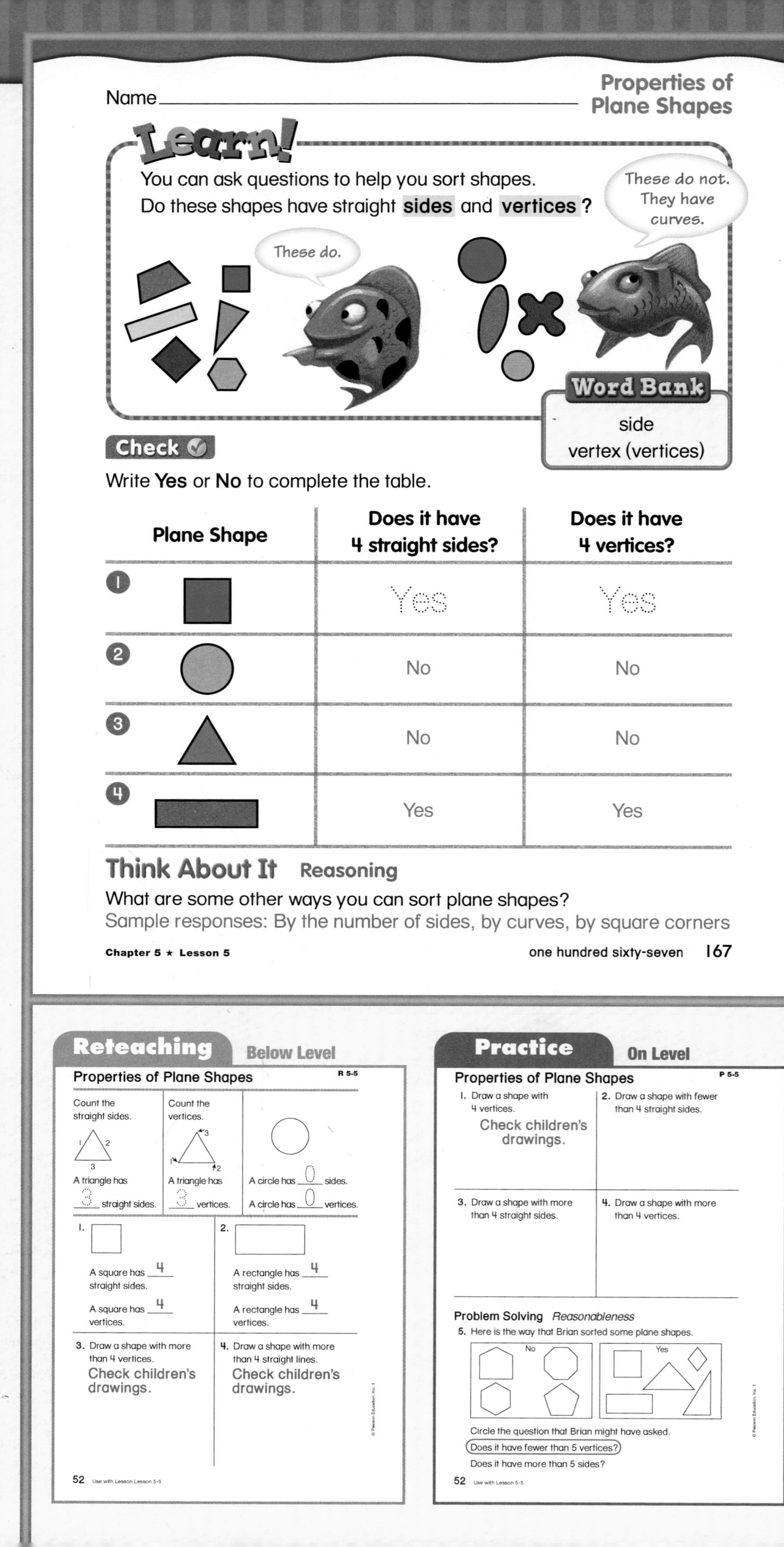

Name ____________________

Properties of Plane Shapes

Learn!

You can ask questions to help you sort shapes.
Do these shapes have straight **sides** and **vertices**?

Word Bank
side
vertex (vertices)

Check

Write **Yes** or **No** to complete the table.

	Plane Shape	Does it have 4 straight sides?	Does it have 4 vertices?
1	square	Yes	Yes
2	circle	No	No
3	triangle	No	No
4	rectangle	Yes	Yes

Think About It Reasoning

What are some other ways you can sort plane shapes?
Sample responses: By the number of sides, by curves, by square corners

Chapter 5 ★ Lesson 5 one hundred sixty-seven 167

Reteaching Below Level

Properties of Plane Shapes R 5-5

Count the straight sides. A triangle has 3 straight sides.

Count the vertices. A triangle has 3 vertices.

A circle has 0 sides. A circle has 0 vertices.

1. A square has 4 straight sides. A square has 4 vertices.

2. A rectangle has 4 straight sides. A rectangle has 4 vertices.

3. Draw a shape with more than 4 vertices. Check children's drawings.

4. Draw a shape with more than 4 straight lines. Check children's drawings.

52 Use with Lesson Lesson 5-5

Practice On Level

Properties of Plane Shapes P 5-5

1. Draw a shape with 4 vertices. Check children's drawings.

2. Draw a shape with fewer than 4 straight sides.

3. Draw a shape with more than 4 straight sides.

4. Draw a shape with more than 4 vertices.

Problem Solving *Reasonableness*

5. Here is the way that Brian sorted some plane shapes.

No Yes

Circle the question that Brian might have asked.

(Does it have fewer than 5 vertices?)

Does it have more than 5 sides?

52 Use with Lesson 5-5

Practice

5. Draw a shape with 3 vertices.

   Check children's drawings.

6. Draw a shape with more than 4 straight sides.

   Check children's drawings.

7. Draw a shape with fewer than 5 straight sides.

   Check children's drawings.

8. Draw a shape with 5 vertices.

   Check children's drawings.

Problem Solving Reasonableness

Here is the way that Sarah sorted some plane shapes.

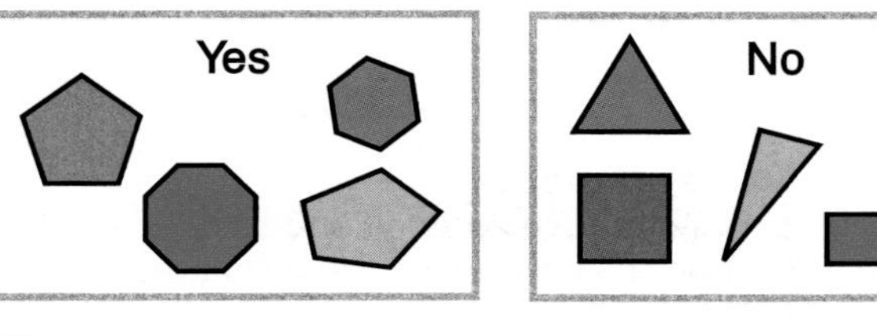

9. Circle the question that Sarah might have asked.

   (Does it have more than 4 vertices?) — circled

   Does it have fewer than 4 straight sides?

Home Connection Your child identified plane shapes and sorted them by the number of vertices and straight sides. **Home Activity** Cut out some shapes for your child to sort into groups. Then talk about the sorting rule.

3 Practice

Point out to children that Exercises 5–8 may have a variety of answers.

Reading Assist: Compare and Contrast To help children sort, compare the properties of two shapes at a time. Hold up a triangle and a circle. **Does the circle have vertices?** *(No)* **the triangle?** *(Yes)* **Does the circle have straight sides?** *(No)* **the triangle?** *(Yes)*

Leveled Practice

Below Level Sort Plane Shape cards (Teaching Tool 16) to complete all exercises.

On Level Complete all exercises as written.

Above Level For Exercises 1–4, write a new question that has the same answers.

Early Finishers One child describes a shape by naming its properties, and a partner tries to identify the shape.

4 Assess

Journal Idea Have children write a riddle, such as: **I have three sides and three vertices. What am I?** Invite partners to solve each other's riddle.

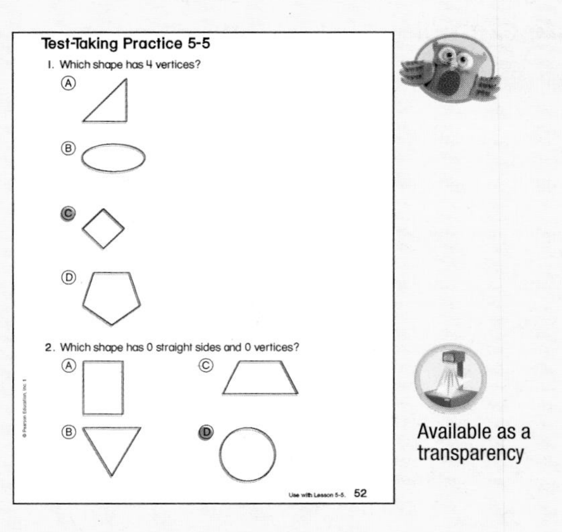

Test-Taking Practice 5-5

1. Which shape has 4 vertices?

   Ⓐ Ⓑ Ⓒ Ⓓ

2. Which shape has 0 straight sides and 0 vertices?

   Ⓐ Ⓑ Ⓒ Ⓓ

Use with Lesson 5-5. 52

Available as a transparency

Enrichment Above Level

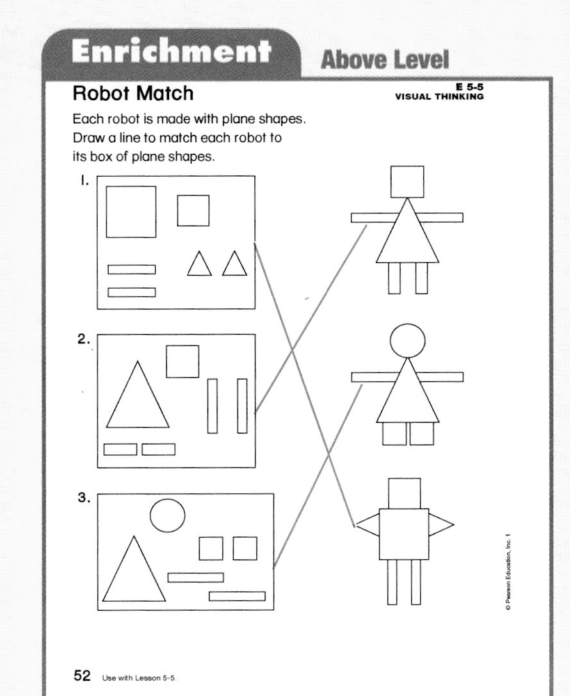

Robot Match — E 5-5 VISUAL THINKING

Each robot is made with plane shapes. Draw a line to match each robot to its box of plane shapes.

1.
2.
3.

52 Use with Lesson 5-5.

Problem Solving

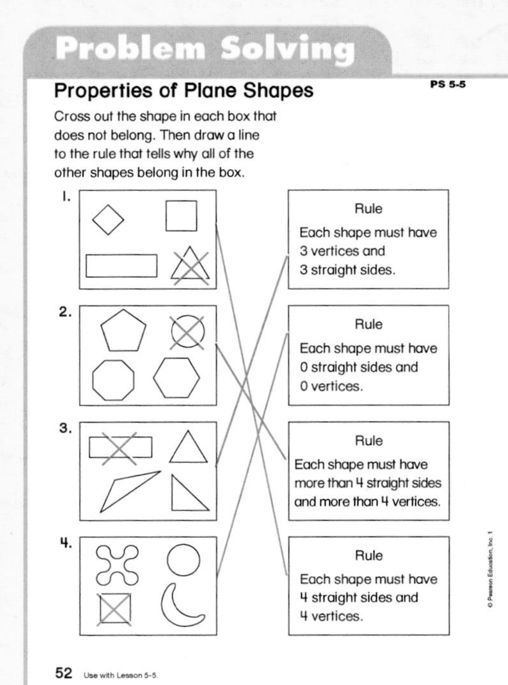

Properties of Plane Shapes — PS 5-5

Cross out the shape in each box that does not belong. Then draw a line to the rule that tells why all of the other shapes belong in the box.

1.
2.
3.
4.

Rule: Each shape must have 3 vertices and 3 straight sides.

Rule: Each shape must have 0 straight sides and 0 vertices.

Rule: Each shape must have more than 4 straight sides and more than 4 vertices.

Rule: Each shape must have 4 straight sides and 4 vertices.

52 Use with Lesson 5-5.

5-6 Same Size and Same Shape

Lesson Organizer

Quick Lesson Overview

Objective Identify and create figures that are the same size and the same shape.

Math Understanding Two shapes can have the same shape and the same size even if they do not share the same orientation.

Vocabulary Same size, same shape

Math Monster Videos Use Episode 15: *Area* with or anytime after Lesson 5-6.

Professional Development Note

Math Background Two shapes are congruent if they fit exactly on top of one other. The concept of congruence is a prerequisite for the concept of symmetry. If two shapes are different in size, but are still the same shape, they are examples of similarity.

NCTM Standards

- Geometry
- Number and Operations

(For a complete correlation to the NCTM Standards and Grades Pre-K through 2 Expectations, see Pages 155G and 155H.)

Getting Started

Spiral Review

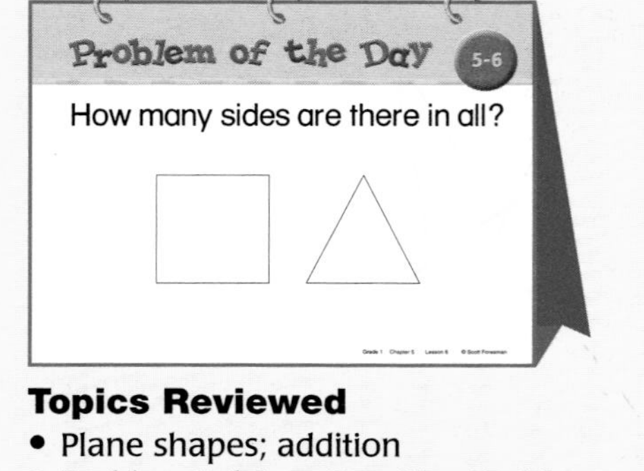

Topics Reviewed

- Plane shapes; addition
- Problem-Solving: One-Step Problem

Answer There are 3 + 4, or 7 sides in all.

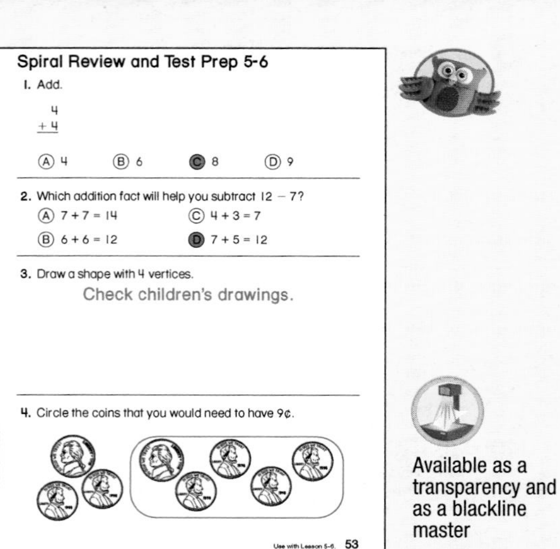

Spiral Review and Test Prep 5-6

1. Add.

$$\begin{array}{r} 4 \\ +4 \end{array}$$

Ⓐ 4 Ⓑ 6 Ⓒ 8 Ⓓ 9

2. Which addition fact will help you subtract 12 − 7?

Ⓐ 7 + 7 = 14 Ⓒ 4 + 3 = 7
Ⓑ 6 + 6 = 12 Ⓓ 7 + 5 = 12

3. Draw a shape with 4 vertices.

Check children's drawings.

4. Circle the coins that you would need to have 9¢.

Use with Lesson 5-6. 53

Available as a transparency and as a blackline master

Topics Reviewed
1. Doubles **2.** Using Addition Facts to Subtract **3.** Properties of Plane Shapes **4.** Dime

Investigating the Concept

Matching Shapes

Materials Large paper models of circles, triangles, squares, and other rectangles of the same and different sizes

What to Do

- Explain that in order for two shapes to *match,* they must be the same shape *and* the same size.
- Hold up two different-sized squares. Have children compare and contrast them. Ask children to tell if the squares match. Lead children to conclude that the shapes do not match because they are not the same size.
- Repeat with different pairs of shapes.

Ongoing Assessment

- **How can you tell if two shapes match?** *(Two shapes match if they are the same size and the same shape.)*
- **Reasoning Could a square ever match a circle? Why or why not?** *(No; they are not the same shape.)*

Reaching All Learners

Oral Language in Math

Understanding *Size* and *Shape*

5–10 MIN **Auditory/Linguistic** WHOLE CLASS

Materials Large and small circles, triangles, squares, and other rectangles cut from tagboard

- Hold up two shapes that are either the same shape or the same size. As you do, children should say either, "They are the same shape," or "They are the same size." Repeat with a variety of pairs.
- Scatter the shapes on a table or the floor. **Sort these shapes by size.** Invite children to sort the shapes by size. Scatter the shapes again. **Sort these shapes by shape.** Invite children to sort the shapes by shape.

Extend Language

English Language Learners

Matchmakers

5–10 MIN **Linguistic** SMALL GROUP

Materials Large models of circles, triangles, squares and other rectangles of the same and different sizes

- Show children two circles that are the same size. **These shapes match because they are the same shape and size.**
- Hold up a large and a small triangle. **Do these shapes match? The shapes do not match because they are not the same size.** Hold up other shapes. Have children give reasons why the shapes match or do not match.

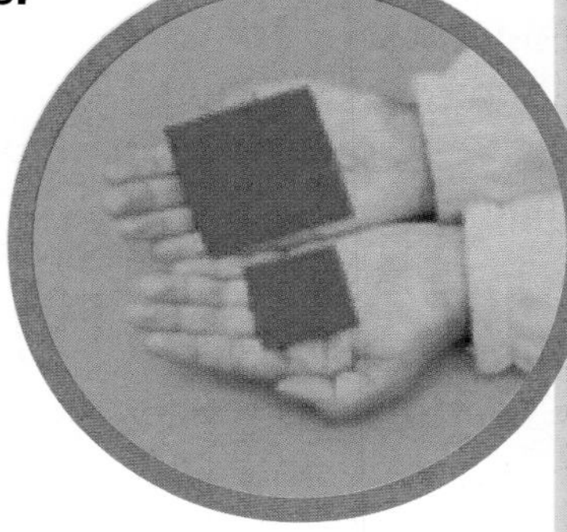

Reteaching

A Good Fit

10–15 MIN **Visual/Spatial** PAIRS

Materials *(per child)* Dot Paper (Teaching Tool 18)

- Have children work in pairs. Invite each child to draw a shape on a piece of dot paper. Have children trade papers.
- Tell children that they will be drawing a shape that is the same size and the same shape as the one drawn by their partner. Before children begin drawing, suggest that they use the dots on the paper as a guide to ensure that their shape matches their partner's shape.
- Have children repeat the activity several times.

Students with Special Needs

Do They Match?

5–10 MIN **Visual/Spatial** SMALL GROUP

Materials Construction paper circles, triangles, squares, and other rectangles of the same and different sizes; chart paper; tape

- Create a two-column chart. Label the left column "Shapes that Match" and the right column "Shapes that Do Not Match."
- Hold up a pair of shapes. Have children decide whether or not the shapes match and tape the pair of shapes in the correct column on the chart. Repeat with other shapes until the chart is complete.

Shapes that Match

Shapes that Do Not Match

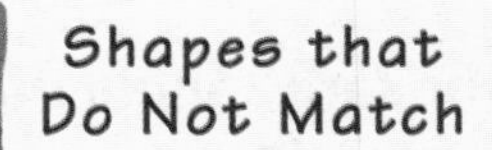

Objective Identify and create figures that are the same size and the same shape.

1 Warm Up

Activate Prior Knowledge Review *same* and *different.* Draw a triangle on the board. Then draw the same triangle, but in a different orientation, such as upside-down. **What is different about the second triangle?** *(It is upside-down.)*

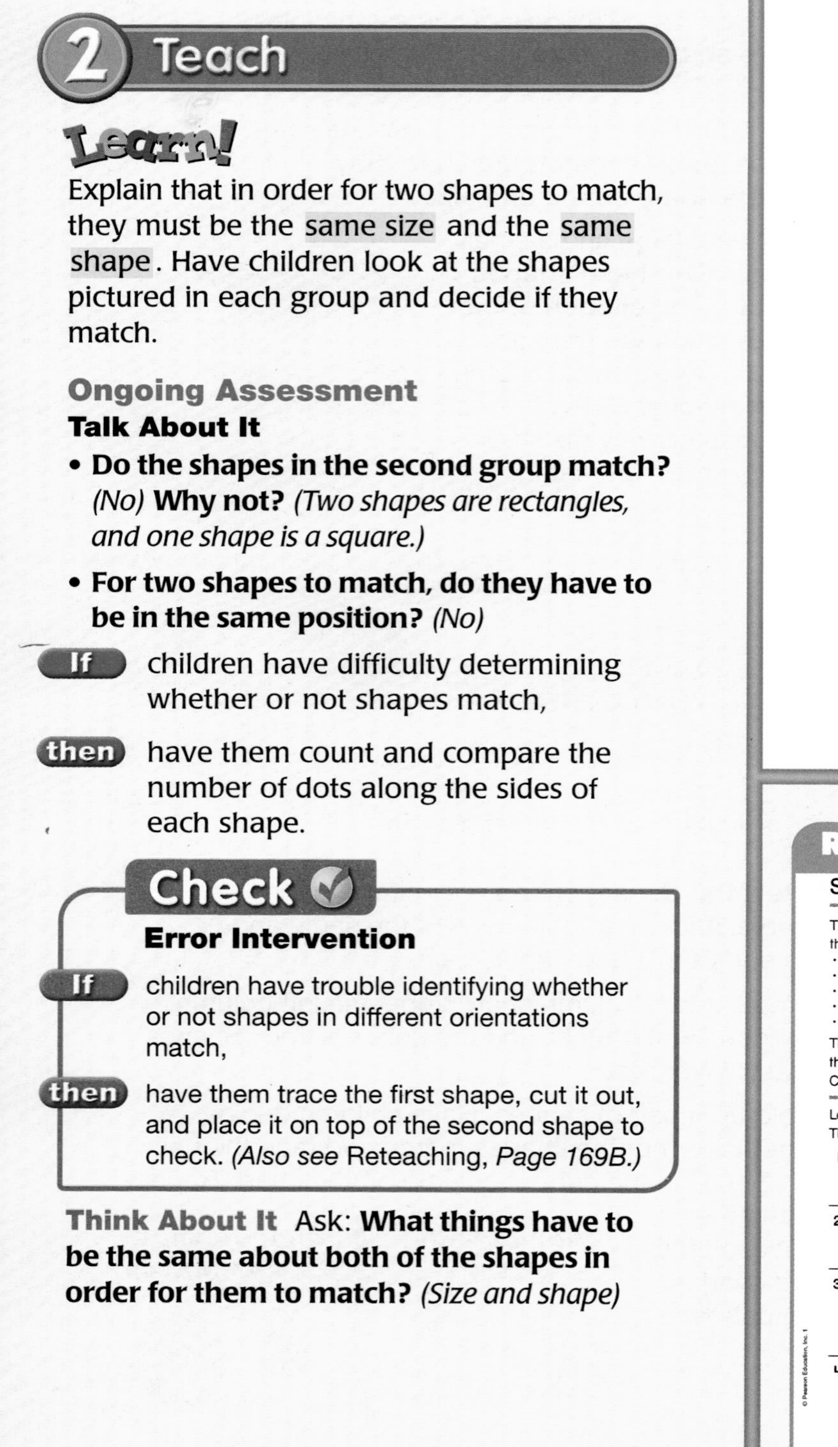

2 Teach

Learn!

Explain that in order for two shapes to match, they must be the same size and the same shape. Have children look at the shapes pictured in each group and decide if they match.

Ongoing Assessment

Talk About It

- **Do the shapes in the second group match?** *(No)* **Why not?** *(Two shapes are rectangles, and one shape is a square.)*
- **For two shapes to match, do they have to be in the same position?** *(No)*

If children have difficulty determining whether or not shapes match,

then have them count and compare the number of dots along the sides of each shape.

Check

Error Intervention

If children have trouble identifying whether or not shapes in different orientations match,

then have them trace the first shape, cut it out, and place it on top of the second shape to check. *(Also see* Reteaching, *Page 169B.)*

Think About It Ask: **What things have to be the same about both of the shapes in order for them to match?** *(Size and shape)*

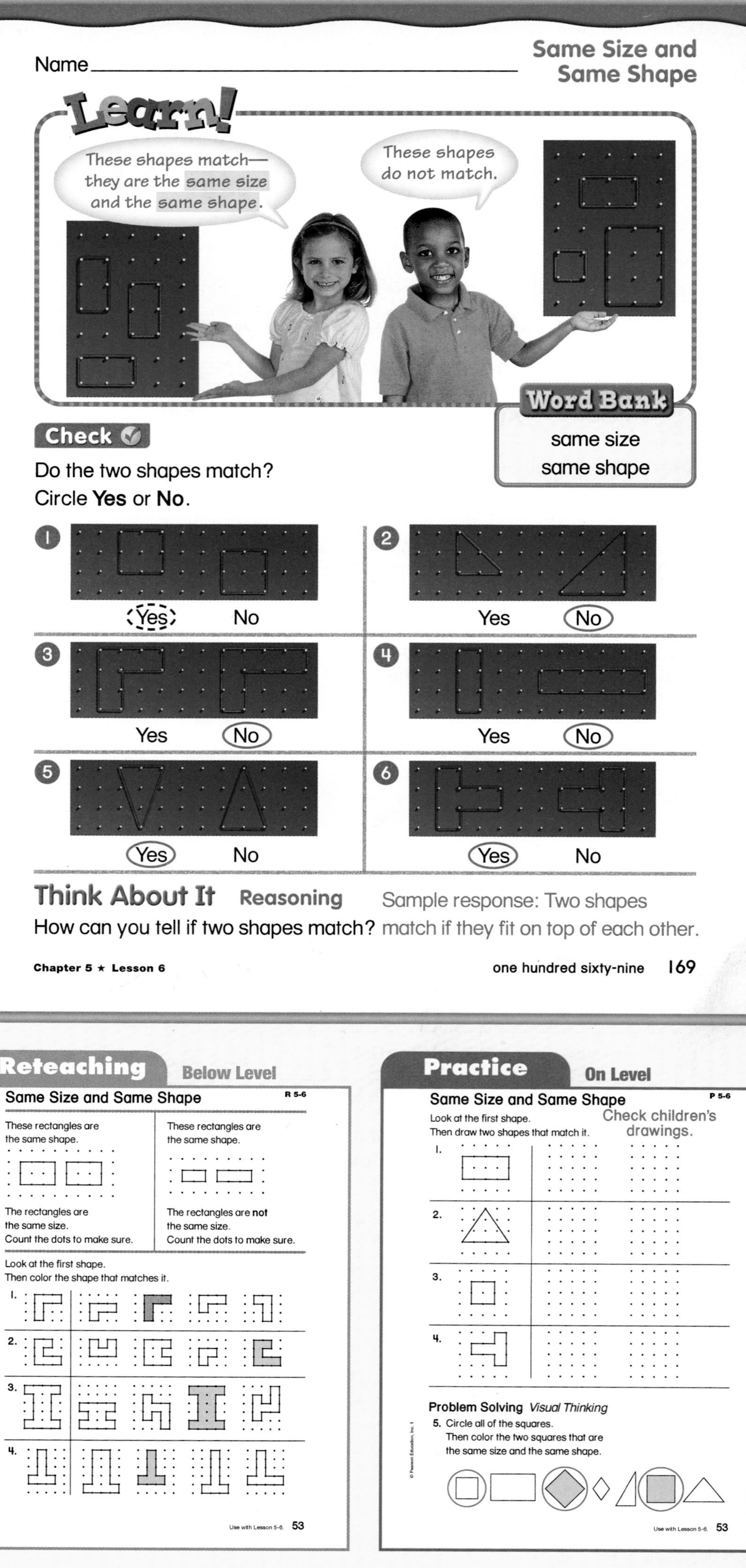

Name ____________________

Same Size and Same Shape

Learn!

Word Bank
same size
same shape

Check

Do the two shapes match?
Circle **Yes** or **No**.

1. Yes No
2. Yes No
3. Yes No
4. Yes No
5. Yes No
6. Yes No

Think About It Reasoning
How can you tell if two shapes match? Sample response: Two shapes match if they fit on top of each other.

Chapter 5 ★ Lesson 6 one hundred sixty-nine 169

Reteaching Below Level

Same Size and Same Shape R 5-6

These rectangles are the same shape. The rectangles are the same size. Count the dots to make sure.

These rectangles are the same shape. The rectangles are **not** the same size. Count the dots to make sure.

Look at the first shape.
Then color the shape that matches it.

1.
2.
3.
4.

Use with Lesson 5-6. 53

Practice On Level

Same Size and Same Shape P 5-6

Look at the first shape.
Then draw two shapes that match it. Check children's drawings.

1.
2.
3.
4.

Problem Solving *Visual Thinking*

5. Circle all of the squares.
Then color the two squares that are the same size and the same shape.

Use with Lesson 5-6. 53

Practice

Look at the first shape.
Then draw two shapes that match it.

7 Check children's drawings.

8 Check children's drawings.

9 Check children's drawings.

10 Check children's drawings.

Problem Solving Visual Thinking

11 Circle all of the triangles.
Then color the two triangles that are the same size and the same shape.

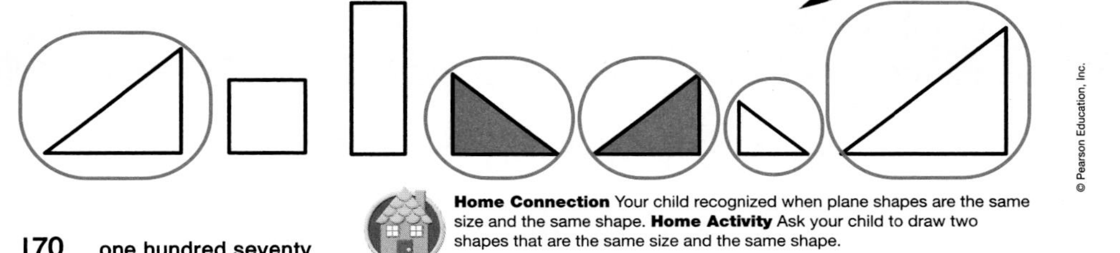

Home Connection Your child recognized when plane shapes are the same size and the same shape. **Home Activity** Ask your child to draw two shapes that are the same size and the same shape.

Enrichment Above Level

E 5-6 REASONING

Matching Shapes

In Exercises 1–2, color the objects with the same shapes red.

1. shade is red

2. shade is red

Color the shapes that match green.

3. shade is green

Use with Lesson 5-6. 53

Problem Solving

PS 5-6

Same Size and Same Shape

Use the shapes in the house to follow the directions.

Blue, Red, Red, Green, Blue, Green, Green, Green

Directions

1. Find the squares that match. Color them blue.
2. Find the triangles that match. Color them red.
3. Find two other shapes that match. Color them green.

Use with Lesson 5-6. 53

3 Practice

After children do Exercise 11, you may wish to introduce the concept of *similarity*. Objects are similar if they are the same shape, but a different size.

Reading Assist: Compare and Contrast Have children compare and contrast the shapes in Exercise 8 and Exercise 10.

Leveled Practice

Below Level Trace and cut out the sample shapes to help draw matching shapes.

On Level Complete all exercises as written.

Above Level Draw a shape in each row that is similar (the same shape, but *not* the same size).

Early Finishers Arrange children in pairs. Have the first child draw a shape, and then have the partner draw a matching shape.

4 Assess

Journal Idea On the board, write "These shapes match." and " These shapes do not match." Have children copy the sentences and then draw pairs of shapes that illustrate each sentence.

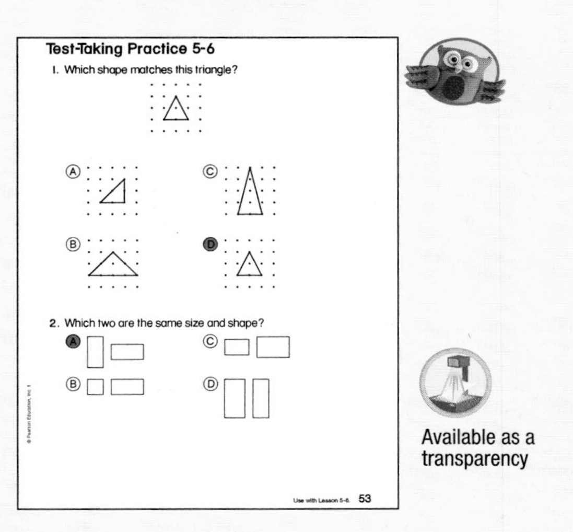
Test-Taking Practice 5-6

1. Which shape matches this triangle?
A B C D

2. Which two are the same size and shape?
A B C D

Use with Lesson 5-6. 53

Available as a transparency

Lesson Organizer

Quick Lesson Overview

Objective Identify objects that show symmetry and draw lines of symmetry.

Math Understanding Symmetric figures have two congruent halves.

Vocabulary Symmetry, line of symmetry

Professional Development Note

Math Background A line of symmetry divides a shape into two parts that are exactly the same size and the same shape (congruent). Some shapes have more than one line of symmetry. For example, a square has four lines of symmetry, and a circle has an infinite number of lines of symmetry.

NCTM Standards

- Geometry
- Number and Operations

(For a complete correlation to the NCTM Standards and Grades Pre-K through 2 Expectations, see Pages 155G and 155H.)

Getting Started

Spiral Review

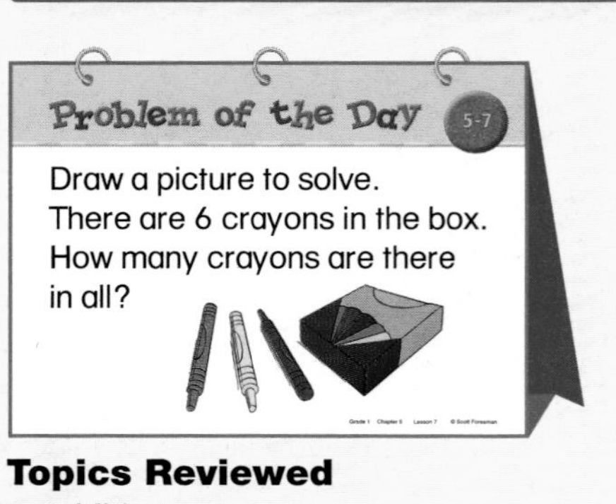

Problem of the Day
5-7
Draw a picture to solve.
There are 6 crayons in the box.
How many crayons are there in all?

Topics Reviewed
- Addition
- Problem-Solving Strategy: Draw a Picture

Answer There are 9 crayons in all. Check children's drawings.

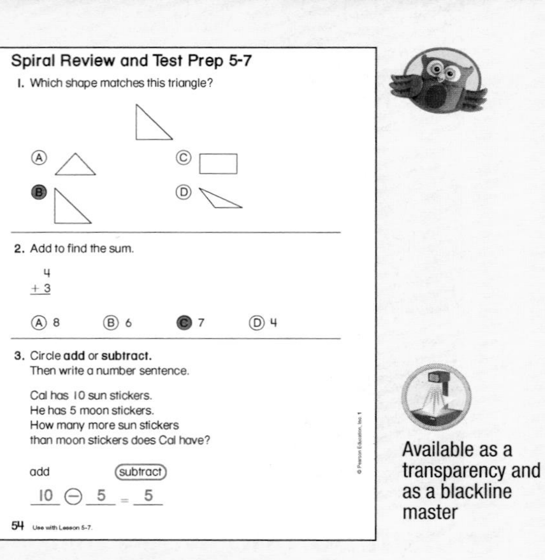
Spiral Review and Test Prep 5-7

1. Which shape matches this triangle?

Ⓐ Ⓑ Ⓒ Ⓓ

2. Add to find the sum.

4
+ 3

Ⓐ 8 Ⓑ 6 Ⓒ 7 Ⓓ 4

3. Circle **add** or **subtract**. Then write a number sentence.

Cal has 10 sun stickers.
He has 5 moon stickers.
How many more sun stickers than moon stickers does Cal have?

add (subtract)

10 − 5 = 5

54 Use with Lesson 5-7

Available as a transparency and as a blackline master

Topics Reviewed
1. Same Size and Same Shape
2. Doubles Plus 1
3. Choose an Operation

Investigating the Concept

Making Matching Parts

Materials *(per child)* Construction paper; scissors

What to Do

- Demonstrate how to make a shape that shows symmetry, such as a leaf, by cutting a folded piece of paper along the nonfolded side. Invite children to make their own symmetric shapes.
- Have children compare the two sides of their shape. Ask children to tell how they are the same. Explain that a shape shows symmetry if it has two matching parts. Tell children that the fold lines on their paper shapes are called lines of symmetry.

Ongoing Assessment

- **How can you tell if a shape shows symmetry?** *(A shape shows symmetry if you can fold it and the two parts match.)*
- **Reasoning Name a shape that has more than one line of symmetry.** *(Sample response: Square)*

Reaching All Learners

Math and Literature

A Story with Symmetry

10–15 MIN **Linguistic**

Materials *Let's Fly a Kite* by Stuart J. Murphy (HarperCollins, 2000)

- Read the book *Let's Fly a Kite* to children.
- Children will learn how a brother and sister find the matching parts of objects as they prepare for an outing at the beach.
- Stop periodically in the reading to have children find the lines of symmetry illustrated in the story.
- As a follow up activity, children may wish to sketch their own symmetrical designs for kites.

Activate Prior Knowledge/Build Background

English Language Learners

Follow the Instructions

10–15 MIN **Auditory/Linguistic**

Materials *(per child)* Construction paper; scissors; posterboard; glue

- Check children's listening skills by asking them to follow these instructions: **Fold your paper in half. At the top, ending at the fold, draw a half circle. Under the circle, draw a half square. Below that, draw a half heart. At the bottom, draw a half leaf.**
- Have children cut out the shapes and draw a line along the fold of each one. Children can paste their shapes on posterboard under the heading "Lines of Symmetry."

Reteaching

Searching for Symmetry

15–20 MIN **Visual/Spatial**

SMALL GROUP

Materials Magazines; scissors; glue; posterboard

- Write the heading "These Things Show Symmetry," at the top of a posterboard. Invite children to cut out pictures of symmetrical objects from magazines, fold them to make a line of symmetry, and paste them on the posterboard.
- Leave space for children to add other examples of symmetry as they encounter them during the week.

Math and Science

Tree Symmetry

15–20 MIN **Visual/Spatial**

WHOLE CLASS

Materials *Autumn Leaves* by Ken Robbins (Scholastic, 1998)

- Show children how symmetry exists in nature by reading *Autumn Leaves.* Give children time to examine the life-size photos of leaves in the book. Children will learn that the leaves of many trees—but not all—show symmetry.
- Weather permitting, take a walk to allow children to search for leaves with and without symmetry.

Objective Identify objects that show symmetry and draw lines of symmetry.

1 Warm Up

Activate Prior Knowledge Review congruence. **How can you find out whether or not two shapes match?** *(Put one shape on top of the other.)* Invite children to look around the classroom for objects that match.

2 Teach

Learn!

Have children compare the two parts of the heart on the page. Lead children to conclude that the two parts are the same shape and the same size. Introduce the word *symmetry*. A shape shows symmetry if it has two matching parts. Explain that the dividing line is called a *line of symmetry*.

Ongoing Assessment

Talk About It

- **Does a square show symmetry? Explain.** *(Yes, because it has two matching parts.)*
- **Can a shape have more than one line of symmetry?** *(Yes)* **Name one shape that does.** *(Sample response: A circle)*

If children have difficulty seeing that both parts of a heart are the same shape and size,

then trace the heart, cut it out, and fold it in half.

Check

Error Intervention

If children have trouble deciding if shapes with horizontal or diagonal lines show symmetry,

then have them rotate the page so that the lines are vertical. *(Also see Reteaching, Page 171B.)*

Think About It Have children fold paper rectangles or index cards diagonally to prove that their answers are correct.

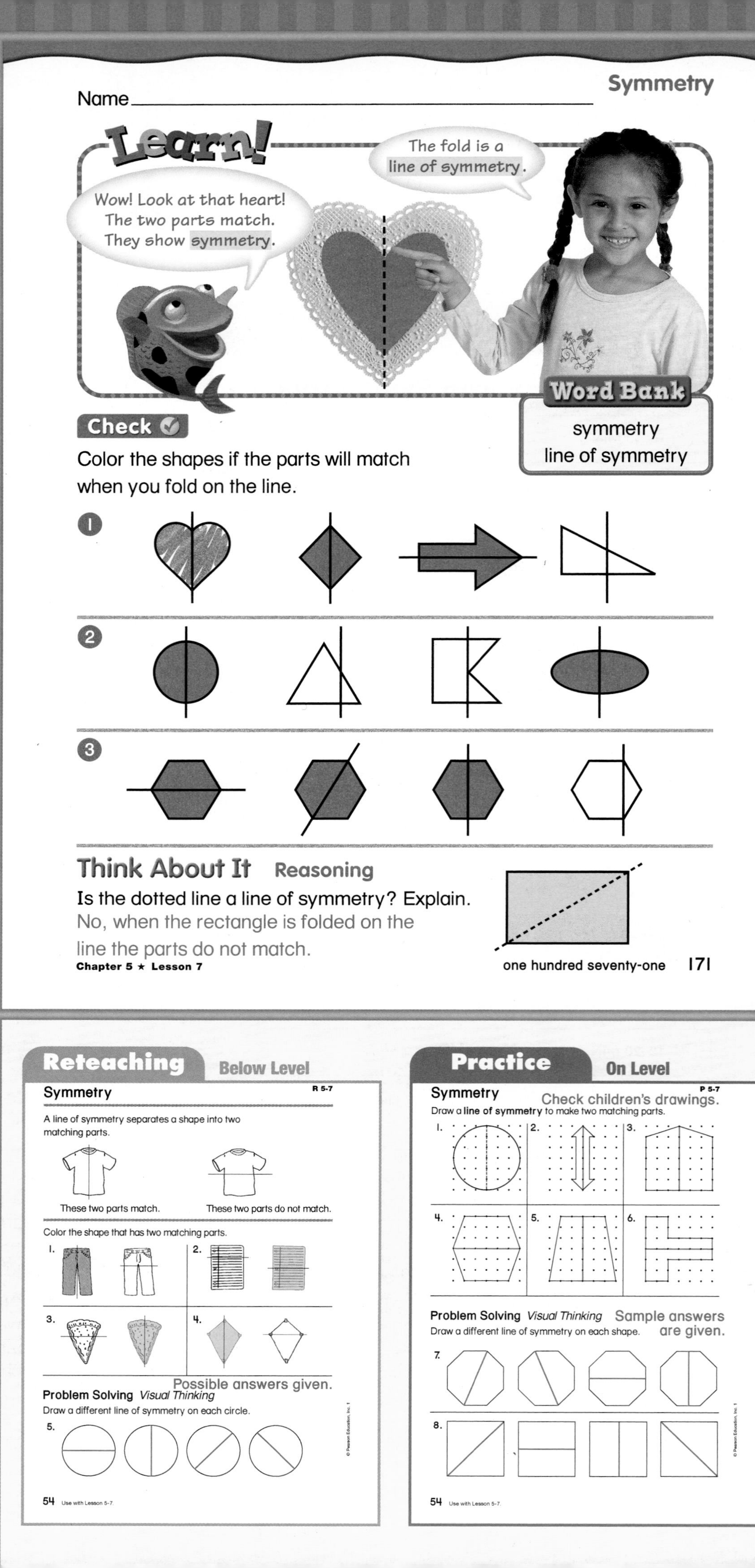

Symmetry

Name ______

Learn!

The fold is a line of symmetry.
Wow! Look at that heart! The two parts match. They show symmetry.

Word Bank
symmetry
line of symmetry

Check

Color the shapes if the parts will match when you fold on the line.

1
2
3

Think About It Reasoning

Is the dotted line a line of symmetry? Explain.
No, when the rectangle is folded on the line the parts do not match.

Chapter 5 ★ Lesson 7 — one hundred seventy-one 171

Reteaching Below Level

Symmetry R 5-7

A line of symmetry separates a shape into two matching parts.

These two parts match. These two parts do not match.

Color the shape that has two matching parts.

1. 2. 3. 4.

Problem Solving *Visual Thinking* Possible answers given.

Draw a different line of symmetry on each circle.

5.

54 Use with Lesson 5-7.

Practice On Level

Symmetry P 5-7

Check children's drawings.

Draw a **line of symmetry** to make two matching parts.

1. 2. 3. 4. 5. 6.

Problem Solving *Visual Thinking* Sample answers are given.

Draw a different line of symmetry on each shape.

7.

8.

54 Use with Lesson 5-7.

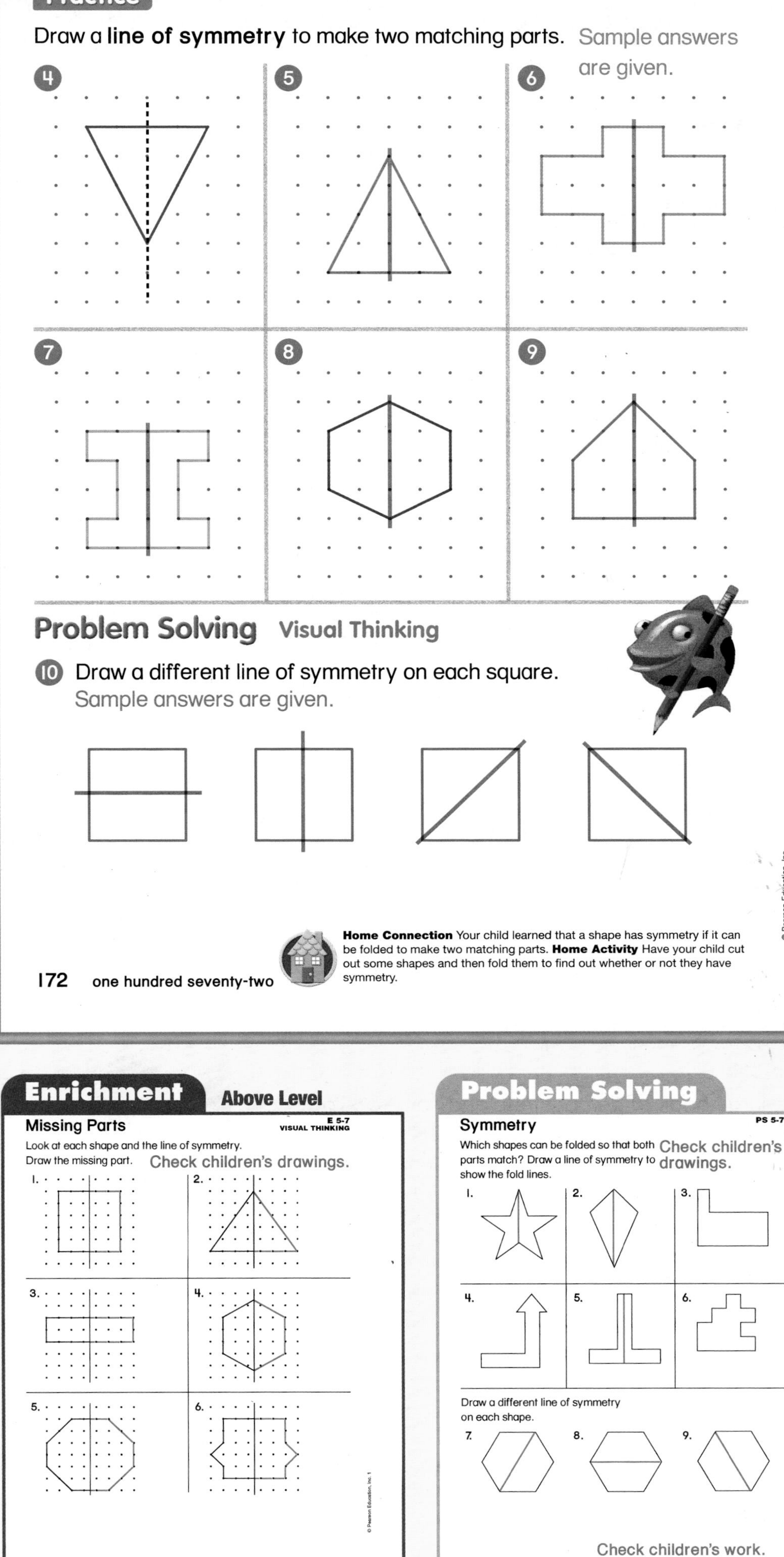

Practice

Draw a **line of symmetry** to make two matching parts. Sample answers are given.

4 5 6

7 8 9

Problem Solving Visual Thinking

10 Draw a different line of symmetry on each square.
Sample answers are given.

Home Connection Your child learned that a shape has symmetry if it can be folded to make two matching parts. **Home Activity** Have your child cut out some shapes and then fold them to find out whether or not they have symmetry.

Enrichment Above Level

Missing Parts E 5-7 VISUAL THINKING

Look at each shape and the line of symmetry.
Draw the missing part. Check children's drawings.

1. 2. 3. 4. 5. 6.

Problem Solving

Symmetry PS 5-7

Which shapes can be folded so that both parts match? Draw a line of symmetry to show the fold lines. Check children's drawings.

1. 2. 3. 4. 5. 6.

Draw a different line of symmetry on each shape.

7. 8. 9.

Check children's work.

3 Practice

For Exercises 4–9, children only need to draw one line of symmetry.

Reading Assist: Compare and Contrast Have children compare the hexagon in Exercise 8 with the pentagon in Exercise 9. **How are they alike? How are they different?**

Leveled Practice

Below Level For Exercises 4–9, trace and cut out the shapes. Fold them to find a line of symmetry.

On Level Complete the exercises as written.

Above Level For Exercises 4–9, draw all of the lines of symmetry on each shape.

Early Finishers Ask children to write the alphabet in capital letters. Then for each letter that shows symmetry, have them draw one line of symmetry with a crayon.

4 Assess

Journal Idea Have children copy the headings "Shows Symmetry" and "Does Not Show Symmetry" onto dot paper. Ask them to draw shapes under each.

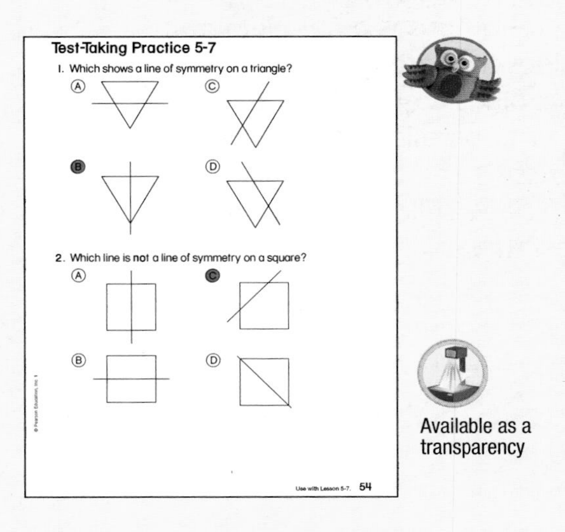

Test-Taking Practice 5-7

1. Which shows a line of symmetry on a triangle?

Ⓐ Ⓑ Ⓒ Ⓓ

2. Which line is not a line of symmetry on a square?

Ⓐ Ⓑ Ⓒ Ⓓ

Available as a transparency

5-8 Slides, Flips, and Turns

Lesson Organizer

Quick Lesson Overview

Objective Perform a slide, flip, or turn on an object and identify the resulting position.

Math Understanding Slides, flips, and turns can be used to change an object's position in space.

Vocabulary Slide, flip, turn

Materials for Student Pages *(per child)* Pattern blocks: 1 triangle, 1 parallelogram, and 1 trapezoid

Professional Development Note

Math Background In this lesson, children use shapes that have not been previously introduced: a parallelogram (diamond) and a trapezoid. A parallelogram is a quadrilateral with two sets of parallel sides. A rhombus is a parallelogram with sides that are all equal in length. A trapezoid is a quadrilateral with one pair of parallel sides. The shape in Exercise 1 is a trapezoid. You may wish to have children compare and contrast these shapes.

NCTM Standards

- Geometry
- Number and Operations

(For a complete correlation to the NCTM Standards and Grades Pre-K through 2 Expectations, see Pages 155G and 155H.)

Getting Started

Spiral Review

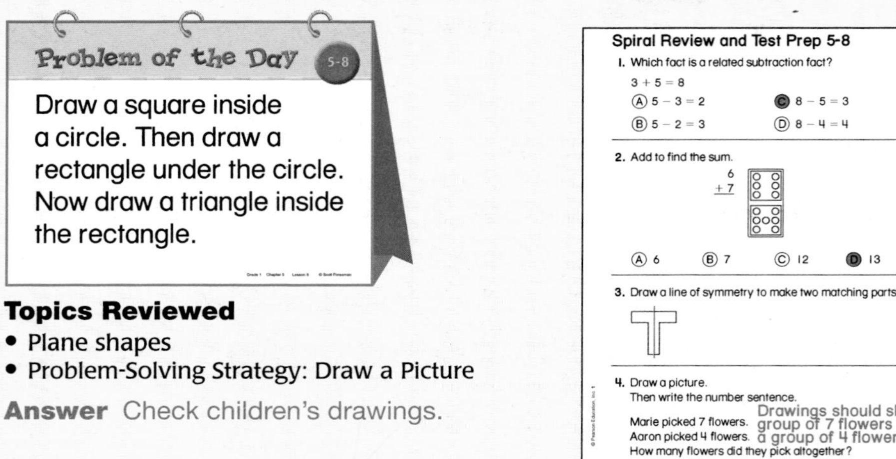

Problem of the Day 5-8

Draw a square inside a circle. Then draw a rectangle under the circle. Now draw a triangle inside the rectangle.

Spiral Review and Test Prep 5-8

1. Which fact is a related subtraction fact?
   3 + 5 = 8
   Ⓐ 5 − 3 = 2 Ⓒ 8 − 5 = 3
   Ⓑ 5 − 2 = 3 Ⓓ 8 − 4 = 4
2. Add to find the sum.
   6
   + 7
   Ⓐ 6 Ⓑ 7 Ⓒ 12 Ⓓ 13
3. Draw a line of symmetry to make two matching parts.
4. Draw a picture.
   Then write the number sentence.
   Marie picked 7 flowers.
   Aaron picked 4 flowers.
   How many flowers did they pick altogether?
   Drawings should show a group of 7 flowers and a group of 4 flowers.
   7 + 4 = 11 flowers or 4 + 7 = 11

55

Topics Reviewed

- Plane shapes
- Problem-Solving Strategy: Draw a Picture

Answer Check children's drawings.

Available as a transparency and as a blackline master

Topics Reviewed

1. Using Related Facts **2.** Vertical Addition
3. Symmetry **4.** Draw a Picture

Investigating the Concept

Slide, Flip, or Turn?

15–20 MIN **Visual/Spatial/Kinesthetic** WHOLE CLASS

Materials Large book; *(per child)* book or magazine

What to Do

- Use the large book to demonstrate and name a slide, a flip, and a turn. Always start in the same position.
- Explain that a slide moves the book to a different location on the surface. A turn rotates the book, and a flip rolls the book over. Be sure children understand that for a slide and a turn, the book stays faceup, but for a flip, it lands facedown.
- Have children use their own books or magazines to copy your motions.

Ongoing Assessment

- **Which movement rolls the book over so it is facedown?** *(Flip)*
- **Reasoning In which ways could you move the book without picking it up?** *(Turn or slide)*

 EC NTL 12 11 10 9

Reaching All Learners

Reading in Math

Reading Directions

10–15 MIN **Linguistic/Kinesthetic**

Materials *(per child)* Nonsymmetrical shape cut from construction paper

- Write these sentences on the board: "Slide it. Flip it. Turn it." Invite children to read the sentences with you. Ask a child to point to each direction and read it.
- Using the same nonsymmetrical shape that each of the children have, show children how to follow each direction.
- Repeat, giving children turns to read and follow the directions. Have the class follow along, each child using his or her own shape.

Access Content

English Language Learners

Put Your Whole Self In

5–10 MIN **Auditory/Kinesthetic**

SMALL GROUP

Materials Books

- To teach the words *slide, flip,* and *turn* invite children to stand and follow your lead as you do each of the following movements.
- Say: **Slide your right foot to the right.** Say: **Flip one hand from palm down to palm up.** Say: **Turn your body to the right.**
- Repeat once more. Then give the slide, flip, turn commands having children follow with books.

Reteaching

Simon Says, "Slide it."

5–10 MIN **Auditory/Kinesthetic**

SMALL GROUP

Materials *(per child)* Pattern block

- Review with children how to slide, flip, and turn the pattern blocks.
- Play Simon Says, using: **slide it, flip it,** and **turn it** as directions. After you give each command, make sure that children have followed each direction using their pattern blocks.
- Practice with a few more rounds, and then give individuals in the group a chance to be "Simon." Tell children that "Simon" has the responsibility of seeing that the directions have been followed.

Math and Art

Make a Pattern

15–20 MIN **Visual/Spatial**

INDIVIDUAL

Materials *(per child)* Pattern blocks; construction paper; crayons

- Show children how they can make designs with repeating patterns by flipping or turning shapes.
- Have children trace a shape and then flip, turn, and trace it. Children can keep repeating the process to make an overall design or a border for a picture. Children can color in the shapes in their design if they wish.
- Display the designs to allow all of the children to appreciate their classmates' artwork.

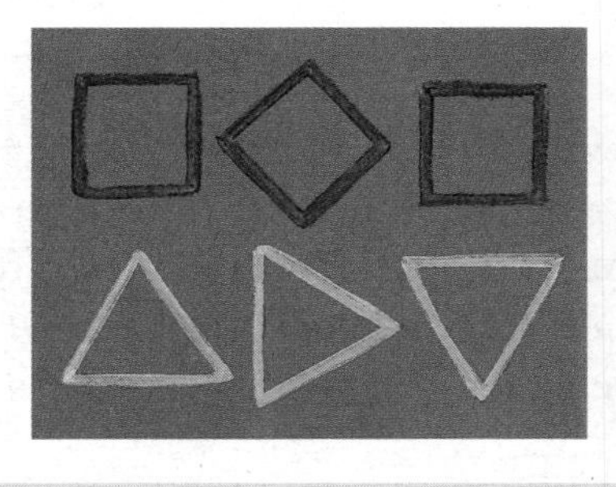

Objective Perform a slide, flip, or turn on an object and identify the resulting position.

1 Warm Up

Activate Prior Knowledge Review vocabulary. Have children give meanings that they may already know for *slide, flip,* and *turn.* Have them use these words in sentences.

2 Teach

Learn!

Point out the different ways the pattern block at the top of the page is being moved. Introduce the terms slide, flip, and turn. Demonstrate them using a classroom object. If you wish, you may introduce more advanced language for each of the terms. A flip is also known as a *reflection,* a slide is also known as a *translation,* and a turn is also known as a *rotation.*

Ongoing Assessment

Talk About It

- **How is a flip different from a turn?** *(Sample response: A turn can be made without picking up an object.)*
- **Who can make their hands show a slide? a flip? a turn?** *(Children should slide, flip, and turn their hands.)*

If children have difficulty demonstrating slides, flips, and turns with their hands,

then have them use classroom objects.

Check

Error Intervention

If children pick up pattern blocks from the surface of the page to do a slide or a turn,

then demonstrate how to slide and turn objects without picking them up. *(Also see* Reteaching, *Page 173B.)*

Think About It Ask children to flip their papers. Then ask them to turn their papers. **How is a flip different from a turn?** *(A flip lands the paper facedown. A turn keeps the same side up.)*

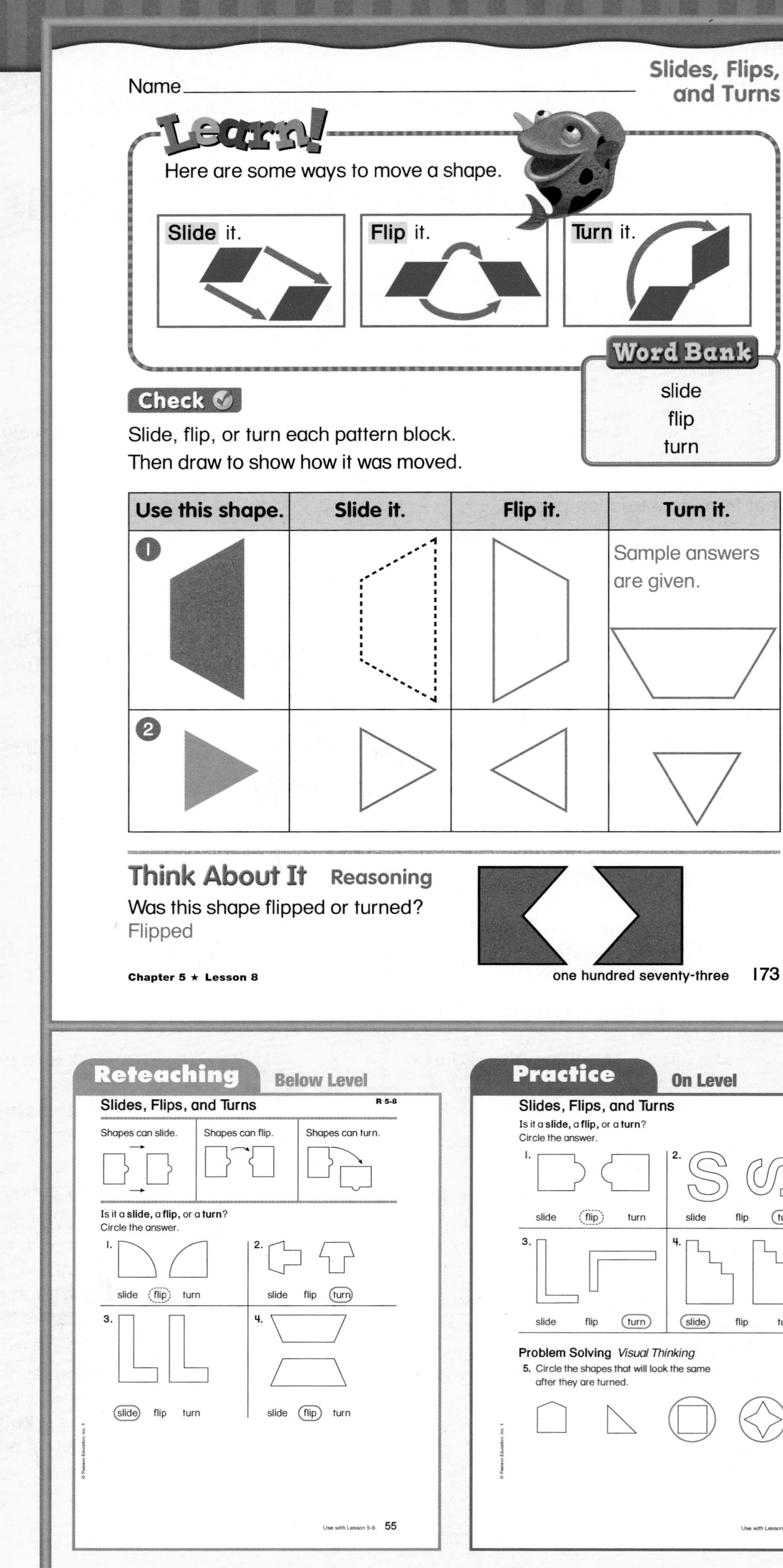

Name ____________________

Slides, Flips, and Turns

Learn!

Here are some ways to move a shape.

Slide it. Flip it. Turn it.

Word Bank
slide
flip
turn

Check

Slide, flip, or turn each pattern block.
Then draw to show how it was moved.

Use this shape.	Slide it.	Flip it.	Turn it.
1			Sample answers are given.
2			

Think About It Reasoning

Was this shape flipped or turned?
Flipped

Chapter 5 ★ Lesson 8 one hundred seventy-three 173

Reteaching Below Level

Slides, Flips, and Turns R 5-8

Shapes can slide. Shapes can flip. Shapes can turn.

Is it a **slide**, a **flip**, or a **turn**?
Circle the answer.

1. slide (flip) turn
2. slide flip (turn)
3. (slide) flip turn
4. slide (flip) turn

Use with Lesson 5-8. 55

Practice On Level

Slides, Flips, and Turns P 5-8

Is it a **slide**, a **flip**, or a **turn**?
Circle the answer.

1. slide (flip) turn
2. slide flip (turn)
3. slide flip (turn)
4. (slide) flip turn

Problem Solving *Visual Thinking*

5. Circle the shapes that will look the same after they are turned.

Use with Lesson 5-8. 55

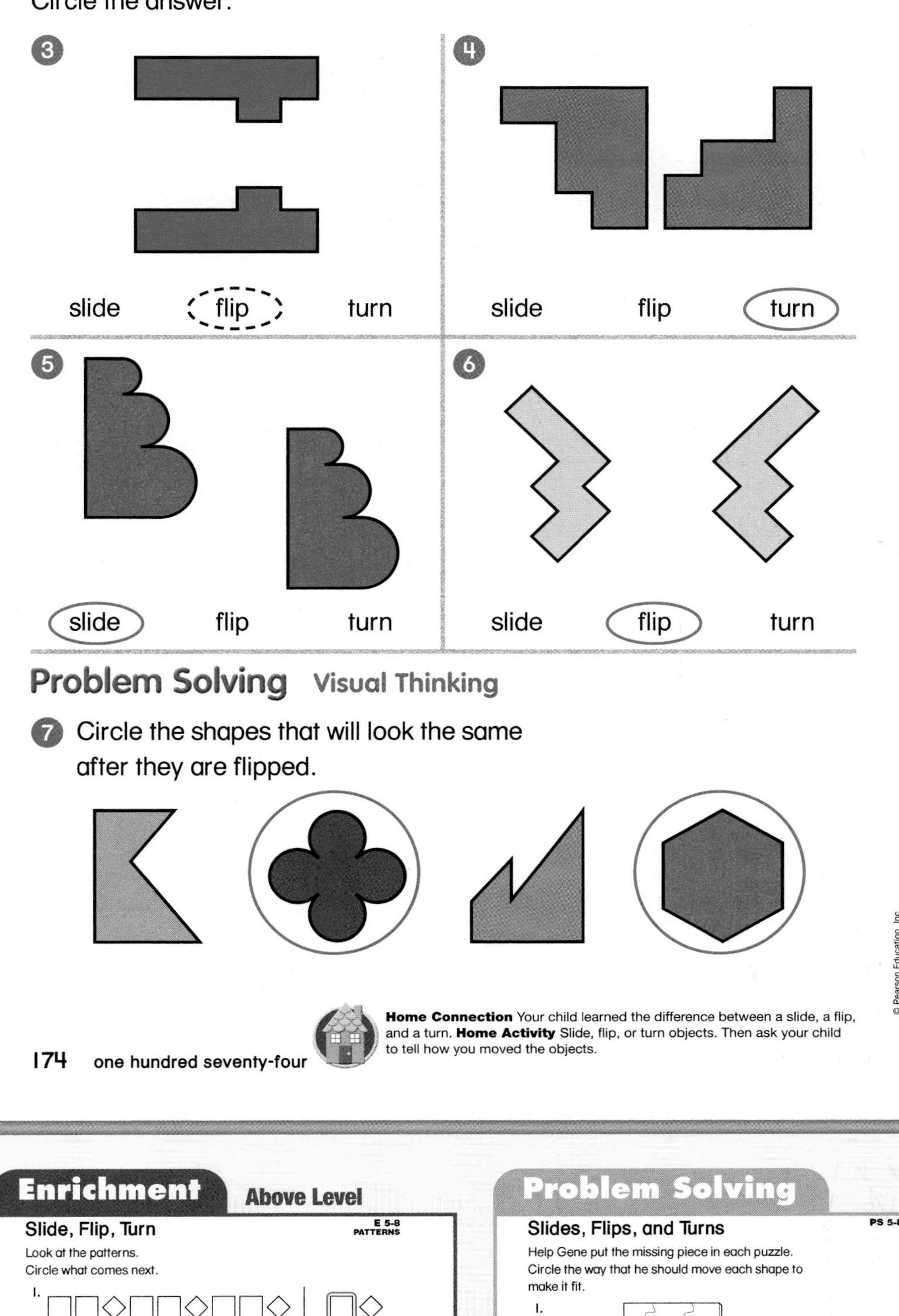

Practice

Is it a **slide**, a **flip**, or a **turn**?
Circle the answer.

3. slide (flip) turn

4. slide flip (turn)

5. (slide) flip turn

6. slide (flip) turn

Problem Solving Visual Thinking

7. Circle the shapes that will look the same after they are flipped.

Home Connection Your child learned the difference between a slide, a flip, and a turn. **Home Activity** Slide, flip, or turn objects. Then ask your child to tell how you moved the objects.

3 Practice

Remind children that a flip can be side-to-side (horizontal) or top-to-bottom (vertical). This will help them with Exercises 3, 6, and 7.

Leveled Practice

Below Level For Exercises 3–7, trace and cut out the shapes and move them to check your work.

On Level For Exercise 7, trace and cut out the shapes.

Above Level Complete all exercises by transforming the shapes mentally.

Early Finishers Have children work in pairs. One partner moves a shape, and the other partner tells whether the move was a slide, flip, or turn. Children take turns moving shapes and naming moves.

4 Assess

Journal Idea Have children draw a shape and then draw what the shape looks like after a slide, a flip, and a turn.

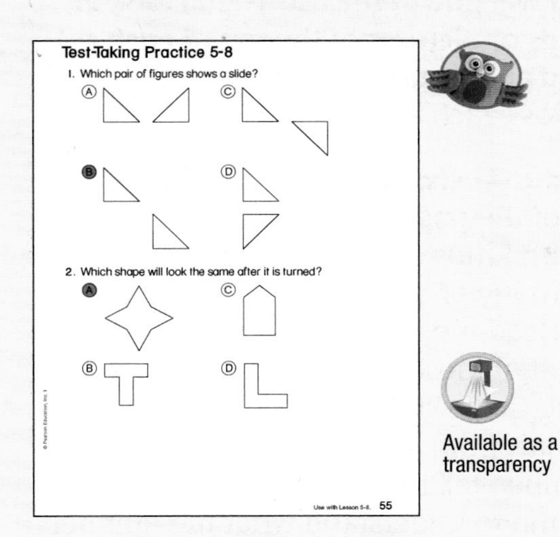

Test-Taking Practice 5-8

1. Which pair of figures shows a slide?
Ⓐ Ⓑ Ⓒ Ⓓ

2. Which shape will look the same after it is turned?
Ⓐ Ⓑ Ⓒ Ⓓ

Use with Lesson 5-8. 55

Available as a transparency

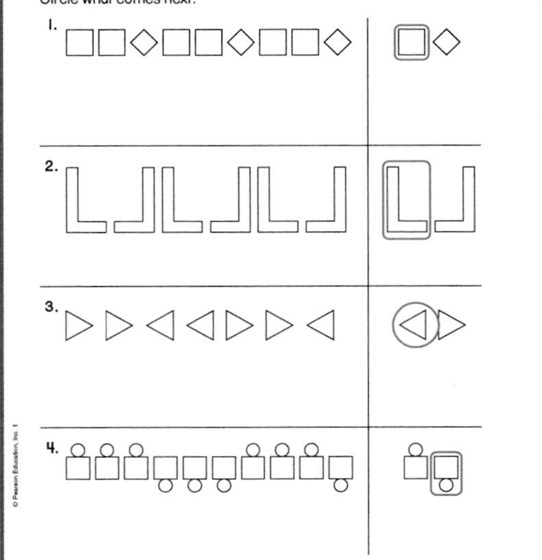

Enrichment Above Level

Slide, Flip, Turn — E 5-8 PATTERNS

Look at the patterns.
Circle what comes next.

1.
2.
3.
4.

Use with Lesson 5-8. 55

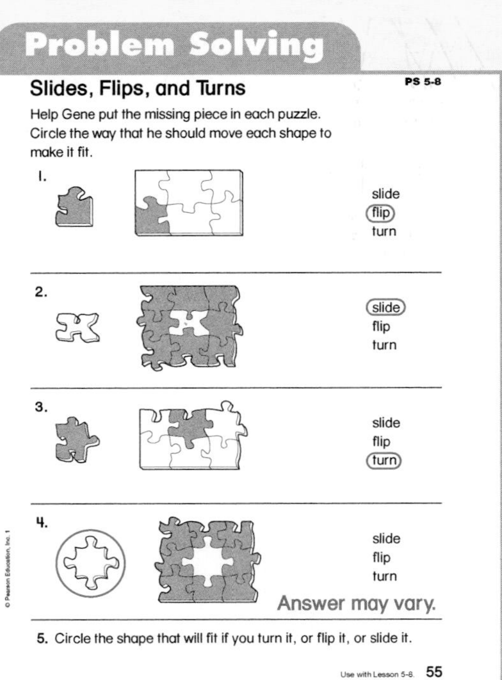

Problem Solving

Slides, Flips, and Turns — PS 5-8

Help Gene put the missing piece in each puzzle.
Circle the way that he should move each shape to make it fit.

1. slide (flip) turn
2. (slide) flip turn
3. slide flip (turn)
4. slide flip turn — Answer may vary.
5. Circle the shape that will fit if you turn it, or flip it, or slide it.

Use with Lesson 5-8. 55

Reading for Math Success

Purpose Show children how to apply the reading skill, *Understand Graphic Sources: Lists,* to their math work. Help prepare children for the problem-solving strategy lesson, *Make an Organized List,* which follows.

Using Student Page 175

Reading Skills and Math Understanding Knowing how to understand graphic sources such as lists is an essential reading skill because a list can make information easier to understand. Making a list is helpful when solving story problems because information can be organized in a list and a list makes it easier to see all possible solutions to a problem.

Model the Process Tell children that they will learn how to read information in a list. Explain that a list is a way of keeping track of information. Model reading a list: **When I read a list, the first thing I do is to read the title at the top. The title tells me what information I will find in the list. Then I look at the words or pictures at the top of each column and at the start of each row. Then I read across each row.**

Guide the Activity Read the direction at the top of the page. Say: **Each child picked 3 different kinds of flowers. This list tells us how many of each flower the children picked.** Read the title of the list and remind children that these words tell what the list is all about. Guide children in reading each line of the chart from left to right. When they get to a number, tell them to look at the top of the column to understand what the number means. To test their understanding of reading a list, have them answer the questions in Exercises 1–3.

Think About It Ask children to imagine that, instead of a list, they read 9 sentences telling them how many of each flower the children picked. Ask them which would be faster, reading the 9 sentences or looking at the list? Help children see that the list is faster because it is organized into rows and has fewer words to read.

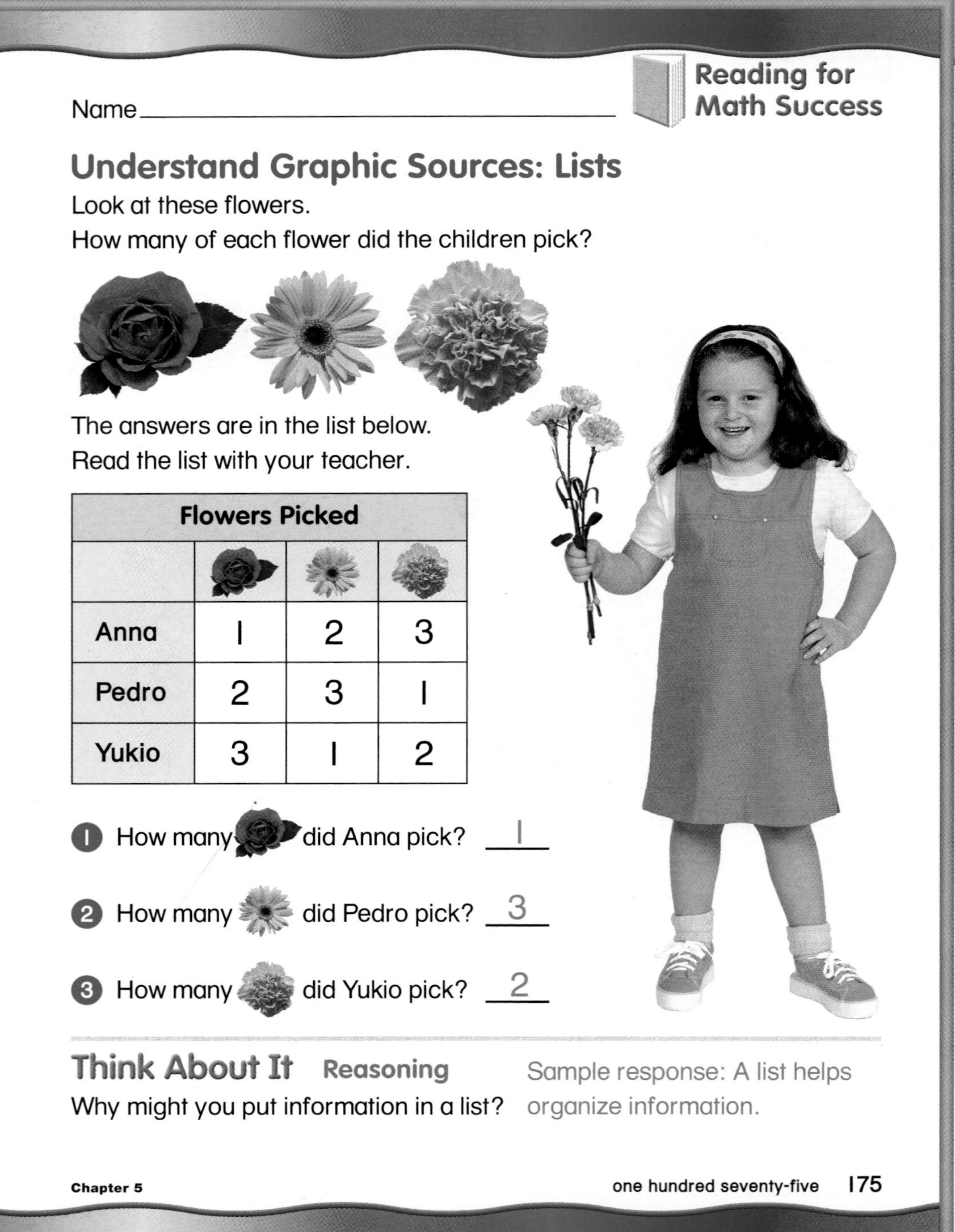

Name ____________________ Reading for Math Success

Understand Graphic Sources: Lists

Look at these flowers.
How many of each flower did the children pick?

The answers are in the list below.
Read the list with your teacher.

Flowers Picked			
	rose	daisy	carnation
Anna	1	2	3
Pedro	2	3	1
Yukio	3	1	2

1. How many (rose) did Anna pick? 1
2. How many (daisy) did Pedro pick? 3
3. How many (carnation) did Yukio pick? 2

Think About It Reasoning
Why might you put information in a list? Sample response: A list helps organize information.

Chapter 5 one hundred seventy-five 175

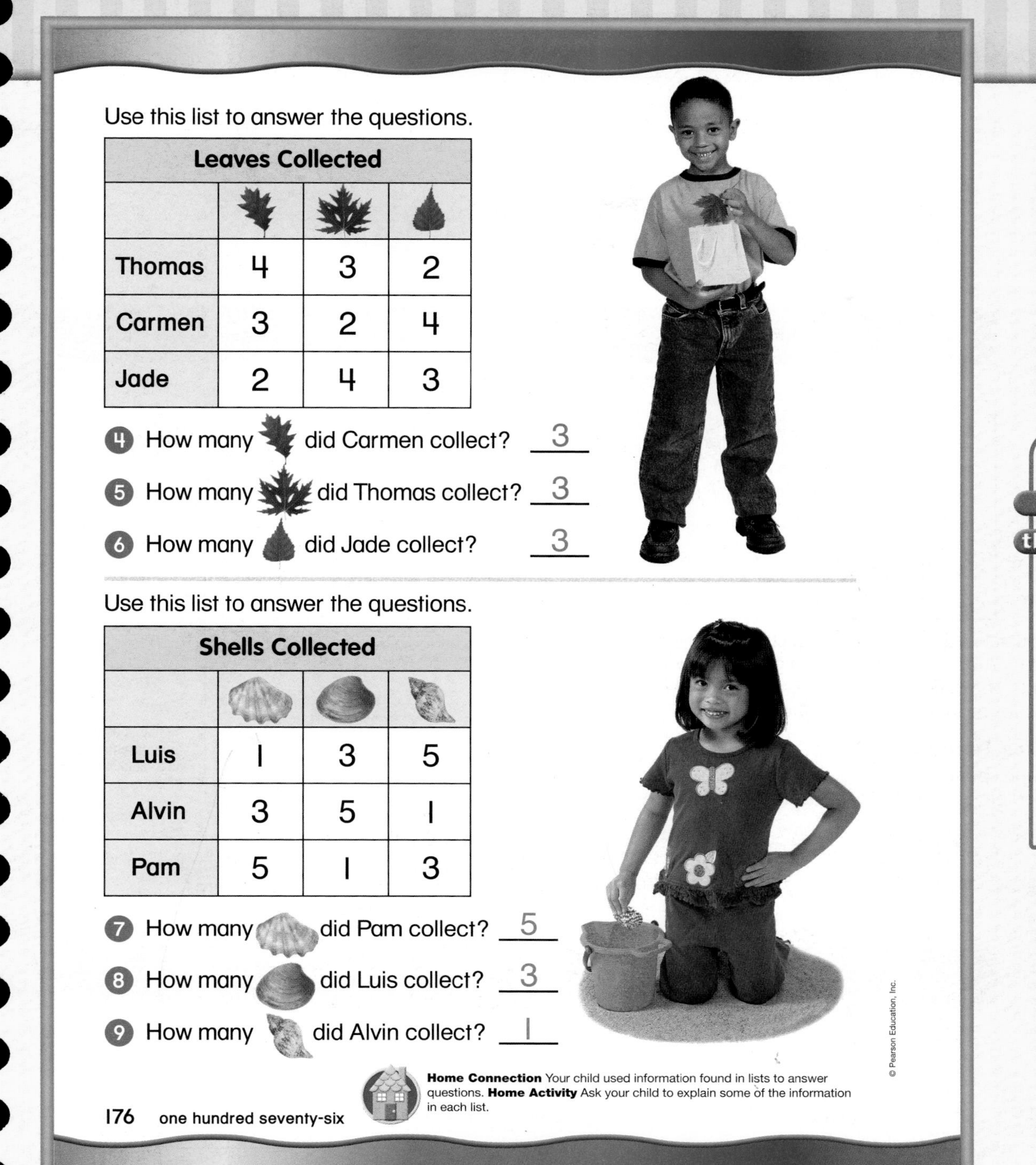

Use this list to answer the questions.

Leaves Collected			
Thomas	4	3	2
Carmen	3	2	4
Jade	2	4	3

4 How many did Carmen collect? 3

5 How many did Thomas collect? 3

6 How many did Jade collect? 3

Use this list to answer the questions.

Shells Collected			
Luis	1	3	5
Alvin	3	5	1
Pam	5	1	3

7 How many did Pam collect? 5

8 How many did Luis collect? 3

9 How many did Alvin collect? 1

Home Connection Your child used information found in lists to answer questions. **Home Activity** Ask your child to explain some of the information in each list.

176 one hundred seventy-six

Using Student Page 176

Have children read the directions independently and use the lists on the page to answer the questions.

When children have completed the page, have them compare their answers and practice asking and answering other questions about each list with a partner.

Error Intervention

If children are having difficulty reading lists,

then make a simpler list. Write *Our Stickers* at the top and draw 2 simple shapes, such as a star and a heart, on the board. In the first row, put the name *Sue* and *3* under one shape and *2* under the other shape. In the second row, put the name *Ken* and *4* under one shape and *2* under the other shape. Read across each row with the children. Ask: **How many star stickers does Sue have? How many heart stickers does Sue have?** Repeat the process for the second row of the list.

Journal Idea Children can write simple lists to learn how to compile information. They can record titles of books they have read, or write lists of new vocabulary words. Later, this information can be used to make a class chart such as "Books We Read This Week." Numbers of books can be tallied by categories such as books about animals, fairy tales, or holidays.

Make an Organized List

Lesson Organizer

Quick Lesson Overview 

Objective Solve problems by making organized lists.

Math Understanding Writing down all of the possible ways of doing something can be a good way to solve a problem.

Materials for Student Pages *(per pair)* Pattern blocks: 1 hexagon, 2 trapezoids, 3 parallelograms, and 6 triangles

Professional Development Note

Managing Instruction Place correct numbers of pattern blocks in small bags ahead of time. Have one or two children collect the bags after the lesson, checking to be sure that all of the blocks are back in each bag.

NCTM Standards

- Geometry
- Number and Operations

(For a complete correlation to the NCTM Standards and Grades Pre-K through 2 Expectations, see Page 155G and 155H.)

Getting Started

Spiral Review

Problem of the Day 5-9

How many triangles are in each symbol? Name any other shapes in the symbols.

Read Aloud These special pictures, or symbols, were used by Arapaho Native Americans to show things in nature. The symbol at the left is for rocks. The middle symbol is for mountains. The symbol at the right is for a frog.

Topics Reviewed

- Plane shapes
- Problem-Solving Skill: Use Data from a Picture

Answer There are 3 triangles in the symbol for rocks, 2 triangles in the symbol for mountains, and 3 triangles in the symbol for a frog. The symbol for a frog also has 2 rectangles and the symbol for mountains also has a diamond.

Spiral Review and Test Prep 5-9

1. Which shows a flip of this shape?
   Ⓐ Ⓑ Ⓒ Ⓓ
2. Which one is **not** in the fact family for 3 + 7 = 10?
   Ⓐ 10 − 7 = 3 Ⓒ 3 + 4 = 7
   Ⓑ 7 + 3 = 10 Ⓓ 10 − 3 = 7
3. Circle the part that repeats. Draw what comes next.
4. Cross out the bowl that can hold the least. Circle the bowl that can hold the most.

56 Use with Lesson 5-9.

Available as a transparency and as a blackline master

Topics Reviewed

1. Slides, Flips, and Turns **2.** Fact Families
3. Identifying and Extending Patterns
4. Comparing and Ordering by Capacity

Investigating the Concept

Pattern Block Puzzles

Materials *(per group)* Pattern blocks: 1 trapezoid, 2 parallelograms, 4 triangles, and 1 square; *(per child)* Pattern-Block Puzzles (Teaching Tool 19)

What to Do

- Distribute Pattern-Block Puzzles to children. Ask them to decide which pattern blocks can be used to cover the first shape. *(2 triangles or 1 parallelogram)*
- Have children find solutions for the other puzzles and draw in the outlines of the shapes they used. Invite children to share their solutions. On the board, keep a record of the different ways.

Ongoing Assessment

- **For which puzzle did we find the most ways?** *(The last puzzle, the largest parallelogram, has four ways.)*
- **Reasoning Why is it useful to make a list of the different ways you find?** *(Sample response: If you write them down as you find them, you can look back to see if any of the ways are repeated.)*

Ways to Make

Shapes I Used	triangle	parallelogram	trapezoid	square
Way 1	2	0	0	1
Way 2	0	1	0	1

Reaching All Learners

Reading in Math

Reading a List

5–10 MIN **Visual/Spatial/Linguistic**

- Write a list on the board like the one shown below. Give children a few minutes to familiarize themselves with the contents. Explain that the list shows different ways to make the green circle using the different shapes shown on the list.
- Talk children through reading the list. Ask questions such as: **What pieces were used for Way 2? How many of each piece was used?**

Ways to Make ●

Shapes I Used	●	◗	◔
Way 1	1	0	0
Way 2	0	2	0
Way 3	0	1	2

Access Content

English Language Learners

Parallelograms and Trapezoids

10–15 MIN **Linguistic/Logical/Mathematical**

Materials *(per group)* Pattern blocks

- Introduce the new shape words *parallelogram* and *trapezoid.*
- Have one group of children make an organized list titled "Ways to Make a Parallelogram" and the other group make a list titled "Ways to Make a Trapezoid." Children should decide which pattern blocks can cover the shape, and then record the answers in their lists.
- Have children explain and demonstrate their findings to the other group.

Reteaching

Making New Shapes

10–15 MIN **Visual/Spatial**

Materials Pattern blocks made from construction paper

- Pass out some construction paper pattern blocks to each child in the group.
- On the board, draw an outline of a figure that can be made using pattern blocks. Invite children to work together to find different ways to make the figure using combinations of pattern blocks. Record each of their ways in a chart similar to the charts found on Student Pages 177 and 178.

Math and Art

Pattern Block Pictures

15–20 MIN **Logical/Mathematical**

Materials Construction paper; glue; pattern block shapes cut from construction paper

- Give each child a piece of construction paper and a handful of construction paper pattern blocks. Assist children in seeing that the sides of many of the blocks are the same size and, thus, are easy to connect.
- Invite children to make seasonal scenes by gluing the pattern blocks onto the paper. Encourage children to add lots of detail to their scenes.

Objective Solve problems by making organized lists.

1 Warm Up

Activate Prior Knowledge Review the word *list*. Invite children to talk about when and where they may have seen lists used before.

2 Teach

Learn!

Explain that there are many ways to cover the shape using different combinations of other shapes. If they use the same blocks in different positions, then the way should only be counted once. Work with children to fill in Way 1, for each column asking how many of each of the shapes were used.

Ongoing Assessment

Talk About It

- **Is there another way to solve the problem?** *(No, everything that we can think of is already on the list.)*
- **Can you use two parallelograms (diamonds) to fill the trapezoid? Explain.** *(No, the two parallelograms are larger than the trapezoid.)*

If children list solutions that do not fit,

then have them place the blocks beside the original shape and compare the shapes.

Check

Error Intervention

If children have trouble finding solutions,

then place one of the correct blocks in place and let them find the remaining blocks. *(Also see* Reteaching, *Page 177B.)*

Think About It Help children consider all of the possible block combinations. **Could you use two blue blocks to cover the red one? Would two green blocks cover the red one? 4 green blocks?**

Name ____________________

PROBLEM-SOLVING STRATEGY
Make an Organized List

Learn!

1. How many ways can you make this shape using pattern blocks?

Read and Understand
You need to find all the ways to use pattern blocks to make the shape.

Plan and Solve
Make a list to keep track of the different ways you find.

Write how many of each shape you use.

Ways to Make (trapezoid)			
	trapezoid	parallelogram	triangle
Way 1	1	0	0
Way 2	0	1	1
Way 3	0	0	3

Look Back and Check
Did you find all the ways?
How do you know?

Think About It Reasoning
How does making an organized list help you?

Sample response: An organized list shows that all of the possible ways have been used.

Reteaching Below Level

PROBLEM-SOLVING STRATEGY R 5-9
Make an Organized List

Give 3 ways you can make this shape using pattern blocks.

Read and Understand
You need to find all the ways that pattern blocks can make the shape.

Plan and Solve
A list can help you keep track.

Ways to Make (trapezoid)			
Shapes I Used	trapezoid	triangle	parallelogram
Way 1	1	0	0
Way 2	0	3	0
Way 3	0	1	1

Look Back and Check
Did you find 3 ways? How do you know?

Give 3 ways you can make this shape using pattern blocks. Complete the list.

1.

Ways to Make (parallelogram)			
Shapes I Used	trapezoid	parallelogram	triangle
Way 1	1	0	1
Way 2	0	2	0
Way 3	0	0	4

Practice On Level

PROBLEM-SOLVING STRATEGY P 5-9
Make an Organized List

1. Show 5 ways you can make this shape using pattern blocks. Complete the list.

Ways to Make (triangle)			
Shapes I Used	hexagon	parallelogram	triangle
Way 1	0	0	9
Way 2	0	1	7
Way 3	0	2	5
Way 4	0	3	3
Way 5	1	0	3

Writing in Math

2. How many ways can you use the pattern blocks to make a (rhombus)? Explain.
Two ways. You can use the parallelogram shape once, or you can use two triangles.

Practice

2 How many ways can you make this shape using pattern blocks? Complete the list. Order may vary.

Ways to Make ⬡				
	⬡	⏢	◆	▲
Way 1	1	0	0	0
Way 2	0	1	0	3
Way 3	0	1	1	1
Way 4	0	2	0	0
Way 5	0	0	1	4
Way 6	0	0	2	2
Way 7	0	0	3	0
Way 8	0	0	0	6

Writing in Math

3 How many ways can you use the pattern blocks to make ▲? Explain.

Only one way. The green triangle is the smallest pattern block.

Home Connection Your child made a list of all the solutions to a problem. **Home Activity** Ask your child to explain how he or she made the list in Exercise 2, above.

Enrichment Above Level

E 5-9
DECISION MAKING

Shape Making

Use these three pattern blocks to make different shapes.
Draw a picture of the shape you make.
Write how many of each shape you used.

Possible answers given.

Shapes I Made	Shapes I Used		
Check children's work.	⏢	◇	△
1.	2		
2.			6
3.	1	1	1

56 Use with Lesson 5-9

Problem Solving

PROBLEM-SOLVING STRATEGY PS 5-9

Make an Organized List

How many ways can you make this shape?
Use pattern blocks.
Make a list to keep track.

Step 1: Decide which blocks you can use.

Step 2: Decide how many of each block you need to make the shape.

1 1

Step 3: Try other shapes. Fill in as many spaces as you can.

Ways to Make △			
Shapes I Used	⏢	△	◇
Way 1	1	1	0
Way 2	0	2	1
Way 3	0	4	0

There are 3 ways to make a shape the same size.

Using the page Have children *look back* at their shapes by placing pattern blocks over the shape to *check* that the blocks make the same shape.

56 Use with Lesson 5-9

3 Practice

Remind children to look for solutions that use different blocks. They should check the list to be sure that there are no duplicates.

Reading Assist: Make Predictions Have children compare the large shape on the front of the page with the shape on the back of the page. **Which shape do you think will have more ways of covering it?**

Leveled Practice

Below Level Find as many ways as you can.

On Level Fill in each row with a different way.

Above Level After completing the list, prove that you have found all the ways.

Early Finishers Children work in pairs. Each child makes a shape with three pattern blocks, traces around the shape, and then removes the blocks. Children switch papers and solve their partner's puzzle.

4 Assess

Journal Idea Have children trace a yellow hexagon and list the ways to cover it with only one kind of block each time.

Test-Taking Practice 5-9

1. What number completes the list?

Ways to Make a ◇		
Shapes I used	◇	△
Way 1	1	0
Way 2	0	___

Ⓐ 0 Ⓑ 1 **Ⓒ 2** Ⓓ 3

2. What number completes the list?

Ways to Make a ▱			
Shapes I used	⏢	▱	▽
Way 1	1	0	1
Way 2	0	___	2
Way 3	0	2	0
Way 4	0	0	4

Ⓐ 4 Ⓑ 3 Ⓒ 2 **Ⓓ 1**

Use with Lesson 5-9. 56

Available as a transparency

Diagnostic Checkpoint

Purpose Provide assessment of children's progress to date by checking their understanding of key content covered in the previous section.

Vocabulary Review

You may wish to review these terms before assigning the page:

circle A plane figure in which all the points are the same distance from a point called the center *(pp. 165–166)*

flip To turn a plane figure over *(pp. 173–174)*

line of symmetry A line on which a figure can be folded so that both halves are congruent *(pp. 171–172)*

plane shape A shape that lies on a flat surface *(pp. 165–166)*

rectangle A quadrilateral with four right angles and opposite sides parallel and the same length *(pp. 165–166)*

same shape/same size A way to describe figures that are identical *(pp. 169–170)*

side A line segment forming part of a plane figure *(pp. 167–168)*

slide To move a plane figure in one direction *(pp. 173–174)*

square A polygon that has four equal sides and four right angles *(pp. 165–166)*

symmetry A figure has symmetry if it can be folded along a line so that both parts match exactly. *(pp. 171–172)*

triangle A polygon with three sides *(pp. 165–166)*

turn To rotate a plane figure *(pp. 173–174)*

vertex (vertices) A point where two sides or two or more edges meet *(pp. 167–168)*

Activities for this section are available in the Math Vocabulary Kit.

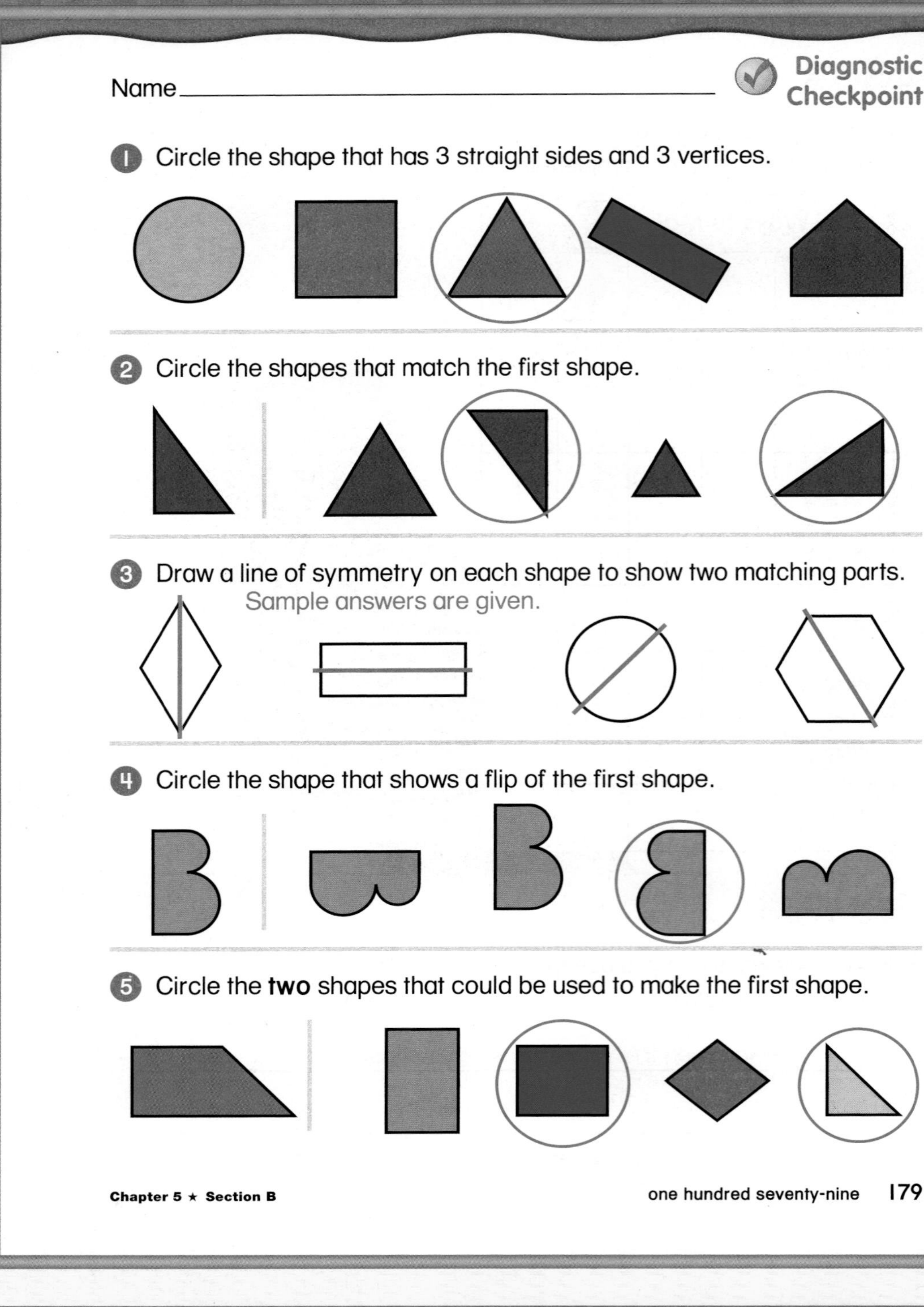

Name ____________________ Diagnostic Checkpoint

1. Circle the shape that has 3 straight sides and 3 vertices.

2. Circle the shapes that match the first shape.

3. Draw a line of symmetry on each shape to show two matching parts.
Sample answers are given.

4. Circle the shape that shows a flip of the first shape.

5. Circle the **two** shapes that could be used to make the first shape.

Chapter 5 ★ Section B — one hundred seventy-nine 179

Item Analysis for Diagnosis and Intervention

Objective	Items	Student Book Pages*	Intervention System
Sort plane shapes and identify their properties.	1	167–168	D49, D50
Identify and create figures that are the same size and the same shape.	2	169–170	D51
Identify objects that show symmetry and draw lines of symmetry.	3	171–172	D52
Perform a slide, flip, or turn on an object and identify the resulting position.	4	173–174	D53
Solve a problem by making an organized list.	5	177–178	E23

*For each lesson, there is a *Reteaching* activity in *Reaching All Learners* and a *Reteaching* master.

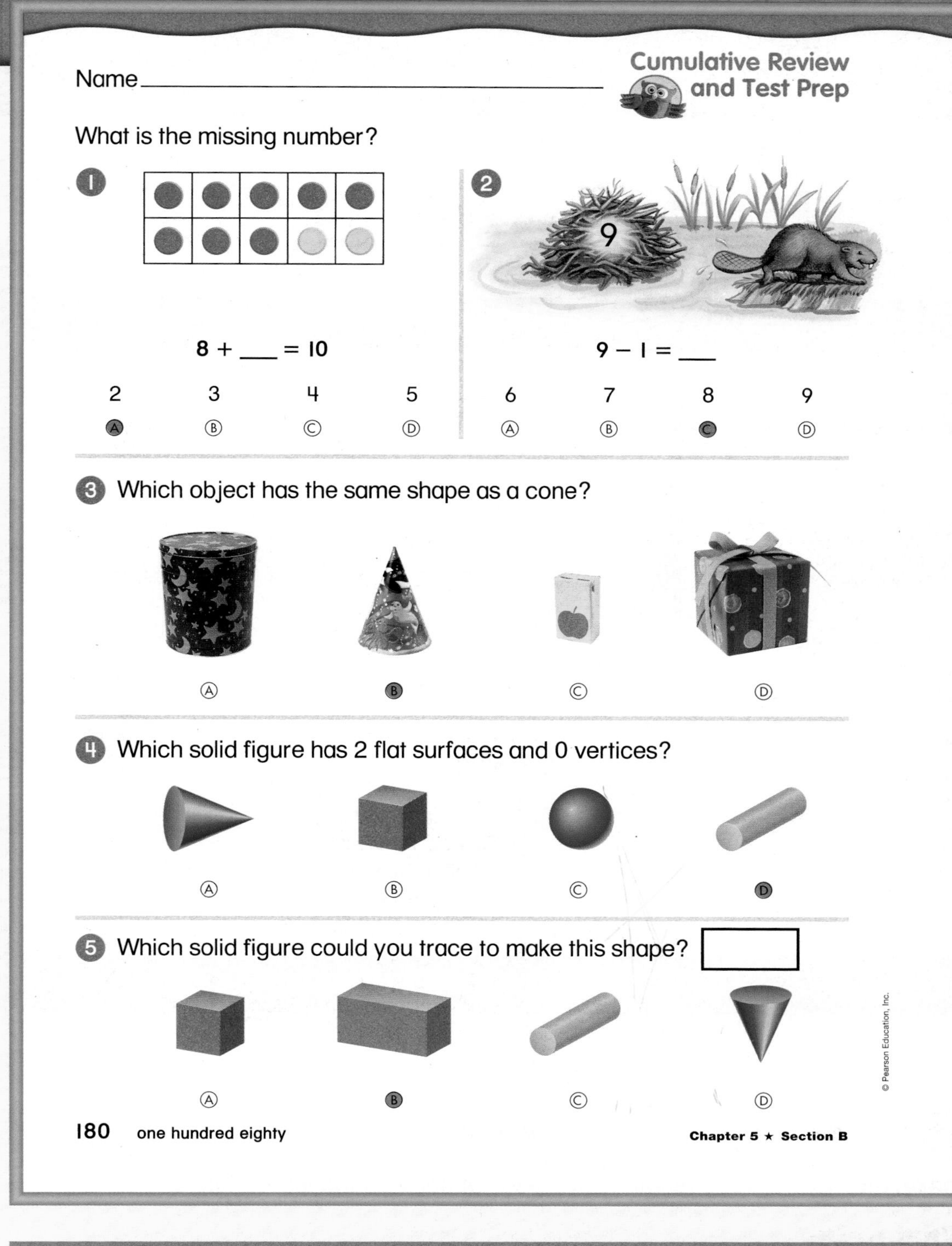
Name ______________________

Cumulative Review and Test Prep

What is the missing number?

1. $8 + \_\_\_ = 10$

   Ⓐ 2 Ⓑ 3 Ⓒ 4 Ⓓ 5

2. $9 - 1 = \_\_\_$

   Ⓐ 6 Ⓑ 7 Ⓒ 8 Ⓓ 9

3. Which object has the same shape as a cone?

   Ⓐ Ⓑ Ⓒ Ⓓ

4. Which solid figure has 2 flat surfaces and 0 vertices?

   Ⓐ Ⓑ Ⓒ Ⓓ

5. Which solid figure could you trace to make this shape?

   Ⓐ Ⓑ Ⓒ Ⓓ

Item Analysis for Diagnosis and Intervention

Objective	Items	Student Book Pages*	Intervention System
Recognize facts that have sums of 10.	1	107–108	B23
Find differences by counting back 1 or 2.	2	127–128	B25
Identify and name standard geometric solids and recognize them in the environment.	3	157–158	D45
Count the number of flat surfaces and vertices on geometric solids.	4	159–160	D46
Match a geometric solid to an outline of one of its flat surfaces.	5	161–162	D47, D48

*For each lesson, there is a *Reteaching* activity in *Reaching All Learners* and a *Reteaching* master.

Cumulative Review and Test Prep

Purpose Provide children with a review of math concepts. Items appear as they would on a standardized test so children become familiar with that format.

5-10 Equal Parts

Lesson Organizer

Quick Lesson Overview

Objective Determine whether a shape has been divided into equal or unequal parts and, if applicable, count the number of equal parts into which it has been divided.

Math Understanding A shape can be divided into any number of equal parts in a variety of ways.

Vocabulary Equal parts

Professional Development Note

Research Base

Most young children will begin to understand fractions by connecting them to their already existing informal notions of sharing and partitioning. Cutting a piece of fruit into two "equal parts" or giving each of three children "fair shares" of a collection of crackers are activities that translate directly into mathematical language and symbols (National Research Council, 2001; Behr, Lesh, Post, & Silver, 1983). In this section, dividing shapes and sets of objects equally provides the students with a familiar activity to which they can then attach the appropriate mathematics.

NCTM Standards

- Number and Operations
- Geometry

(For a complete correlation to the NCTM Standards and Grades Pre-K through 2 Expectations, see Page 155G and 155H.)

Getting Started

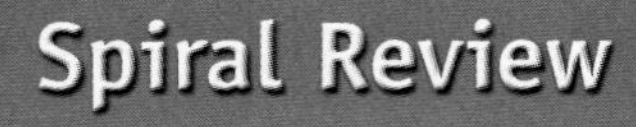

Spiral Review

Problem of the Day 5-10

Solve.
Carol made some towers like this one. She used 6 cubes. How many towers did Carol make?

Topics Reviewed
- Addition
- Problem-Solving: One-Step Problem

Answer Carol made 2 towers. Since 1 tower is made of 3 cubes, 2 towers are made of 3 + 3, or 6 cubes.

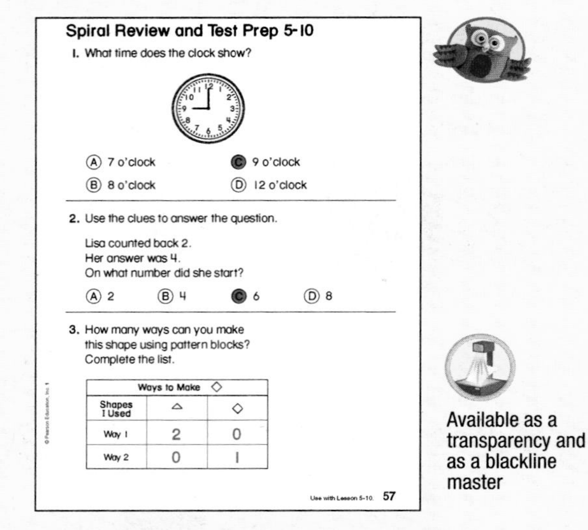

Spiral Review and Test Prep 5-10

1. What time does the clock show?

Ⓐ 7 o'clock Ⓑ 8 o'clock Ⓒ 9 o'clock Ⓓ 12 o'clock

2. Use the clues to answer the question.
Lisa counted back 2.
Her answer was 4.
On what number did she start?

Ⓐ 2 Ⓑ 4 Ⓒ 6 Ⓓ 8

3. How many ways can you make this shape using pattern blocks? Complete the list.

Ways to Make ◇		
Shapes I Used	△	◇
Way 1	2	0
Way 2	0	1

Use with Lesson 5-10. 57

Available as a transparency and as a blackline master

Topics Reviewed
1. Telling Time on an Analog Clock
2. Counting Back
3. Make an Organized List

Investigating the Concept

Folding Equal Parts

Materials *(per child)* 6 rectangular pieces of paper (4 inches x 6 inches)

What to Do

- Have children fold three pieces of paper in half: one horizontally, one vertically, and one diagonally. Then have children determine which rectangles have 2 matching parts.
- Introduce the phrase equal parts. Then ask children to fold a new piece of paper to show 2 *unequal* parts. Ask children to tell how they folded their papers.
- Model two different ways to make 4 equal parts.

Ongoing Assessment

- **How could you fold the paper into 3 equal parts?** *(By making two folds in the paper)*
- **Reasoning Two children share a sandwich. Should they share a sandwich with 2 equal parts or a sandwich with 2 unequal parts? Explain.** *(Equal parts so that they each get the same amount)*

Reaching All Learners

Oral Language in Math

Fair Share

5–10 MIN **Linguistic**

Materials Two paper circles; marker; scissors

- Explain that two children will share 1 cracker, represented by a circle. Divide the circle into 2 unequal parts. Give 1 to each child. **Are you happy with your share? Why or why not?** Encourage children to say that the parts are not the same, or *not equal.*
- Next, divide a circle equally. Ask children if they are now happy with their share. Lead children to say these are *equal parts.*

Extend Language

English Language Learners

Making Equal Parts

10–15 MIN **Kinesthetic**

Materials *(per pair)* Construction paper rectangles, squares, and circles; scissors

- Demonstrate how to fold and cut a shape into 2 and 4 equal parts.
- Have pairs of children work together. Have one child say, "Please give me one equal part." Have the other child cut the shape into two equal parts and give one part to the partner.
- Repeat with the other child requesting an equal part.

Reteaching

Sorting by Number of Parts

10–15 MIN **Visual/Spatial**

Materials *(per group)* Paper shapes; chart paper; tape

- Prior to the activity, draw lines dividing paper shapes into 2 to 8 equal parts. Then create a chart with the numbers 2, 3, 4, 6, and 8 written along the left side. Title the chart "Equal Parts."
- Distribute the shapes and have children sort the shapes by the number of equal parts in each. Invite each child to tape a shape to the chart in the appropriate row.

Equal Parts	
2	
3	
4	
6	
8	

Math and Health

Sharing Food

15–20 MIN **Visual/Spatial**

Materials *(per child)* Construction paper; crayons or markers

- Create a list of healthy foods that the children enjoy eating. Encourage children to name foods that can be shared with one or more people.
- Have children draw pictures of foods that can be shared. After they have drawn the pictures, have them draw lines to divide each of the foods into equal parts. Under each picture, have children write the number of equal parts shown.

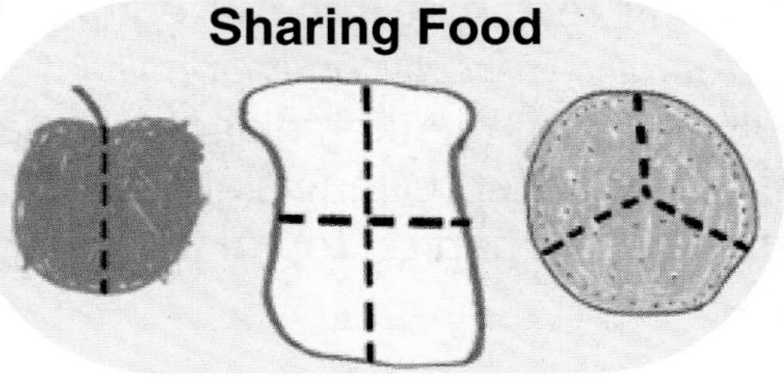

Objective Determine whether a shape has been divided into equal or unequal parts and, if applicable, count the number of equal parts into which it has been divided.

1 Warm Up

Activate Prior Knowledge Review *congruence.* Make the following labels: "Same Size and Same Shape," "Different Sizes," and "Different Shapes." Have children draw pairs of shapes for each label.

2 Teach

Learn!

Point out the child in the picture, and explain that he wants to share the food with friends. Ask children to tell which pizza would be easier to share fairly and explain why. Introduce the phrase equal parts.

Ongoing Assessment

Talk About It

- **Which sandwich will be easier to share fairly?** *(The first one. Its parts are equal.)*
- **Can you divide a shape into 3 equal parts?** *(Yes)* **5 equal parts?** *(Yes)*

If children have difficulty determining which foods show equal parts,

then trace the foods, cut out the parts, and try to fit them on top of one another.

Check

Error Intervention

If children circle a shape that shows unequal parts,

then point to each part. **Is this part the same as that part?** *(Also see* Reteaching, *Page 181B.)*

Think About It Ask: **What is one way to divide this rectangle into two equal parts?** *(Horizontally, vertically, or diagonally)* If children do not mention diagonally, have them cut a paper rectangle along a diagonal and place one part on top of the other.

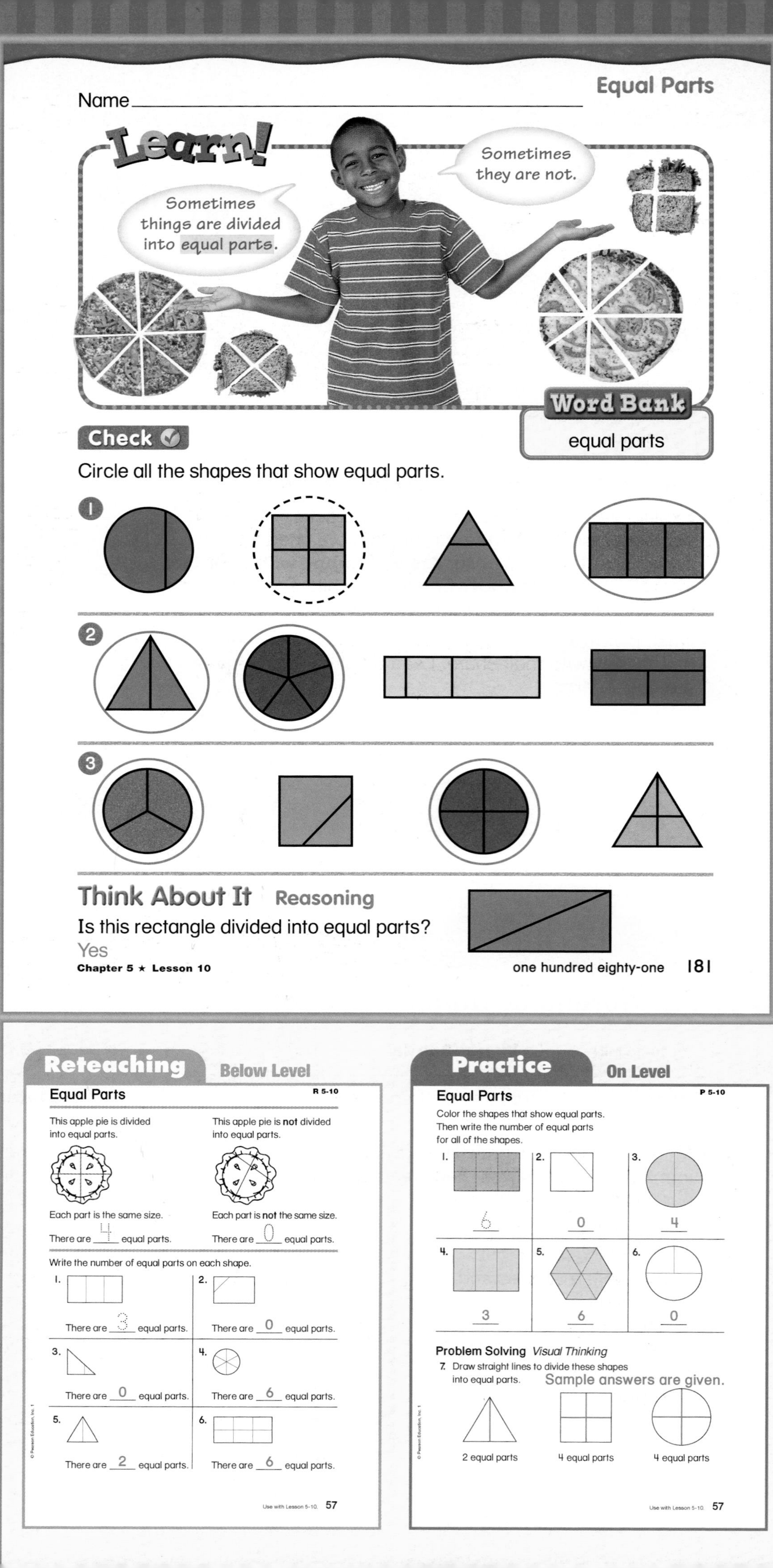

Name ______________________ **Equal Parts**

Learn!

Word Bank
equal parts

Check

Circle all the shapes that show equal parts.

1
2
3

Think About It Reasoning

Is this rectangle divided into equal parts?
Yes

Chapter 5 ★ Lesson 10 one hundred eighty-one 181

Reteaching Below Level

Equal Parts R 5-10

This apple pie is divided into equal parts.
Each part is the same size.
There are 4 equal parts.

This apple pie is **not** divided into equal parts.
Each part is **not** the same size.
There are 0 equal parts.

Write the number of equal parts on each shape.

1. There are 3 equal parts.
2. There are 0 equal parts.
3. There are 0 equal parts.
4. There are 6 equal parts.
5. There are 2 equal parts.
6. There are 6 equal parts.

Use with Lesson 5-10. 57

Practice On Level

Equal Parts P 5-10

Color the shapes that show equal parts.
Then write the number of equal parts for all of the shapes.

1. 6
2. 0
3. 4
4. 3
5. 6
6. 0

Problem Solving *Visual Thinking*

7. Draw straight lines to divide these shapes into equal parts. Sample answers are given.

2 equal parts 4 equal parts 4 equal parts

Use with Lesson 5-10. 57

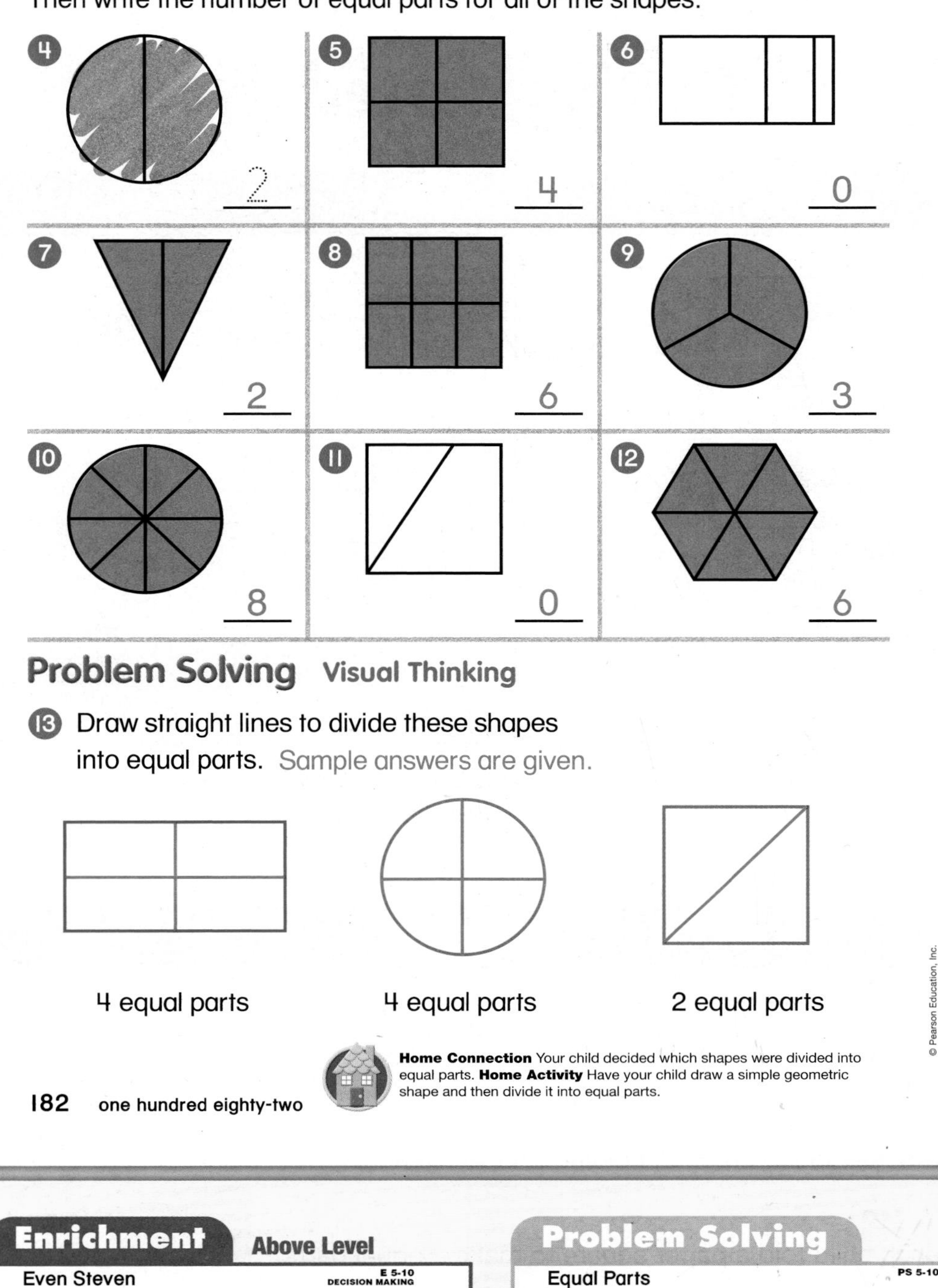

Practice

Color the shapes that show equal parts.
Then write the number of equal parts for all of the shapes.

4. 2
5. 4
6. 0
7. 2
8. 6
9. 3
10. 8
11. 0
12. 6

Problem Solving Visual Thinking

13. Draw straight lines to divide these shapes into equal parts. Sample answers are given.

4 equal parts | 4 equal parts | 2 equal parts

Home Connection Your child decided which shapes were divided into equal parts. **Home Activity** Have your child draw a simple geometric shape and then divide it into equal parts.

3 Practice

Explain to children that they should write the number of parts only if the parts are equal. If the parts are unequal, they should write *0.*

Reading Assist: Sequence Ask children to sequence the steps for completing Exercises 4–12. **What is the first thing you need to do? What should you do next? What should you do last?**

Leveled Practice

Below Level Use cutout shapes for Exercise 13.

On Level Complete all exercises as written.

Above Level Trace the shapes with unequal parts, and show a way to divide them equally.

Early Finishers Have children use square pieces of paper to see how many ways they can fold them into 2 and 4 equal parts.

4 Assess

Journal Idea Draw several shapes on the board. Ask children to copy each shape twice. Have them divide the first of each pair into equal parts and the second into unequal parts.

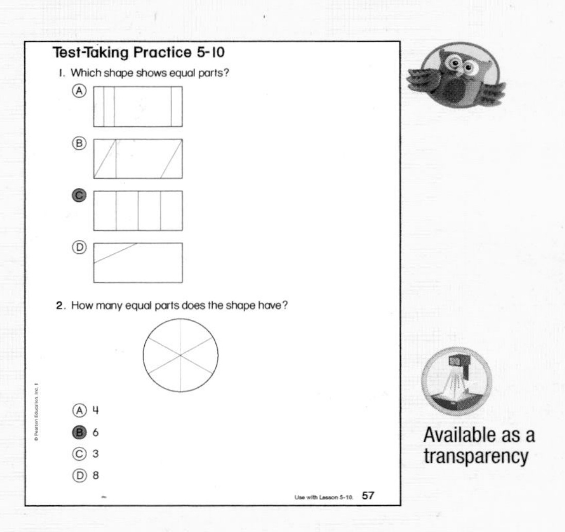

Test-Taking Practice 5-10

1. Which shape shows equal parts?
   - Ⓐ
   - Ⓑ
   - Ⓒ
   - Ⓓ
2. How many equal parts does the shape have?
   - Ⓐ 4
   - Ⓑ 6
   - Ⓒ 3
   - Ⓓ 8

Use with Lesson 5-10. 57

Enrichment Above Level

Even Steven E 5-10 DECISION MAKING

Help the children share.
Draw lines to show equal parts. Possible answers given.

1. 2 boys share an apple.
2. 3 girls share a pizza.
3. 4 children share the sandwich.
4. 6 children share the banana bread.

Use with Lesson 5-10. 57

Problem Solving

Equal Parts PS 5-10

Read each story. Circle the shape that shows what Maya did.

1. Maya drew a flag. The flag had 4 equal parts.
2. Maya cut a cake into 6 equal parts.
3. Maya planted flowers in the garden. She put different flowers in each of 8 equal parts.
4. Help Maya divide this shape into 6 equal parts. Draw straight lines.

Check children's work.

Use with Lesson 5-10. 57

5-11

Halves

Lesson Organizer

Quick Lesson Overview 

Objective Identify and show halves of a region.

Math Understanding A half of a region is one of two equally sized parts.

Vocabulary Fraction, whole, halves, one half ($\frac{1}{2}$)

Professional Development Note

How Children Learn Math
Fraction notation may look strange to some children. To help children become familiar with it, label halves of different objects around the room. For example, cover one half of a circular clock with colored cellophane and label each part $\frac{1}{2}$.

NCTM Standards

- Number and Operations
- Geometry

(For a complete correlation to the NCTM Standards and Grades Pre-K through 2 Expectations, see Page 155G and 155H.)

Getting Started

Spiral Review

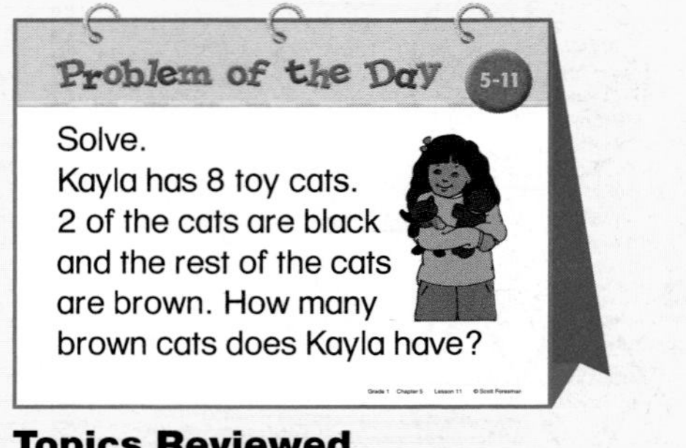
Problem of the Day 5-11

Solve.
Kayla has 8 toy cats.
2 of the cats are black and the rest of the cats are brown. How many brown cats does Kayla have?

Topics Reviewed

- Addition and subtraction
- Problem-Solving: One-Step Problem

Answer Kayla has 6 brown cats; 6 + 2 = 8, or 8 − 6 = 2

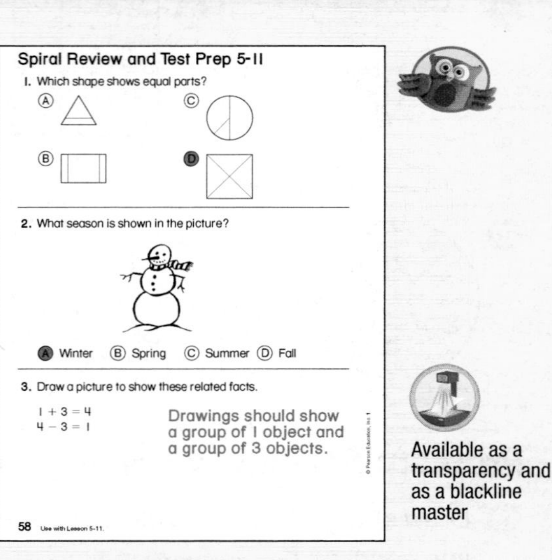
Spiral Review and Test Prep 5-11

1. Which shape shows equal parts?
Ⓐ Ⓑ Ⓒ Ⓓ

2. What season is shown in the picture?
Ⓐ Winter Ⓑ Spring Ⓒ Summer Ⓓ Fall

3. Draw a picture to show these related facts.
1 + 3 = 4
4 − 3 = 1
Drawings should show a group of 1 object and a group of 3 objects.

58 Use with Lesson 5-11.

Available as a transparency and as a blackline master

Topics Reviewed

1. Equal Parts
2. Months and Seasons
3. Using Related Facts

Investigating the Concept

Folding Halves

Materials *(per child)* Fraction Folding Shapes (Teaching Tool 20)

What to Do

- Have each child fold a paper square to make 2 equal parts.
- Explain that when a shape is divided into 2 equal parts, we call the parts halves. Each part is one half of the whole.
- Draw a square on the board. Shade one half. Write the fraction notation for one half ($\frac{1}{2}$) below the shaded part.
- Have children write $\frac{1}{2}$ on each part of their squares. Then invite them to fold other paper shapes to show halves.

Ongoing Assessment

- **What does the bottom number tell us?** *(How many equal parts there are)* **the top number?** *(How many parts we are talking about)*
- **Reasoning Is half of one shape always the same size as half of another shape?** *(No; half of a big shape is larger than half of a small shape.)*

Reaching All Learners

Math Vocabulary

The Language of Fractions

5–10 MIN **Linguistic**

Materials 5 sentence strips; 5 index cards; markers

- Write the following sentences on sentence strips. Draw an illustration beside numbers 1–3.
  1. This is a ___ orange.
  2. This orange has ___.
  3. This is ___ of the orange.
  4. One half is a ___.
  5. You can write one half like this ___.
- On index cards write the following: "whole, two equal parts, half, fraction, $\frac{1}{2}$."
- Have children choose the word that completes each sentence.

This is a ___ whole ___ orange.

English Language Learners

Access Content

Speaking of Fractions

5–10 MIN **Linguistic/Auditory**

Materials 3 apples; plastic knife

- Hold an apple and say: **This is a *whole* apple.** Have children repeat after you. Cut a second apple in half, point to each half and say: **This is *one half* of an apple.** Have children repeat after you and write $\frac{1}{2}$ on the board. Cut an apple in 2 unequal parts and say: **This is *not* one half.** Again, have children repeat after you.
- Display the whole apple, 2 halves, and 2 unequal parts. Ask children to pick out a *whole* and *one half.*

Reteaching

Two Halves Make a Whole

15–20 MIN **Visual/Spatial**

Materials *(per group)* chart paper; tape; *(per child)* construction paper shape

- Prior to the activity, use a marker to divide several shapes into 2 equal and unequal parts. Create a two-column chart. Title the left column, "Halves" and the right column, "Not Halves."
- Give one shape to each child. One at a time, have a child tape his or her shape to the chart and explain why it was placed in that column.

Halves | Not Halves

Math and Social Studies

Fair Is Fair

5–10 MIN **Linguistic/Social/Cooperative**

- List the following on the board:
  - Sharing a piece of fruit
  - Sharing a pizza
  - Sharing a table with a partner
  - Sharing space on a playground
- Encourage children to explain why equal parts would be important in those situations. Invite children to think of other situations in which things should be divided equally. Add children's suggestions to the list.
- Discuss the importance of fairness and why equal is fair and unequal is unfair.

Sharing a piece of fruit
Sharing a pizza

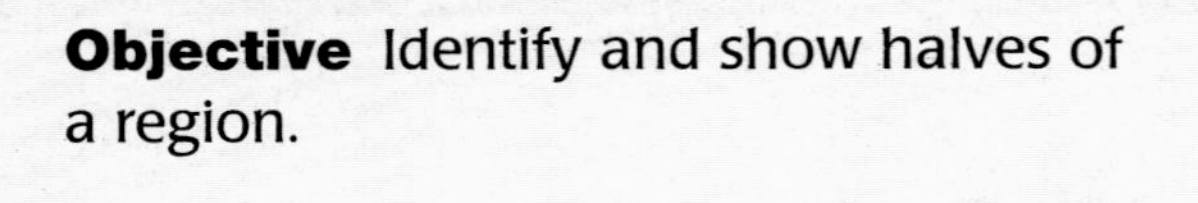

Objective Identify and show halves of a region.

1 Warm Up

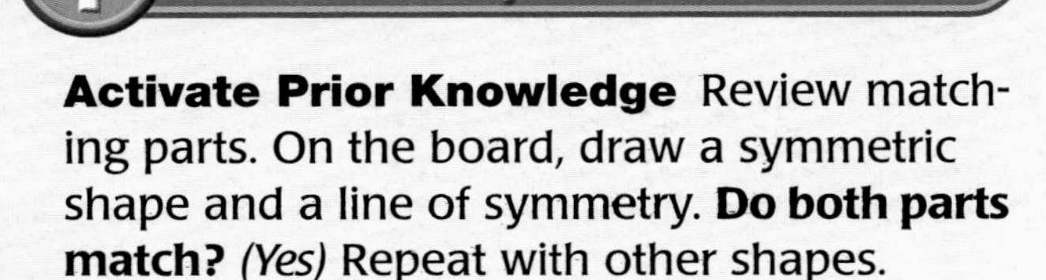

Activate Prior Knowledge Review matching parts. On the board, draw a symmetric shape and a line of symmetry. **Do both parts match?** *(Yes)* Repeat with other shapes.

2 Teach

Learn!

Discuss how the objects in the first group are different from those in the second group. Explain that when a shape has two equal parts, the parts are called halves. Each is one half of the whole. The bottom number in the fraction $\frac{1}{2}$ tells the number of equal parts and the top number refers to one part.

Ongoing Assessment

Talk About It

- **Why are the parts of the apple not called halves?** *(They are not equal.)*
- **Why are the parts of the cracker not called halves?** *(The cracker has 3 equal parts.)*

If children identify objects with 3 or more equal parts as showing halves,

then remind them that only objects divided into 2 equal parts show halves.

Check

Error Intervention

If children circle only one shape in each row,

then remind them to look for more than one shape. *(Also see* Reteaching, *Page 183B.)*

Think About It Ask: **If a shape is divided into halves, how many equal parts does it have?** *(Two)* **Do the shapes pictured have two parts?** *(One has 2 parts, and one has 3 parts.)* **Do the shapes have equal parts?** *(One does. One does not.)* **Do either of the shapes have two equal parts?** *(No)*

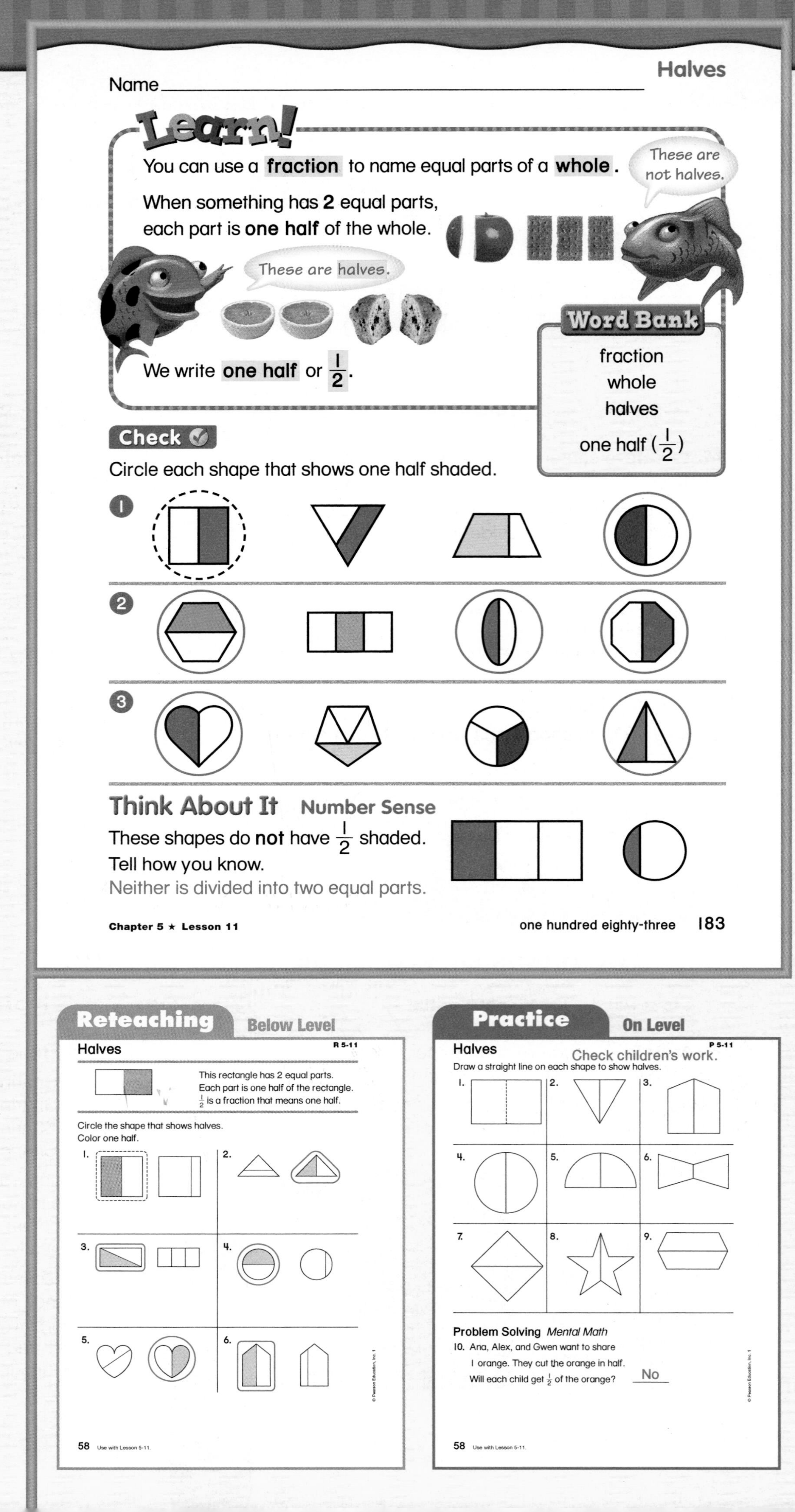

Name ____________________ **Halves**

Learn!

You can use a **fraction** to name equal parts of a **whole**.

When something has **2** equal parts, each part is **one half** of the whole.

These are not halves.
These are halves.

We write **one half** or $\frac{1}{2}$.

Word Bank
fraction
whole
halves
one half ($\frac{1}{2}$)

Check

Circle each shape that shows one half shaded.

1
2
3

Think About It Number Sense

These shapes do **not** have $\frac{1}{2}$ shaded. Tell how you know.
Neither is divided into two equal parts.

Reteaching Below Level

Halves R 5-11

This rectangle has 2 equal parts. Each part is one half of the rectangle. $\frac{1}{2}$ is a fraction that means one half.

Circle the shape that shows halves. Color one half.

1. 2. 3. 4. 5. 6.

58 Use with Lesson 5-11

Practice On Level

Halves P 5-11

Check children's work.

Draw a straight line on each shape to show halves.

1. 2. 3. 4. 5. 6. 7. 8. 9.

Problem Solving *Mental Math*

10. Ana, Alex, and Gwen want to share 1 orange. They cut the orange in half. Will each child get $\frac{1}{2}$ of the orange? No

58 Use with Lesson 5-11

Practice

Draw a straight line on each shape to show halves. Sample answers are given.

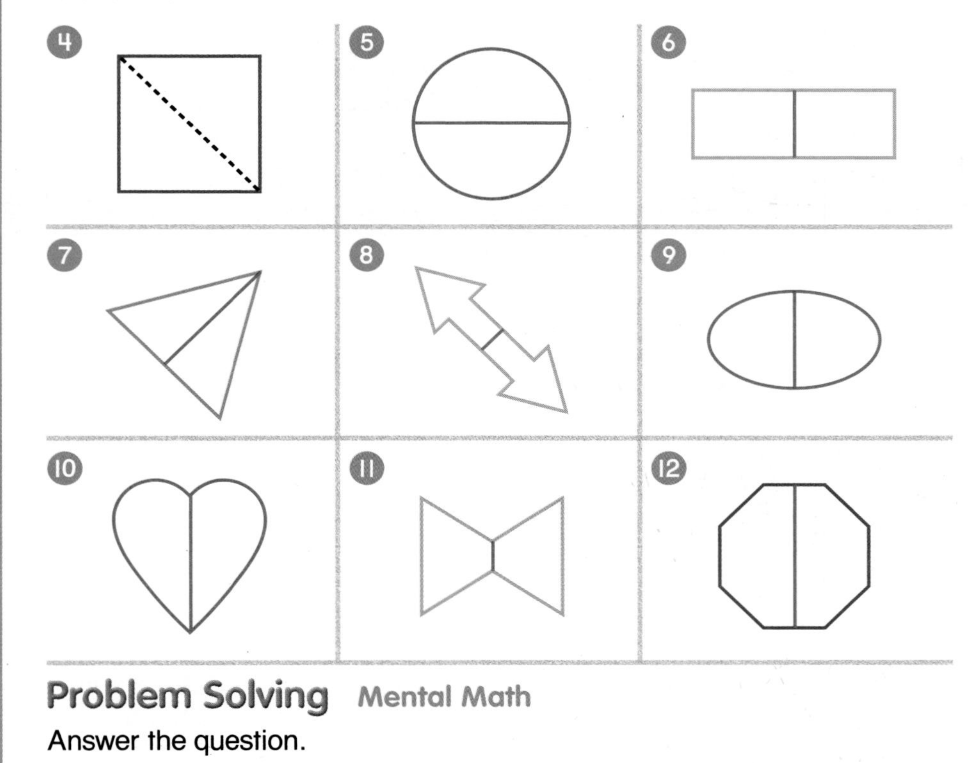

Problem Solving Mental Math

Answer the question.

13. Jack, James, and David shared 1 apple for their snack.
Jack ate $\frac{1}{2}$ of the apple.
James ate $\frac{1}{2}$ of the apple.
Was there any apple left for David?

No

Home Connection Your child divided shapes in half. **Home Activity** With your child, draw a series of four identical rectangles and then divide them in half four different ways.

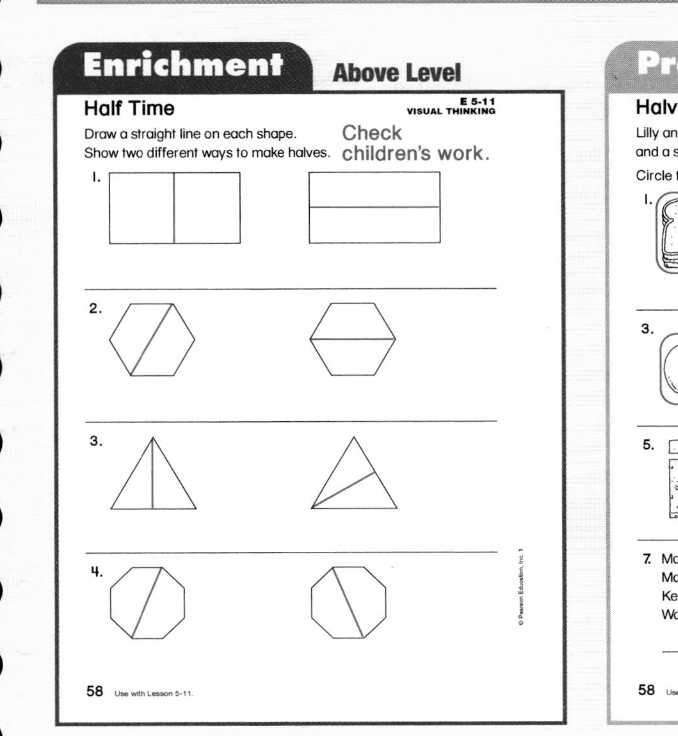

Enrichment Above Level

Half Time — E 5-11 VISUAL THINKING

Draw a straight line on each shape. Show two different ways to make halves. Check children's work.

1.
2.
3.
4.

58 Use with Lesson 5-11.

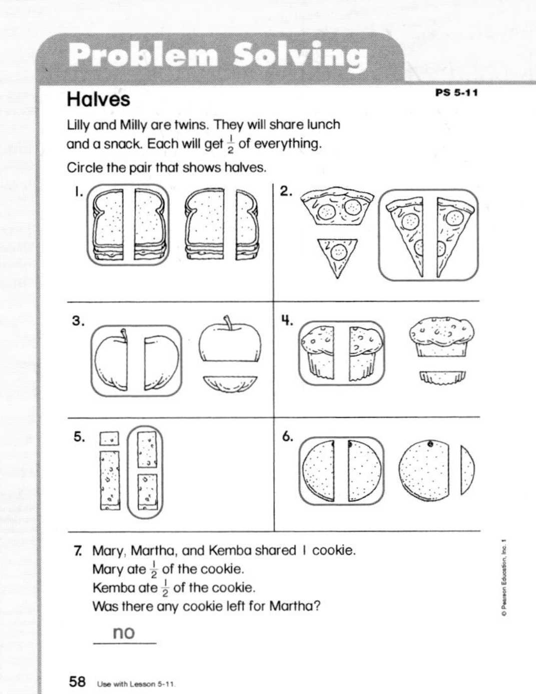

Problem Solving

Halves — PS 5-11

Lilly and Milly are twins. They will share lunch and a snack. Each will get $\frac{1}{2}$ of everything.

Circle the pair that shows halves.

1. 2. 3. 4. 5. 6.

7. Mary, Martha, and Kemba shared 1 cookie.
Mary ate $\frac{1}{2}$ of the cookie.
Kemba ate $\frac{1}{2}$ of the cookie.
Was there any cookie left for Martha?

no

58 Use with Lesson 5-11.

3 Practice

In Exercises 4–12, there may be different ways of dividing the shapes in half.

Leveled Practice

Below Level Fold paper circles in half to help complete Exercise 13.

On Level Complete all exercises as written.

Above Level Complete all exercises. Then shade one half of each shape and write $\frac{1}{2}$.

Early Finishers Have children work in pairs to draw shapes on slips of paper. Ask them to divide some of the shapes into halves and some into 2 unequal parts. Then they take turns choosing a shape and telling whether or not it shows halves.

4 Assess

Journal Idea On dot paper, have children draw shapes that can be divided into halves and shade one half of each shape.

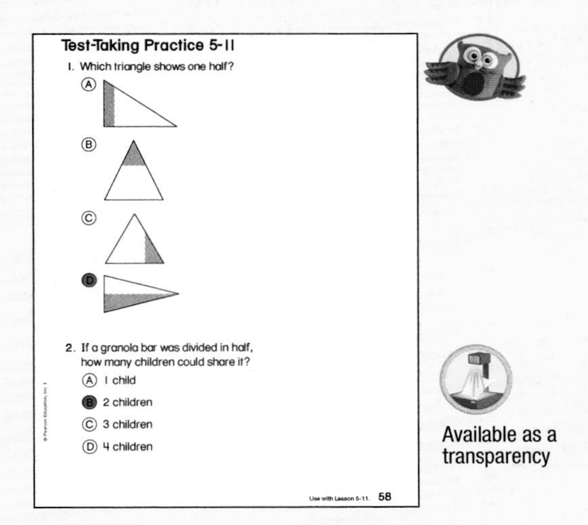

Test-Taking Practice 5-11

1. Which triangle shows one half?
Ⓐ
Ⓑ
Ⓒ
● D

2. If a granola bar was divided in half, how many children could share it?
Ⓐ 1 child
● 2 children
Ⓒ 3 children
Ⓓ 4 children

Use with Lesson 5-11. 58

Available as a transparency

5-12 Thirds and Fourths

Lesson Organizer

Quick Lesson Overview 

Objective Identify and show one third or one fourth of a region.

Math Understanding A unit fraction of a region names one of a number of equally sized parts.

Vocabulary Thirds, one third ($\frac{1}{3}$), fourths, one fourth ($\frac{1}{4}$)

Professional Development Note

Effective Questioning Techniques Ask comparative questions that focus on the size of one third in relation to the size of the whole. Shade one third of three different-sized squares. **Why aren't these thirds all the same?** *(The squares are different sizes, so the thirds are different also.)* Repeat with fourths.

NCTM Standards

- Number and Operations
- Geometry

(For a complete correlation to the NCTM Standards and Grades Pre-K through 2 Expectations, see Pages 155G and 155H.)

Getting Started

Spiral Review

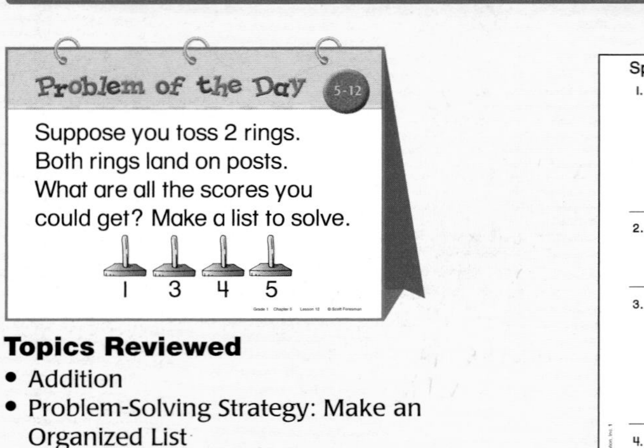

Problem of the Day
5-12
Suppose you toss 2 rings.
Both rings land on posts.
What are all the scores you could get? Make a list to solve.
1 3 4 5

Topics Reviewed

- Addition
- Problem-Solving Strategy: Make an Organized List

Answer 2, 4, 5, 6, 7, 8, 9, and 10

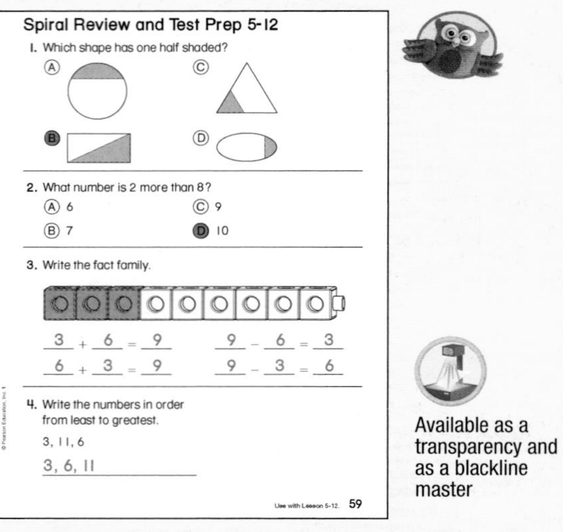

Spiral Review and Test Prep 5-12

1. Which shape has one half shaded?
   Ⓐ Ⓑ Ⓒ Ⓓ
2. What number is 2 more than 8?
   Ⓐ 6 Ⓑ 7 Ⓒ 9 Ⓓ 10
3. Write the fact family.
   3 + 6 = 9   9 − 6 = 3
   6 + 3 = 9   9 − 3 = 6
4. Write the numbers in order from least to greatest.
   3, 11, 6
   3, 6, 11

Use with Lesson 5-12. 59

Available as a transparency and as a blackline master

Topics Reviewed
1. Halves **2.** 1 and 2 More Than
3. Fact Families **4.** Comparing and Ordering Numbers Through 12

Investigating the Concept

Folding Thirds and Fourths

10–15 MIN | Visual/Spatial | WHOLE CLASS

Materials *(per child)* Fraction Folding Shapes (Teaching Tool 20)

What to Do

- Ask children to fold the rectangle so that it shows 3 equal parts and then refold it to show 4 equal parts. Have them share their approaches.
- Explain that when a shape is divided into 3 equal parts, we call the parts thirds. Each part is one third of the whole. When there are 4 equal parts, we call the parts fourths. Each part is one fourth of the whole. Then introduce $\frac{1}{3}$ and $\frac{1}{4}$.
- Have children label the parts of their shapes $\frac{1}{3}$ or $\frac{1}{4}$. Invite them to fold other shapes into thirds and fourths.

Ongoing Assessment

- **What does the 3 stand for in $\frac{1}{3}$?** *(The shape is divided into 3 equal parts.)*
- **Reasoning How are thirds different from fourths?** *(3 equal parts are thirds; 4 equal parts are fourths.)*

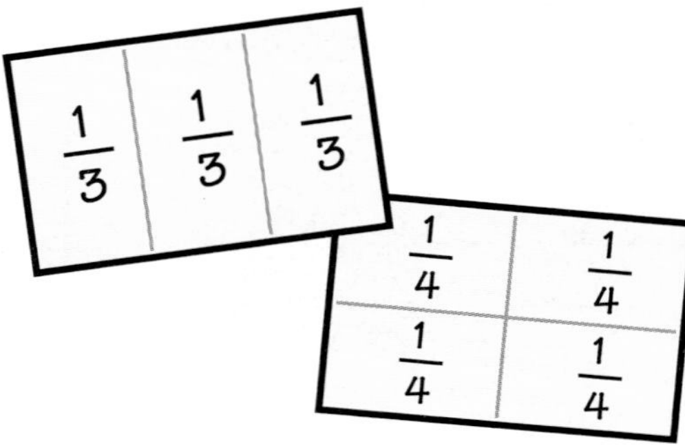

Reaching All Learners

Math and Literature

Eating Fractions

10–15 MIN **Linguistic/Visual/Spatial**

Materials *Eating Fractions* by Bruce McMillan (Scholastic, 1992); *(per child)* 2 construction paper circles; crayons

- Before reading *Eating Fractions,* have children preview the first few pages to predict what the book will be about.
- Pause periodically while reading to have children point out the fractions illustrated in the photographs.
- After reading, distribute the paper circles to the children. Have children color one half of one circle and one fourth of the second circle.

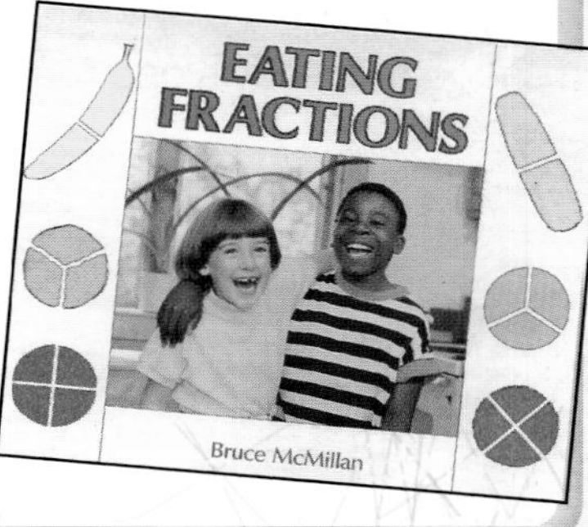

Activate Prior Knowledge/Build Background

English Language Learners

Fraction Glossary

5–10 MIN **Linguistic**

Materials *(per group)* Posterboard; paper rectangles; marker

- To help children make a poster-size glossary of fraction terms write the words *thirds, one third, fourths, one fourth* on the posterboard, leaving space for illustrations of each.
- Have children write $\frac{1}{3}$ and $\frac{1}{4}$ in the appropriate places and attach paper rectangles to illustrate each of the words.
- Say the glossary words and have children repeat them. Post the glossary in the classroom.

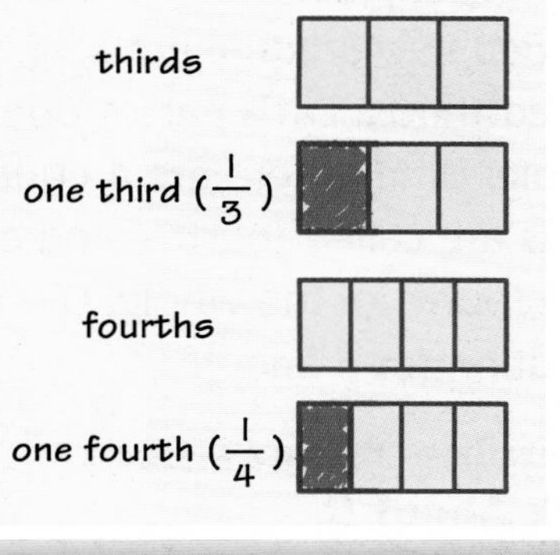

Reteaching

Fraction Sort

10–15 MIN **Linguistic/Visual/Spatial**

SMALL GROUP

Materials Rectangles divided into fourths and thirds; various shapes divided and colored to show one third or one fourth

- Introduce the terms *thirds* and *fourths* using the rectangles to illustrate each term. Color one fourth, and one third, respectively, and ask children what part is colored in by completing the sentence "This is ___ out of ___ parts." Introduce the terms *one third* and *one fourth.*
- Give children shapes to sort into thirds and fourths.

Advanced Learners

Comparing and Ordering Fractions

15–20 MIN **Logical/Mathematical**

Materials Measuring cups ($\frac{1}{4}$ cup, $\frac{1}{3}$ cup, $\frac{1}{2}$ cup); beads; 3 clear plastic cups labeled $\frac{1}{2}$, $\frac{1}{3}$, $\frac{1}{4}$

- On the board, write $\frac{1}{2}$, $\frac{1}{3}$, and $\frac{1}{4}$. Have children predict which is the most and which is the least.
- Invite children to use each of the measuring cups to fill the cups with beads. Have children compare the amount of beads in each cup and order the cups from least to most. Lead children to see that the amount of beads increases as the denominator of the fraction decreases.

Objective Identify and show one third or one fourth of a region.

1 Warm Up

Activate Prior Knowledge Review halves. On the board, draw four or five symmetric shapes. Challenge volunteers to draw a line that divides each shape into halves.

2 Teach

Learn!

Have children tell into how many equal parts each of the shapes at the top of the page is divided. Explain that the first shape is divided into 3 equal parts, and the parts are called thirds. Each part is one third of the whole. When there are 4 equal parts, the parts are called fourths and each part is one fourth of the whole. Discuss the fraction notation for $\frac{1}{3}$ and $\frac{1}{4}$.

Ongoing Assessment

Talk About It

- **What does the 4 in $\frac{1}{4}$ mean?** *(The shape is divided into 4 equal parts.)*
- **What does the 1 in $\frac{1}{4}$ mean?** *(It refers to 1 of those parts.)*

If children confuse thirds and fourths,

then point out that the word *three* begins like *thirds,* and the word *four* begins like *fourths.*

Check

Error Intervention

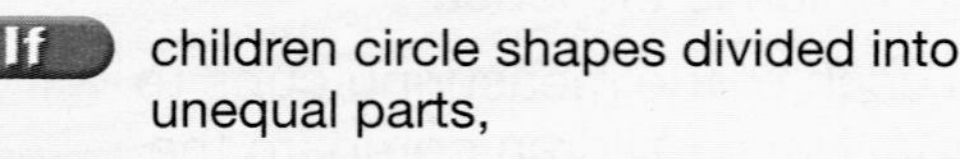

If children circle shapes divided into unequal parts,

then remind them that all of the parts must be equal. *(Also see* Reteaching, *Page 185B.)*

Think About It Have children use the shapes at the top of the page to answer the question.

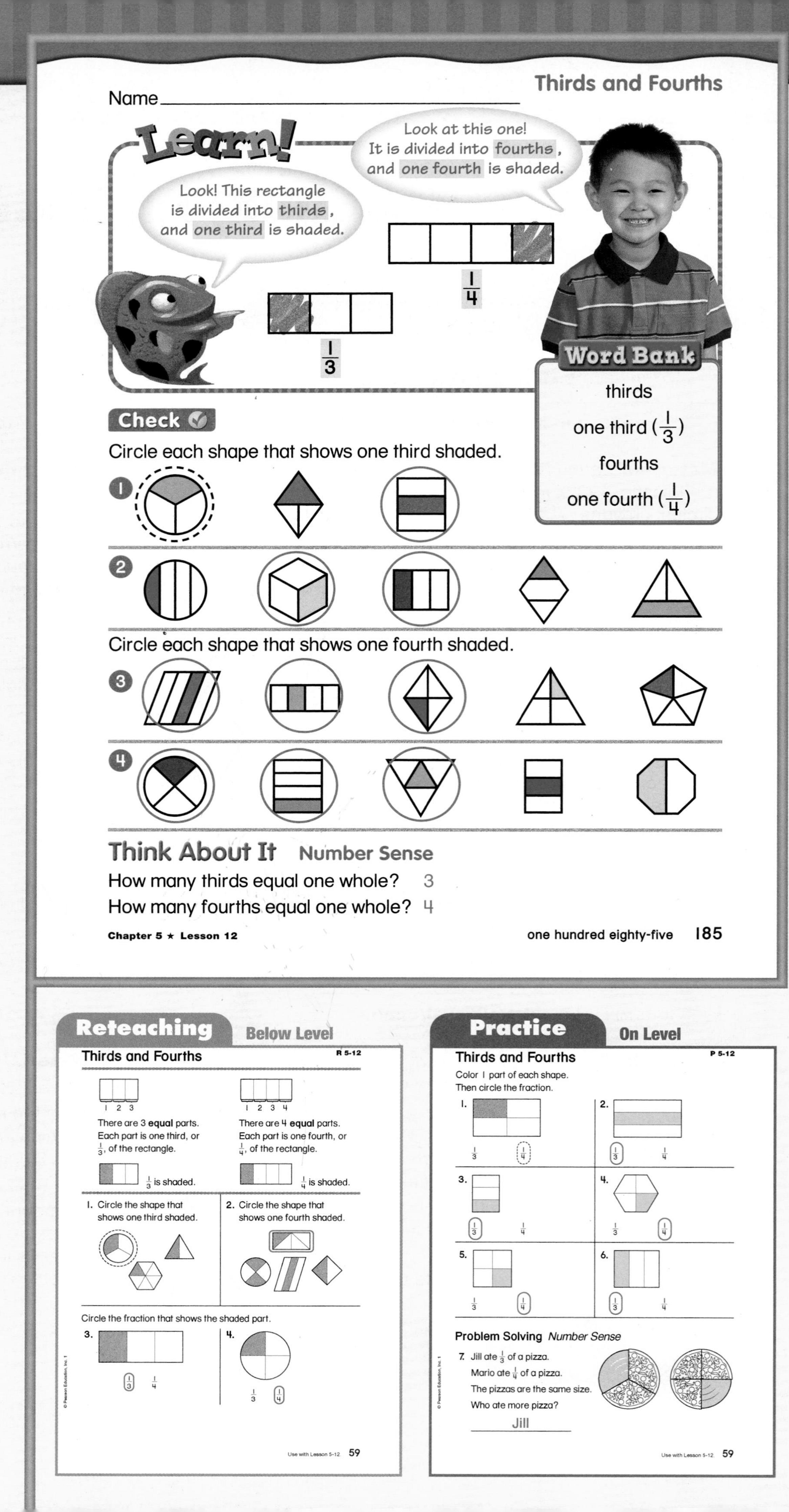

Name ____________________ Thirds and Fourths

Learn!

Look! This rectangle is divided into thirds, and one third is shaded.
Look at this one! It is divided into fourths, and one fourth is shaded.
$\frac{1}{3}$
$\frac{1}{4}$

Word Bank

thirds

one third ($\frac{1}{3}$)

fourths

one fourth ($\frac{1}{4}$)

Check

Circle each shape that shows one third shaded.

1

2

Circle each shape that shows one fourth shaded.

3

4

Think About It Number Sense

How many thirds equal one whole? 3

How many fourths equal one whole? 4

Chapter 5 ★ Lesson 12 — one hundred eighty-five 185

Reteaching Below Level

Thirds and Fourths R 5-12

1 2 3 — There are 3 **equal** parts. Each part is one third, or $\frac{1}{3}$, of the rectangle. $\frac{1}{3}$ is shaded.

1 2 3 4 — There are 4 **equal** parts. Each part is one fourth, or $\frac{1}{4}$, of the rectangle. $\frac{1}{4}$ is shaded.

1. Circle the shape that shows one third shaded.

2. Circle the shape that shows one fourth shaded.

Circle the fraction that shows the shaded part.

3. $\frac{1}{3}$ $\frac{1}{4}$

4. $\frac{1}{3}$ $\frac{1}{4}$

Use with Lesson 5-12. 59

Practice On Level

Thirds and Fourths P 5-12

Color 1 part of each shape. Then circle the fraction.

1. $\frac{1}{3}$ $\frac{1}{4}$

2. $\frac{1}{3}$ $\frac{1}{4}$

3. $\frac{1}{3}$ $\frac{1}{4}$

4. $\frac{1}{3}$ $\frac{1}{4}$

5. $\frac{1}{3}$ $\frac{1}{4}$

6. $\frac{1}{3}$ $\frac{1}{4}$

Problem Solving *Number Sense*

7. Jill ate $\frac{1}{3}$ of a pizza. Mario ate $\frac{1}{4}$ of a pizza. The pizzas are the same size. Who ate more pizza? Jill

Use with Lesson 5-12. 59

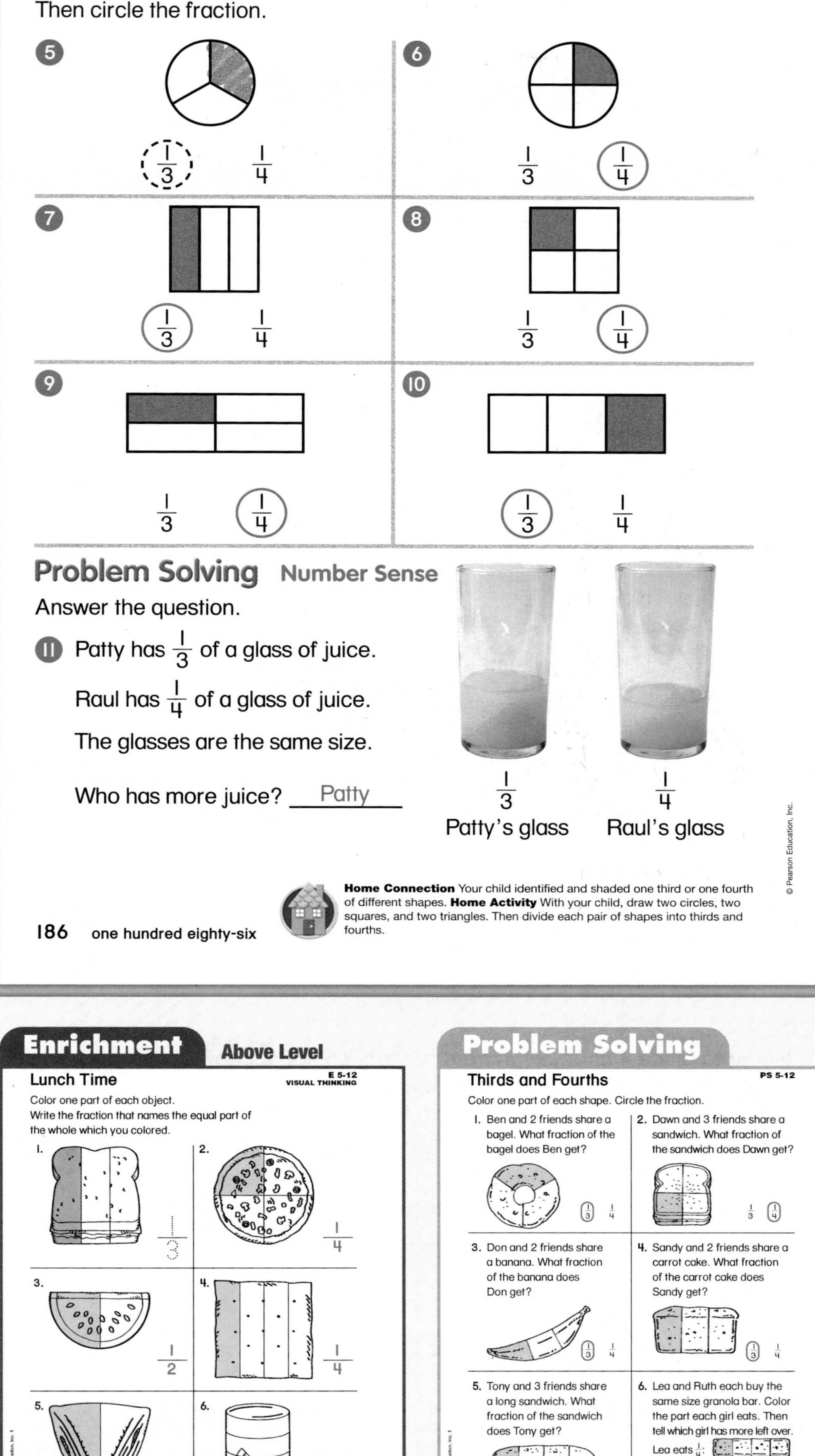

Practice

Color 1 part of each shape.
Then circle the fraction.

5. $\frac{1}{3}$ $\frac{1}{4}$

6. $\frac{1}{3}$ $\frac{1}{4}$

7. $\frac{1}{3}$ $\frac{1}{4}$

8. $\frac{1}{3}$ $\frac{1}{4}$

9. $\frac{1}{3}$ $\frac{1}{4}$

10. $\frac{1}{3}$ $\frac{1}{4}$

Problem Solving Number Sense

Answer the question.

11. Patty has $\frac{1}{3}$ of a glass of juice.
Raul has $\frac{1}{4}$ of a glass of juice.
The glasses are the same size.

Who has more juice? Patty

$\frac{1}{3}$ Patty's glass $\frac{1}{4}$ Raul's glass

Home Connection Your child identified and shaded one third or one fourth of different shapes. **Home Activity** With your child, draw two circles, two squares, and two triangles. Then divide each pair of shapes into thirds and fourths.

Enrichment Above Level

Lunch Time E 5-12 VISUAL THINKING

Color one part of each object.
Write the fraction that names the equal part of the whole which you colored.

1. $\frac{1}{3}$
2. $\frac{1}{4}$
3. $\frac{1}{2}$
4. $\frac{1}{4}$
5. $\frac{1}{2}$
6. $\frac{1}{4}$

Problem Solving

Thirds and Fourths PS 5-12

Color one part of each shape. Circle the fraction.

1. Ben and 2 friends share a bagel. What fraction of the bagel does Ben get? $\frac{1}{3}$ $\frac{1}{4}$
2. Dawn and 3 friends share a sandwich. What fraction of the sandwich does Dawn get? $\frac{1}{3}$ $\frac{1}{4}$
3. Don and 2 friends share a banana. What fraction of the banana does Don get? $\frac{1}{3}$ $\frac{1}{4}$
4. Sandy and 2 friends share a carrot cake. What fraction of the carrot cake does Sandy get? $\frac{1}{3}$ $\frac{1}{4}$
5. Tony and 3 friends share a long sandwich. What fraction of the sandwich does Tony get? $\frac{1}{3}$ $\frac{1}{4}$
6. Lea and Ruth each buy the same size granola bar. Color the part each girl eats. Then tell which girl has more left over.
Lea eats $\frac{1}{4}$.
Ruth eats $\frac{1}{3}$.
Lea has more left over.

3 Practice

For Exercise 11, prompt children to compare the height of the juice in each glass. **In which glass is the juice higher? In which glass is the juice lower?**

Leveled Practice

Below Level Use paper cutouts for Exercise 11.

On Level Complete all exercises as written.

Above Level After completing Exercises 5–10, go back and write the fraction next to each shaded part.

Early Finishers Have children show thirds by building shapes with 3 identical pattern blocks. Similarly, they can show fourths by using 4 identical blocks. They can record their shapes and make fraction books.

4 Assess

Journal Idea Have children draw 2 different shapes and shade one third of each shape. Repeat for one fourth. Ask them to label the shaded part of each shape with the correct fraction name: "one third" or "one fourth."

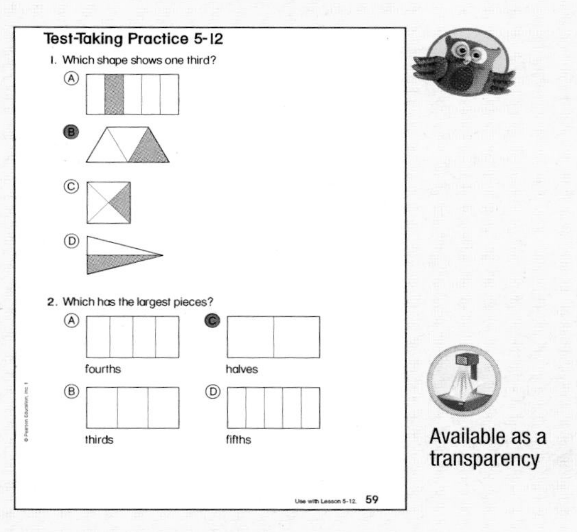

Test-Taking Practice 5-12

1. Which shape shows one third?
Ⓐ
Ⓑ
Ⓒ
Ⓓ

2. Which has the largest pieces?
Ⓐ fourths
Ⓒ halves
Ⓑ thirds
Ⓓ fifths

Use with Lesson 5-12. 59

Available as a transparency

5-13 Fractions of a Set

Lesson Organizer

Quick Lesson Overview

Objective Identify and show one half, one third, or one fourth of a group of two, three, or four objects, respectively.

Math Understanding Groups can be divided into equal parts in the same way that shapes can be divided into equal parts.

Professional Development Note

Effective Questioning Techniques Help children connect fractions of groups with fractions of regions. Compare a shape with four equal parts to a group of four counters. **Are the parts of the shape equal?** *(Yes)* **How do you know the parts of the group are also equal?** *(They are all the same.)*

NCTM Standards

- Number and Operations
- Geometry

(For a complete correlation to the NCTM Standards and Grades Pre-K through 2 Expectations, see Page 155G and 155H.)

Getting Started

Spiral Review

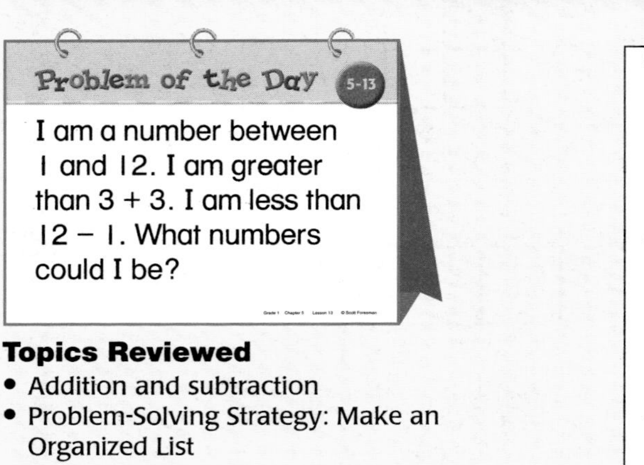

Problem of the Day 5-13

I am a number between 1 and 12. I am greater than 3 + 3. I am less than 12 − 1. What numbers could I be?

Topics Reviewed

- Addition and subtraction
- Problem-Solving Strategy: Make an Organized List

Answer The number must be greater than 3 + 3, or 6, and less than 12 − 1, or 11. So the number could be 7, 8, 9, or 10.

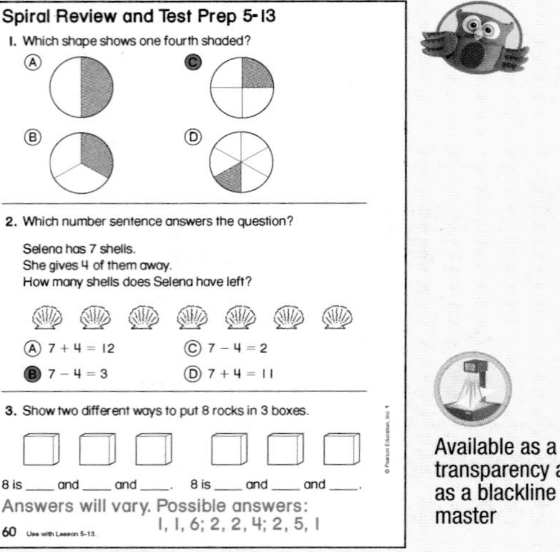

Spiral Review and Test Prep 5-13

1. Which shape shows one fourth shaded?

Ⓐ Ⓒ Ⓑ Ⓓ

2. Which number sentence answers the question?

Selena has 7 shells.
She gives 4 of them away.
How many shells does Selena have left?

Ⓐ 7 + 4 = 12 Ⓒ 7 − 4 = 2
Ⓑ 7 − 4 = 3 Ⓓ 7 + 4 = 11

3. Show two different ways to put 8 rocks in 3 boxes.

8 is ___ and ___ and ___. 8 is ___ and ___ and ___.

Answers will vary. Possible answers: 1, 1, 6; 2, 2, 4; 2, 5, 1

60 Use with Lesson 5-13.

Available as a transparency and as a blackline master

Topics Reviewed

1. Thirds and Fourths
2. Choose an Operation
3. Use Objects

Investigating the Concept

Showing Fractions

10–15 MIN | **Logical/Mathematical** | WHOLE CLASS

Materials *(per child)* 4 two-color counters

What to Do

- Ask children to place 4 counters in front of them so that 3 show yellow and 1 shows red. **How many of the counters are red?** *(1)* **How many counters are there in all?** *(4)* Explain to the children that 1 out of 4 equal parts is red.
- Draw a square and divide it into 4 equal parts. Shade 1 part. **How much of this square is shaded?** *(One fourth or $\frac{1}{4}$)*
- Explain that 1 out of 4 counters is one fourth, also.
- Have children arrange their counters so that 1 out of 3 is red.

Ongoing Assessment

- **What fraction do we use to show 1 out of 3?** *(One third or $\frac{1}{3}$)*
- **Reasoning What is one way to model one fourth using children in our class?** *(Sample response: 4 children—only 1 of them is wearing green)*

Reaching All Learners

Oral Language in Math

Fill in the Blanks

5–10 MIN **Linguistic** SMALL GROUP

Materials Crayons of different colors

- Hold a blue crayon and a red crayon and say: **1 out of 2 crayons is blue. What fraction is blue?** *(One half)*
- Hand out a different combination of colored crayons to each child. Have children complete this sentence: "___ out of ___ crayons is ___." Then have children name the fraction for their combination of crayons.
- Redistribute the crayons and repeat the activity.

One out of three crayons is yellow.

Access Content

English Language Learners

Fractions to Words

10–15 MIN **Auditory/Linguistic** SMALL GROUP

Materials Classroom objects of two different colors such as blocks or crayons

- Write $\frac{1}{2}$, $\frac{1}{3}$, and $\frac{1}{4}$ on the board. Have children read aloud each fraction. If necessary, help children with their pronunciations of the fraction words.
- Show 2 red blocks and 1 yellow block. **Which fraction tells how many are yellow?** Have children point to the fraction on the board and say the words for the fraction.
- Repeat with other fractions.

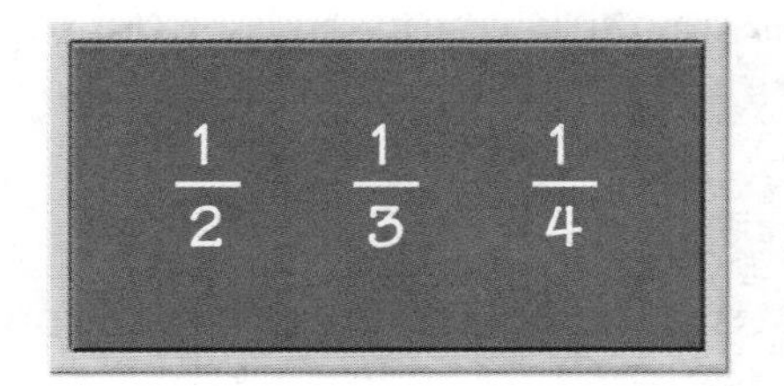

Reteaching

Finding a Fraction of a Group

10–15 MIN **Logical/Mathematical** SMALL GROUP

Materials *(per child)* Two-color counters; 3 outlines of circles divided into halves and thirds and fourths

- Have children place 1 counter with the red-side up in each of the halves of the circle outline. Then have children flip one of the red counters to yellow. Have children color the halves of the circle to match the colors of the counters. **What fraction of the circle is yellow?** *($\frac{1}{2}$)* **What fraction of the counters is red?** *($\frac{1}{2}$)*
- Repeat with thirds and fourths on the other outlines.

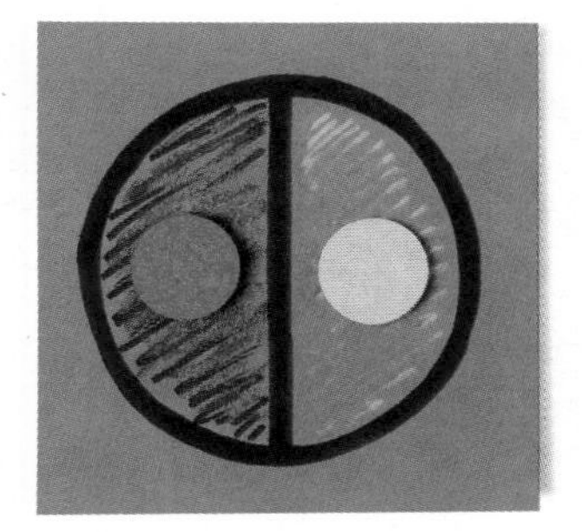

Students with Special Needs

Fraction Book

15–20 MIN **Kinesthetic** INDIVIDUAL

Materials *(per child)* Markers; magazines; drawing paper

- Invite children to make a fraction book showing fractions of a group. Help children think of a theme for their book, such as animals or flowers. Have them label each page with a fraction, $\frac{1}{2}$, $\frac{1}{3}$, and $\frac{1}{4}$, and draw pictures or cut pictures from magazines to represent that fraction.
- Bind the pages together and have children write a title and decorate the cover. Place the books in the classroom library for all to read.

Objective Identify and show one half, one third, or one fourth of a group of two, three, or four objects, respectively.

1 Warm Up

Activate Prior Knowledge Review *same* and *different.* Have children take turns naming objects that are the same and different.

2 Teach

Learn!

Have children count the apples. Then have them tell how many of the apples are green. **1 out of 2 equal parts is green.** Draw a circle. Shade one half. Ask children to tell what fraction we would write to tell about 1 out of 2 equal parts of the circle. **1 out of 2 apples is one half, also.**

Ongoing Assessment

Talk About It

- **What fraction of the group of tomatoes is green?** *($\frac{1}{3}$)*
- **What fraction of the group of peppers is green?** *($\frac{1}{4}$)*

If children have difficulty naming the correct fraction for a part of a group,

then remind them that the number of parts in the whole group goes on the bottom of the fraction.

Check ✓

Error Intervention

If children circle the wrong fraction for a group of pasta,

then have them write numerals above the pictures as they count the objects. *(Also see Reteaching, Page 187B.)*

Think About It On the board draw a triangle divided in half and a group of 2 stars with only one shaded. Write $\frac{1}{2}$. **What does the bottom number tell you about the triangle?** *(It has 2 equal parts.)* **What does the bottom number tell you about the stars?** *(There are 2 stars.)*

Name ____________________

Fractions of a Set

Learn!

1 green apple
2 apples in all
$\frac{1}{2}$ of the apples is green.

1 out of 2 is green.

1 green tomato
3 tomatoes in all
$\frac{1}{3}$ of the tomatoes is green.

1 out of 3 is green.

1 green pepper
4 peppers in all
$\frac{1}{4}$ of the peppers is green.

1 out of 4 is green.

Check ✓

Circle the fraction that tells what part of the set is green.

1. $\frac{1}{2}$ $\frac{1}{3}$ $\frac{1}{4}$
2. $\frac{1}{2}$ $\frac{1}{3}$ $\frac{1}{4}$
3. $\frac{1}{2}$ $\frac{1}{3}$ $\frac{1}{4}$
4. $\frac{1}{2}$ $\frac{1}{3}$ $\frac{1}{4}$

Think About It Reasoning

How is finding a fraction of a **set** like finding a fraction of a **shape?**

Sample response: Each one names equal parts of a whole.

Reteaching Below Level

Fractions of a Set R 5-13

1 ball is gray. 2 balls in all. $\frac{1}{2}$ of the balls are gray.	1 ball is gray. 3 balls in all. $\frac{1}{3}$ of the balls are gray.	1 ball is gray. 4 balls in all. $\frac{1}{4}$ of the balls are gray.

Tell how many are gray. Tell how many in all. Circle the fraction.

1. 1 hat is gray. 4 hats in all. $\frac{1}{2}$ $\frac{1}{3}$ $\frac{1}{4}$
2. 1 doll is gray. 3 dolls in all. $\frac{1}{2}$ $\frac{1}{3}$ $\frac{1}{4}$
3. 1 yo yo is gray. 2 yo yos in all. $\frac{1}{2}$ $\frac{1}{3}$ $\frac{1}{4}$

Circle the fraction that tells what part of the group is gray.

4. $\frac{1}{2}$ $\frac{1}{3}$ $\frac{1}{4}$
5. $\frac{1}{2}$ $\frac{1}{3}$ $\frac{1}{4}$
6. $\frac{1}{2}$ $\frac{1}{3}$ $\frac{1}{4}$
7. $\frac{1}{2}$ $\frac{1}{3}$ $\frac{1}{4}$

Practice On Level

Fractions of a Set P 5-13

Color one object.
Then circle the fraction that tells what part of the group you colored.

1. $\frac{1}{2}$ $\frac{1}{3}$ $\frac{1}{4}$
2. $\frac{1}{2}$ $\frac{1}{3}$ $\frac{1}{4}$
3. $\frac{1}{2}$ $\frac{1}{3}$ $\frac{1}{4}$
4. $\frac{1}{2}$ $\frac{1}{3}$ $\frac{1}{4}$
5. $\frac{1}{2}$ $\frac{1}{3}$ $\frac{1}{4}$
6. $\frac{1}{2}$ $\frac{1}{3}$ $\frac{1}{4}$

Problem Solving *Writing in Math*

7. Tim has a group of balloons. $\frac{1}{3}$ of them are blue. Draw Tim's balloons.

Check that $\frac{1}{3}$ of the balloons are blue.

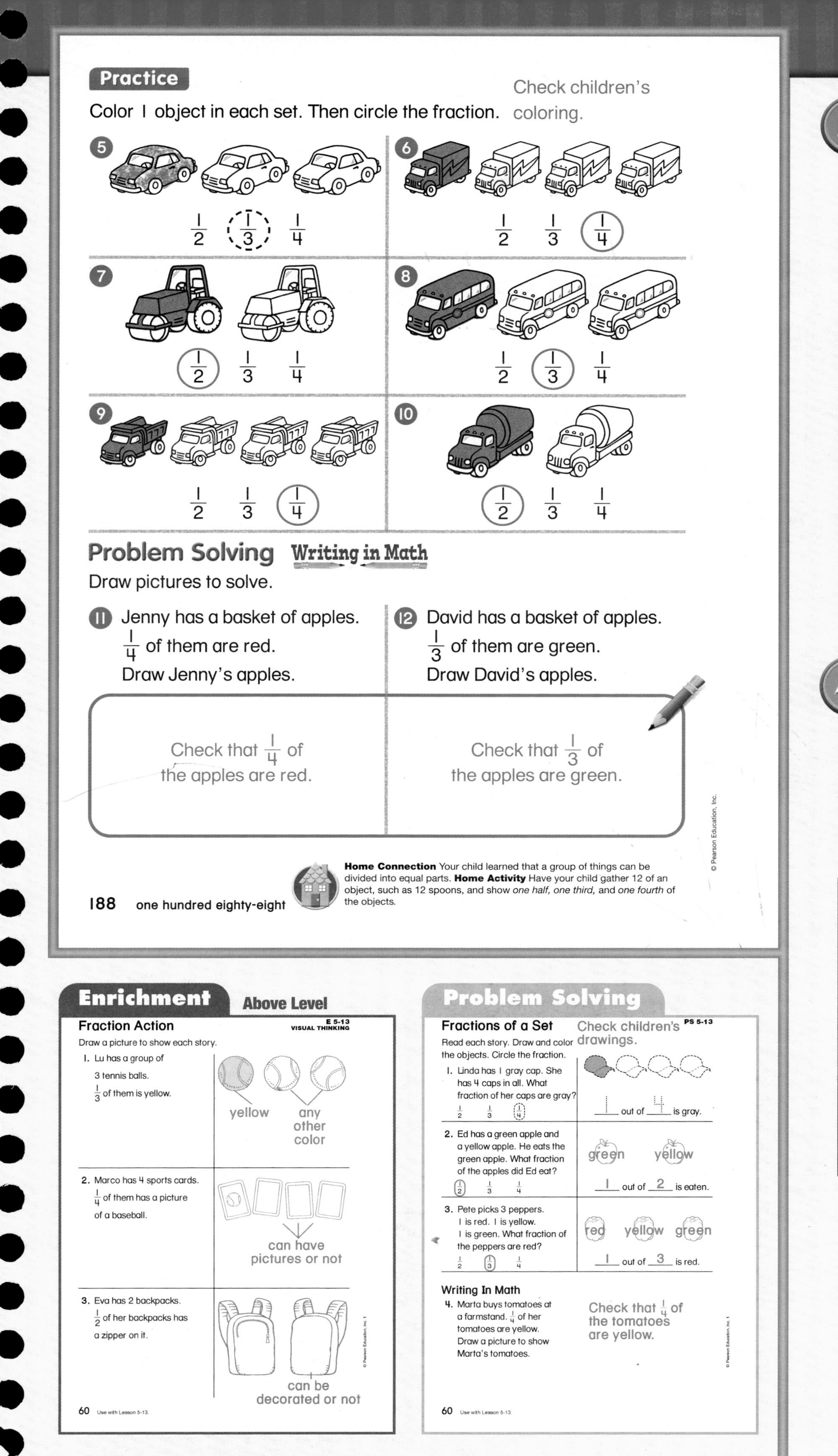

Practice

Color 1 object in each set. Then circle the fraction. Check children's coloring.

5. $\frac{1}{2}$ $\frac{1}{3}$ $\frac{1}{4}$

6. $\frac{1}{2}$ $\frac{1}{3}$ $\frac{1}{4}$

7. $\frac{1}{2}$ $\frac{1}{3}$ $\frac{1}{4}$

8. $\frac{1}{2}$ $\frac{1}{3}$ $\frac{1}{4}$

9. $\frac{1}{2}$ $\frac{1}{3}$ $\frac{1}{4}$

10. $\frac{1}{2}$ $\frac{1}{3}$ $\frac{1}{4}$

Problem Solving Writing in Math

Draw pictures to solve.

11. Jenny has a basket of apples. $\frac{1}{4}$ of them are red. Draw Jenny's apples.

12. David has a basket of apples. $\frac{1}{3}$ of them are green. Draw David's apples.

Check that $\frac{1}{4}$ of the apples are red.

Check that $\frac{1}{3}$ of the apples are green.

Home Connection Your child learned that a group of things can be divided into equal parts. **Home Activity** Have your child gather 12 of an object, such as 12 spoons, and show *one half, one third,* and *one fourth* of the objects.

Enrichment Above Level

Fraction Action E 5-13 VISUAL THINKING

Draw a picture to show each story.

1. Lu has a group of 3 tennis balls. $\frac{1}{3}$ of them is yellow.

2. Marco has 4 sports cards. $\frac{1}{4}$ of them has a picture of a baseball.

3. Eva has 2 backpacks. $\frac{1}{2}$ of her backpacks has a zipper on it.

Problem Solving

Fractions of a Set PS 5-13

Check children's drawings.

Read each story. Draw and color the objects. Circle the fraction.

1. Linda has 1 gray cap. She has 4 caps in all. What fraction of her caps are gray? $\frac{1}{2}$ $\frac{1}{3}$ $\frac{1}{4}$

1 out of 4 is gray.

2. Ed has a green apple and a yellow apple. He eats the green apple. What fraction of the apples did Ed eat? $\frac{1}{2}$ $\frac{1}{3}$ $\frac{1}{4}$

1 out of 2 is eaten.

3. Pete picks 3 peppers. 1 is red. 1 is yellow. 1 is green. What fraction of the peppers are red? $\frac{1}{2}$ $\frac{1}{3}$ $\frac{1}{4}$

1 out of 3 is red.

Writing In Math

4. Marta buys tomatoes at a farmstand. $\frac{1}{4}$ of her tomatoes are yellow. Draw a picture to show Marta's tomatoes.

Check that $\frac{1}{4}$ of the tomatoes are yellow.

3 Practice

Explain that for Exercises 11 and 12, children should think about more than one part of the group. Remind them that the number at the top of the fraction tells how many are red or green.

Leveled Practice

Below Level Use connecting cubes to complete Exercises 5–12.

On Level Complete all exercises as written.

Above Level Write the fraction next to each part you shaded.

Early Finishers Invite children to use connecting cubes to show $\frac{1}{2}$, $\frac{1}{3}$, and $\frac{1}{4}$. Have them use one color to show all of the cubes in the group. Next, have them trade one cube for a different color cube.

4 Assess

Journal Idea Ask children to draw pictures to show one half of a group, one third of a group, and one fourth of a group. Have them label each picture with the appropriate fraction.

Test-Taking Practice 5-13

1. What fraction tells what part of the group are stars?

Ⓐ $\frac{1}{2}$
Ⓑ $\frac{1}{3}$
Ⓒ $\frac{1}{4}$
Ⓓ $\frac{2}{3}$

2. Marc drew a group of triangles. $\frac{1}{4}$ of them are shaded. Which shows the triangles Marc drew?

Ⓐ △ ▲ ▲ ▲
Ⓑ △ △ △ △ ▲
Ⓒ △ △ ▲
Ⓓ △ △ △ ▲

Available as a transparency

5-14 Non-Unit Fractions

Lesson Organizer

Quick Lesson Overview 

Objective Identify and show non-unit fractions of a region or set.

Math Understanding A non-unit fraction names more than one equally-sized part; the number of equal parts is the denominator and the number of parts being named is the numerator.

Professional Development Note

How Children Learn Math Prior to introducing the concept of non-unit fractions, provide children with plenty of unit fraction experiences. Ask children to name 1 out of 2, 3, or 4 equal parts of a region or set. Include practice with manipulatives, folded paper, drawings, and flash cards.

NCTM Standards

- Number and Operations
- Geometry

(For a complete correlation to the NCTM Standards and Grades Pre-K through 2 Expectations, see Page 155G and 155H.)

Getting Started

Spiral Review

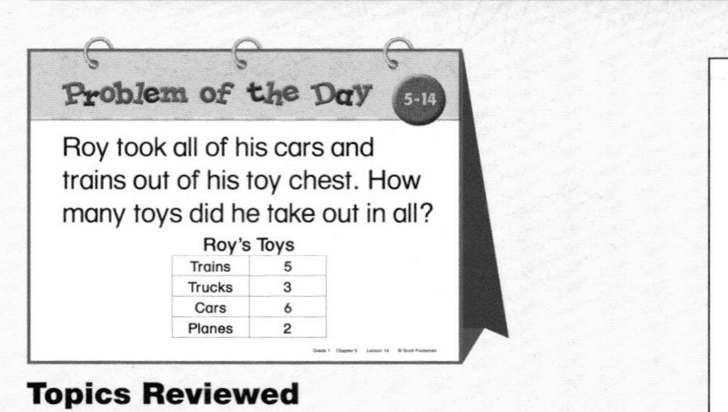

Problem of the Day 5-14

Roy took all of his cars and trains out of his toy chest. How many toys did he take out in all?

Roy's Toys

Trains	5
Trucks	3
Cars	6
Planes	2

Topics Reviewed

- Addition
- Problem-Solving Skill: Use Data from a Table

Answer Roy took out 6 + 5, or 11 toys.

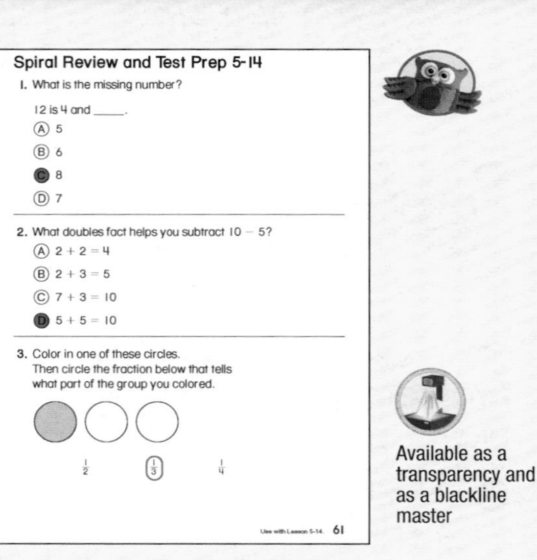

Spiral Review and Test Prep 5-14

1. What is the missing number?
12 is 4 and ____.
(A) 5
(B) 6
(C) 8
(D) 7

2. What doubles fact helps you subtract 10 − 5?
(A) 2 + 2 = 4
(B) 2 + 3 = 5
(C) 7 + 3 = 10
(D) 5 + 5 = 10

3. Color in one of these circles.
Then circle the fraction below that tells what part of the group you colored.
$\frac{1}{2}$ $\frac{1}{3}$ $\frac{1}{4}$

Use with Lesson 5-14. 61

Available as a transparency and as a blackline master

Topics Reviewed
1. Making 11 and 12 **2.** Using Doubles to Subtract **3.** Fractions of a Set **4.** Doubles Plus 1

Investigating the Concept

More Than One Part

10–15 MIN | **Visual/Spatial** | WHOLE CLASS

Materials *(per child)* 4 two-color counters; 5 paper squares

What to Do

- Have children arrange 3 counters to show 2 yellow and 1 red. Ask them to tell how many there are in all and how many are yellow. Write $\frac{2}{3}$ on the board. Point to the denominator and numerator as you explain that there are 3 counters in all and 2 of them are yellow.
- Have children fold a paper square into thirds and shade 2 of the parts yellow. Have them tell the fraction that names the shaded parts. ($\frac{2}{3}$) Repeat the activity for $\frac{3}{3}$, $\frac{2}{4}$, $\frac{3}{4}$, and $\frac{4}{4}$.

Ongoing Assessment

- **Reasoning How are the group of counters and the paper square alike? How are they different?** *(Sample answer: For both we are naming 2 of 3 equal parts. The counters show a fraction of a group. The square shows a fraction of a shape.)*
- **If you have 2 yellow counters and 2 red counters, what fraction names the red counters?** ($\frac{2}{4}$)

Reaching All Learners

Math Vocabulary

Reading Fractions

5–10 MIN **Linguistic**

Materials Chart paper; markers

- Draw a square on the chart. Divide it into 4 equal parts. Color in 1 part and ask: **What fraction tells how much is colored?** *($\frac{1}{4}$)* Ask a volunteer to read the fraction, "one fourth."
- Color 2 squares and show how to write the fraction, $\frac{2}{4}$. Explain that $\frac{2}{4}$ is read: **two fourths** because *two* of the fourths are colored in.
- Continue to color in parts of other shapes to practice reading fractions.

two fourths

Access Content

English Language Learners

Describing Fractions

10–15 MIN **Visual/Spatial/Linguistic**

Materials *(per pair)* Connecting cubes

- On the board draw 3 squares, shading parts of each square to show $\frac{2}{4}$, $\frac{3}{4}$, and $\frac{2}{3}$. Name the fractions for children to repeat.
- Have pairs of children use different colored connecting cubes to show the same fractions, $\frac{2}{3}$, $\frac{2}{4}$, and $\frac{3}{4}$. Then have children write sentences to describe the cubes, such as, "Two fourths of the cubes are red."

Two fourths of the cubes are red.

Reteaching

Working with Non-Unit Fractions

15–20 MIN **Visual/Spatial** SMALL GROUP

Materials *(per child)* Plane Shape Cards (Teaching Tool 16)

- Prior to copying the teaching tool for children, draw lines to divide the shapes into halves, thirds, and fourths.
- Have children color 1 part of each shape and identify what fraction is shown in each, $\frac{1}{2}$, $\frac{1}{3}$, or $\frac{1}{4}$. Then have children color a second part of each shape. Explain to children that their fractions have changed from $\frac{1}{2}$, $\frac{1}{3}$, and $\frac{1}{4}$ to $\frac{2}{2}$, $\frac{2}{3}$, and $\frac{2}{4}$ because there are now 2 parts colored instead of 1.
- Invite children to color the third and fourth parts of those shapes that have 3 and 4 parts. Challenge them to tell what fractions each shows.

Advanced Learners

Adding and Subtracting Fractions

10–15 MIN **Visual/Spatial** SMALL GROUP

Materials 8 inch x 10 inch pieces of red and white construction paper

- Cut the red paper into fourths and label each section $\frac{1}{4}$. Draw lines to divide the white paper into fourths.
- Attach one white paper to the board and write the equation $\frac{1}{4} + \frac{1}{4} =$ ___. Invite children to attach one red section for each fourth added as the group says, "One fourth plus one fourth equals ___." **What is the fraction for the sum?** *(Two fourths)*
- Repeat adding and subtracting fourths, thirds, and halves.

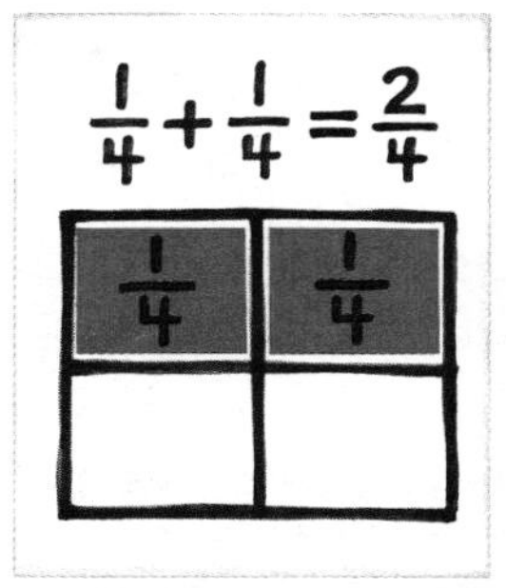

Objective Identify and show non-unit fractions of a region or set.

1 Warm Up

Activate Prior Knowledge Review unit fractions of regions and sets. On the board, draw 4 circles and shade 1 of them. Then draw a square divided into fourths and shade $\frac{1}{4}$. Ask children to name the fractions.

2 Teach

Learn!

Direct children's attention to the square and the group of stars on the student page. Ask them to tell how many equal parts there are and how many of them are shaded. Write $\frac{2}{4}$ on the board, and explain that for both examples, two fourths is shaded.

Ongoing Assessment

Talk About It

- **How would you show three-fourths of the square?** *(Color 3 parts)*
- **How would you show four-fourths?** *(Color all 4 parts)*

If children are confused about which number on the fraction tells how many shaded parts there are,

then draw pictures to show $\frac{1}{4}$, $\frac{2}{4}$, $\frac{3}{4}$, and $\frac{4}{4}$. Ask children to write the fraction for each. Point out that the bottom number always tells the number of equal parts.

Check

Error Intervention

If children make errors when circling fractions,

then have them first cross out any fractions that do not have the correct number of equal parts. *(Also see* Reteaching, *Page 189B.)*

Think About It Discuss the meaning of $\frac{3}{6}$. **How many equal parts are there?** *(6)* **How many of them should you shade?** *(3)*

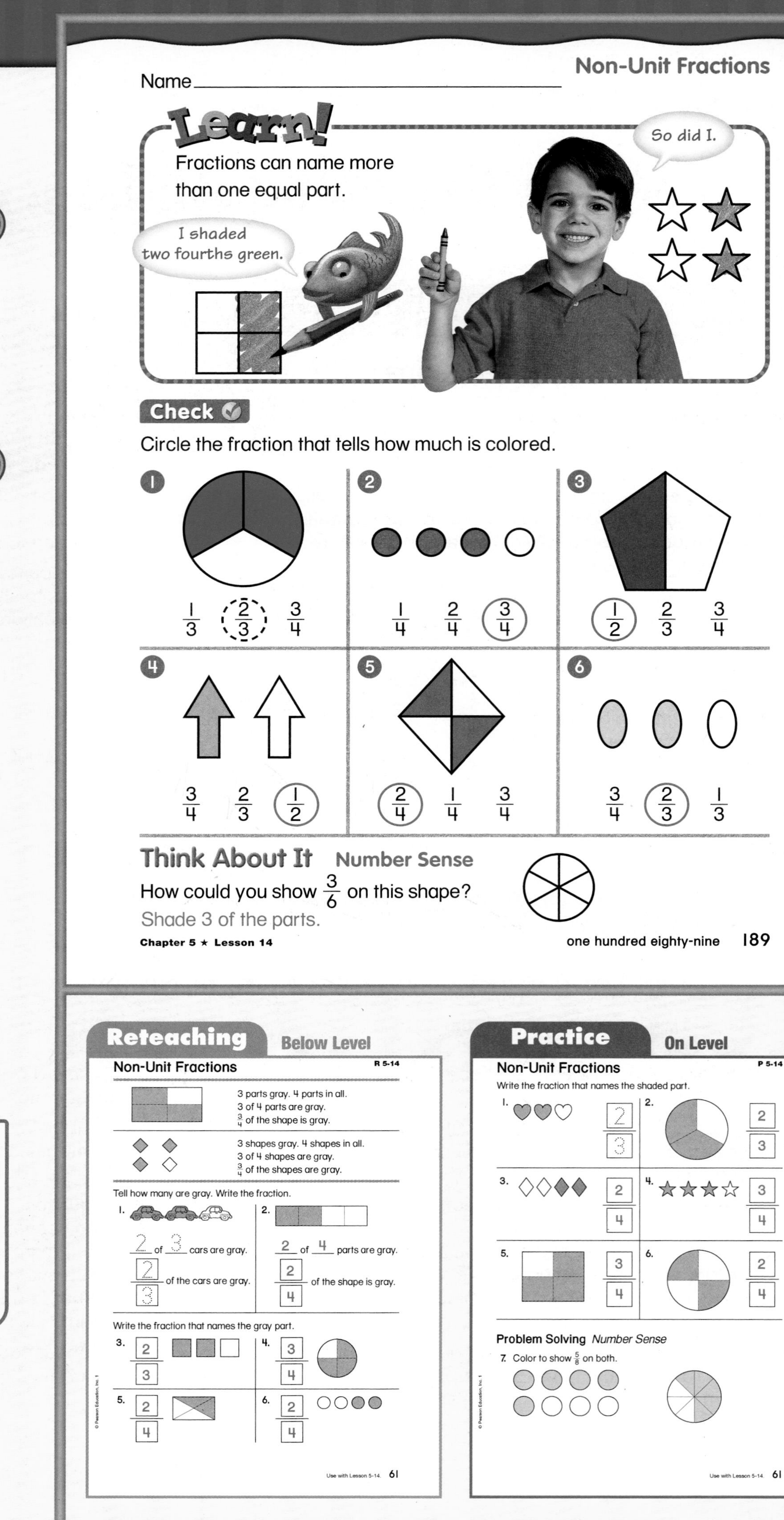

Name ____________________

Non-Unit Fractions

Learn!

Fractions can name more than one equal part.

Check

Circle the fraction that tells how much is colored.

1. $\frac{1}{3}$ $\frac{2}{3}$ $\frac{3}{4}$
2. $\frac{1}{4}$ $\frac{2}{4}$ $\frac{3}{4}$
3. $\frac{1}{2}$ $\frac{2}{3}$ $\frac{3}{4}$
4. $\frac{3}{4}$ $\frac{2}{3}$ $\frac{1}{2}$
5. $\frac{2}{4}$ $\frac{1}{4}$ $\frac{3}{4}$
6. $\frac{3}{4}$ $\frac{2}{3}$ $\frac{1}{3}$

Think About It Number Sense

How could you show $\frac{3}{6}$ on this shape?

Shade 3 of the parts.

Chapter 5 ★ Lesson 14 one hundred eighty-nine 189

Reteaching Below Level

Non-Unit Fractions R 5-14

3 parts gray. 4 parts in all.
3 of 4 parts are gray.
$\frac{3}{4}$ of the shape is gray.

3 shapes gray. 4 shapes in all.
3 of 4 shapes are gray.
$\frac{3}{4}$ of the shapes are gray.

Tell how many are gray. Write the fraction.

1. 2 of 3 cars are gray. $\frac{2}{3}$ of the cars are gray.
2. 2 of 4 parts are gray. $\frac{2}{4}$ of the shape is gray.

Write the fraction that names the gray part.

3. $\frac{2}{3}$
4. $\frac{3}{4}$
5. $\frac{2}{4}$
6. $\frac{2}{4}$

Use with Lesson 5-14. 61

Practice On Level

Non-Unit Fractions P 5-14

Write the fraction that names the shaded part.

1. $\frac{2}{3}$
2. $\frac{2}{3}$
3. $\frac{2}{4}$
4. $\frac{3}{4}$
5. $\frac{3}{4}$
6. $\frac{2}{4}$

Problem Solving *Number Sense*

7. Color to show $\frac{5}{8}$ on both.

Use with Lesson 5-14. 61

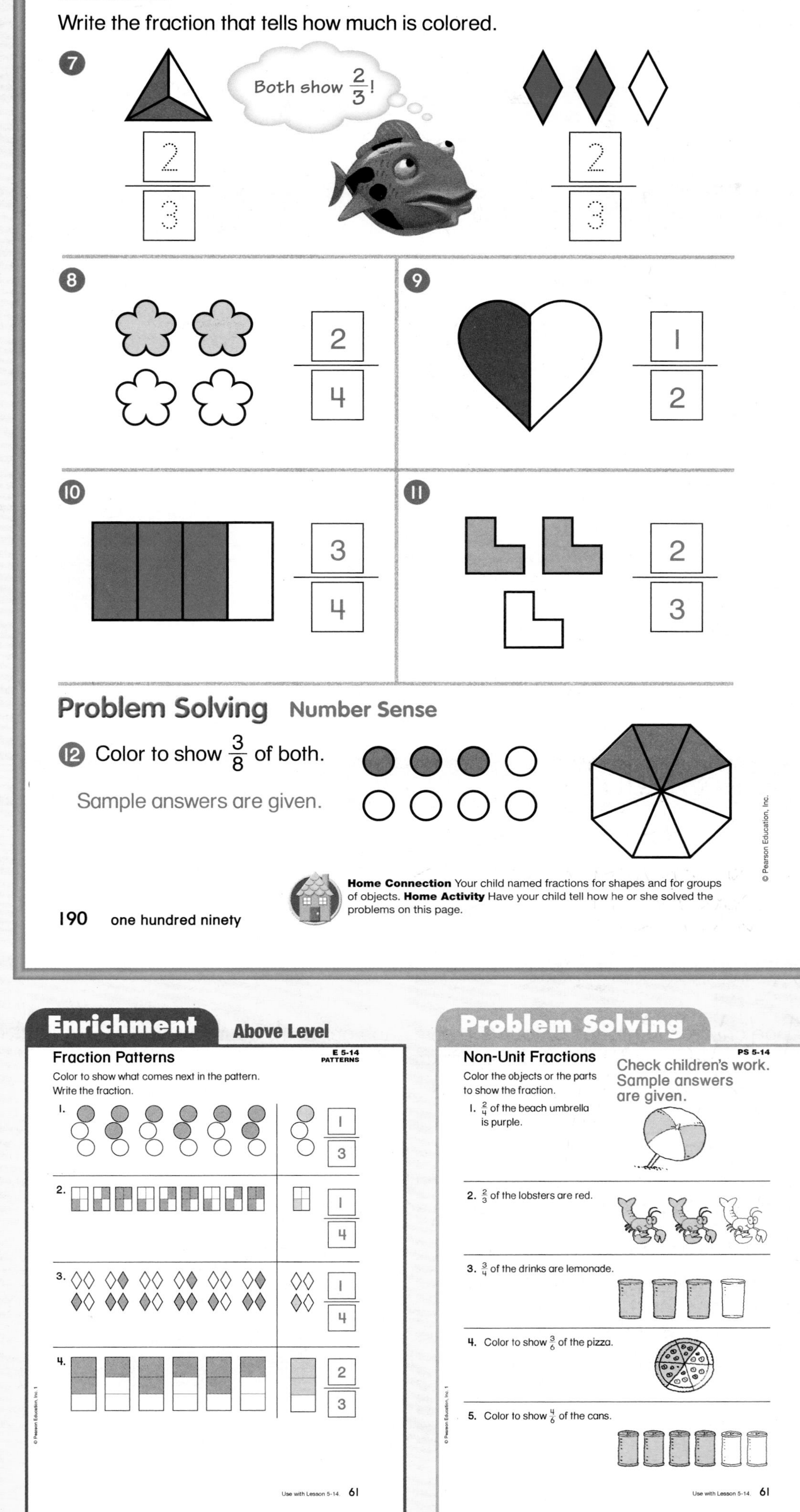

Practice

Write the fraction that tells how much is colored.

7. $\frac{2}{3}$ $\frac{2}{3}$

Both show $\frac{2}{3}$!

8. $\frac{2}{4}$

9. $\frac{1}{2}$

10. $\frac{3}{4}$

11. $\frac{2}{3}$

Problem Solving Number Sense

12. Color to show $\frac{3}{8}$ of both.

Sample answers are given.

Home Connection Your child named fractions for shapes and for groups of objects. Home Activity Have your child tell how he or she solved the problems on this page.

190 one hundred ninety

© Pearson Education, Inc.

Enrichment Above Level

Fraction Patterns E 5-14 PATTERNS

Color to show what comes next in the pattern. Write the fraction.

1. $\frac{1}{3}$

2. $\frac{1}{4}$

3. $\frac{1}{4}$

4. $\frac{2}{3}$

Use with Lesson 5-14. 61

Problem Solving

Non-Unit Fractions PS 5-14

Check children's work. Sample answers are given.

Color the objects or the parts to show the fraction.

1. $\frac{2}{4}$ of the beach umbrella is purple.

2. $\frac{2}{3}$ of the lobsters are red.

3. $\frac{3}{4}$ of the drinks are lemonade.

4. Color to show $\frac{3}{6}$ of the pizza.

5. Color to show $\frac{4}{6}$ of the cans.

Use with Lesson 5-14. 61

3 Practice

Remind children to count the number of equal parts first and write that number on the bottom. Then ask them to count the number of shaded parts and write that number on the top.

Reading Assist: Draw Conclusions Have children look at Exercise 7. **Which number is greater? Which number is less? Do you think the bottom number is always going to be greater? Why or why not?**

Leveled Practice

Below Level Complete Exercises 7–12 in pairs.

On Level Complete Exercises 7–12 individually.

Above Level Write each fraction in words.

Early Finishers Have pairs of children make fraction fact cards and take turns flashing a card and naming the fraction.

4 Assess

Journal Idea Write $\frac{2}{3}$ and $\frac{3}{4}$ on the board. Ask children to draw pictures to show the fractions. Then have them label each picture.

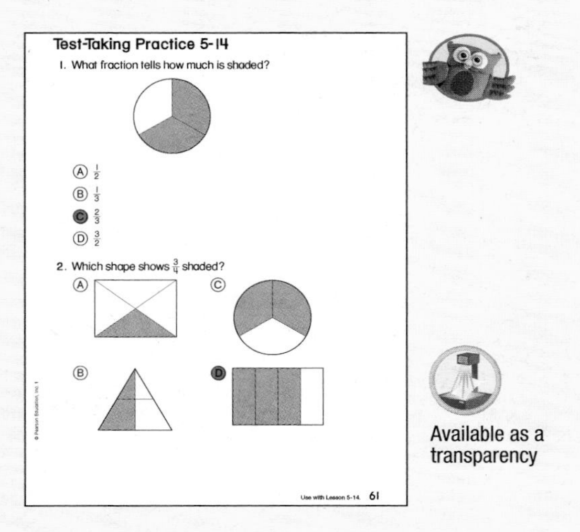

Test-Taking Practice 5-14

1. What fraction tells how much is shaded?

2. Which shape shows $\frac{3}{4}$ shaded?

Use with Lesson 5-14. 61

Available as a transparency

Use Data from a Chart

Lesson Organizer

Quick Lesson Overview

Objective Solve problems by using data from a chart.

Math Understanding A chart can hold data that is useful in solving problems.

Vocabulary Equal share

Materials for Student Pages *(per child)* 15 counters

Professional Development Note

Math Background Separating a group into equal parts is a prerequisite skill for understanding fractions with numerators greater than one, multiplying, and dividing. Help children devise strategies for giving equal shares, such as giving one item to each child before giving a second item to any child.

NCTM Standards

- Algebra
- Problem Solving
- Number and Operations

(For a complete correlation to the NCTM Standards and Grades Pre-K through 2 Expectations, see Page 155G and 155H.)

Getting Started

Spiral Review

Problem of the Day 5-15

Ellen made a beaded necklace. She used 5 spheres and some cubes. She used 10 beads in all. How many cubes did Ellen use for her necklace?

Topics Reviewed
- Addition and subtraction
- Problem-Solving: One-Step Problem

Answer Ellen used 5 cubes for her necklace.

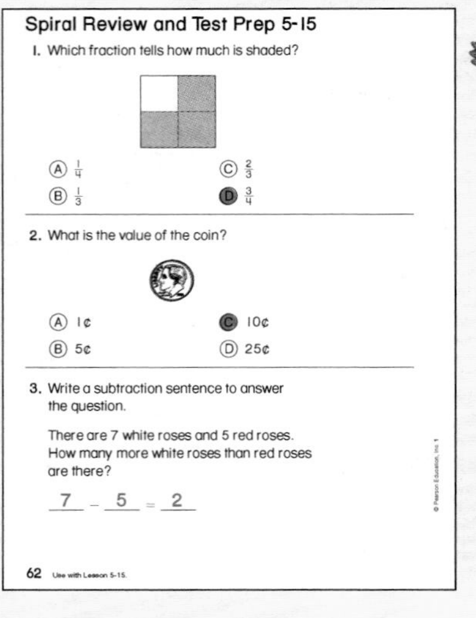
Spiral Review and Test Prep 5-15

1. Which fraction tells how much is shaded?

   Ⓐ $\frac{1}{4}$ Ⓑ $\frac{1}{3}$ Ⓒ $\frac{2}{3}$ Ⓓ $\frac{3}{4}$

2. What is the value of the coin?

   Ⓐ 1¢ Ⓑ 5¢ Ⓒ 10¢ Ⓓ 25¢

3. Write a subtraction sentence to answer the question.

   There are 7 white roses and 5 red roses. How many more white roses than red roses are there?

   7 – 5 = 2

62 Use with Lesson 5-15.

Available as a transparency and as a blackline master

Topics Reviewed
1. Non-Unit Fractions
2. Dime
3. Write a Number Sentence

Investigating the Concept

Equal Shares

Materials *(per group)* 12 counters

What to Do

- Arrange children in groups of four and give each group 12 counters. Ask children to pretend that the counters are carrots.
- Have each group decide how they would divide 12 carrots equally among the group.
- Discuss children's different strategies for solving the problem.
- Explain that the number of carrots each child gets is called an equal share. Have children suggest why it is called an equal share.

Ongoing Assessment

- **Number Sense What is each child's equal share when 12 carrots are shared among 6 children?** *(2)*
- **What is each child's equal share when 10 carrots are shared among 2 children?** *(5)*

Reaching All Learners

Math Vocabulary

Understanding Equal Shares

5–10 MIN | **Linguistic** | WHOLE CLASS

Materials Counters

- Ask children to pretend that they are having a party. They have 8 treats to share. Give 4 children 2 counters each.
- Ask if each of the children got an equal share.
- Have children demonstrate their understanding of equal share by offering explanations, such as "They all have the same," or "Everyone has a fair share."
- Repeat the activity with a different number of counters and children.

Access Content

English Language Learners

Sharing Equally

15–20 MIN | **Linguistic**

Materials Paper plates; connecting cubes

- Organize children into groups of three. Give the group 3 plates and 9 cubes. Encourage children to work as a group to decide how to share the cubes equally. Allow them to dialogue in their primary languages.
- Bring the entire group together. **What is each child's share?** Invite a child from each group to explain how they divided the cubes.
- Repeat using different numbers of cubes and plates.

Reteaching

Equal Shares in the Classroom

10–15 MIN | **Social/Cooperative**

Materials Chart paper; markers; classroom objects

- Prepare a two-column chart with the head: *Things to Share.* List classroom objects that are to be shared in centers, such as new library books, toys, and snacks. Then write how many of each are to be shared.
- Arrange for different-sized groups of children to share these things. Refer to the chart for the number to be shared and have children decide how to make sure that every-one will get an equal share.

Math and Science

Planting Seeds

15–20 MIN | **Logical/Mathematical** | SMALL GROUP

Materials Variety of seeds; paper cups; soil; water

- Discuss with the children how seeds need room to grow and that too many seeds should not be planted in one pot.
- Prepare a chart that lists different types of seeds and the number of each type of seed that the class has to plant. Have children use the chart to figure out how many seeds to plant in each cup.
- Children can then add soil, seeds, and water.

Objective Solve problems by using data from a chart.

1 Warm Up

Activate Prior Knowledge Review reading a chart. Draw a chart on the board. **What is the title of this chart? What is included in the chart?**

2 Teach

Learn!

Have children read the question aloud. Explain that they need to find out how many erasers each child will get. **How can you find the number of erasers that the class has?** *(Look at the chart.)* Have children suggest ways to solve the problem.

Ongoing Assessment

Talk About It

- **What is each child's equal share?** *(4)*
- **How could you check your answer?** *(Sample response: Ask, "Did I start with 12 counters? Are the groups equal?")*

If children have difficulty making equal groups,

then show them how to hand out the counters one at a time to each child.

Check

Error Intervention

If children do not draw four groups of 2 counters for Exercise 1,

then have them count all of the counters to be sure that they started with the correct number. *(Also see* Reteaching, *Page 191B.)*

Think About It Ask: **Could two children share 2 crayons equally?** *(Yes)* **How about 3 crayons equally?** *(No)* **4?** *(Yes)* **5?** *(No)* **What pattern do you see?** *(Sample response: Yes, no, yes, no, …)*

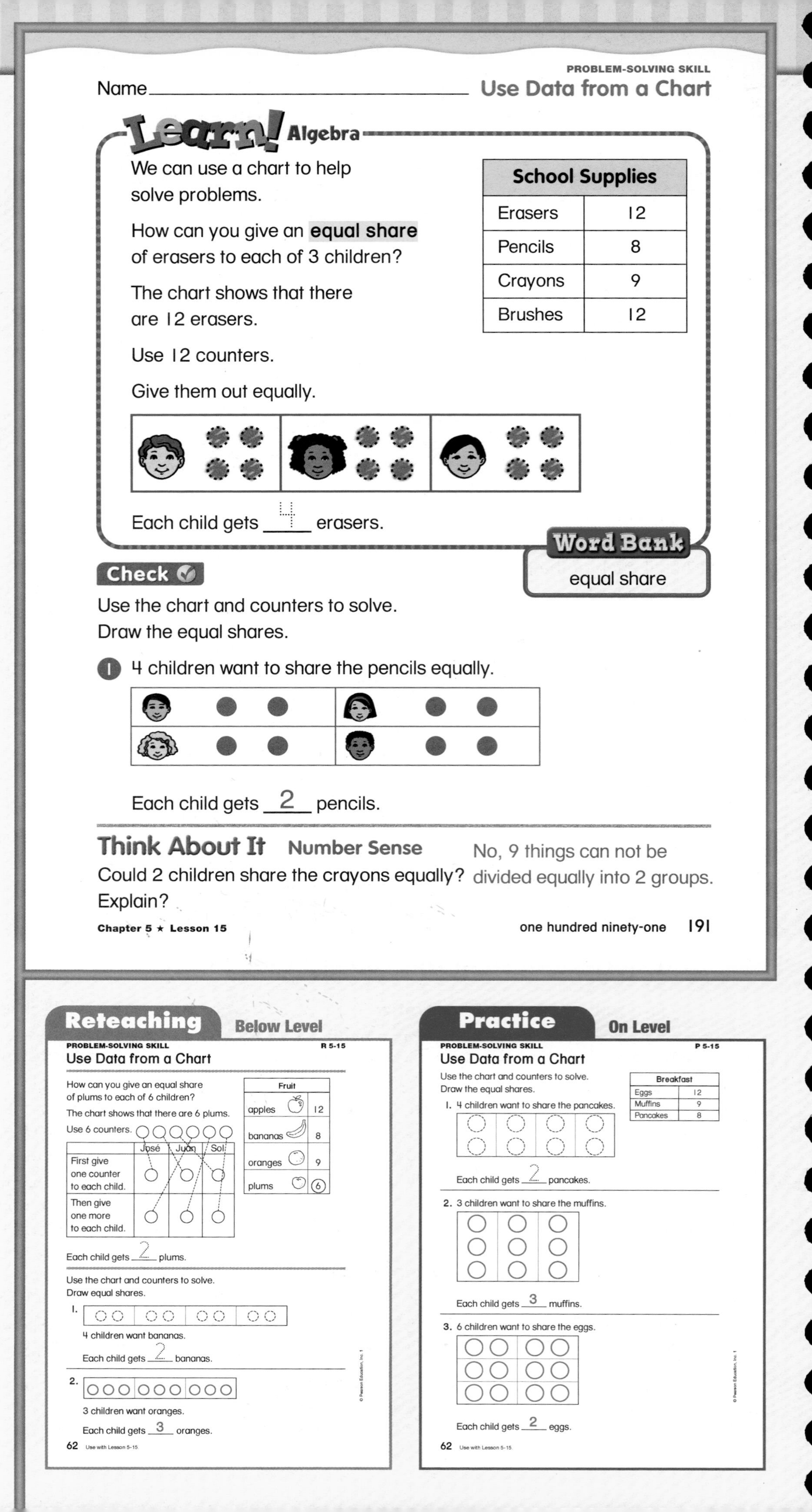

PROBLEM-SOLVING SKILL
Name ____________ Use Data from a Chart

Learn! Algebra

We can use a chart to help solve problems.

How can you give an **equal share** of erasers to each of 3 children?

The chart shows that there are 12 erasers.

Use 12 counters.

Give them out equally.

School Supplies	
Erasers	12
Pencils	8
Crayons	9
Brushes	12

Each child gets __4__ erasers.

Word Bank: equal share

Check

Use the chart and counters to solve.
Draw the equal shares.

1. 4 children want to share the pencils equally.

Each child gets __2__ pencils.

Think About It Number Sense
Could 2 children share the crayons equally? Explain?
No, 9 things can not be divided equally into 2 groups.

Chapter 5 ★ Lesson 15 one hundred ninety-one 191

Reteaching Below Level

PROBLEM-SOLVING SKILL R 5-15
Use Data from a Chart

How can you give an equal share of plums to each of 6 children?
The chart shows that there are 6 plums.
Use 6 counters.

Fruit	
apples	12
bananas	8
oranges	9
plums	6

	José	Juan	Sol
First give one counter to each child.			
Then give one more to each child.			

Each child gets __2__ plums.

Use the chart and counters to solve.
Draw equal shares.

1. 4 children want bananas.
Each child gets __2__ bananas.

2. 3 children want oranges.
Each child gets __3__ oranges.

62 Use with Lesson 5-15

Practice On Level

PROBLEM-SOLVING SKILL P 5-15
Use Data from a Chart

Use the chart and counters to solve.
Draw the equal shares.

Breakfast	
Eggs	12
Muffins	9
Pancakes	8

1. 4 children want to share the pancakes.
Each child gets __2__ pancakes.

2. 3 children want to share the muffins.
Each child gets __3__ muffins.

3. 6 children want to share the eggs.
Each child gets __2__ eggs.

62 Use with Lesson 5-15

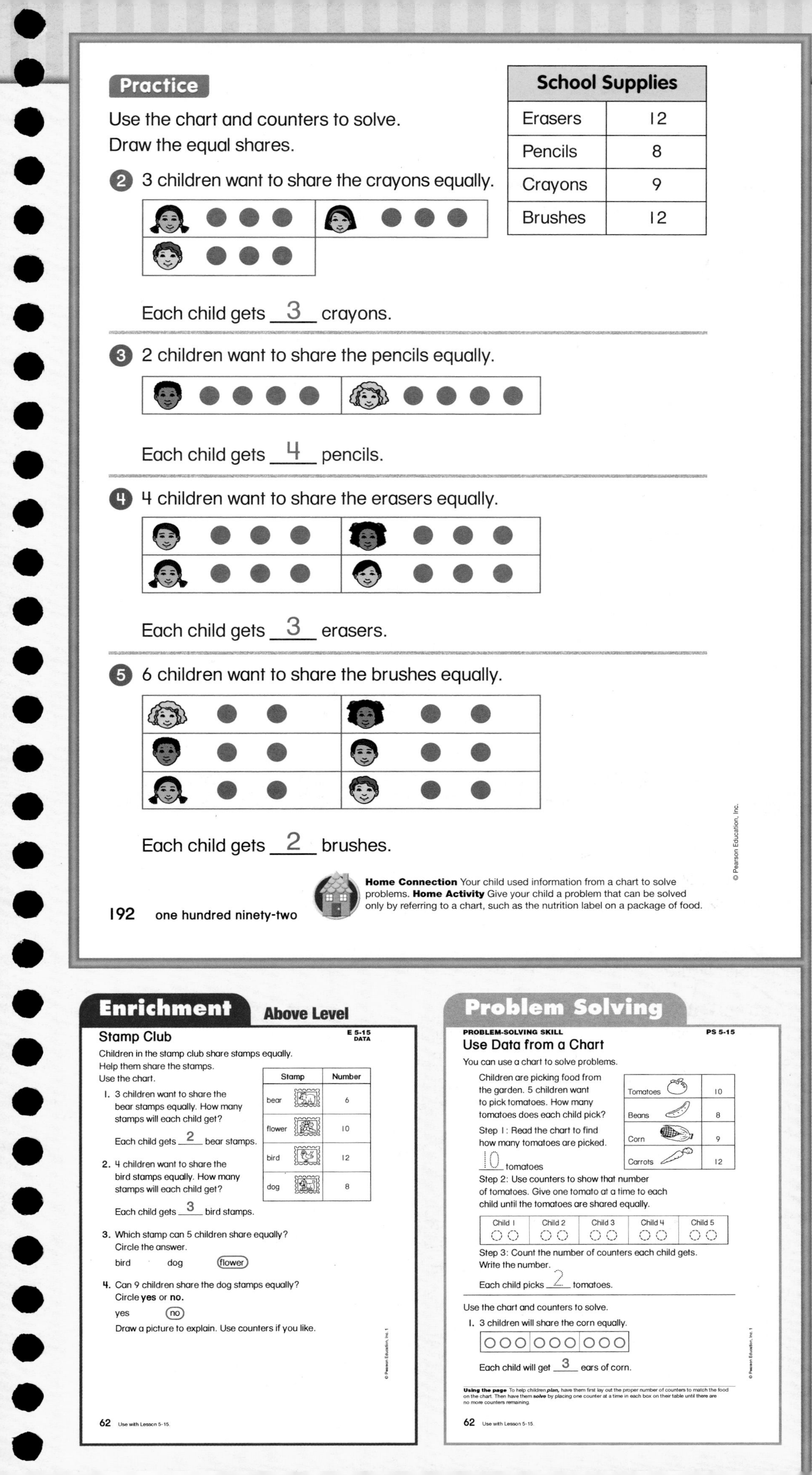

Practice

School Supplies	
Erasers	12
Pencils	8
Crayons	9
Brushes	12

Use the chart and counters to solve.
Draw the equal shares.

2. 3 children want to share the crayons equally.

Each child gets 3 crayons.

3. 2 children want to share the pencils equally.

Each child gets 4 pencils.

4. 4 children want to share the erasers equally.

Each child gets 3 erasers.

5. 6 children want to share the brushes equally.

Each child gets 2 brushes.

Home Connection Your child used information from a chart to solve problems. **Home Activity** Give your child a problem that can be solved only by referring to a chart, such as the nutrition label on a package of food.

Enrichment — Above Level

Stamp Club

E 5-15 DATA

Children in the stamp club share stamps equally.
Help them share the stamps.
Use the chart.

Stamp	Number
bear	6
flower	10
bird	12
dog	8

1. 3 children want to share the bear stamps equally. How many stamps will each child get?

   Each child gets 2 bear stamps.

2. 4 children want to share the bird stamps equally. How many stamps will each child get?

   Each child gets 3 bird stamps.

3. Which stamp can 5 children share equally? Circle the answer.

   bird dog (flower)

4. Can 9 children share the dog stamps equally? Circle **yes** or **no.**

   yes (no)

   Draw a picture to explain. Use counters if you like.

Problem Solving

PROBLEM-SOLVING SKILL PS 5-15

Use Data from a Chart

You can use a chart to solve problems.

Children are picking food from the garden. 5 children want to pick tomatoes. How many tomatoes does each child pick?

Tomatoes	10
Beans	8
Corn	9
Carrots	12

Step 1: Read the chart to find how many tomatoes are picked.

10 tomatoes

Step 2: Use counters to show that number of tomatoes. Give one tomato at a time to each child until the tomatoes are shared equally.

Child 1	Child 2	Child 3	Child 4	Child 5
○ ○	○ ○	○ ○	○ ○	○ ○

Step 3: Count the number of counters each child gets. Write the number.

Each child picks 2 tomatoes.

Use the chart and counters to solve.

1. 3 children will share the corn equally.

   Each child will get 3 ears of corn.

Using the page To help children *plan,* have them first lay out the proper number of counters to match the food on the chart. Then have them *solve* by placing one counter at a time in each box on their table until there are no more counters remaining.

3 Practice

Remind children to look at the chart to find the data needed to solve each problem.

Reading Assist: Main Idea Explain to children that in each of these problems, the main idea involves making equal groups. For Exercises 2–5, ask children to tell the number of counters they should begin with, the number of groups they will make, and the number of counters that end up in each group.

Leveled Practice

Below Level Work in pairs and use counters.

On Level Work individually and use counters.

Above Level Complete all exercises without counters.

Early Finishers Invite each child to make up a problem similar to those in this lesson. Have partners exchange problems and solve.

4 Assess

Journal Idea Ask children to solve the following problem and draw a picture to show what they did. **Two children want to share 12 grapes equally. How many grapes will each child get?** *(6)*

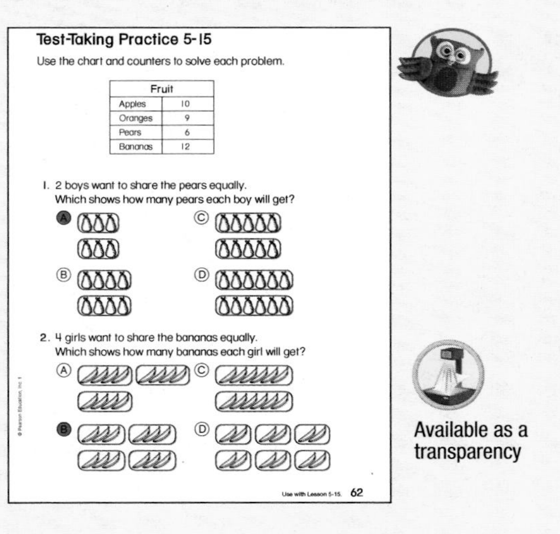

Test-Taking Practice 5-15

Use the chart and counters to solve each problem.

Fruit	
Apples	10
Oranges	9
Pears	6
Bananas	12

1. 2 boys want to share the pears equally. Which shows how many pears each boy will get?

   Ⓐ (marked) Ⓑ Ⓒ Ⓓ

2. 4 girls want to share the bananas equally. Which shows how many bananas each girl will get?

   Ⓐ Ⓑ (marked) Ⓒ Ⓓ

Use with Lesson 5-15. 62

Available as a transparency

Shapes All Around Us

Lesson Organizer

Quick Lesson Overview

Objective Review and apply concepts, skills, and strategies learned in this and previous chapters.

Math Understanding Some real-world problems can be solved using known concepts, skills, and strategies.

Professional Development Note

Math Background Children apply what they know about geometry to solve new problems. If a child has difficulty solving a problem, determine if the child does not understand the geometry term or does not know a prerequisite skill or strategy. To help children understand the content, read problems aloud to them.

NCTM Standards

- Number and Operations
- Geometry

(For a complete correlation to the NCTM Standards and Grades Pre-K through 2 Expectations, see Pages 155G and 155H.)

Getting Started

Spiral Review

Problem of the Day 5-16

Solve.
Betty has 10 peanuts.
Sue has 3 more peanuts than Betty.
How many peanuts does Sue have?

Topics Reviewed
- Addition
- Problem-Solving: One-Step Problem

Answer Sue has 10 + 3, or 13 peanuts.

Spiral Review and Test Prep 5-16

1. There were 3 fish in Sam's tank.
He put 2 more fish in the tank.
How many fish are in the tank now?
(A) 1 fish (C) 3 fish
(B) 2 fish (D) 5 fish

2. What is the missing number?
7 is greater than ____.
(A) 7 (C) 9
(B) 11 (D) 6

3. Use the chart and counters to solve.
Draw the equal shares.

Animal Stamps	
Lion	6
Tiger	12
Bear	8

3 children want to share the lion stamps.

Each child gets 2 lion stickers.

Use with Lesson 5-16. 63

Available as a transparency and as a blackline master

Topics Reviewed
1. Write a Number Sentence
2. Comparing Numbers to 5 and to 10
3. Use Data from a Chart

Investigating the Concept

Reviewing Geometry

Materials Geometric solids; index cards labeled with the names of each solid figure

What to Do

- Display all five geometric solids and labels in random order. Discuss each shape, its characteristics, and its name. Encourage children to use the words *flat surface, face,* and *vertex* in their descriptions. Remind children that the word *face* can be used only to refer to cubes and other prisms.
- Have children take turns choosing a shape and matching it with the index card that says its name.

Ongoing Assessment

- **Reasoning How are a sphere and a cube different?** *(Sample response: A sphere has no flat surfaces; a cube has 6 flat surfaces.)*
- **What objects do you know that are shaped like a cylinder?** (*Sample response: A can, a glass, a paper towel tube)*

cylinder

Reaching All Learners

Math and Literature

Geometry All Around

10–15 MIN **Visual/Spatial**

Materials *The Wing on a Flea: A Book About Shapes* by Ed Emberley (Little, Brown & Company, 2001); *(per child)* shapes cut from colored paper; glue; paper

- Read the rhyming text on each page. Have children figure out which shapes were used to make the animals on each page.
- Children can point to the rectangles, triangles, and circles that form the fleas' wings, birds' beaks, and cats' noses in the art.
- As a follow-up activity, provide children with paper shapes to create animal collages.

Access Content

English Language Learners

Tracing Shapes

10–15 MIN **Kinesthetic**

- Draw squares, circles, rectangles, and triangles on the board. Invite children to say the shape names with you.
- Ask a child to face away as another child traces a shape on his or her back. The child is to guess the name of the shape traced. Accept either a word answer or the child pointing to the shape on the board.
- Partners take turns tracing and guessing shapes on each other's backs.
- You may wish to extend the activity by adding other shapes.

Reteaching

Shape Gallery

5–10 MIN **Visual/Spatial**

Materials Boxes and other solid figures (dry cereal boxes, oatmeal boxes, balls, juice containers)

- Suggest objects with various shapes that children can bring from home. Also, gather classroom disposables that can be recycled, such as milk cartons.
- Children can paint or decorate the shape and then identify the shape by writing an accompanying description of the artwork. For example help children write a label that reads: *Blue and Yellow Cylinder* by Jorge Rodriguez.
- Display the objects and invite the principal and school staff to visit the gallery.

Blue and Yellow Cylinder by Jorge Rodriguez

Math and Physical Education

Living Shapes

10–15 MIN **Kinesthetic**

Materials *(per group)* Large loop made from rope or string

- Demonstrate how to form a shape using the loop and positioning children at various points to form vertices.
- Invite three children to stand at three places around the loop. Have them pick up the loop and pull it taut. Ask the other children to tell what shape the children have formed. *(Triangle)*
- Challenge groups to make other shapes. Have them think about how many children are needed for each shape and where the children should be positioned.

Objective Review and apply concepts, skills, and strategies learned in this and previous chapters.

1 Warm Up

Activate Prior Knowledge Review comparing numbers of items. Show a group of 5 triangles and a group of 7 circles. **Which group has more?** *(Circles)* Then ask a volunteer to match the items in the groups and tell how many shapes do not have a match. *(2)* Invite a child to write a subtraction sentence to compare the numbers. *(7 – 5 = 2)*

2 Teach

Explain to children that they will use what they already know about geometry to solve the problems on the student page. Read the first problem aloud.

Ongoing Assessment

Talk About It

- **What do we need to do?** *(Circle each sphere.)*
- **What do we know?** *(A sphere has no flat surfaces or vertices.)*
- **How can we solve this problem?** *(Think about what a sphere is and find it on the page.)*

If children cannot find the spheres,

then look at each shape and discuss its characteristics.

Error Intervention

If children circle the cubes,

then remind them that spheres are shaped like balls. *(Also see* Reteaching, *Page 193B.)*

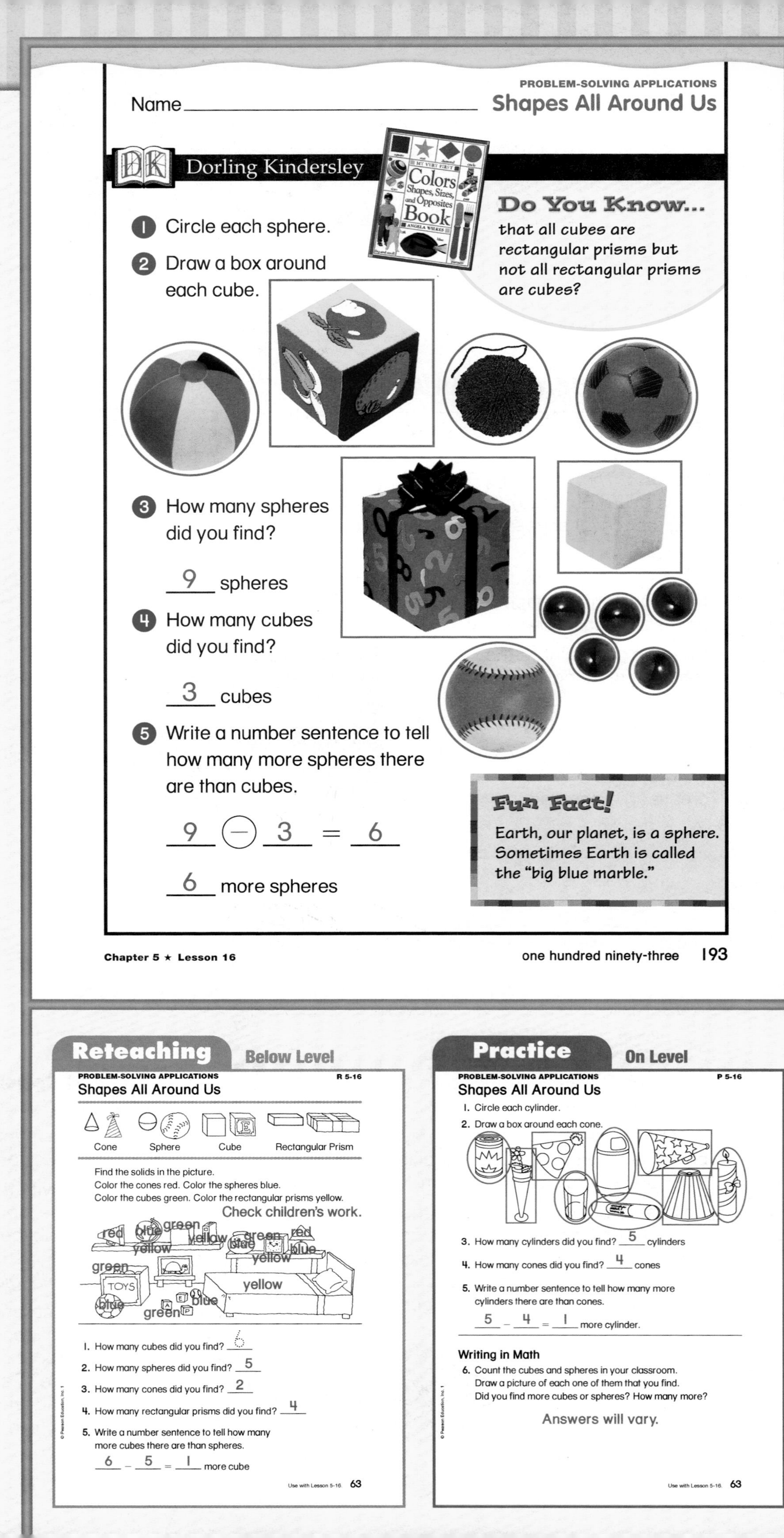

Name ____________ PROBLEM-SOLVING APPLICATIONS
Shapes All Around Us

Dorling Kindersley

1. Circle each sphere.
2. Draw a box around each cube.

Do You Know... that all cubes are rectangular prisms but not all rectangular prisms are cubes?

3. How many spheres did you find? 9 spheres
4. How many cubes did you find? 3 cubes
5. Write a number sentence to tell how many more spheres there are than cubes.

9 − 3 = 6

6 more spheres

Fun Fact! Earth, our planet, is a sphere. Sometimes Earth is called the "big blue marble."

Chapter 5 ★ Lesson 16 one hundred ninety-three 193

Reteaching Below Level

PROBLEM-SOLVING APPLICATIONS R 5-16
Shapes All Around Us

Cone Sphere Cube Rectangular Prism

Find the solids in the picture.
Color the cones red. Color the spheres blue.
Color the rectangular prisms yellow.
Color the cubes green.
Check children's work.

1. How many cubes did you find? 6
2. How many spheres did you find? 5
3. How many cones did you find? 2
4. How many rectangular prisms did you find? 4
5. Write a number sentence to tell how many more cubes there are than spheres.
6 − 5 = 1 more cube

Use with Lesson 5-16. 63

Practice On Level

PROBLEM-SOLVING APPLICATIONS P 5-16
Shapes All Around Us

1. Circle each cylinder.
2. Draw a box around each cone.
3. How many cylinders did you find? 5 cylinders
4. How many cones did you find? 4 cones
5. Write a number sentence to tell how many more cylinders there are than cones.
5 − 4 = 1 more cylinder.

Writing in Math

6. Count the cubes and spheres in your classroom. Draw a picture of each one of them that you find. Did you find more cubes or spheres? How many more?
Answers will vary.

Use with Lesson 5-16. 63

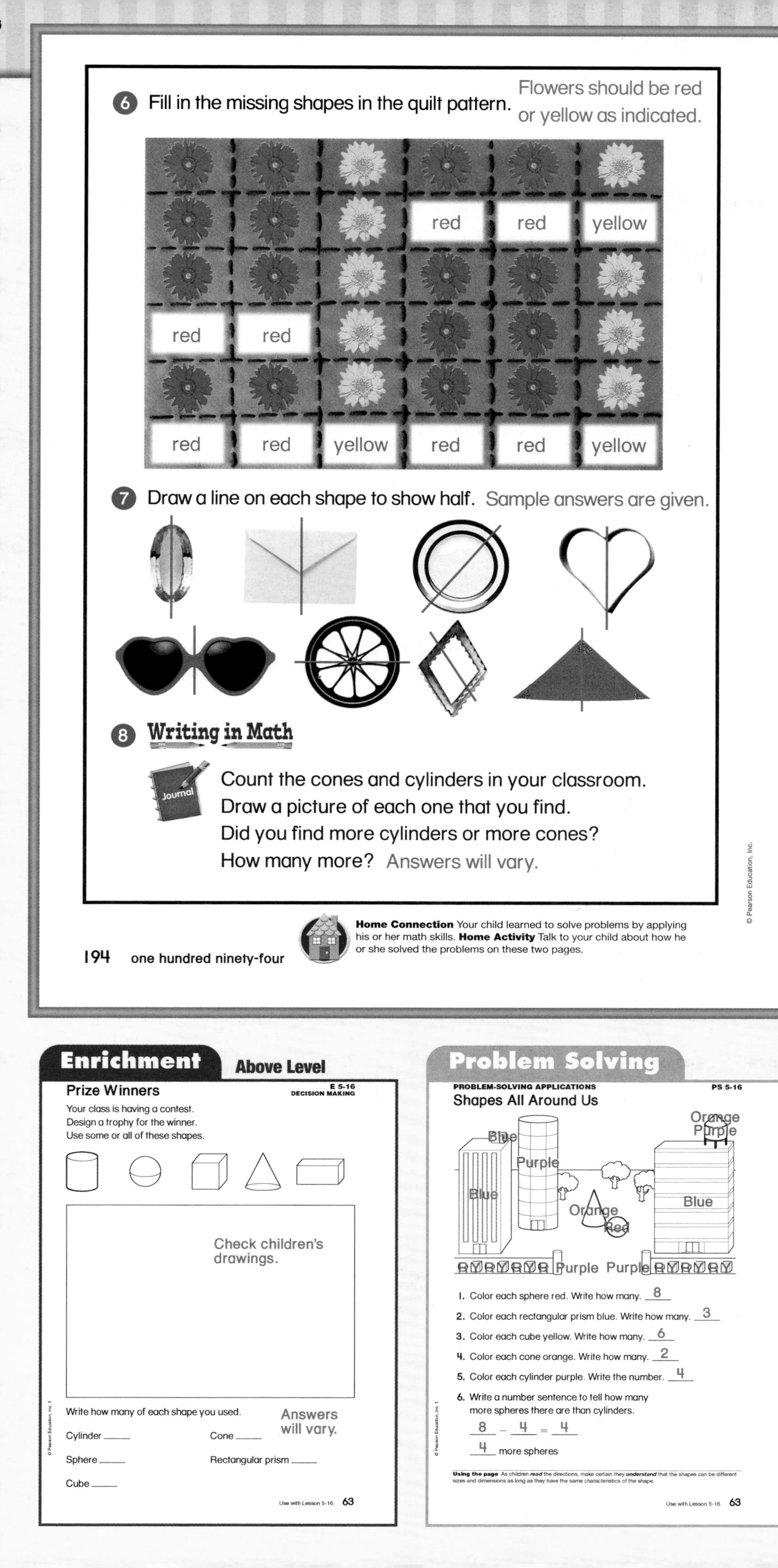

6 Fill in the missing shapes in the quilt pattern. Flowers should be red or yellow as indicated.

7 Draw a line on each shape to show half. Sample answers are given.

8 **Writing in Math**

Count the cones and cylinders in your classroom.
Draw a picture of each one that you find.
Did you find more cylinders or more cones?
How many more? Answers will vary.

Home Connection Your child learned to solve problems by applying his or her math skills. **Home Activity** Talk to your child about how he or she solved the problems on these two pages.

Enrichment Above Level

Prize Winners — E 5-16 DECISION MAKING

Your class is having a contest.
Design a trophy for the winner.
Use some or all of these shapes.

Check children's drawings.

Write how many of each shape you used. Answers will vary.

Cylinder ____ Cone ____
Sphere ____ Rectangular prism ____
Cube ____

Use with Lesson 5-16. 63

Problem Solving

PROBLEM-SOLVING APPLICATIONS — PS 5-16

Shapes All Around Us

1. Color each sphere red. Write how many. 8
2. Color each rectangular prism blue. Write how many. 3
3. Color each cube yellow. Write how many. 6
4. Color each cone orange. Write how many. 2
5. Color each cylinder purple. Write the number. 4
6. Write a number sentence to tell how many more spheres there are than cylinders.
   8 − 4 = 4
   4 more spheres

Using the page As children *read* the directions, make certain they *understand* that the shapes can be different sizes and dimensions as long as they have the same characteristics of the shape.

Use with Lesson 5-16. 63

3 Practice

Read each question aloud. The questions used to help solve the problem in Exercise 1 may be used as a guide for questioning children as they do the remaining exercises.

Reading Assist: Draw Conclusions Help children draw a conclusion about what happens when a shape is divided into two parts that are exactly the same.

Leveled Practice

Below Level Work with a partner to solve problems in all exercises.

On Level Work with a partner only to complete Exercise 8.

Above Level Solve all problems independently.

Early Finishers Have children draw a picture of "the big blue marble." Then have them draw a line to show half. Tell children that we call half of Earth a *hemisphere.*

4 Assess

Journal Idea Have children draw as many things as they can that have the same shape as one solid figure.

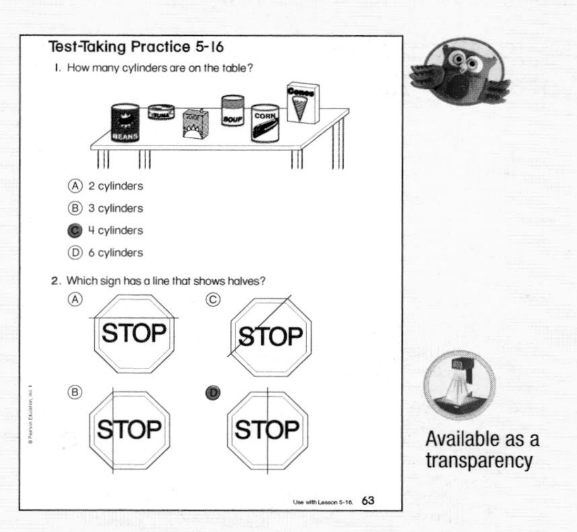

Test-Taking Practice 5-16

1. How many cylinders are on the table?

Ⓐ 2 cylinders
Ⓑ 3 cylinders
Ⓒ 4 cylinders
Ⓓ 6 cylinders

2. Which sign has a line that shows halves?

Use with Lesson 5-16. 63

Available as a transparency

Diagnostic Checkpoint

Purpose Provide assessment of children's progress to date by checking their understanding of key content covered in the previous section.

Vocabulary Review

You may wish to review these terms before assigning the page:

equal parts When parts of a set or shape are the same size *(pp. 181–182)*

equal shares A group of objects is separated so that each subgroup has the same number of objects *(pp. 191–192)*

fourths A region divided into four equal parts *(pp. 185–186)*

fraction A number that names part of a region or a part of a group *(pp. 183–184)*

halves A region divided into two equal parts *(pp. 183–184)*

one fourth ($\frac{1}{4}$) One of four equal parts *(pp. 185–186)*

one half ($\frac{1}{2}$) One of two equal parts *(pp. 183–184)*

one third ($\frac{1}{3}$) One of three equal parts *(pp. 185–186)*

thirds A region divided into three equal parts *(pp. 185–186)*

whole Including all parts; complete *(pp. 183–184)*

Activities for this section are available in the Math Vocabulary Kit.

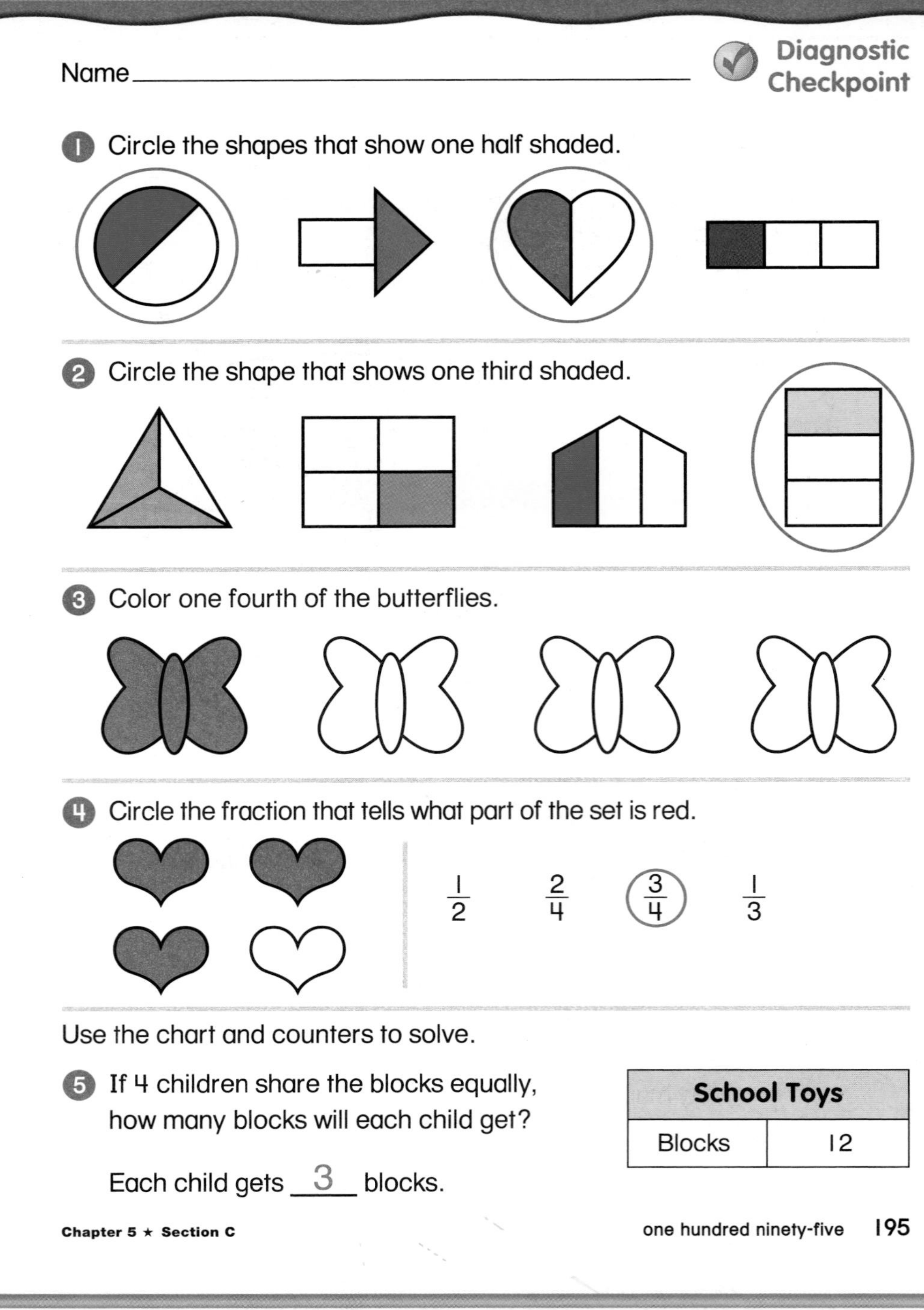

Name ____________________

Diagnostic Checkpoint

1. Circle the shapes that show one half shaded.

2. Circle the shape that shows one third shaded.

3. Color one fourth of the butterflies.

4. Circle the fraction that tells what part of the set is red.

$\frac{1}{2}$ $\frac{2}{4}$ $\frac{3}{4}$ $\frac{1}{3}$

Use the chart and counters to solve.

5. If 4 children share the blocks equally, how many blocks will each child get?

School Toys	
Blocks	12

Each child gets 3 blocks.

Chapter 5 ★ Section C

one hundred ninety-five 195

Item Analysis for Diagnosis and Intervention

Objective	Items	Student Book Pages*	Intervention System
Identify and show halves of a region.	1	183–184	A60
Identify and show one third or one fourth of a region.	2	185–186	A60
Identify and show one half, one third, or one fourth of a group of two, three, or four objects, respectively.	3	187–188	A61
Identify and show non-unit fractions of a region or set.	4	189–190	A62
Solve a problem using data from a chart.	5	191–192	E1

*For each lesson, there is a *Reteaching* activity in *Reaching All Learners* and a *Reteaching* master.

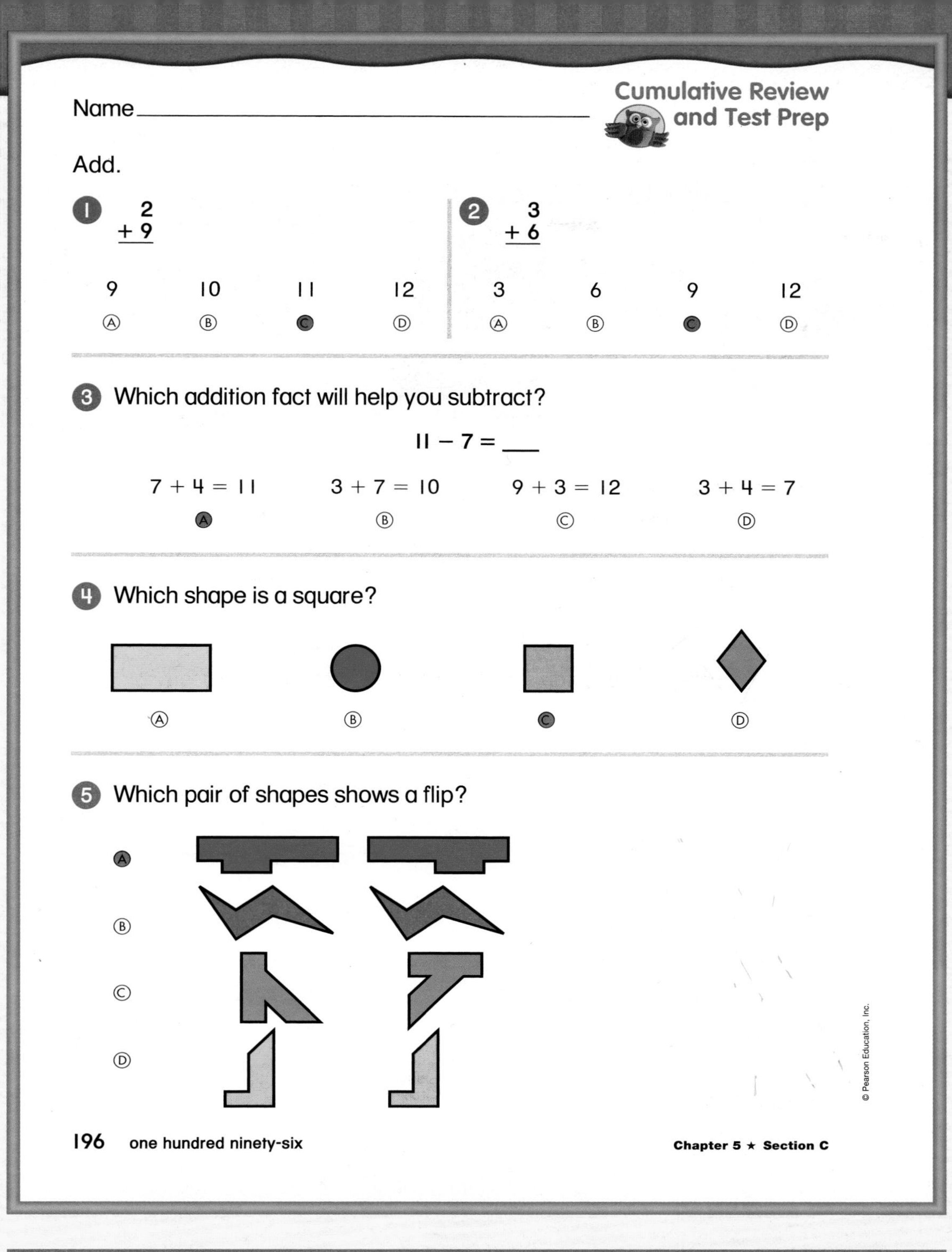
Name ______________________

Cumulative Review and Test Prep

Add.

1. $\begin{array}{r} 2 \\ +\ 9 \\ \hline \end{array}$

9 Ⓐ | 10 Ⓑ | 11 Ⓒ | 12 Ⓓ

2. $\begin{array}{r} 3 \\ +\ 6 \\ \hline \end{array}$

3 Ⓐ | 6 Ⓑ | 9 Ⓒ | 12 Ⓓ

3. Which addition fact will help you subtract?

11 − 7 = ___

7 + 4 = 11 Ⓐ | 3 + 7 = 10 Ⓑ | 9 + 3 = 12 Ⓒ | 3 + 4 = 7 Ⓓ

4. Which shape is a square?

Ⓐ | Ⓑ | Ⓒ | Ⓓ

5. Which pair of shapes shows a flip?

Ⓐ

Ⓑ

Ⓒ

Ⓓ

Item Analysis for Diagnosis and Intervention

Objective	Items	Student Book Pages*	Intervention System
Count on 1, 2, or 3 to add, starting with the greater number.	1–2	95–96	B19
Find differences by using known addition facts.	3	141–142	B29
Identify and name standard plane shapes and recognize them in the environment.	4	165–166	D49
Perform a slide, flip, or turn on an object and identify the resulting position.	5	173–174	D53

*For each lesson, there is a *Reteaching* activity in *Reaching All Learners* and a *Reteaching* master.

Cumulative Review and Test Prep

Purpose Provide children with a review of math concepts. Items appear as they would on a standardized test so children become familiar with that format.

Enrichment

Purpose Provide children with related mathematical topics and applications beyond the basic chapter content.

Using Student Page 197

Remind children that they have already learned about plane shapes. Tell them that on this page, they will learn about shapes that are *not* plane shapes.

Before having children work through the page, you may want to use yarn or string to demonstrate open and closed shapes. Have children create a shape on their desks in which the ends of the yarn meet. Explain that the shape they made is *closed* because nothing can get inside or outside of the shape. Next, have children *open* the shape by separating the ends of the yarn. Ask children to tell why they think this is called an open shape. Then ask them to suggest how it could be closed. Repeat the process several times. Point out that open shapes can become closed shapes by moving the yarn back together.

When children are comfortable with the process, read the directions on the page and make sure children understand how to complete the exercises. Make sure children know that they should draw a line to close any open shapes.

When determining whether or not a shape is open or closed, suggest that children think about whether or not a bug could crawl outside of the shape. To test for an open shape, children might use their fingers to show how the bug might get out.

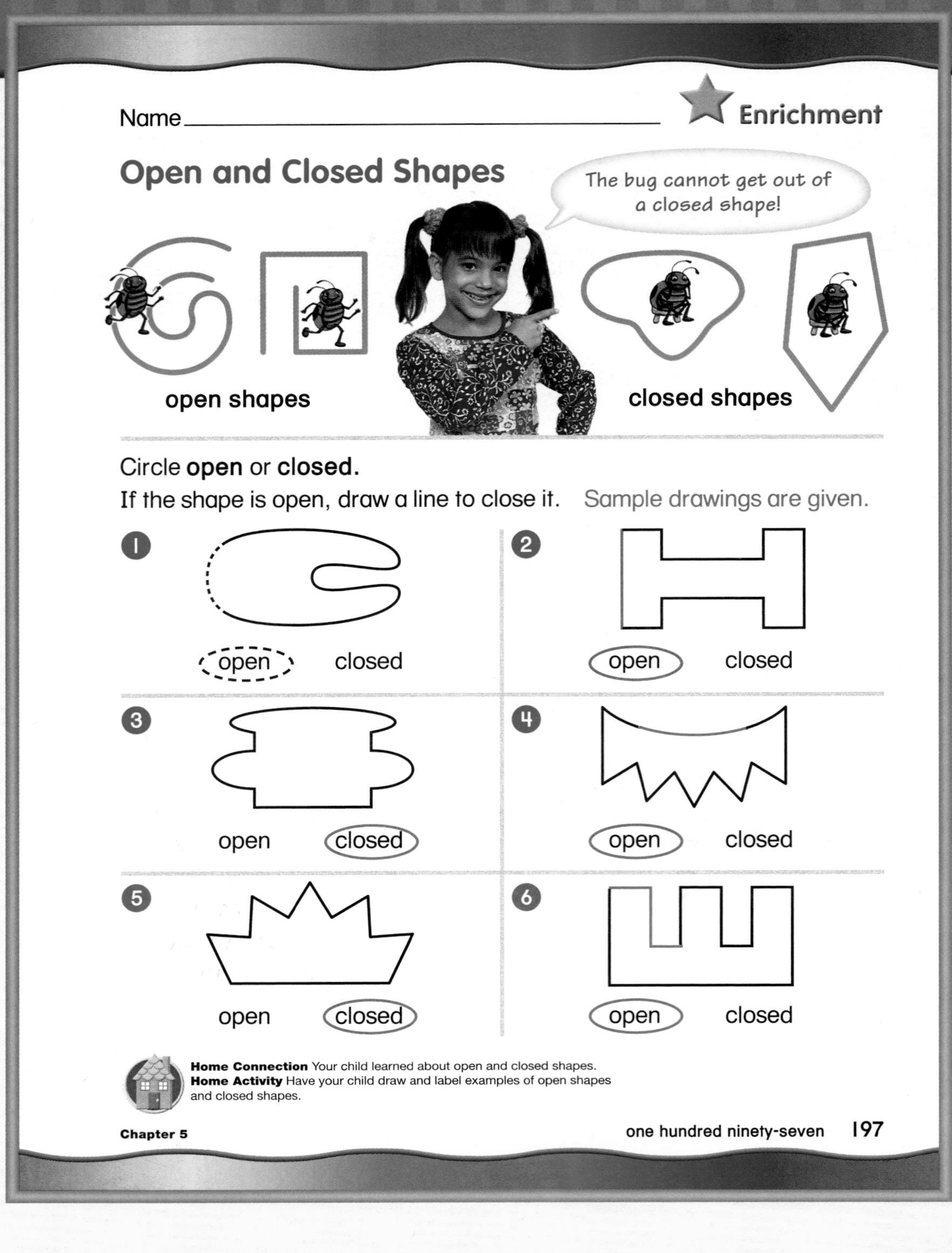

Name____________________________ Enrichment

Open and Closed Shapes

The bug cannot get out of a closed shape!

open shapes

closed shapes

Circle **open** or **closed.**

If the shape is open, draw a line to close it. Sample drawings are given.

1. open closed
2. open closed
3. open closed
4. open closed
5. open closed
6. open closed

Home Connection Your child learned about open and closed shapes.
Home Activity Have your child draw and label examples of open shapes and closed shapes.

Chapter 5 one hundred ninety-seven 197

Name ____________________

Learning with Technology

Slide, Flip, and Turn Shapes Using a Computer

You can use a computer to slide, flip, and turn a shape.

1. Go to the Geometry Shapes eTool.
2. Pick a shape. Place it in the workspace. Draw it on your paper.
3. Flip the shape. Draw your screen. Label the shape as a **flip.**
4. Turn the shape. Draw your screen. Label the shape as a **turn.**
5. Slide the shape. Draw your screen. Label the shape as a **slide.**
6. Turn your paper over and repeat Steps 2–5, using a different shape.

Think About It Reasoning

How are a turn and a slide the same? How are they different?

Sample answers: They are the same because you don't turn the shape over. They are different because when you turn a shape it faces in a different direction.

Home Connection Your child used a computer to move shapes by flipping, sliding, and turning them. **Home Activity** Ask your child to draw a shape and then to draw the shape after it has been flipped, turned, and slid.

Learning with Technology

Purpose Use a computer to slide, flip, and turn a shape.

Using Student Page 198

You will need the Geometry Shapes eTool for this computer activity.

If necessary, put children in pairs or groups. Give them a few minutes to get acquainted with choosing a shape and placing it in the workspace. Ask the children how they can slide, turn, and flip the shape on the screen. Guide them to the correct tool in the program for each movement.

You may want to print and make copies of the screen the children will use in the program. Circle the tools they will need to slide, turn, and flip shapes on the screen. Children can use this screen shot to try this activity on their own.

Think About It Help children understand that a turn and a slide are the same because you don't need to turn a shape over to do either one. A turn and a slide are different because when you slide a shape, it still faces the same direction, but when you turn a shape, it faces a different direction.

Test Talk

Purpose Teach children a particular test-taking strategy and help them become more comfortable with the language and format used on standardized tests.

Using Student Page 199

This page is designed to give children practice in understanding test questions.

Children often have difficulty on standardized tests not because they haven't been introduced to the concept or skill being tested, but because they fail to understand what they are being asked to do or how they are being asked to do it. This page can help with both the what and the how.

Discuss the question in Exercise 1. Ask children how the word *not* changes the meaning of the question. Ask children to explain why the shape in answer choice C does **not** have $\frac{1}{3}$ shaded. If needed, point out to children that since the sections of the rectangle are not the same size, the shaded part does not show $\frac{1}{3}$. Remind children that since this shape does **not** have $\frac{1}{3}$ shaded, it is the correct answer. You may want to discuss the shapes in the other answer choices with children. Stress that each of the other three shapes is divided into 3 equal parts with 1 part shaded. Since each of the other shapes has $\frac{1}{3}$ shaded, the other answer choices are not correct.

Have children complete Exercise 2 independently. When they have finished, ask children how the word *not* changed the meaning of the problem. Then discuss why the triangle in answer choice B is the correct answer choice.

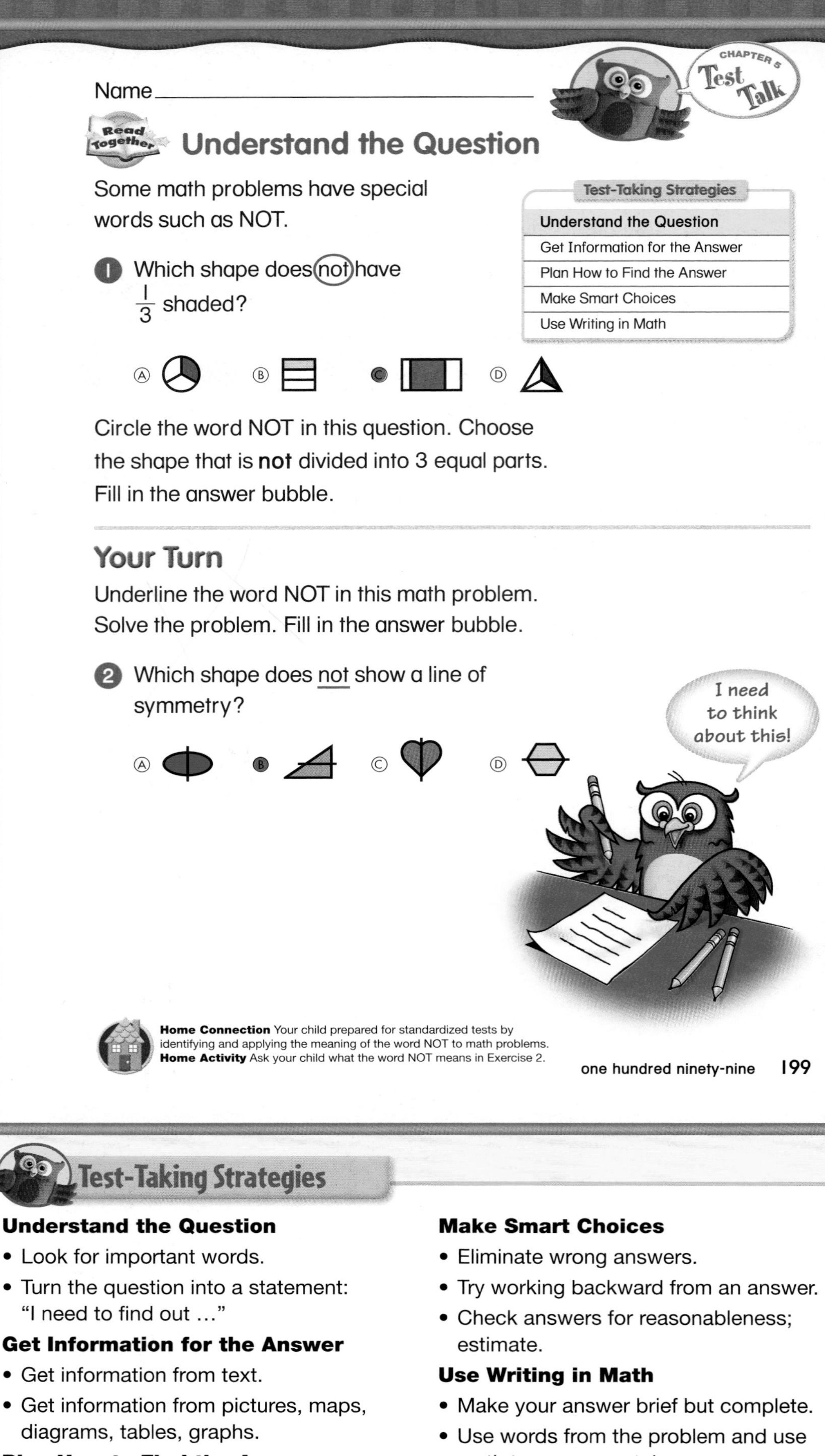

Name ____________________

CHAPTER 5 Test Talk

Read Together

Understand the Question

Some math problems have special words such as NOT.

Test-Taking Strategies
- Understand the Question
- Get Information for the Answer
- Plan How to Find the Answer
- Make Smart Choices
- Use Writing in Math

1. Which shape does not have $\frac{1}{3}$ shaded?

Ⓐ Ⓑ Ⓒ Ⓓ

Circle the word NOT in this question. Choose the shape that is **not** divided into 3 equal parts. Fill in the answer bubble.

Your Turn

Underline the word NOT in this math problem. Solve the problem. Fill in the answer bubble.

2. Which shape does not show a line of symmetry?

Ⓐ Ⓑ Ⓒ Ⓓ

Home Connection Your child prepared for standardized tests by identifying and applying the meaning of the word NOT to math problems. **Home Activity** Ask your child what the word NOT means in Exercise 2.

one hundred ninety-nine 199

Test-Taking Strategies

Understand the Question
- Look for important words.
- Turn the question into a statement: "I need to find out …"

Get Information for the Answer
- Get information from text.
- Get information from pictures, maps, diagrams, tables, graphs.

Plan How to Find the Answer
- Think about problem-solving skills and strategies.
- Choose computation methods.

Make Smart Choices
- Eliminate wrong answers.
- Try working backward from an answer.
- Check answers for reasonableness; estimate.

Use Writing in Math
- Make your answer brief but complete.
- Use words from the problem and use math terms accurately.
- Describe the steps in order.
- Draw pictures to explain your thinking.

Name ______________________________

Discover Math in Your World

Math Music

Today you will play in the Hand-Clap Band. Your teacher will divide the class into three groups.

First, the whole class will practice counting **1 - 2 - 3 - 4, 1 - 2 - 3 - 4.** Try to count the numbers, or beats, at the same pace. Now ...

Musical Parts

1. Group 1 will clap only on beat **1.** Group 1 will be clapping 1 out of every 4 beats. Write this as a fraction. $\frac{1}{4}$
2. Group 2 will clap only on beats **1** and **3.** Group 2 will be clapping 2 out of every 4 beats. Write this as a fraction. $\frac{2}{4}$
3. Group 3 will clap on **every** beat. Group 3 will be clapping 4 out of every 4 beats. Write this as a fraction. $\frac{4}{4}$

Take It to the NET
Video and Activities
www.scottforesman.com

Home Connection Your child solved problems about music by writing fractions. **Home Activity** Ask your child what fraction he or she would write to show clapping 3 out of every 4 beats. ($\frac{3}{4}$)

Take It to the NET
Video and Activities
www.scottforesman.com

The video includes pre-viewing and post-viewing questions. A Discovery Channel Blackline Master is also provided.

Discover Math in Your World

Purpose Help children connect math content to everyday applications.

Using Student Page 200

On this page, children will play in a Hand-Clap Band and write fractions for clapping on different beats.

To introduce children to this musical activity, recite a rhyme with a beat in 4 or play some music, such as "Yankee Doodle," that has a beat in 4. Have children begin by clapping on every beat, then just on every other beat, and then just on the first beat of each measure. Introduce the word *measure* as a group of beats and explain that they are clapping on the first beat of the measure. Next, have children practice clapping on the second, third, and fourth beats of each measure. **If we clap on 3 of the 4 beats in a measure, how can we write that as a fraction?** Write $\frac{3}{4}$ on the chalkboard, explaining that the 3 shows "clapping on 3 of the beats" and the 4 means "4 beats to the measure," or clapping on 3 out of 4 beats. If children are confused, draw a model with 4 parts, 3 parts shaded, and tell children that 4 parts are the beats in a measure and the 3 parts are the beats on which they clapped.

Read through the directions together and have children practice counting beats to a $\frac{4}{4}$ rhythm, emphasizing the first beat in each measure. Then teach each group how to clap its part. Finally, put the 3 groups together as you direct the counting. When finished, have children read and answer the questions by writing fractions.

Note: The answer to Exercise 3 is $\frac{4}{4}$. Children have not yet been introduced to fractions in which the numerator and denominator are the same number. If children seem confused by this fraction, simply draw a model of a figure (bar or circle) with 4 parts, shade all 4 parts, and tell children that this fraction means that you are talking about 4 out of 4 parts.

Chapter Test

Purpose Assess children's progress by checking their understanding of the concepts and skills covered in Chapter 5. Use as a review, practice test, or chapter test.

MindPoint Quiz Show CD-ROM Use *MindPoint Quiz Show* for additional practice on Chapter 5.

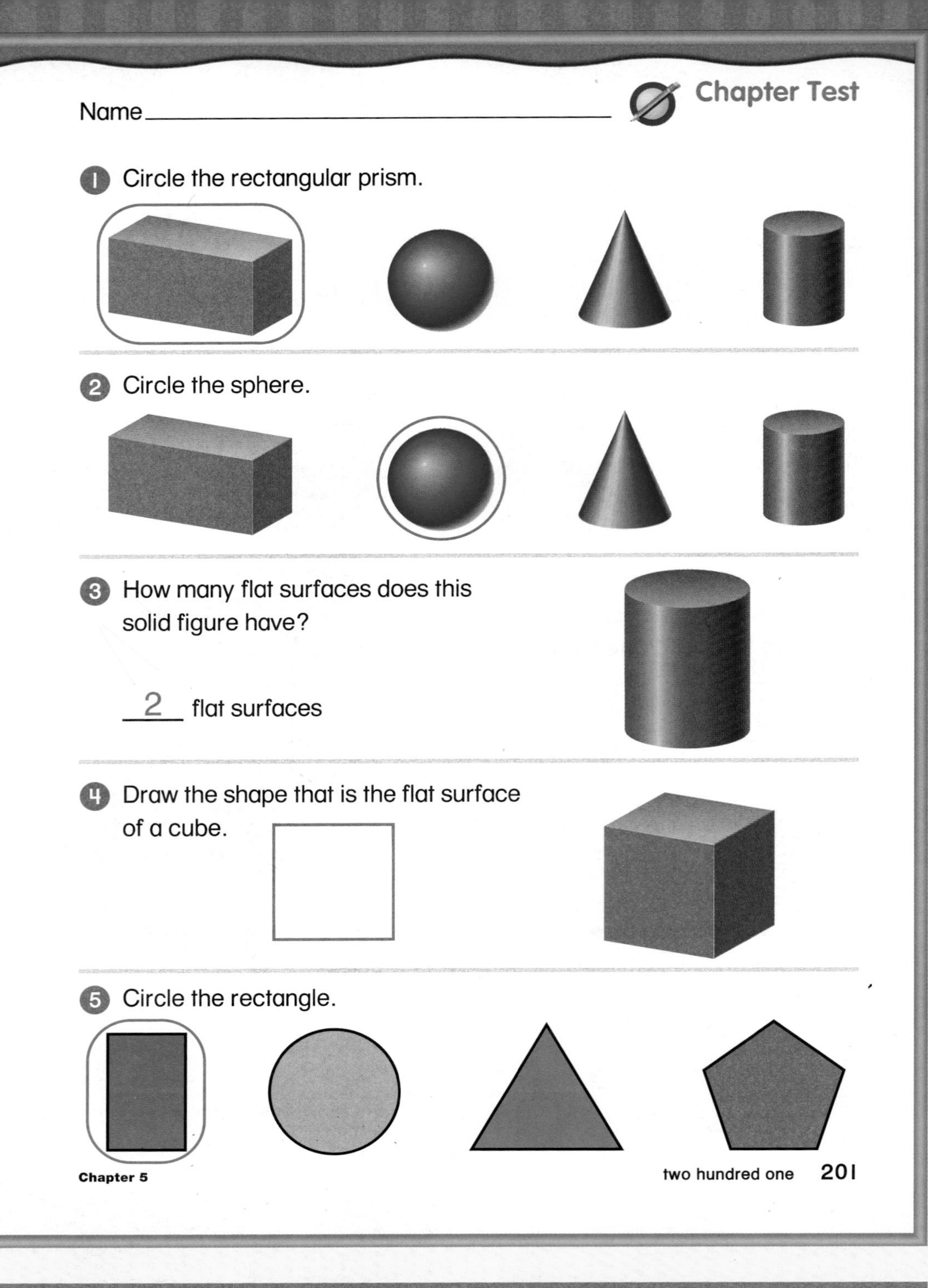

Name ______________________ Chapter Test

1. Circle the rectangular prism.

2. Circle the sphere.

3. How many flat surfaces does this solid figure have?

   2 flat surfaces

4. Draw the shape that is the flat surface of a cube.

5. Circle the rectangle.

Chapter 5 — two hundred one 201

Item Analysis for Diagnosis and Intervention

Objective	Items	Student Book Pages*	Intervention System
Identify and name standard geometric solids and recognize them in the environment.	1–2	157–158	D45
Count the number of flat surfaces and vertices on geometric solids.	3	159–160	D46
Match a geometric solid to an outline of one of its flat surfaces.	4	161–162	D47, D48
Identify and name standard plane shapes and recognize them in the environment.	5	165–166	D49

*For each lesson, there is a *Reteaching* activity in *Reaching All Learners* and a *Reteaching* master.

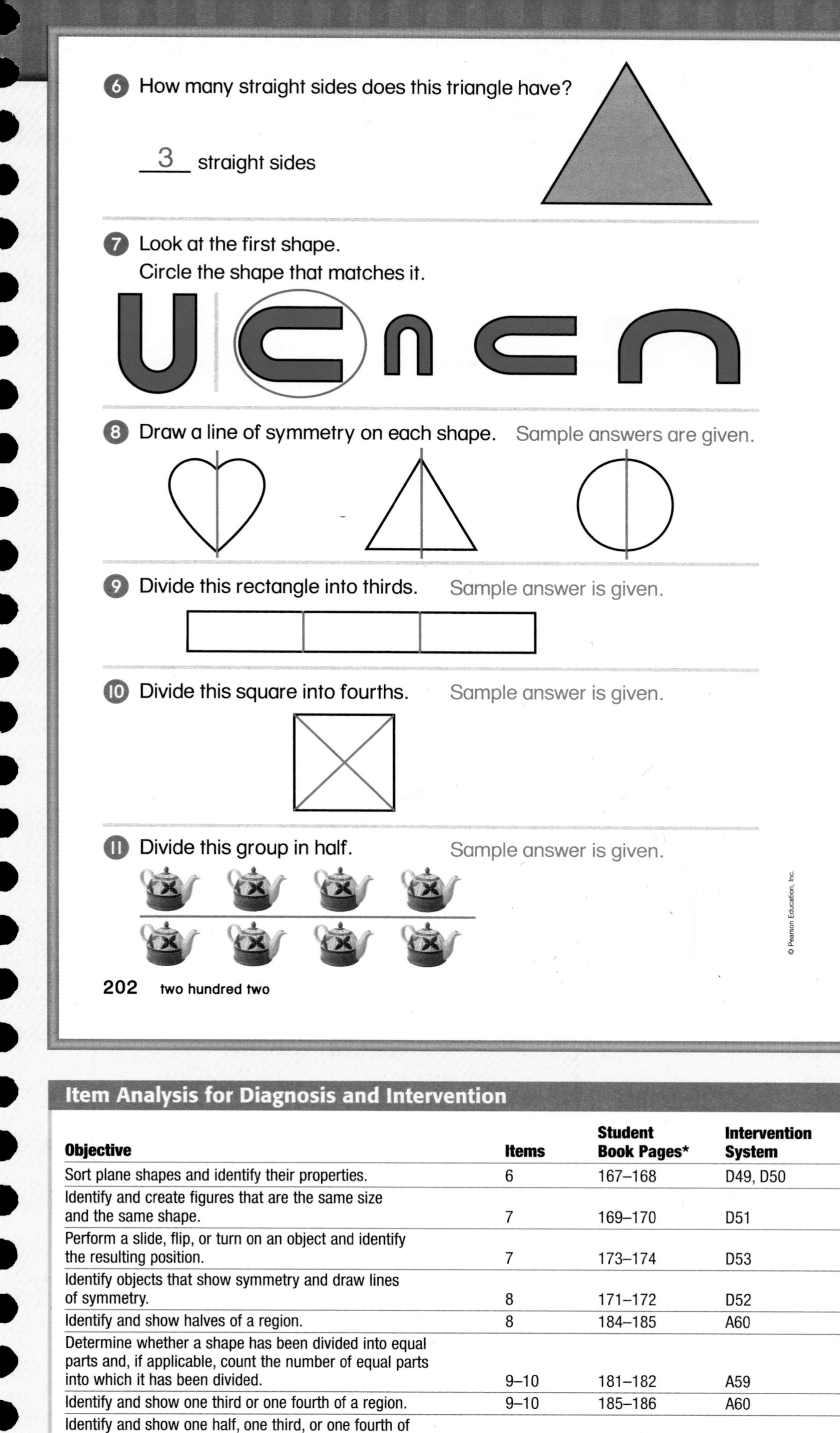

6 How many straight sides does this triangle have?

3 straight sides

7 Look at the first shape.
Circle the shape that matches it.

8 Draw a line of symmetry on each shape. Sample answers are given.

9 Divide this rectangle into thirds. Sample answer is given.

10 Divide this square into fourths. Sample answer is given.

11 Divide this group in half. Sample answer is given.

© Pearson Education, Inc.

202 two hundred two

Assessment Sourcebook

These additional assessment options may be found in the *Assessment Sourcebook:*

- Chapter 5 Free-Response Test (Forms A and B)
- Chapter 5 Multiple-Choice Test (Forms C and D)
- Chapter 5 Performance Assessment

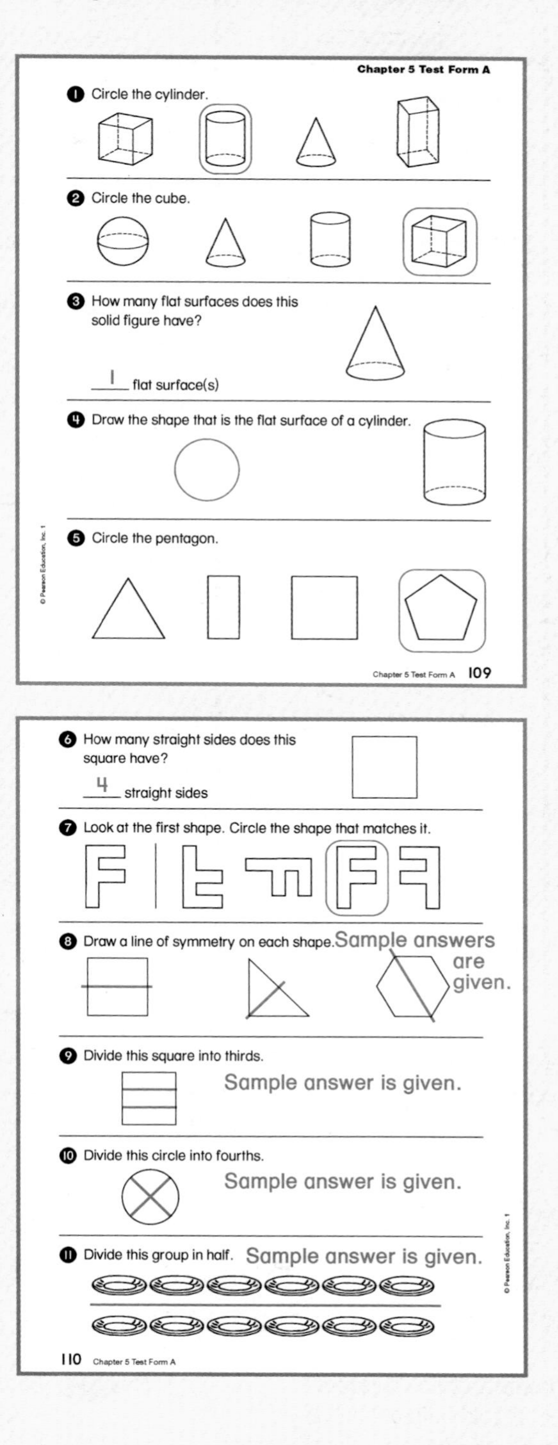

Chapter 5 Test Form A

1 Circle the cylinder.

2 Circle the cube.

3 How many flat surfaces does this solid figure have?

1 flat surface(s)

4 Draw the shape that is the flat surface of a cylinder.

5 Circle the pentagon.

© Pearson Education, Inc. 1

Chapter 5 Test Form A 109

6 How many straight sides does this square have?

4 straight sides

7 Look at the first shape. Circle the shape that matches it.

8 Draw a line of symmetry on each shape. Sample answers are given.

9 Divide this square into thirds. Sample answer is given.

10 Divide this circle into fourths. Sample answer is given.

11 Divide this group in half. Sample answer is given.

© Pearson Education, Inc. 1

110 Chapter 5 Test Form A

Item Analysis for Diagnosis and Intervention

Objective	Items	Student Book Pages*	Intervention System
Sort plane shapes and identify their properties.	6	167–168	D49, D50
Identify and create figures that are the same size and the same shape.	7	169–170	D51
Perform a slide, flip, or turn on an object and identify the resulting position.	7	173–174	D53
Identify objects that show symmetry and draw lines of symmetry.	8	171–172	D52
Identify and show halves of a region.	8	184–185	A60
Determine whether a shape has been divided into equal parts and, if applicable, count the number of equal parts into which it has been divided.	9–10	181–182	A59
Identify and show one third or one fourth of a region.	9–10	185–186	A60
Identify and show one half, one third, or one fourth of a group of two, three, or four objects, respectively.	11	187–188	A61

*For each lesson, there is a *Reteaching* activity in *Reaching All Learners* and a *Reteaching* master.

CHAPTER 6

Lesson Planner

Time

Suggested Pacing: 12 days

Section A Telling Time

6-1 pp. 205–206	6-2 pp. 207–208	6-3 pp. 209–210	6-4 pp. 211–212	6-5 pp. 215–216
Minutes **Objective** Determine if an event takes more or less than a minute. **Math Understanding** Knowing the approximate length of a minute helps to accurately estimate time. **Vocabulary** Minute	**Understanding the Hour and Minute Hands** **Objective** Identify the hour hand and the minute hand on a clock and tell time to the hour. **Math Understanding** The hour hand tells the hour, while the minute hand tells the number of minutes after the hour. **Vocabulary** Hour, hour hand, minute hand, o'clock	**Telling and Writing Time to the Hour** **Objective** Tell and write time to the hour on an analog and on a digital clock. **Math Understanding** Time to the hour can be shown on an analog clock or on a digital clock and written in two ways: *_ o'clock or _ : 00.*	**Telling and Writing Time to the Half Hour** **Objective** Tell and write time to the half hour. **Math Understanding** A half hour is 30 minutes long. **Vocabulary** Half hour Reading For Math Success pp. 213–214	Problem-Solving Strategy **Act It Out** **Objective** Solve problems by acting out given situations. **Math Understanding** One strategy that can be used to solve a problem is to act it out. **Materials for Student Pages** *(per child)* Clock Face (Teaching Tool 22) **Section A Diagnostic Checkpoint, p. 217** **Cumulative Review and Test Prep, p. 218**

Math Story: ***Late for School Again?*, pp. 6A–6F** **Home-School Connection, p. 203**
Practice Game: ***Spin for Time*, p. 204**

Resources in the Student Book

Ongoing Assessment and Test Prep *Also see* pp. 203G–203H.

Instant Check System™
- **Check** before Practice
- **Think About It** after examples
- **Diagnostic Checkpoint** end of sections

Test Prep
- **Test Talk** end of chapter
- **Cumulative Review and Test Prep** end of sections

Daily Real-World Problem Solving plus ...

Problem-Solving Applications lesson on pp. 229–230 uses data from Dorling Kindersley literature.

Discover Math in Your World on p. 236 uses data from a topic in the Discovery Channel School Video Library, Segment 6.

EC NTL 12 11 10 9 8 7 6 5

Notes

Reading and Writing in Math *Throughout*

This feature shows how reading skills and strategies can help with problem-solving skills and strategies in math.
Also, **Reading Assists** are in the Teacher's Edition.

Writing in Math

Some lessons include **Writing in Math** exercises. Also, daily **Journal Ideas** are in the Teacher's Edition.

Technology Resources for Students *Also see* p. T20.

Take It to the NET
More Activities
www.scottforesman.com

More activities, Discovery Channel School Video Library, and Math eTools

Math eTools: electronic manipulatives online, on CD-ROM, and in the Online Student's Edition

All text pages are available online and on CD-ROM. The Online Student's Edition includes Math eTools plus glossary links for vocabulary.

Lesson Planner

Time (continued)

Section B Using Time

6-6 pp. 219–220	6-7 pp. 221–222	6-8 pp. 223–224	6-9 pp. 225–226	6-10 pp. 227–228
Ordering Events **Objective** Determine whether an event takes place in the morning, afternoon, or night. **Math Understanding** The time of an event can be estimated and labeled with the terms *morning, afternoon,* or *night.* **Vocabulary** Morning, afternoon, night	**Estimating Lengths of Time** **Objective** Compare and estimate the length of time it takes for each of three activities. **Math Understanding** The duration of two or more events can be compared.	Problem-Solving Skill **Use Data from a Schedule** **Objective** Solve problems by reading and using the information in a schedule. **Math Understanding** A time schedule is a table that is useful for solving problems.	**Days of the Week** **Objective** Read and use a calendar to name the days of the week. **Math Understanding** A calendar is a chart listing the days of the month in order, grouped in weeks. **Vocabulary** Calendar, day, month, week	**Months of the Year** **Objective** Identify and order the months of the year. **Math Understanding** The months of the year, like the days of the week, have a specific order. **Vocabulary** Year

Additional Resources for ...

Reaching All Learners

- **Practice** Masters/Workbook, every lesson
- **Reteaching** Masters/Workbook, every lesson
- **Enrichment** Masters/Workbook, every lesson
- **Every Student Learns** A teacher resource with daily suggestions for helping students overcome language barriers to learning math
- **Spiral Review and Test Prep** Transparencies and Masters/Workbook, every lesson
- **Math Games** Use *The Farm* anytime after Lesson 6-3. Use *Time's Up* anytime after Lesson 6-4.
- **Investigation** See pp. 203I–203J.

Problem Solving

- **Problem Solving** Masters/Workbook, every lesson
- **Problem of the Day** Flipchart/Transparencies, every lesson
- **Discovery Channel School** Masters, follow-up to Segment 6 in the Discovery Channel School Video Library

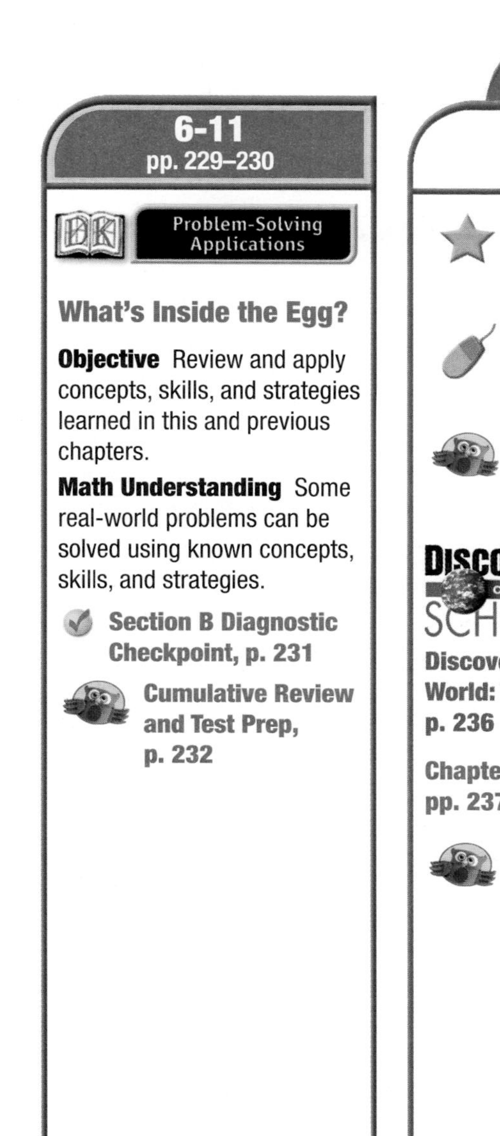

6-11
pp. 229–230

Problem-Solving Applications

What's Inside the Egg?

Objective Review and apply concepts, skills, and strategies learned in this and previous chapters.

Math Understanding Some real-world problems can be solved using known concepts, skills, and strategies.

Section B Diagnostic Checkpoint, p. 231

Cumulative Review and Test Prep, p. 232

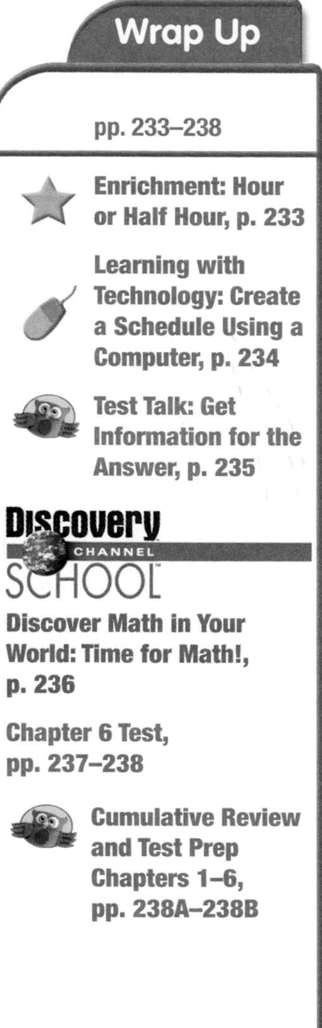

Wrap Up

pp. 233–238

Enrichment: Hour or Half Hour, p. 233

Learning with Technology: Create a Schedule Using a Computer, p. 234

Test Talk: Get Information for the Answer, p. 235

Discovery Channel School

Discover Math in Your World: Time for Math!, p. 236

Chapter 6 Test, pp. 237–238

Cumulative Review and Test Prep Chapters 1–6, pp. 238A–238B

Reading in Math

- **Vocabulary Kit** Word Cards plus transparencies and activities for instructional word walls and for small groups
- **Dorling Kindersley Literature Library** Books with interesting data

Assessment, Intervention, and Test Prep

- **Assessment Sourcebook** See pp. 203G–203H.
- **Math Diagnosis and Intervention System** See pp. 203G–203H.
- **Test-Taking Practice** Transparencies, every lesson
- **SAT 9, SAT 10, TerraNova Practice and Test Prep** Includes practice tests, correlations, and more

Teacher Support

- **Teaching Tools** Masters: paper manipulatives and more
- **Home-School Connection** Masters, use Chapter 6 Family Letter at the start of the chapter. Use Study Buddies 11 and 12 after Lessons 6-1 and 6-5.
- **Professional Development Resources** See p. T18.
- **Technology Resources** See p. T20.

CHAPTER 6

Professional Development

Skills Trace - Time

BEFORE Chapter 6	DURING Chapter 6	AFTER Chapter 6
Grade K developed identifying and ordering the days of the week, naming the months and seasons of the year, sequencing events, estimating and comparing the duration of two or more events, and telling time to the hour. **Chapter 5 in Grade 1** developed identifying halves.	**Chapter 6** focuses on determining whether an event takes more or less than 1 minute, estimating and comparing the duration of two or more events, telling time to the nearest half hour, and listing the days of the week and months of the year in order.	**Grade 2** develops telling time to the nearest 5 minutes, reading a date on a calendar, and finding elapsed time.

Math Background and Teaching Tips

Section A

Telling Time

pp. 205–218

Time is the duration of an event from beginning to end. Time can be measured in standard units such as seconds, minutes, hours, and days, or it can be measured in nonstandard units that repeat predictably such as a metronome or a pendulum swing.

This section focuses on how to read analog and digital clocks to the nearest half hour and the meaning of a minute as a unit of time. The passage of time is compared to various tasks, giving children the opportunity to establish personal references as benchmarks for estimating 1 minute.

TIP! Make Connections *Point out opportunities for children to establish personal references for 1 minute. Ask questions such as: Will it take more or less than 1 minute to take out your reading book? to walk to the gym?*

It is important to convey to children that measuring time, as with measuring all attributes, is approximate. Encourage them to express time measurements as "about a minute" or "about an hour."

TIP! Reinforce Big Ideas *Use language such as "It is about 2 o'clock" to convey the concept that measuring time is an approximate activity. Encourage children to use this language to describe the length of time they estimate an event will take.*

Learning to tell time on an analog clock requires an understanding of the movement of the hands.

It may help children to remember that clock hands do not move at the same speed.

The minute hand moves about 12 times as fast as the hour hand.

It is important to remember that the actions and functions of the two hands are different. The small hour hand indicates broad, approximate time, while the long minute hand indicates time after and before the hour.

Although the digital and analog clocks are paired on the pupil pages, they have distinctly different advantages and disadvantages. The digital clock records the time, but it requires the ability to read two-digit numbers. The analog clock may be more difficult to read, but it conveys the concept of the passage of time, in that the movement of the hands is visible.

Children will use their newly developed skill of estimating 1 minute to support a developing sense of how long 30 minutes, or one half hour, is.

"Since it takes about 1 minute to tie my shoes, 30 minutes is like I tied my shoes 30 times."

Math Understandings

- Knowing the approximate length of a minute helps to accurately estimate time.
- The hour hand tells the hour, while the minute hand tells the number of minutes after the hour.
- Time to the hour can be shown on an analog clock or on a digital clock and written in two ways: *_ o'clock or _:00.*
- A half hour is 30 minutes long.
- One strategy that can be used to solve a problem is to act it out.

Developing a sense of the passage of time aids children when they later read a digital clock that says 7:56, for instance. They will understand that it means "almost 8:00, or 8 o'clock," and that 4 minutes until the hour is not a long time.

Acting out elapsed times allows children to play on a clock model with the hand movements. The activity also emphasizes that the pattern on an analog clock follows the same sequence as the counting numbers.

TIP! Reinforce Big Ideas *Use the counting-on strategy when figuring out elapsed time. If an activity started at 8 and lasts 3 hours, begin at 8… 9, 10, 11.*

Section B

Using Time

pp. 219–232

The process of measurement, in this case using units of time to measure, is the same for every measurable attribute.

- The attribute being measured is identified—time.
- An approximate unit is selected. In this section, three are used: 1 minute, 1 hour, and 1 day.
- That unit is compared to the event being measured.
- The number of units is reported.

Estimating with each unit before measuring helps children develop a sense of the meaning of each unit, that is—about how long is 1 hour? 1 day?

Using time data from a schedule combines several skills—reading a table, reading time notation, ordering events, understanding the concept of elapsed time, and reading digital and analog clocks. Schedules reinforce the concept that time is a convenient tool for ordering the events of our lives.

TIP! Reinforce Big Ideas *Emphasize that schedules report beginning times of events. They do not report interim time, and from the beginning of one event to the beginning of another event, time is passing.*

Train from Grand Station to Point Lewis

Depart	Arrive
3:34	4:12
4:32	5:00
5:04	5:23

The calendar is a table that tracks days, weeks, and months as units of time. Each week is a repeating pattern. However, each month may begin and end on different days. Therefore, one week's time may overlap across two different months.

Repeating pattern unit for one week:

S, M, T, W, T, F, S

Reciting the days of the week beginning with a day other than Sunday is related to counting on from a number other than one.

3 . . . 4, 5, 6

Tuesday . . . Wednesday, Thursday, Friday

Both forms of recitation reinforce counting numbers and days of the week as following a specific sequence and pattern.

The greatest unit of time explored in this chapter is the year. Like the days of the week, the months follow a specific sequence that repeats.

Math Understandings

- The time of an event can be estimated and labeled with the terms *morning, afternoon,* or *night.*
- The duration of two or more events can be compared.
- A time schedule is a form of table useful for solving problems.
- A calendar is a chart listing the days of the month in order, grouped in weeks.
- The months of the year, like the days of the week, have a specific order.

TIP! Reinforce Big Ideas *Emphasize that each unit of time forms a small set within each next greater unit of time—minutes are smaller than hours, hours are smaller than days, days are smaller than weeks, weeks are smaller than months, and months are smaller than years. For example, birthdays happen once a year, Saturdays happen once a week, and lunch happens every day.*

TIP! Encourage Flexibility *Write the date or time of day in different notations on the chalkboard in your daily classroom routine.*

Assessment Resources

DIAGNOSING READINESS

Start of Year Diagnosing Readiness for Grade 1, Assessment Sourcebook pp. 43–46 and in Online Intervention

Start of Chapter Diagnosing Readiness for Chapter 6, Assessment Sourcebook pp. 121–122 and in Online Intervention

Start of Lesson Warm Up, Teacher's Edition pp. 205, 207, 209, 211, 215, 219, 221, 223, 225, 227, 229

Instant Check System™

ONGOING ASSESSMENT

Before Independent Practice Check and Think About It, Student Book, every lesson

After a Section Diagnostic Checkpoint, pp. 217, 231 and in Online Intervention

Basic-Facts Timed Test 6 Assessment Sourcebook, p. 32

FORMAL EVALUATION

Chapter Tests Chapter 6 Test, Student Book pp. 237–238; Assessment Sourcebook Forms A and B Free Response pp. 123–126, Forms C and D Multiple Choice pp. 127–134, Performance Assessment p. 11; Multiple-Choice Chapter Test in Online Intervention

Cumulative Tests Chapters 1–3, 1–6, 1–9, 1–12, Assessment Sourcebook, pp. 89–92, 135–138, 181–184, 227–230; Online Intervention

Test Generator Computer-generated tests; can be customized

Correlation to Assessments, Intervention, and Standardized Tests

	Assessments		Intervention	Standardized Tests				
Lessons	Diagnostic Checkpoint	Chapter Test	Math Diagnosis and Intervention System	SAT 9/10	ITBS	CTBS	CAT	MAT
6-1 Minutes	p. 217: Ex. 5	Ex. 1	Booklet D: D3	•/•	•	•	•	•
6-2 Understanding the Hour and Minute Hands	p. 217: Ex. 1, 2	Ex. 2, 3	Booklet D: D4	•/•	•	•	•	•
6-3 Telling and Writing Time to the Hour	p. 217: Ex. 1, 2	Ex. 2, 3	Booklet D: D5	•/•	•	•	•	•
6-4 Telling and Writing Time to the Half Hour	p. 217: Ex. 3, 4	Ex. 4, 5	Booklet D: D6	•/•	•	•	•	•
6-5 Problem-Solving Strategy: Act It Out	p. 217: Ex. 6	Ex. 11	Booklet E: E30	/•				
6-6 Ordering Events	p. 231: Ex. 1	Ex. 8	Booklet D: D7					
6-7 Estimating Lengths of Time	p. 231: Ex. 2	Ex. 9	Booklet D: D7			•		
6-8 Problem-Solving Skill: Use Data from a Schedule	p. 231: Ex. 3	Ex. 10	Booklet E: E1	•/		•	•	•
6-9 Days of the Week	p. 231: Ex. 4, 5	Ex. 6	Booklet D: D8	•/•				
6-10 Months of the Year		Ex. 7	Booklet D: D8	•/•				

KEY:
SAT 9 Stanford Achievement Test
SAT 10 Stanford Achievement Test
ITBS Iowa Test of Basic Skills
CAT California Achievement Test
CTBS Comprehensive Test of Basic Skills (TerraNova)
MAT Metropolitan Achievement Test

Intervention and Test Prep Resources

INTERVENTION

During Instruction Helpful "If... then..." suggestions in the Teacher's Edition in Ongoing Assessment and Error Intervention

Math Diagnosis and Intervention System Diagnostic tests, individual and class record forms, two-page Intervention Lessons (example, practice, test prep), and one-page Intervention Practice (multiple choice), all in cross-grade strand booklets (Booklets A–E for Grades K–3, Booklets F–M for Grades 4–6).

Online Intervention Diagnostic tests; individual, class, school, and district reports; remediation including tutorials, video, games, practice exercises

TEST PREP

Test Talk before the Chapter Test, p. 235

Cumulative Review and Test Prep end of sections, pp. 218, 232 and end of Chapter 6, pp. 238A–238B

Test-Taking Practice Transparencies for every lesson

Spiral Review and Test Prep for every lesson

SAT 9, SAT 10, TerraNova Practice and Test Prep section quizzes, practice tests

Correlation to NCTM Standards and Grades Pre-K through 2 Expectations

Measurement

Understand measurable attributes of objects and the units, systems, and processes of measurement.

Grades Pre-K through 2 Expectations

- Recognize the attributes of length, volume, weight, area, and time. *Lessons 6-1, 6-2, 6-3, 6-4, 6-5, 6-6, 6-7, 6-8, 6-9, 6-10*
- Compare and order objects according to these attributes. *Lessons 6-1, 6-2, 6-3, 6-4, 6-6, 6-7, 6-8, 6-9, 6-10*
- Understand how to measure using nonstandard and standard units. *Lessons 6-2, 6-3, 6-4, 6-5*
- Select an appropriate unit and tool for the attribute being measured. *Lessons 6-6, 6-7*

Apply appropriate techniques, tools, and formulas to determine measurements.

Grades Pre-K through 2 Expectations

- Develop common referents for measures to make comparisons and estimates. *Lessons 6-1, 6-6, 6-7, 6-10*

Data Analysis and Probability

Select and use appropriate statistical methods to analyze data.

Grades Pre-K through 2 Expectations

- Describe parts of the data and the set of data as a whole to determine what the data show. *Lesson 6-8*

The NCTM 2000 Pre-K through Grade 12 Content Standards are Number and Operations, Algebra, Geometry, Measurement, and Data Analysis and Probability. The Process Standards (Problem Solving, Reasoning and Proof, Communication, Connections, and Representation) are incorporated throughout lessons.

CHAPTER 6 Investigation

Time

Activity I

Use in place of the Investigating the Concept activity in Lesson 6-1.

Exploring 1 Minute

Overview Children investigate length of time and the number of times an activity can be completed in 1 minute.

Materials Classroom clock with a second hand

The Task

- Have children suggest simple activities they can complete at their desks, such as writing a name or snapping cubes together. Choose one activity and ask: **How many times can you complete the activity in 1 minute?**
- Have each child complete the task as many times as possible in 1 minute. Say: **Stop** after 1 minute has passed.
- Have children record the results.

Observing and Questioning

- If a child only completes a task once, ask: **Can you complete the task again before 1 minute is up?**
- Observe whether children are completing the task multiple times before 1 minute has passed. You might ask: **How will you know when 1 minute has passed?**
- **How did you estimate the number of times you could complete the task before you started?** *(I know that I can do it one time quickly.)*

Sharing and Summarizing

- Have children explain how they knew when 1 minute had passed. Also, discuss how many times children were able to complete the task.
- **Key Idea** As children share their strategies for keeping time, point out that in learning how to tell time on a clock, it is important to know what a minute is and how long it is. A minute can be recorded as "60 seconds" or "1 minute."

Follow-Up

- Have children choose a different activity to complete in 1 minute and estimate the number of times they can complete it in 1 minute.

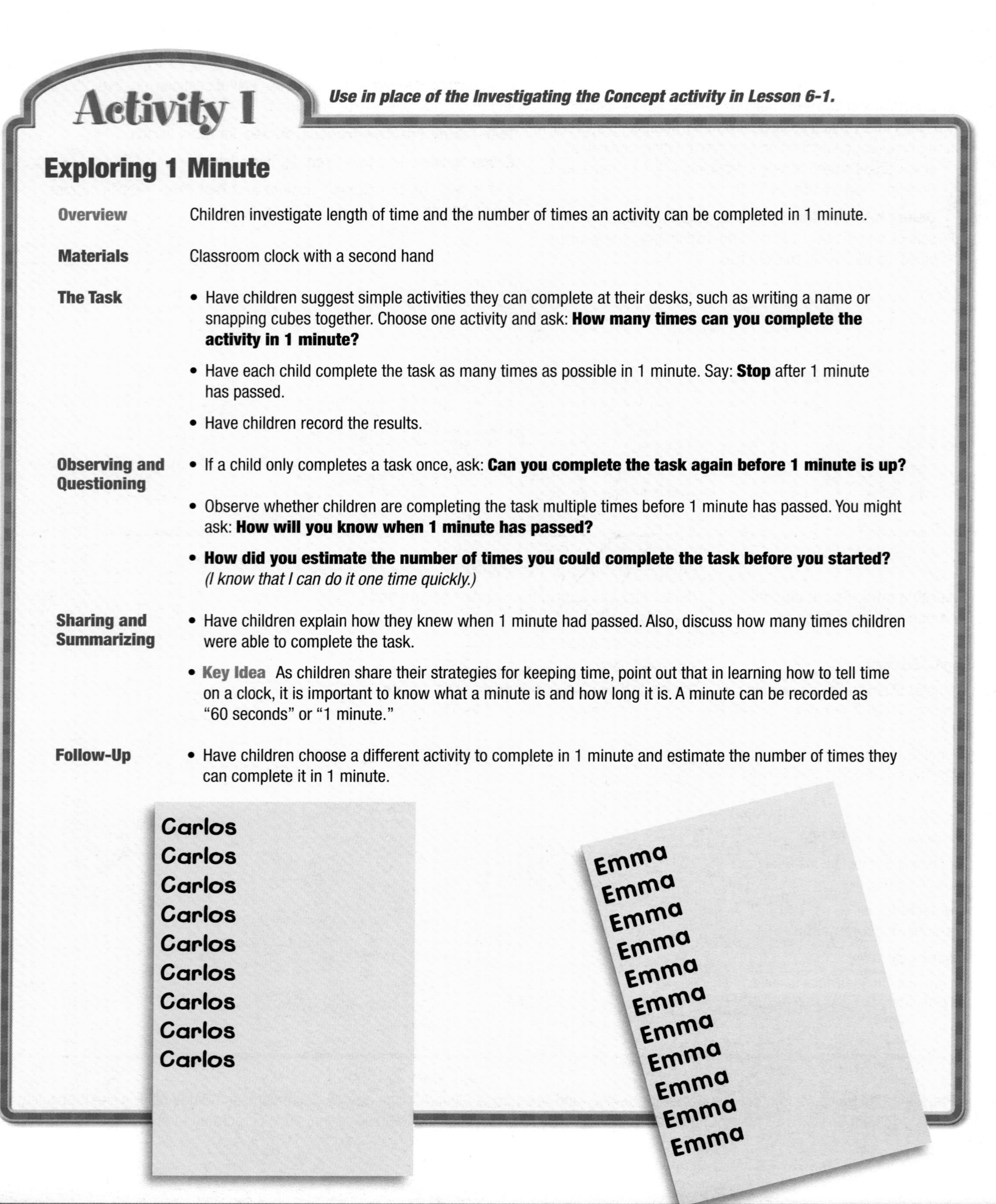

Link to ***Investigations in Number, Data, and Space***® See the **Joint-Usage Plan** available from Pearson Scott Foresman.

Activity 2

Use in place of the Investigating the Concept activity in Lesson 6-6.

Make a Time Line to Sequence Events

Overview

Children investigate the starting times for a variety of common activities and list them in order of occurrence.

Materials

(per group) Clock Face (Teaching Tool 22); 8.5 x 11 inch drawing paper; crayons; scissors

The Task

- As a class, create a list on the board of activities that children complete during the day.
- Discuss with children the time that each activity begins and write these times next to the corresponding activities.
- Working in groups, have each child choose one activity from the board and draw a picture of it. On a clock face, children can then show the time at which the activity begins, and place it beside the picture.
- Children can then paste the pictures and clock faces on drawing paper to create a timeline of events. Each group will create a separate timeline.

Observing and Questioning

- Observe whether children place activities in sequential order, and listen for them to use words such as *before, after, later,* and *earlier.*
- If children are having difficulty putting the activities in order, ask the following questions.
- **Which activities happen early in the day? Which happen later in the day?**
- **How did you decide the order in which to put the activities?** *(We started with the activity that happened earliest in the morning.)*

Sharing and Summarizing

- After children explain what they did, summarize the ways they determined the order for the activities. For example, children may start with the earliest activity and put events in order as they occur through the day. Others may choose one activity and decide what happens before it and after it and then order groups of activities.
- **Key Idea** As children share strategies for telling time and ordering events, point out the importance of showing activities in order of occurrence. Be sure to use the word *sequence* when discussing the order of children's activities.

Follow-Up

- Ask children to draw a picture of one additional activity during the day and point on the timeline to show where this activity would take place.

Math Story

Late for School Again? (Genre: Animal fantasy)

In this story, Bunny jumps out of bed in the morning and is afraid that she will be late for school. After she gets dressed and is ready to go to school, she realizes that it is Saturday morning.

Introducing the Story

Discuss with children what time they get up in the morning. Ask if they get up at the same time on weekends as they do during the school week. Talk with them about what might happen on a school day if they got up late.

Reading the Story

Read the story through once without stopping. Encourage children to listen carefully and to enjoy the story and art along with you.

Read the story again, this time inviting children to close their eyes and see in their minds what is happening on each page of the story. Tell children that they can use this reading strategy, picturing a story in their minds, whenever they read stories or solve math problems. (For more on *Visualize,* see Reading for Math Success, pp. 213–214.)

Page 6A

Bunny jumped up out of bed.
It was 6:30.
"Oh, no! I know I'm going to be late for school again!" she said.
6B
Bunny brushed her teeth.
She washed her face and ears.
She made her bed.
She looked at her clock.
It was 7:00.
"Why is it so quiet?" wondered Bunny.
"I don't hear Mother calling me."
6C

Page 6B **Page 6C**

"Where are my socks?
Where are my shoes?
I can't find anything!"
Oh, no! It was already 7:30.
6D
Bunny hopped down the stairs.
She was almost out of breath.
"It's time for breakfast," said Bunny.
"I have to hurry! It's already 8:00!"
6E

Page 6D

Page 6E

Then Bunny remembered. It was Saturday!
"There is no school today!" said Bunny.
"Silly, silly me! Oh, well."
Bunny ate her breakfast and read some
books until her mom and dad woke up.
6F

Page 6F

Follow-Up Activities

- **Create Elapsed-Time Stories** Ask children to recall what time Bunny gets up this morning *(6:30)*, brushes her teeth *(7:00)*, gets dressed *(7:30)*, and eats breakfast *(8:00)*. Then challenge them to create elapsed-time stories using this information, giving them an example such as: **How long after Bunny brushes her teeth does she eat breakfast?** *(1 hour)*
- **Sequence** Write these tasks on the board: "wash face, eat breakfast, get up, get dressed." Challenge children to describe the sequence of events in the story by giving the order in which Bunny performs these tasks.
- **Extend the Story** Ask: **What do you think Bunny will do when she gets up for the second time? What do you think Bunny will do Sunday morning? What time do you think Bunny will get up Monday morning?**

Home-School Connection

Purpose Provide families with a quick overview of the material that will be covered in Chapter 6. Included on this page: a family letter, a math activity, references to literature related to the chapter, and new math vocabulary words.

Using Student Page 203

You may wish to read and discuss the family letter with children prior to having them sign it and sending the page home.

Literature: Dorling Kindersley

Available in the Scott Foresman Dorling Kindersley Literature Library

A Day in the Life of a Firefighter
by Linda Hayward
(Dorling Kindersley Ltd., 2001)

This book uses time as a measure to follow a firefighter through his day, from early morning to late evening.

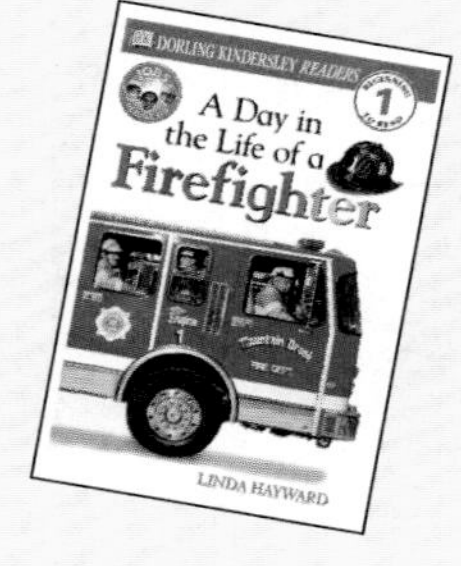

The Home-School Connection booklet includes:

- Chapter 6 Family Letter in English and Spanish
- Study Buddies 11
- Study Buddies 12

Study Buddies pages provide reinforcement activities for children to work on with a partner. Each Study Buddy has a page for the child and a page of prompts to help the partner guide the child's learning.

Vocabulary

minute *(pp. 205–206)*
hour *(pp. 207–208)*
hour hand *(pp. 207–208)*
minute hand *(pp. 207–208)*
o'clock *(pp. 207–208)*
half hour *(pp. 211–212)*
morning *(pp. 219–220)*
afternoon *(pp. 219–220)*
night *(pp. 219–220)*
calendar *(pp. 225–226)*
day *(pp. 225–226)*
month *(pp. 225–226)*
week *(pp. 225–226)*
year *(pp. 227–228)*

Home-School Connection

Dear Family,

Today my class started Chapter 6, **Time.** I will learn about time to the hour and to the half hour. I will also learn about the days of the week and the months of the year by using a calendar. Here are some of the math words I will be learning and some things we can do to help me with my math.

Love,

____

Math Activity to Do at Home

Help your child keep a picture diary of one activity he or she did each day for a week. Ask your child to write the name of the day and the time the activity was done beside each picture. Discuss with your child about how long each activity took.

Books to Read Together

Reading math stories reinforces concepts. Look for these titles in your local library:

10 Minutes till Bedtime
By Peggy Rathmann
(G.P. Putnam's Sons, 1998)

Bunny Day: Telling Time from Breakfast to Bedtime
By Rick Walton
(HarperCollins, 2002)

Take It to the NET
More Activities
www.scottforesman.com

My New Math Words

hour There are 60 minutes in an hour.

half hour A half hour is 30 minutes.

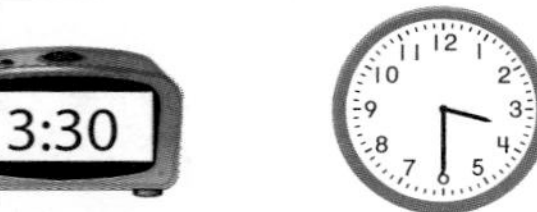

calendar

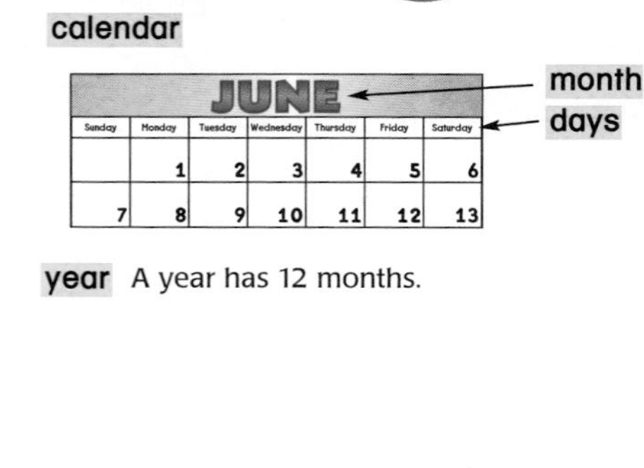

year A year has 12 months.

Math Vocabulary Kit

Every vocabulary word is written on a card with the definition of the word printed on the back. Vocabulary activities are provided in the *Math Vocabulary Kit Teacher's Guide*.

Add the words from the Vocabulary list at left to your Math Word Wall as they are introduced.

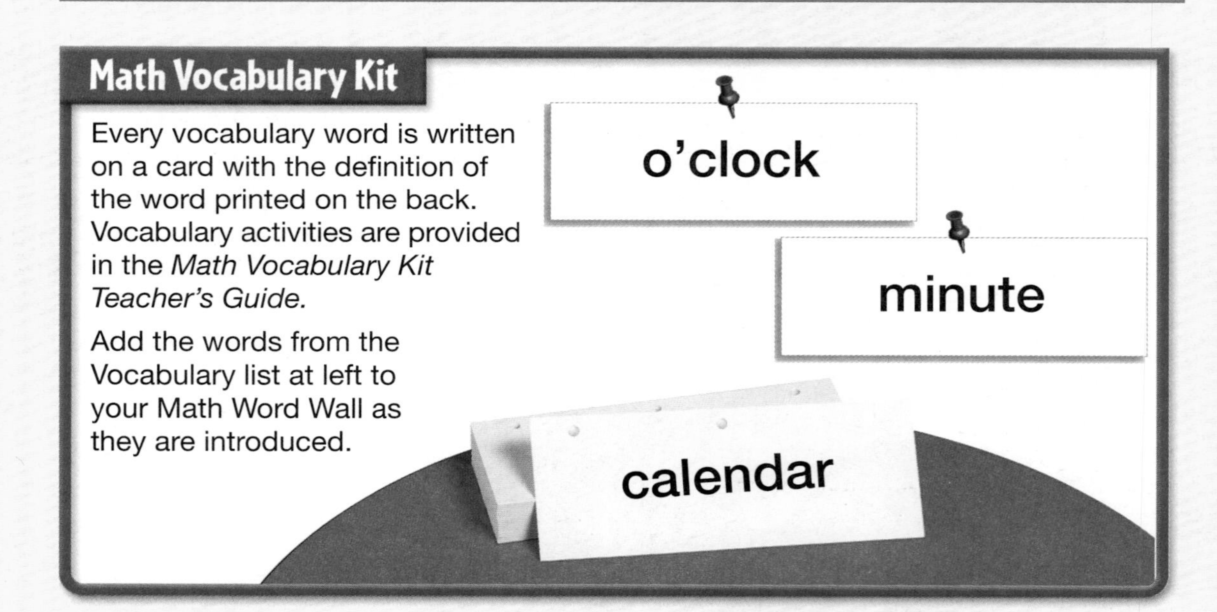

Name ______________________

Practice Game

Spin for Time

What You Need
paper clip
pencil
12 game markers

How to Play
1. Pretend that the paper clip is the **hour hand** on a clock.
2. Take turns spinning the spinner. Say the time.
3. Place a marker on the clock that shows that time.
4. If you land on the clock that Bunny is holding, you get an extra turn!
5. Keep playing until you and your partner cover all of the clocks.

© Pearson Education, Inc.

204 two hundred four

Practice Game
for School or Home

Purpose Provide children with an opportunity to practice skills they have previously learned.

Using Student Page 204

You may choose to discuss these questions before children play "Spin for Time."

- **If it is 3:00, where is the short hand? Where is the long hand?**
- **How do you use the hands of a clock to tell time?**

Give children the materials for the game.

Describe the game, explaining how the children will follow the directions. Lead children through the process of spinning and placing a marker on the clock that shows the corresponding time. Make sure children understand that they get an extra turn if they land on the clock Bunny is holding. Allow children to complete the game.

Describe another way to play: Have children place markers on each number of the clock. They spin, say the time, and remove a marker from the corresponding time on the clock. (There is no extra turn for landing on the Bunny clock.) When all of the markers have been removed, the player with the most markers is the winner.

Chapter 6 Diagnosing Readiness

1. Circle the event that takes more time.
2. Write the time shown on the clock. 2 o'clock
3. Show 9 o'clock by writing the time on the digital clock and drawing the hour hand on the analog clock. 9:00 9 o'clock
4. Match the pictures with the symbols for morning, afternoon, and evening. morning afternoon evening
5. Write the missing dates.
6. Color November 13 red.

November						
Sun	Mon	Tue	Wed	Thur	Fri	Sat
					1	2
3	4	5	6	7	8	9
10	11	12	13	14	15	16
17	18	19	20	21	22	23
24	25	26	27	28	29	30

© Pearson Education, Inc. 1

Chapter 6 Diagnosing Readiness 121

Item Analysis for Diagnosis and Intervention

Objective	Items	Student Book Pages*	Intervention System
Identify the activity or event that takes more time or less time.	1	Kindergarten	D2
Tell time to the hour on an analog clock and a digital clock.	2–3	Kindergarten	D2
Identify the time of day as day or night; morning, afternoon, or evening.	4	Kindergarten	D2
Identify the different parts of a calendar.	5–6	Kindergarten	D2

*For each lesson, there is a *Reteaching* activity in *Reaching All Learners* and a *Reteaching* master.

Math Leveled Literature Library

Ox-Cart Man (Challenging)★
Donald Hall. New York: Puffin Books, 1979.

Describes the day-to-day activities of an early nineteenth century family during the calendar year as the seasons change.

Minutes

Lesson Organizer

Quick Lesson Overview

Objective Determine if an event takes more or less than 1 minute.

Math Understanding Knowing the approximate length of 1 minute helps to accurately estimate time.

Vocabulary Minute

Professional Development Note

Research Base

Understanding of number is a powerful idea used by children for organizing quantitative information and developing quantitative skills such as telling time (Case & Griffin, 1990). The lessons in this section connect the skill of telling time to children's previous work with numbers through 60.

NCTM Standards

- Measurement

(For a complete correlation to the NCTM Standards and Grades Pre-K through 2 Expectations, see Pages 203G and 203H.)

Getting Started

Spiral Review

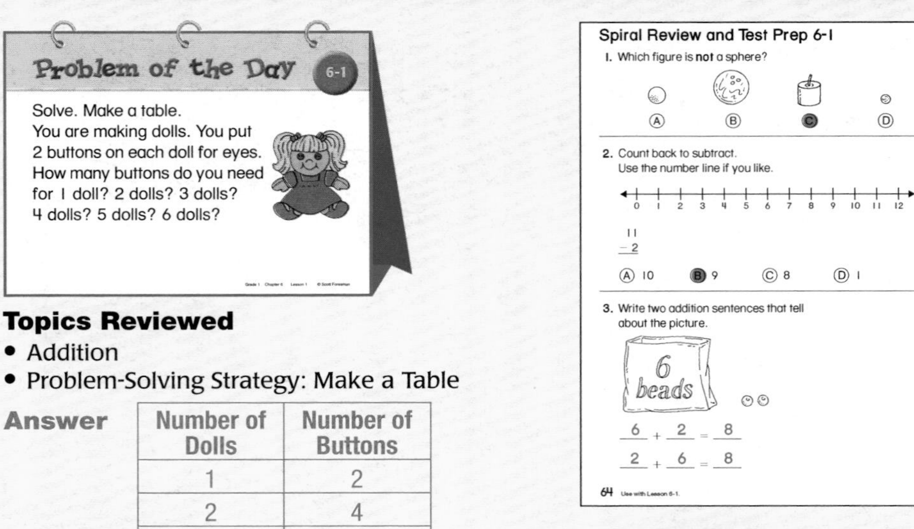

Problem of the Day 6-1

Solve. Make a table.
You are making dolls. You put 2 buttons on each doll for eyes. How many buttons do you need for 1 doll? 2 dolls? 3 dolls? 4 dolls? 5 dolls? 6 dolls?

Spiral Review and Test Prep 6-1

1. Which figure is **not** a sphere?
Ⓐ Ⓑ Ⓒ Ⓓ

2. Count back to subtract.
Use the number line if you like.
0 1 2 3 4 5 6 7 8 9 10 11 12
11
− 2
Ⓐ 10 Ⓑ 9 Ⓒ 8 Ⓓ 1

3. Write two addition sentences that tell about the picture.
6 beads
6 + 2 = 8
2 + 6 = 8

64 Use with Lesson 6-1.

Topics Reviewed
- Addition
- Problem-Solving Strategy: Make a Table

Answer

Number of Dolls	Number of Buttons
1	2
2	4
3	6
4	8
5	10
6	12

Available as a transparency and as a blackline master

Topics Reviewed
1. Solid Figures
2. Counting Back Using a Number Line
3. Adding in Any Order

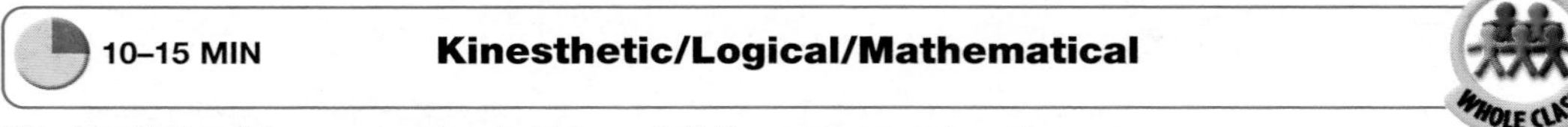

Investigating the Concept

More or Less Than a Minute

10–15 MIN **Kinesthetic/Logical/Mathematical** WHOLE CLASS

Materials Timer or clock; *(per child)* crayons; drawing paper

What to Do

- To help children understand how long 1 minute is, ask them to stand "as still as a statue" for 1 minute.
- Write "less than 1 minute" and "more than 1 minute" on the board. Ask children to predict whether it will take less or more than 1 minute to clap four times. Have them clap four times and see that the timer shows that it took less than 1 minute. **Was your prediction correct?**
- Continue predicting and timing children as they do several activities, such as drawing simple pictures or singing songs.

Ongoing Assessment

- **Reasoning What activity do you like to do that takes more than 1 minute?** *(Sample responses: Read a book, play a game, finger paint)*
- **Would a sneeze take less or more than 1 minute?** *(Less than 1 minute)*

Reaching All Learners

Math and Literature

A Matter of Minutes

10–15 MIN **Auditory/Linguistic**

Materials *10 Minutes Till Bedtime* by Peggy Rathman (Putnam, 1998)

- Read this book about a very unusual visit from a family of hamsters just before bedtime.
- After reading about the fantastic experiences of the boy, ask children to share their pre-bedtime routines.
- **How long do your pre-bedtime activities take? Does it take more or less than 1 minute to brush your teeth? Does it take more than 1 minute to take a bath? Does it take less than 1 minute to listen to a bedtime story?**

Reteaching

Just a Minute

10–15 MIN **Kinesthetic**

Materials Chart paper; markers; timer or clock

- Ask children to close their eyes for 1 minute. Tell them you will tell them when time is up. **Is a minute a long time or a short time?**
- After children have a feeling for how long 1 minute is, make a chart with the headings: "Takes Less Than 1 Minute" and "Takes More Than 1 Minute."
- Have children perform everyday classroom activities, time the activities, and record them on the chart. Begin by having children sharpen a pencil.

Activate Prior Knowledge/Build Background

English Language Learners

What Is Less Than 1 Minute? What Is More?

Materials Timer or clock

- Focus attention on the timer as children stand for 1 minute. When time is up, say: **That took 1 minute.**
- Open a window. **That took less than 1 minute.** Ask children to recall actions they have done in less than 1 minute.
- Pantomime eating lunch. **Eating lunch takes more than 1 minute.** Invite children to act out what they can do in more than 1 minute.

Takes more than one minute.

Math and Physical Education

Ready, Set, Go!

10–15 MIN **Kinesthetic**

SMALL GROUP

Materials *(per group)* Table tennis balls; basket; scorecard

- Write the name of each child on a scorecard. Assign a scorekeeper for the group. The other members have the job of helping the scorekeeper keep track of the points.
- Explain that each member of the group has 1 minute to throw as many balls as possible into the basket. Children may retrieve balls and throw them again to gain more points.
- The child who scores the most points in 1 minute wins.

Objective Determine if an event takes more or less than 1 minute.

1 Warm Up

Activate Prior Knowledge Review *less than* and *more than.* Ask questions, such as: **Are there more than 5 teachers in this room?** or **Is 6 less than 10?** Help children determine the correct answer by counting.

2 Teach

Learn!

Demonstrate how long 1 minute is by asking children to tap their shoulders for 1 minute. Then call attention to the activity at the top of the student page. Share ideas about how long it takes to play checkers. Have children circle the answer to show it takes more than 1 minute to play a game of checkers.

Ongoing Assessment

Talk About It

- **What are some things that take less than 1 minute to do?** *(Samples responses: Blink, wink, turn on a light)*
- **What are some things that take more than 1 minute to do?** (*Sample responses: Ride a bike, play the piano, practice handwriting)*

If children cannot tell how long an activity takes,

then time children as they pantomime the activity.

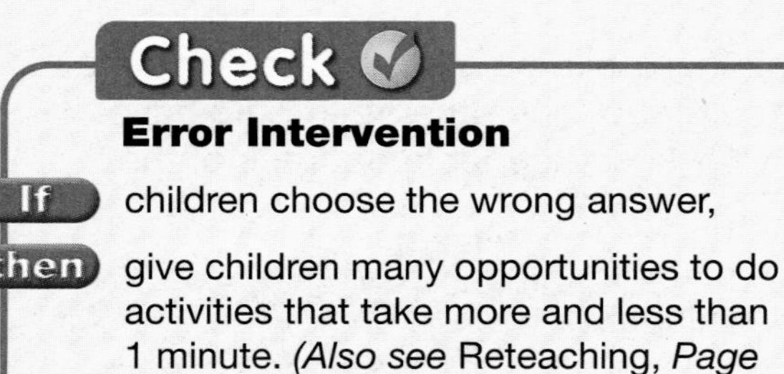

Check

Error Intervention

If children choose the wrong answer,

then give children many opportunities to do activities that take more and less than 1 minute. *(Also see* Reteaching, *Page 205B.)*

Think About It Encourage children to support their answers with sensible reasons, pointing out that either answer could be right depending on how fast a person does the activity.

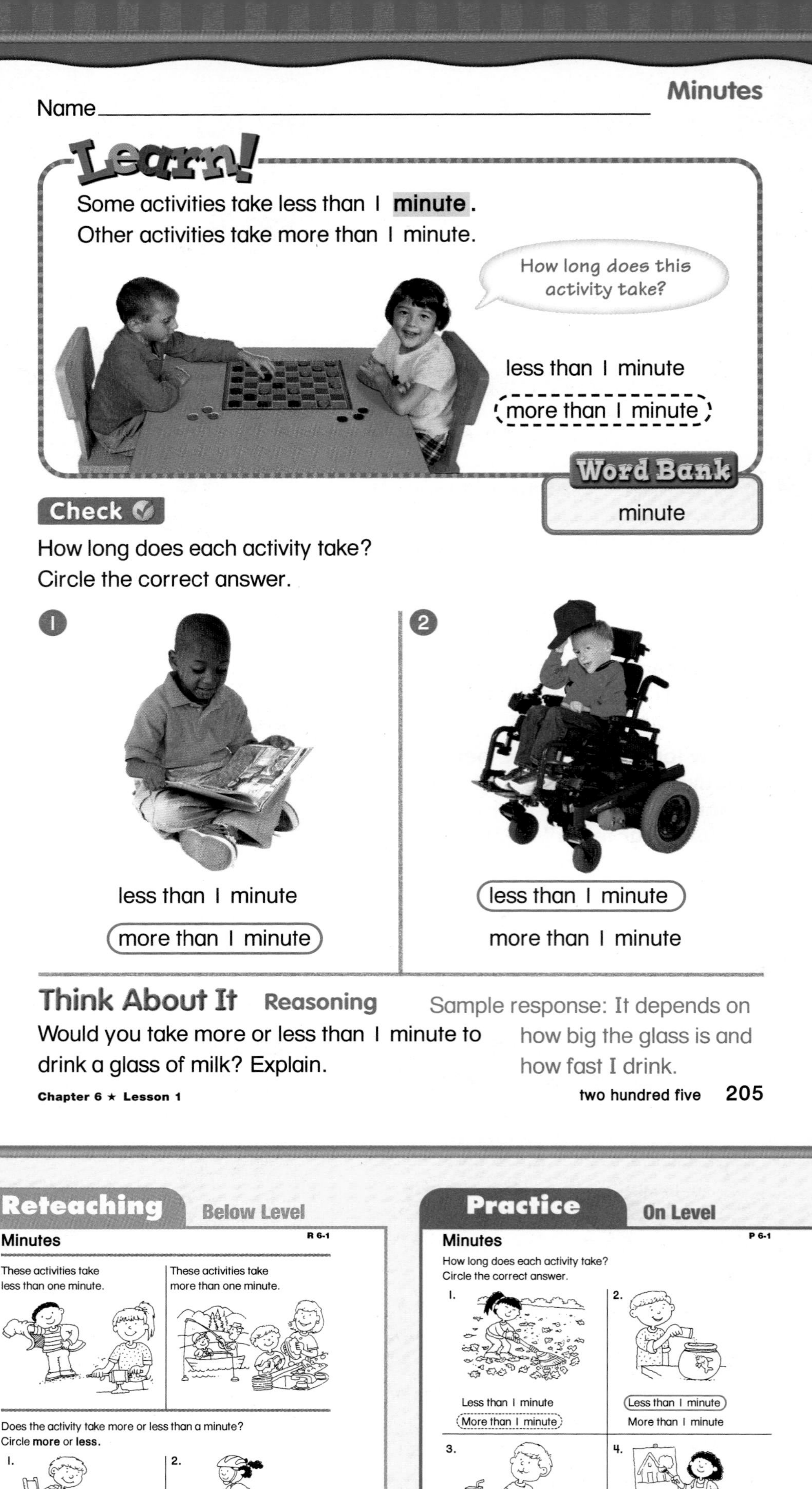

Name ____________ **Minutes**

Learn!

Some activities take less than 1 **minute**.
Other activities take more than 1 minute.

less than 1 minute
(more than 1 minute)

Word Bank
minute

Check

How long does each activity take?
Circle the correct answer.

1. less than 1 minute / (more than 1 minute)
2. (less than 1 minute) / more than 1 minute

Think About It Reasoning
Would you take more or less than 1 minute to drink a glass of milk? Explain.
Sample response: It depends on how big the glass is and how fast I drink.

Chapter 6 ★ Lesson 1 two hundred five 205

Reteaching Below Level

Minutes R 6-1

These activities take less than one minute. | These activities take more than one minute.

Does the activity take more or less than a minute?
Circle **more** or **less**.

1. more (less)
2. (more) less
3. more (less)
4. (more) less

64 Use with Lesson 6-1

Practice On Level

Minutes P 6-1

How long does each activity take?
Circle the correct answer.

1. Less than 1 minute / (More than 1 minute)
2. (Less than 1 minute) / More than 1 minute
3. Less than 1 minute / (More than 1 minute)
4. Less than 1 minute / (More than 1 minute)

Problem Solving *Estimation*
5. Draw a picture to show something that you can do in about the same time it takes to make your bed.
Check children's drawings.

64 Use with Lesson 6-1

Practice

How long does each activity take?
Circle the correct answer.

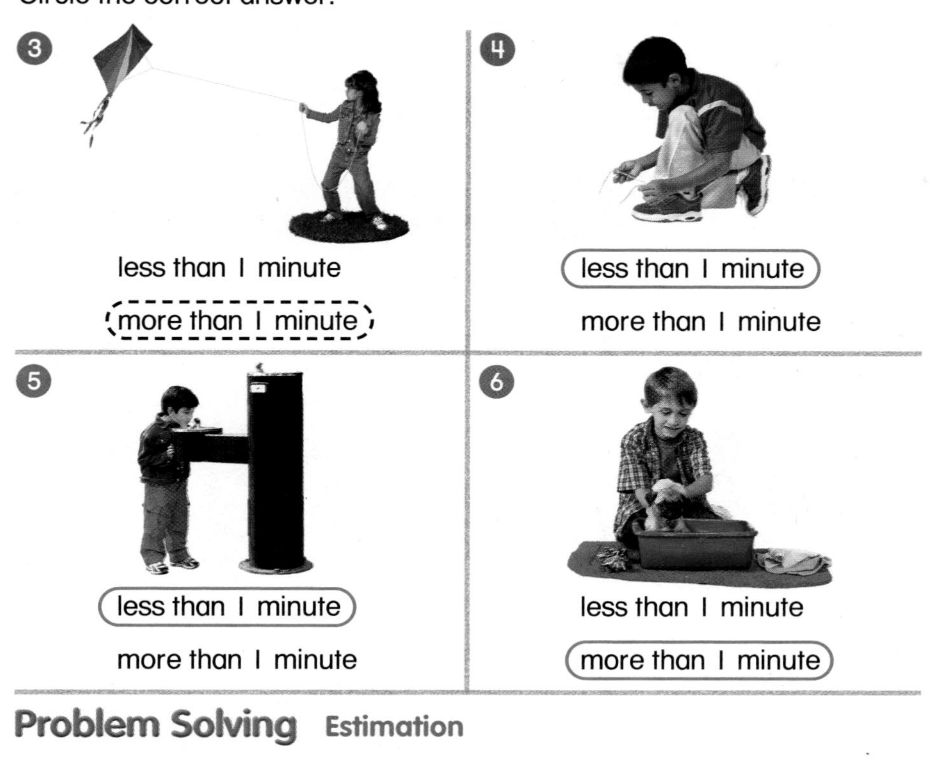

3. less than 1 minute / **(more than 1 minute)**

4. **(less than 1 minute)** / more than 1 minute

5. **(less than 1 minute)** / more than 1 minute

6. less than 1 minute / **(more than 1 minute)**

Problem Solving Estimation

7. Draw a picture to show something that you can do in about the same time as it takes to write your name.

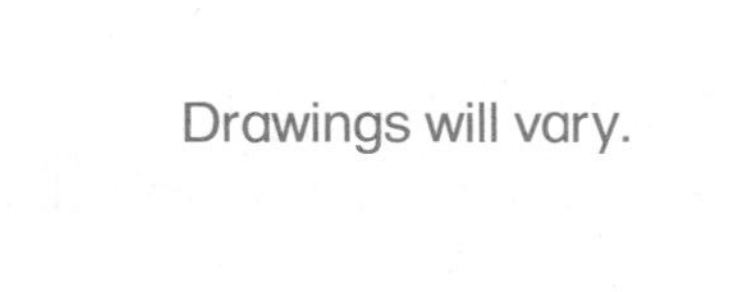

Drawings will vary.

Home Connection Your child decided if activities take more or less than 1 minute. **Home Activity** Before you and your child do an activity, ask your child to predict whether it will take more or less than 1 minute. Then time yourselves to see if he or she was correct.

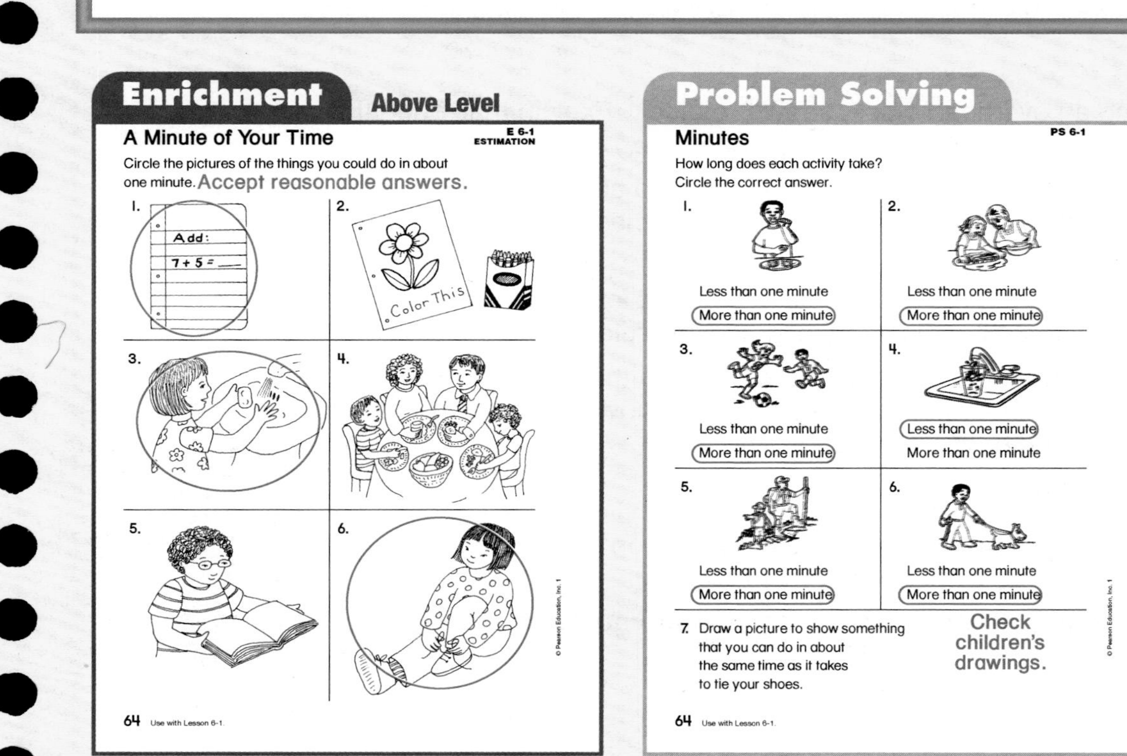

Enrichment Above Level

A Minute of Your Time E 6-1 ESTIMATION

Circle the pictures of the things you could do in about one minute. Accept reasonable answers.

1. 2. 3. 4. 5. 6.

64 Use with Lesson 6-1.

Problem Solving

Minutes PS 6-1

How long does each activity take?
Circle the correct answer.

1. Less than one minute / (More than one minute)
2. Less than one minute / (More than one minute)
3. Less than one minute / (More than one minute)
4. (Less than one minute) / More than one minute
5. Less than one minute / (More than one minute)
6. Less than one minute / (More than one minute)

7. Draw a picture to show something that you can do in about the same time as it takes to tie your shoes. Check children's drawings.

64 Use with Lesson 6-1.

3 Practice

For Exercises 4 and 5, consider having children act out the activity, while their class-mates time them using a timer or a clock.

Reading Assist: Use Picture Clues Before doing Exercises 3–6, ask children to tell what is happening in each picture.

Leveled Practice

Below Level Listen as the teacher describes each activity.

On Level Complete all exercises as written.

Above Level Circle the activity that takes the longest time.

Early Finishers Invite children to think of four activities that take more than 1 minute to do. Ask them to illustrate each.

4 Assess

Journal Idea Ask children to guess how many times they can write their own names in 1 minute. Time children as they do so. Have children compare their own writings with their predictions.

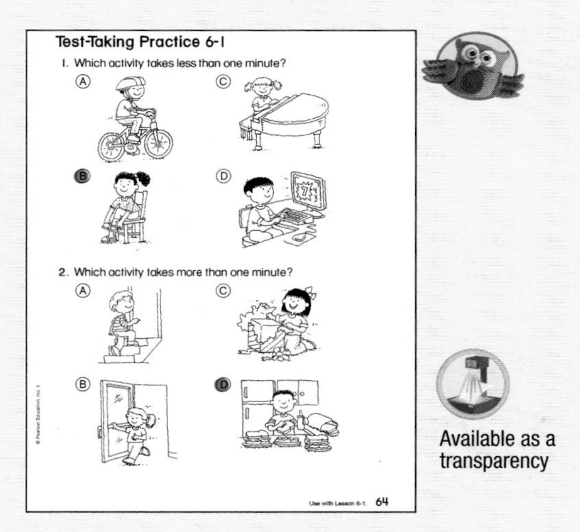

Test-Taking Practice 6-1

1. Which activity takes less than one minute?
Ⓐ Ⓑ Ⓒ Ⓓ

2. Which activity takes more than one minute?
Ⓐ Ⓑ Ⓒ Ⓓ

Use with Lesson 6-1. 64

Available as a transparency

6-2 Understanding the Hour and Minute Hands

Lesson Organizer

Quick Lesson Overview

Objective Identify the hour hand and the minute hand on a clock and tell time to the hour.

Math Understanding The hour hand tells the hour, while the minute hand tells the number of minutes after the hour.

Vocabulary Hour, hour hand, minute hand, o'clock

Managing Instruction For direct experience with measuring tools, create an overhead transparency from the Clock Face (Teaching Tool 22). Allow each child to create a personal clock face for hands-on activities. Consider copying the clock faces onto heavy stock paper, laminating them, and collecting them daily for reuse.

NCTM Standards

- Measurement

(For a complete correlation to the NCTM Standards and Grades Pre-K through 2 Expectations, see Pages 203G and 203H.)

Getting Started

Spiral Review

Problem of the Day 6-2

10 + 0 is one way to make 10. How many other ways are there to make 10 by adding 2 numbers? Write all the other ways.

Topics Reviewed

- Addition
- Problem-Solving Strategy: Make a Table

Answer There are 10 other ways: 0 + 10, 1 + 9, 2 + 8, 3 + 7, 4 + 6, 5 + 5, 6 + 4, 7 + 3, 8 + 2, and 9 + 1. Check children's tables.

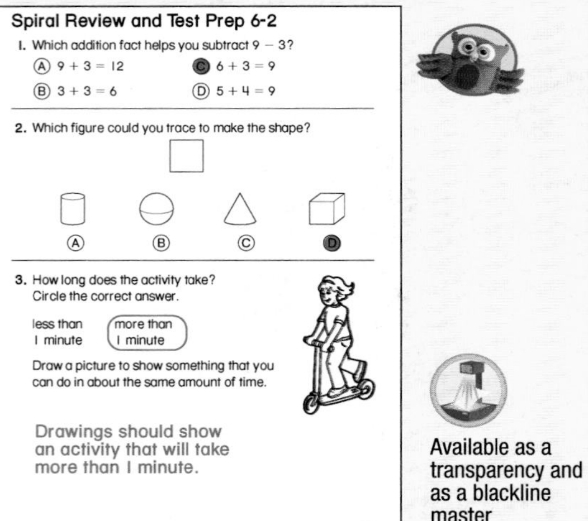

Spiral Review and Test Prep 6-2

1. Which addition fact helps you subtract 9 − 3?
   - Ⓐ 9 + 3 = 12
   - Ⓑ 3 + 3 = 6
   - Ⓒ 6 + 3 = 9
   - Ⓓ 5 + 4 = 9
2. Which figure could you trace to make the shape?
   - Ⓐ Ⓑ Ⓒ Ⓓ
3. How long does the activity take? Circle the correct answer.

   less than 1 minute | more than 1 minute

   Draw a picture to show something that you can do in about the same amount of time.

   Drawings should show an activity that will take more than 1 minute.

Use with Lesson 6-2. 65

Available as a transparency and as a blackline master

Topics Reviewed

1. Using Addition Facts to Subtract **2.** Relating Plane Shapes to Solid Figures **3.** Minutes

Investigating the Concept

Show the Time to the Hour

Materials Overhead clock; *(per child)* Clock Face (Teaching Tool 22)

What to Do

- Using an overhead clock, show 8 o'clock. Explain that when the hour hand points to 8 and the minute hand points to 12, we say *8 o'clock.*
- Move the minute hand all the way around and the hour hand to 9 to show that one hour (60 minutes) has passed, and now it is 9 o'clock.
- Have children predict what each time will look like on the clock before you show it; 6 o'clock, 12 o'clock, and 5 o'clock.
- Give children their own clock faces. Help them identify the minute and hour hands. Have children show several different times to the hour.

Ongoing Assessment

- **Reasoning When the minute hand is on 12 and the hour hand is on 6, what time is it?** *(6 o'clock)*
- **How many different times to the hour can be shown on a clock?** *(12)*

Reaching All Learners

Oral Language in Math

Rhyme Time

10–15 MIN **Auditory/Linguistic**

- Draw a tall clock with a blank clock face on the board.
- Have children listen for the time in this rhyme.

  Hickory, dickory, dock
  The mouse ran up the clock.
  The clock struck one
  The mouse ran down.
  Hickory, dickory, dock.

- Explain that "The clock struck one" means 1 o'clock. Ask children to tell you how to show 1 o'clock on the clock face.
- Repeat the rhyme and activity, substituting other times for 1 o'clock.

Access Content

English Language Learners

Clock Talk

5–10 MIN **Linguistic/Visual/Spatial**

Materials Clock Face (Teaching Tool 22); sets of index cards labeled *hour, hour hand, minute hand,* and *o'clock;* Number Cards 0–11 (Teaching Tool 9); Number Cards 12–20 (Teaching Tool 11)

- Post copies of the clock face on the wall and draw various times to the hour on the clocks.
- Point to each index card as you name a term for children to repeat.
- Have children label each clock with word cards and a number card.

Reteaching

What Time Is It?

5–10 MIN **Linguistic/Kinesthetic**

Materials *(per child)* Clock Face (Teaching Tool 22)

- Demonstrate how to set a clock at 9 o'clock. Use the words *minute hand* and *hour hand* as you set the time. **We start school at 9 o'clock.**
- Ask children to set their clocks to 10 o'clock. Emphasize that the minute hand moves all the way around the clock and the hour hand only moves to the next number. **1 hour later, we have math. Set your clocks for 10 o'clock.**
- Continue demonstrating times and having children show them on their clocks.

Math and Social Studies

Work Days

15–20 MIN **Linguistic/Visual/Spatial**

Materials Books about jobs and workers; *(per child)* paper; crayons

- Share books about the work that people do. Discuss what firefighters, chefs, zookeepers, and storeowners do during the day.
- Invite children to write and illustrate books that show a day in the life of one of these workers. Have them decide what a worker would do in a seven-hour day.
- Give children a model for the text at the bottom of each page: "At ___ o'clock the ___ starts to work."

At 8 o'clock the zookeeper starts to work.

Objective Identify the hour hand and the minute hand on a clock and tell time to the hour.

1 Warm Up

Activate Prior Knowledge Review ordering numbers. On the board, write sets of numbers in sequence with blanks in place of some of the numbers. Have volunteers fill in the blanks.

2 Teach

Learn!

Call attention to the clock at the top of the student page. Help children identify the hour hand and the minute hand. Explain that when the minute hand points to 12, we say o'clock. If the hour hand points to 3, the clock shows 3 o'clock. Tell children that it takes 60 minutes (1 hour) for the minute hand to move once around the clock.

Ongoing Assessment

Talk About It

- **Which hand tells the hour?** *(The shorter hand)*
- **If the hour hand and the minute hand are both on 12, what time is it?** *(12 o'clock)*

If children have difficulty telling time,

then go once around the clock, naming each hour, noting where the red and blue hands are.

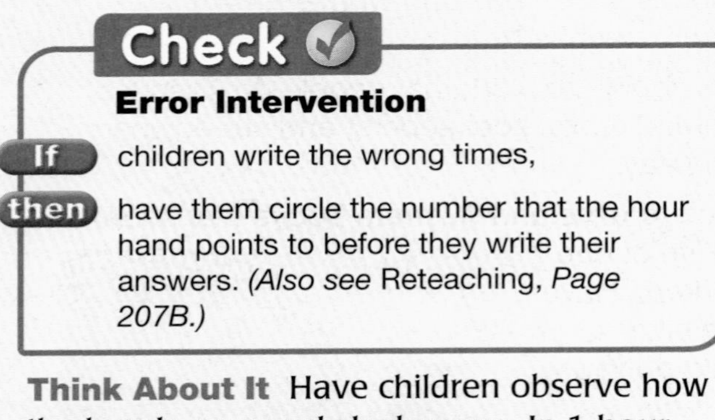

Check

Error Intervention

If children write the wrong times,

then have them circle the number that the hour hand points to before they write their answers. *(Also see* Reteaching, *Page 207B.)*

Think About It Have children observe how the hands on a real clock move. In 1 hour the minute hand travels all the way around the clock, while the hour hand just moves to the next number.

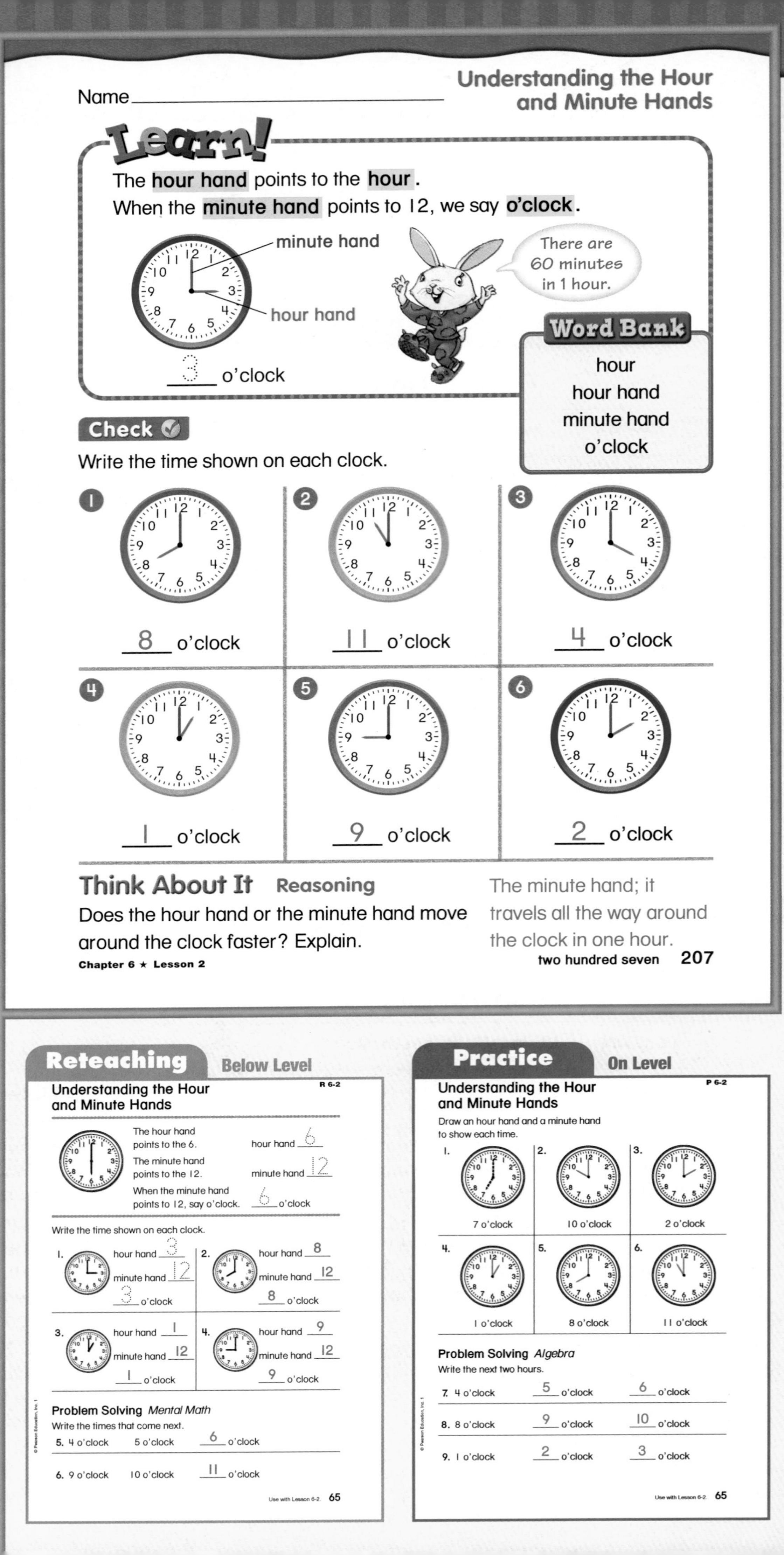

Name ____________________

Understanding the Hour and Minute Hands

Learn!

The **hour hand** points to the **hour**.
When the **minute hand** points to 12, we say **o'clock**.

3 o'clock

Word Bank
hour
hour hand
minute hand
o'clock

Check

Write the time shown on each clock.

1. 8 o'clock
2. 11 o'clock
3. 4 o'clock
4. 1 o'clock
5. 9 o'clock
6. 2 o'clock

Think About It Reasoning

Does the hour hand or the minute hand move around the clock faster? Explain.

The minute hand; it travels all the way around the clock in one hour.

Chapter 6 ★ Lesson 2 — two hundred seven 207

Reteaching Below Level

R 6-2

Understanding the Hour and Minute Hands

The hour hand points to the 6. — hour hand 6
The minute hand points to the 12. — minute hand 12
When the minute hand points to 12, say o'clock. — 6 o'clock

Write the time shown on each clock.

1. hour hand 3, minute hand 12, 3 o'clock
2. hour hand 8, minute hand 12, 8 o'clock
3. hour hand 1, minute hand 12, 1 o'clock
4. hour hand 9, minute hand 12, 9 o'clock

Problem Solving *Mental Math*

Write the times that come next.

5. 4 o'clock 5 o'clock 6 o'clock
6. 9 o'clock 10 o'clock 11 o'clock

Use with Lesson 6-2 65

Practice On Level

P 6-2

Understanding the Hour and Minute Hands

Draw an hour hand and a minute hand to show each time.

1. 7 o'clock
2. 10 o'clock
3. 2 o'clock
4. 1 o'clock
5. 8 o'clock
6. 11 o'clock

Problem Solving *Algebra*

Write the next two hours.

7. 4 o'clock 5 o'clock 6 o'clock
8. 8 o'clock 9 o'clock 10 o'clock
9. 1 o'clock 2 o'clock 3 o'clock

Use with Lesson 6-2 65

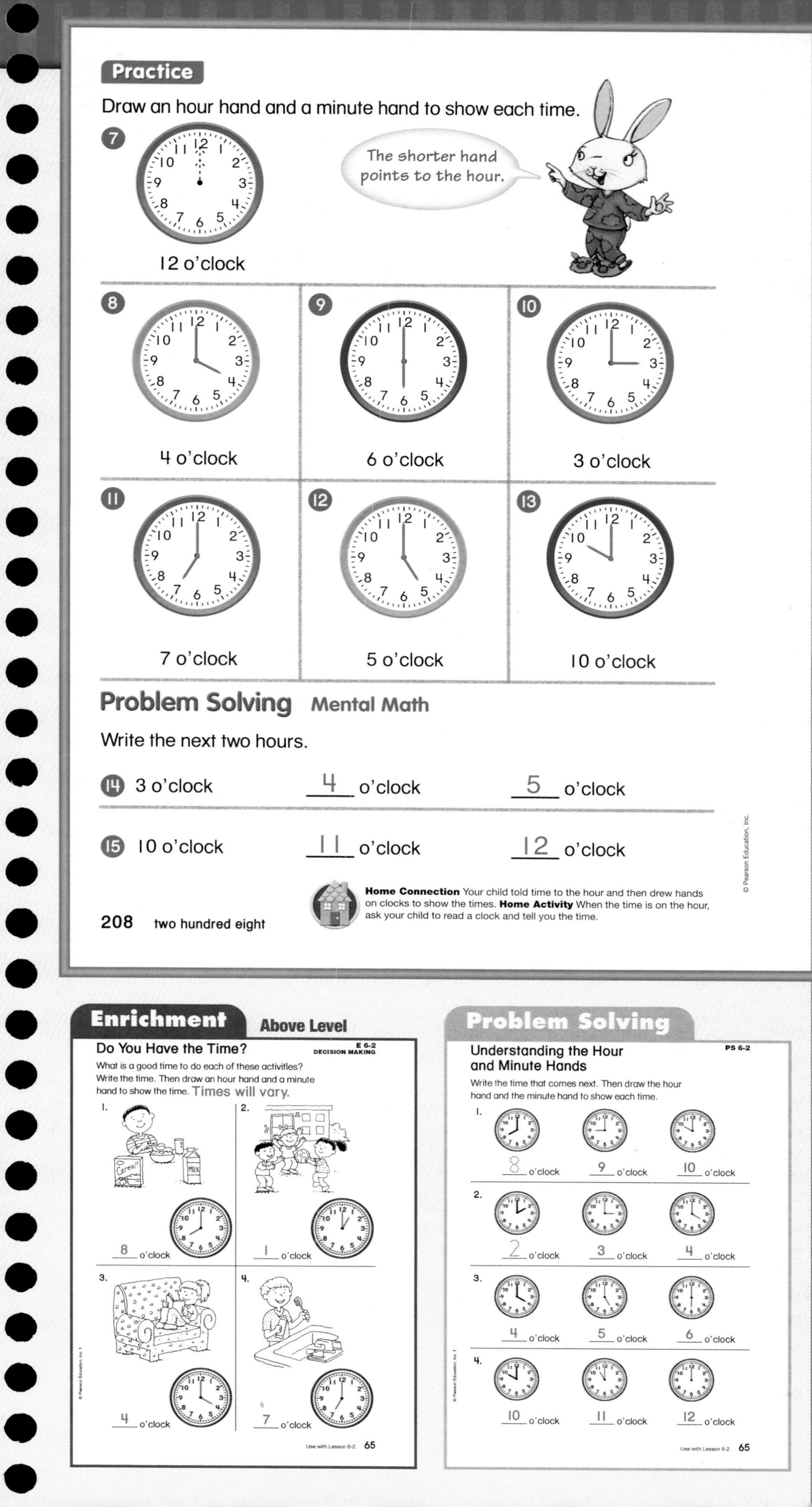

Practice

Draw an hour hand and a minute hand to show each time.

The shorter hand points to the hour.

7. 12 o'clock
8. 4 o'clock
9. 6 o'clock
10. 3 o'clock
11. 7 o'clock
12. 5 o'clock
13. 10 o'clock

Problem Solving Mental Math

Write the next two hours.

14. 3 o'clock 4 o'clock 5 o'clock
15. 10 o'clock 11 o'clock 12 o'clock

Home Connection Your child told time to the hour and then drew hands on clocks to show the times. **Home Activity** When the time is on the hour, ask your child to read a clock and tell you the time.

© Pearson Education, Inc.

208 two hundred eight

Enrichment Above Level

Do You Have the Time? E 6-2 DECISION MAKING

What is a good time to do each of these activities? Write the time. Then draw an hour hand and a minute hand to show the time. Times will vary.

1. 8 o'clock
2. 1 o'clock
3. 4 o'clock
4. 7 o'clock

Use with Lesson 6-2. 65

Problem Solving

Understanding the Hour and Minute Hands PS 6-2

Write the time that comes next. Then draw the hour hand and the minute hand to show each time.

1. 8 o'clock 9 o'clock 10 o'clock
2. 2 o'clock 3 o'clock 4 o'clock
3. 4 o'clock 5 o'clock 6 o'clock
4. 10 o'clock 11 o'clock 12 o'clock

Use with Lesson 6-2. 65

3 Practice

After children complete Exercises 7–13, ask them to tell what is alike and what is different about each of the clocks.

Leveled Practice

Below Level Use a clock to show each time.

On Level Circle the number each hour hand will point to before drawing it.

Above Level Complete all exercises as written.

Early Finishers In Exercises 7–13, have children write the time it will be 1 hour later.

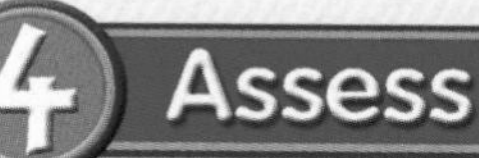

4 Assess

Journal Idea Have children draw pictures to show activities they like to do. Then have them draw clocks to show the times that they usually do them.

Test-Taking Practice 6-2

1. What time does the clock show?
   - Ⓐ 6 o'clock
   - Ⓑ 12 o'clock
   - Ⓒ 5 o'clock
   - Ⓓ 1 o'clock
2. What time comes next?
   6 o'clock ____ o'clock
   - Ⓐ 5
   - Ⓑ 7
   - Ⓒ 12
   - Ⓓ 8
3. What time came before?
   ____ o'clock 6 o'clock
   - Ⓐ 2
   - Ⓑ 3
   - Ⓒ 4
   - Ⓓ 5

Use with Lesson 6-2. 65

Available as a transparency

6-3 Telling and Writing Time to the Hour

Lesson Organizer

Quick Lesson Overview 

Objective Tell and write time to the hour on an analog clock and on a digital clock.

Math Understanding Time to the hour can be shown on an analog clock or on a digital clock and can be written in two ways: _ *o'clock* or _ *:00.*

Professional Development Note

Effective Questioning Techniques Conversations and questions about the units of time will build children's vocabularies and provide opportunities for the teacher to learn about their understandings and misconceptions. Focus questions on the procedure children follow to tell time to the hour. For example: **How do you know the clock shows 4 o'clock?**

NCTM Standards

- Measurement

(For a complete correlation to the NCTM Standards and Grades Pre-K through 2 Expectations, see Pages 203G and 203H.)

Getting Started

Spiral Review

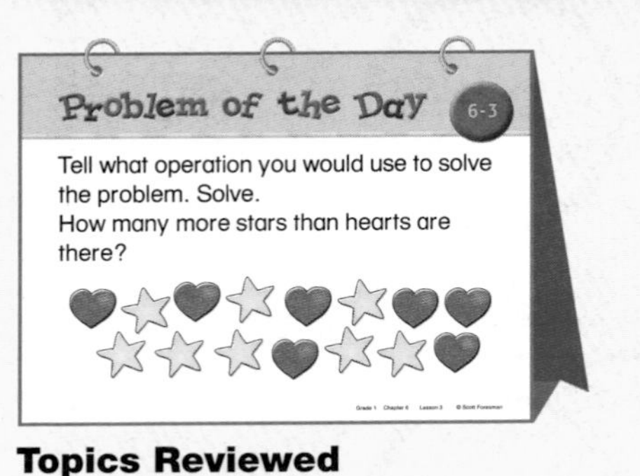

Topics Reviewed

- Subtraction
- Problem-Solving Skill: Choose an Operation

Answer Sample: Use subtraction to solve. There are 8 − 7, or 1 more star than hearts.

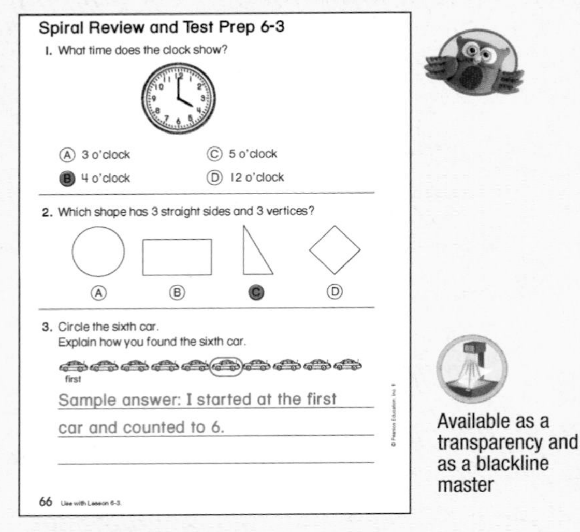
Spiral Review and Test Prep 6-3

1. What time does the clock show?

Ⓐ 3 o'clock Ⓒ 5 o'clock
Ⓑ 4 o'clock Ⓓ 12 o'clock

2. Which shape has 3 straight sides and 3 vertices?

Ⓐ Ⓑ Ⓒ Ⓓ

3. Circle the sixth car.
Explain how you found the sixth car.

first

Sample answer: I started at the first car and counted to 6.

66 Use with Lesson 6-3.

Available as a transparency and as a blackline master

Topics Reviewed
1. Understanding the Hour and Minute Hands **2.** Properties of Plane Shapes
3. Ordinal Numbers Through Tenth

Investigating the Concept

Time to Write the Time

Materials *(per child)* Clock Face (Teaching Tool 22); index cards

What to Do

- Write "4 o'clock" on the board and have children show the time using their clock faces. Then show the same time on a digital clock by drawing a simple digital clock on the board.
- Tell children that time can be written just as it is shown on the digital clock. Write "4:00" under "4 o'clock" on the board. Point out that the number before the two dots (colon) tells the hour and that the two zeros after the colon mean that we say *o'clock.*
- Continue having children show a given time on their clock faces and write on an index card what the digital clock would say.

4 o'clock

Ongoing Assessment

- **Reasoning How does the digital clock show time?** *(With numbers)*
- **How does the clock face show time?** *(With numbers and hands)*

Reaching All Learners

Oral Language in Math

You're Late!

10–15 MIN **Auditory/Linguistic**

- Read these rhymes to children.

  A diller, a dollar,
  A ten o'clock scholar,
  What makes you come so soon?
  You used to come at 9 o'clock
  But now you come at noon.

  Elsie Marley is grown so fine,
  She won't get up to feed the swine,
  But lies in bed till eight or nine.
  Lazy Elsie Marley.

- **A ten o'clock scholar is a student who comes to school at ten o'clock. How would you show ten o'clock?** Ask a volunteer to show the time on a blank analog and digital clock face on the board.
- Continue with the other times in the rhymes.

Access Content

English Language Learners

Find Your Partner in Time

10–15 MIN **Visual/Spatial**

Materials Small pieces of paper, each with a time to the hour drawn on an analog clock; small pieces of paper with the same times written on digital clocks

- Distribute the pieces of paper to children. Call out a time. Invite children who have the corresponding time to hold up their papers.
- Then invite children to find someone who has the same time. Children with a digital reading of 5:00 should look for someone who has an analog reading of 5 o'clock.

Reteaching

Time Match Up

10–15 MIN **Logical/Mathematical**

PAIRS

Materials *(per pair)* Index cards labeled with times to each hour on analog clocks and digital clocks

- Hold up the card showing 3 o'clock on an analog clock. Match it with a card that shows 3 o'clock on a digital clock. Tell children these are two ways to show three o'clock.
- Turn upside down 16 cards that show 8 different hours on analog clocks and digital clocks.
- Have children work in pairs to make matches. Encourage them to say each time as they make a match.

8:00

Math and Science

Another Way to Tell Time

10–15 MIN **Linguistic/Visual/Spatial**

Materials Sundial (if available)

- Explain that, long ago, before clocks were invented, people used the Sun to determine the time of day.
- Take children outside at different times of the day to show them how the Sun moves across the sky from east to west. Explain that at noon the Sun is directly overhead.
- If a sundial is available, show children how sun and shadow are used to show time of day.

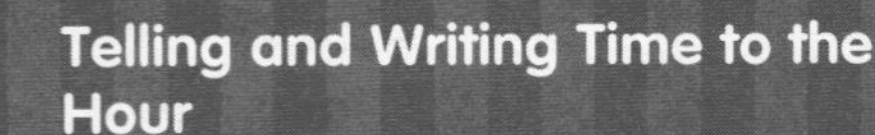

Objective Tell and write time to the hour on an analog clock and on a digital clock.

1 Warm Up

Activate Prior Knowledge Review children's knowledge of analog and digital clocks. Show examples and compare the two. **How are these clocks alike? How are they different?**

2 Teach

Learn!
Direct attention to the picture of the clock face. Have a volunteer tell what time the hands on the clock show. *(6 o'clock)* Then have children locate the digital clock. Explain that the digital clock also says 6 o'clock. Point out that the number 6 before the two dots (colon) tells the hour and the two zeros after the colon mean that we say *o'clock.*

Ongoing Assessment

Talk About It

- **What time is it if you see 8:00 on the clock?** *(8 o'clock)*
- **How would you show 12 o'clock on a digital clock?** *(By writing 12:00)*

If children do not understand that both clocks show the same time,

then have children locate 6 on each clock.

Check

Error Intervention

If children write 12 instead of 00,

then then remind them that though the minute hand is pointing to the 12, we write "o'clock" with 00. *(Also see* Reteaching, *Page 209B.)*

Think About It Show children, minute-by-minute, how the minute hand travels from 4:00 to 5:00, until it has returned to the 12. Point out that the hour hand only moves from one number to the next.

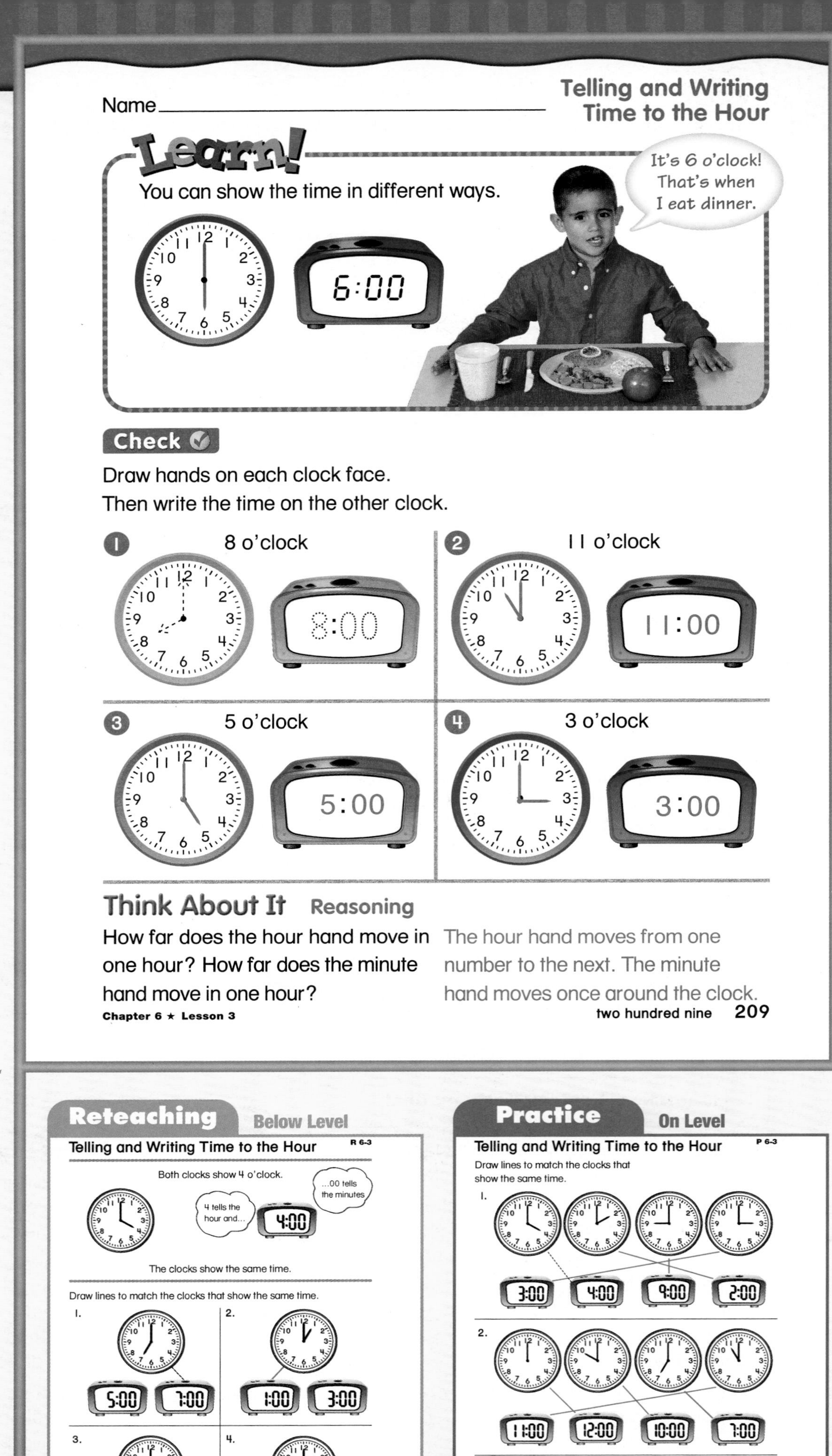

Name ____________________

Telling and Writing Time to the Hour

Learn!

You can show the time in different ways.

6:00
It's 6 o'clock! That's when I eat dinner.

Check

Draw hands on each clock face.
Then write the time on the other clock.

1. 8 o'clock — 8:00
2. 11 o'clock — 11:00
3. 5 o'clock — 5:00
4. 3 o'clock — 3:00

Think About It Reasoning

How far does the hour hand move in one hour? How far does the minute hand move in one hour? The hour hand moves from one number to the next. The minute hand moves once around the clock.

Chapter 6 ★ Lesson 3 — two hundred nine 209

Reteaching Below Level

Telling and Writing Time to the Hour R 6-3

Both clocks show 4 o'clock.

4 tells the hour and... ...00 tells the minutes 4:00

The clocks show the same time.

Draw lines to match the clocks that show the same time.

1. 5:00 7:00
2. 1:00 3:00
3. 12:00 9:00
4. 5:00 6:00

66 Use with Lesson 6-3

Practice On Level

Telling and Writing Time to the Hour P 6-3

Draw lines to match the clocks that show the same time.

1. 3:00 4:00 9:00 2:00
2. 11:00 12:00 10:00 7:00

Problem Solving *Algebra*
Look for the pattern. Then write each missing time.

3. 12:00, 1:00, 2 : 00, 3:00, 4:00
4. 10:00, 11:00, 12 : 00, 1:00, 2:00

66 Use with Lesson 6-3

EC NTL 12 11 10 9 8 7 6 5

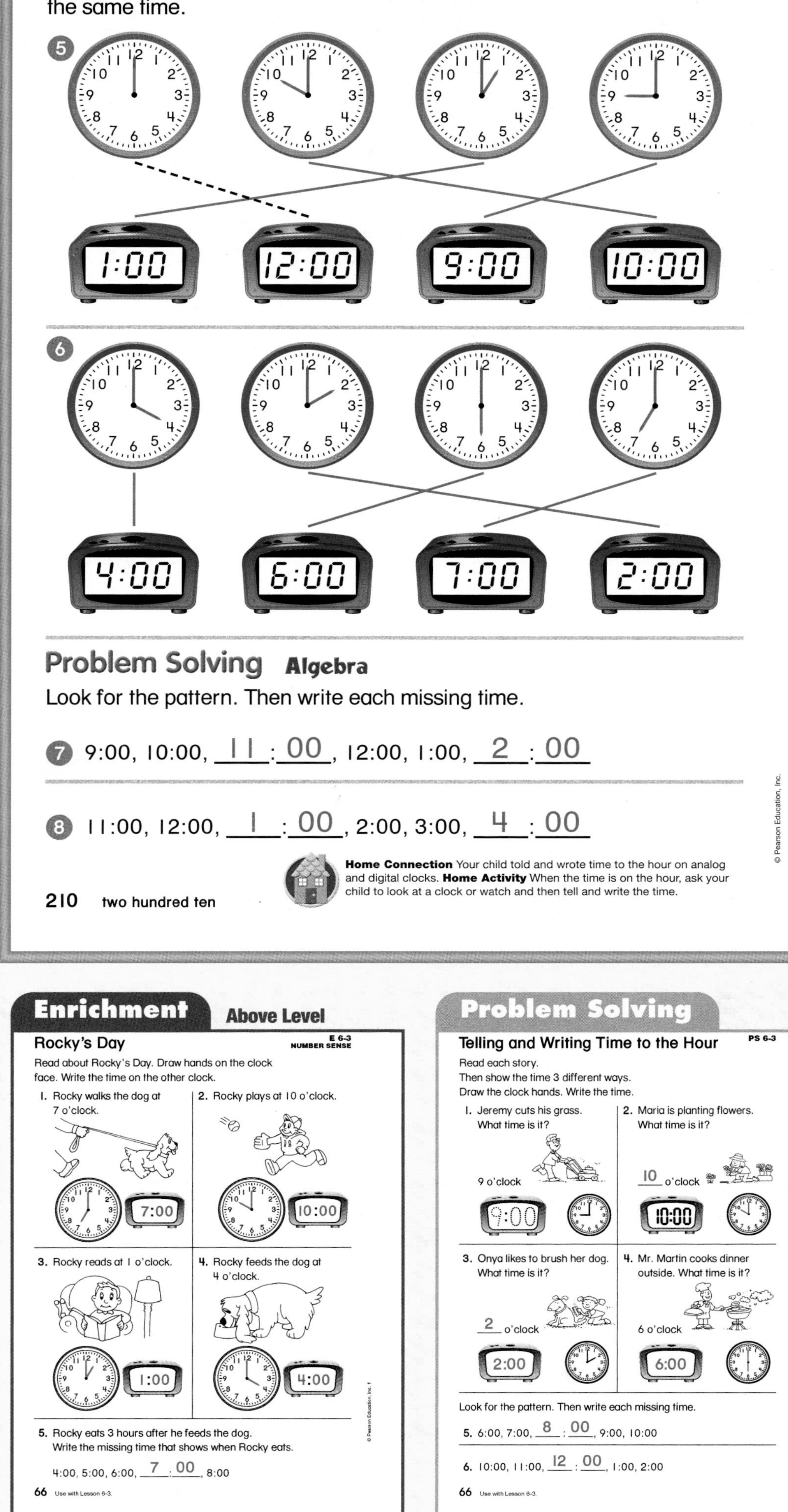

Practice

Draw lines to match the clocks that show the same time.

5

1:00	12:00	9:00	10:00

6

4:00	6:00	7:00	2:00

Problem Solving Algebra

Look for the pattern. Then write each missing time.

7 9:00, 10:00, 11 : 00, 12:00, 1:00, 2 : 00

8 11:00, 12:00, 1 : 00, 2:00, 3:00, 4 : 00

Home Connection Your child told and wrote time to the hour on analog and digital clocks. **Home Activity** When the time is on the hour, ask your child to look at a clock or watch and then tell and write the time.

Enrichment Above Level

Rocky's Day E 6-3 NUMBER SENSE

Read about Rocky's Day. Draw hands on the clock face. Write the time on the other clock.

1. Rocky walks the dog at 7 o'clock. 7:00
2. Rocky plays at 10 o'clock. 10:00
3. Rocky reads at 1 o'clock. 1:00
4. Rocky feeds the dog at 4 o'clock. 4:00
5. Rocky eats 3 hours after he feeds the dog. Write the missing time that shows when Rocky eats.
4:00, 5:00, 6:00, 7 : 00, 8:00

66 Use with Lesson 6-3.

Problem Solving

Telling and Writing Time to the Hour PS 6-3

Read each story.
Then show the time 3 different ways.
Draw the clock hands. Write the time.

1. Jeremy cuts his grass. What time is it? 9 o'clock 9:00
2. Maria is planting flowers. What time is it? 10 o'clock 10:00
3. Onya likes to brush her dog. What time is it? 2 o'clock 2:00
4. Mr. Martin cooks dinner outside. What time is it? 6 o'clock 6:00

Look for the pattern. Then write each missing time.

5. 6:00, 7:00, 8 : 00, 9:00, 10:00
6. 10:00, 11:00, 12 : 00, 1:00, 2:00

66 Use with Lesson 6-3.

3 Practice

After children complete Exercises 7 and 8, invite them to choose a time and tell what they do at that time of the day.

Reading Assist: Summarize Give each child a yellow crayon. Ask children to highlight each of the following: a clock face, a digital clock, a colon, two zeros, a minute hand, and an hour hand.

Leveled Practice

Below Level Circle the number the hour hand points to before matching it.

On Level Complete all exercises as written.

Above Level For each clock face, tell what time it will be in 1 hour.

Early Finishers Invite children to write a missing-time pattern, similar to Exercise 8 for a classmate to fill in with the missing times.

4 Assess

Journal Idea Ask children to draw a picture of something they usually do at 4 o'clock in the afternoon. Then have them draw a clock face and a digital clock.

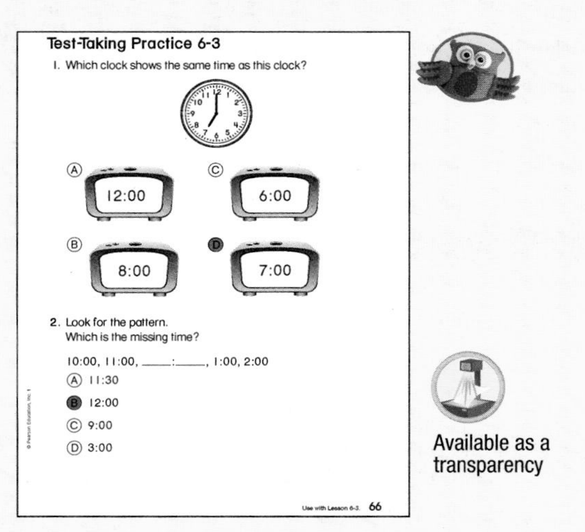

Test-Taking Practice 6-3

1. Which clock shows the same time as this clock?

Ⓐ 12:00 Ⓒ 6:00
Ⓑ 8:00 ● 7:00

2. Look for the pattern. Which is the missing time?

10:00, 11:00, ___:___, 1:00, 2:00

Ⓐ 11:30
● 12:00
Ⓒ 9:00
Ⓓ 3:00

Use with Lesson 6-3. 66

Available as a transparency

6-4 Telling and Writing Time to the Half Hour

Lesson Organizer

Quick Lesson Overview

Objective Tell and write time to the half hour.

Math Understanding A half hour is 30 minutes long.

Vocabulary Half hour

Materials for Student Pages
Overhead clock

Professional Development Note

How Children Learn Math Telling time to the hour is a prerequisite skill for telling time to the half hour. In particular, children need to understand the difference between the hour hand and the minute hand and what each shows. Provide additional practice with telling time to the hour for children who have not yet mastered those understandings.

NCTM Standards

- Measurement

(For a complete correlation to the NCTM Standards and Grades Pre-K through 2 Expectations, see Pages 203G and 203H.)

Getting Started

Spiral Review

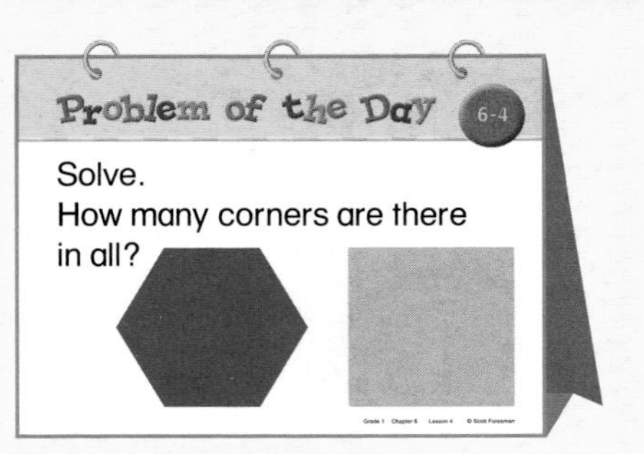

Problem of the Day
6-4
Solve.
How many corners are there in all?

Topics Reviewed

- Plane shapes; addition
- Problem-Solving Skill: One-Step Problem

Answer There are 6 + 4, or 10 corners in all.

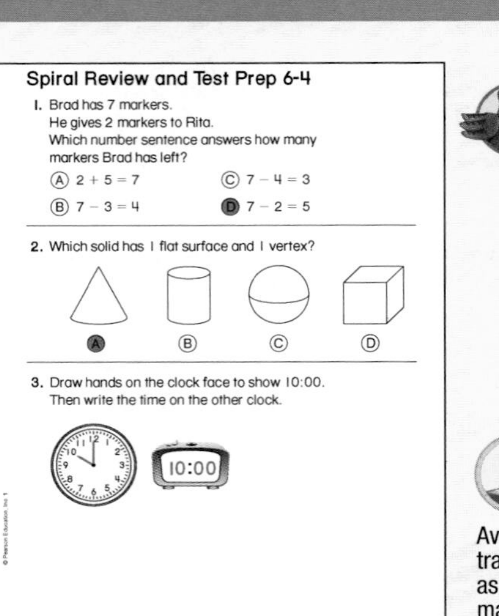
Spiral Review and Test Prep 6-4

1. Brad has 7 markers. He gives 2 markers to Rita. Which number sentence answers how many markers Brad has left?
   Ⓐ 2 + 5 = 7 Ⓒ 7 − 4 = 3
   Ⓑ 7 − 3 = 4 Ⓓ 7 − 2 = 5
2. Which solid has 1 flat surface and 1 vertex?
   Ⓐ Ⓑ Ⓒ Ⓓ
3. Draw hands on the clock face to show 10:00. Then write the time on the other clock.
   10:00

Use with Lesson 6-4. 67

Available as a transparency and as a blackline master

Topics Reviewed

1. Write a Number Sentence
2. Flat Surfaces and Vertices
3. Telling and Writing Time to the Hour

Investigating the Concept

Time to the Half hour

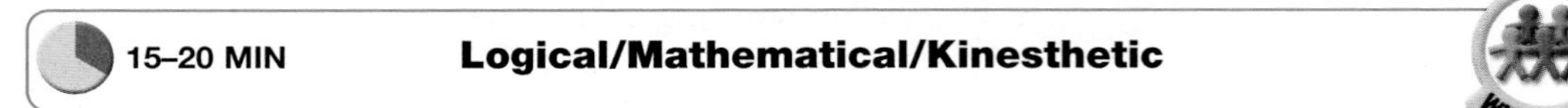
15–20 MIN **Logical/Mathematical/Kinesthetic** WHOLE CLASS

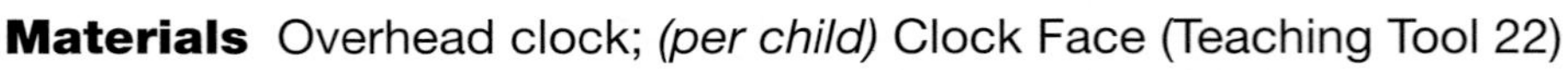
Materials Overhead clock; *(per child)* Clock Face (Teaching Tool 22)

What to Do

- Using an overhead clock, show 3 o'clock. Slowly move the minute hand to the 6 as you explain that a half hour (30 minutes) has passed, and the minute hand is halfway to the next hour. Show children that the hour hand is now halfway between the 3 and the 4.
- Count to 30 as you move the minute hand from 12 to 6. Tell children that when the minute hand points to 6, we say *thirty.* Write 3:30 on the board and say the time together.
- Have children write 5:30 and 12:30 and show each on their clock faces.

Ongoing Assessment

- **Reasoning** **Why is the hour hand halfway between 3 and 4 when it is 3:30?** *(Because 3:30 is halfway between 3 o'clock and 4 o'clock)*
- **Where does the minute hand point when it is 7:30?** *(To 6)*

Reaching All Learners

Reading in Math

Reading the Class Schedule

10–15 MIN **Linguistic**

Materials Class schedule

- Read the schedule of daily events with children.
- If you do not have anything scheduled on the half hour, work in an activity to give children practice reading those times.
- Show children how a time to the half hour, 10:30 for example, is shown on an analog and a digital clock.
- Draw the clocks on the schedule. Invite children to show clocks for other times of the schedule.

CLASS SCHEDULE		
9:00	School starts	9:00
9:30	Reading	9:30
11:00	Math	11:00
11:30	Lunch	11:30

Access Content

English Language Learners

Understanding Clock Words

5–10 MIN **Auditory/Kinesthetic**

Materials *(per child)* Clock Face (Teaching Tool 22)

- Use the clock face to introduce or review the meanings of *hour hand, minute hand, half hour, halfway, between.* Then have children follow your instructions.
- **Show 1:00 on your clock face. Move the minute hand ahead a half hour. What number is the minute hand pointing to?** *(6)* **Move the hour hand to halfway between the 1 and the 2. The time is 1:30. Say "1:30" and write it on a piece of paper.** Repeat the instructions for another time to the half hour.

Reteaching

Showing the Hour and Half Hour

10–15 MIN **Kinesthetic**

Materials *(per child)* Clock Face (Teaching Tool 22)

- Review that a half hour means 30 minutes. On an overhead transparency of the teaching tool, show 10:00. Move the hour hand between 10 and 11. Then move the minute hand to 6.
- Have children show various times to the hour, and then to the half hour on their clocks.

Math and Art

Fancy Clocks

15–20 MIN **Visual/Spatial**

INDIVIDUAL

Materials Books about clocks; *(per child)* paper plate; hour and minute hands cut from construction paper; metal brad; crayons or markers

- In a group, share books with pictures of antique or unusual clocks. Invite children to make their own decorative clock faces, using the designs in the books for inspiration. Help each child attach the hour and minute hands to the face with the metal brads.
- Display the clocks in a classroom clock shop.

Objective Tell and write time to the half hour.

1 Warm Up

Activate Prior Knowledge Review telling time to the hour. Display a clock set to 1:00. **What time is it? What time will it be in 1 hour?** Then move the hands to show 1 hour passing.

2 Teach

Learn!

Using an overhead clock, show 4 o'clock. Slowly count as you move the minute hand to 6. Explain that 30 minutes (a half hour) have passed. **The minute hand points to 6, which is halfway to the next hour. The hour hand is now halfway between 4 and 5.** Tell children that when the minute hand points to 6, we say *thirty.*

Ongoing Assessment

Talk About It

- **How much time has passed when the minute hand moves from 12 to 6?** *(30 minutes)*
- **Where will the hour hand be when it is 8:30?** *(Between 8 and 9)*

If children do not understand the term *half hour,*

then shade the right half of a circle to show that *half* of the circle is the same as *half* of an hour.

Check

Error Intervention

If children confuse the hands,

then have them first find the hour hand, the shorter hand, and say which numbers it is between. *(Also see* Reteaching, *Page 211B.)*

Think About It Show children other examples of time to the half hour and ask why the hour hand is between the two numbers.

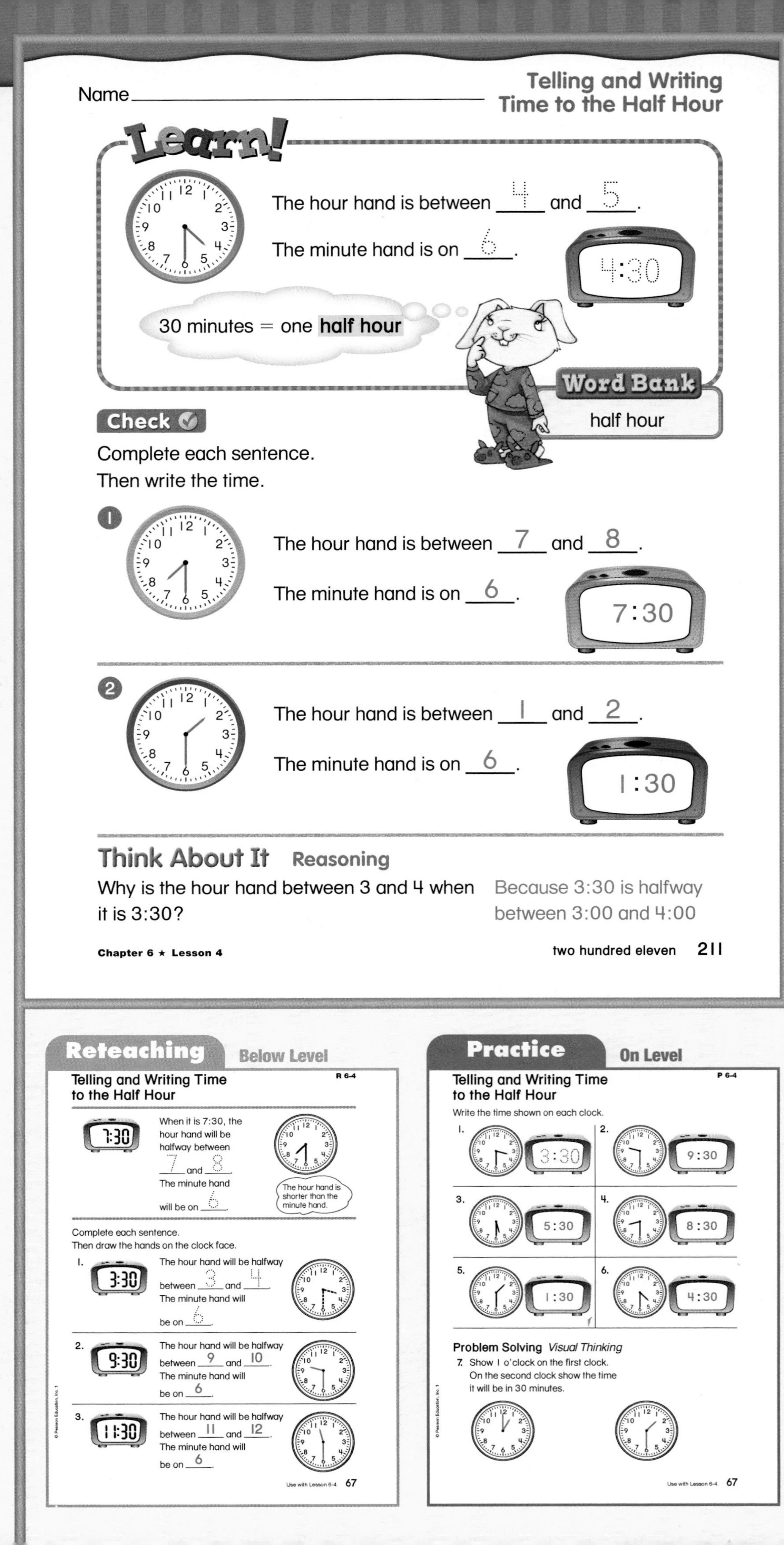

Name ______________________

Telling and Writing Time to the Half Hour

Learn!

The hour hand is between 4 and 5.

The minute hand is on 6.

4:30

30 minutes = one half hour

Word Bank

half hour

Check

Complete each sentence.
Then write the time.

1. The hour hand is between 7 and 8.
   The minute hand is on 6.
   7:30

2. The hour hand is between 1 and 2.
   The minute hand is on 6.
   1:30

Think About It Reasoning

Why is the hour hand between 3 and 4 when it is 3:30? Because 3:30 is halfway between 3:00 and 4:00

Chapter 6 ★ Lesson 4 — two hundred eleven 211

Reteaching Below Level

Telling and Writing Time to the Half Hour R 6-4

7:30 — When it is 7:30, the hour hand will be halfway between 7 and 8. The minute hand will be on 6.

The hour hand is shorter than the minute hand.

Complete each sentence.
Then draw the hands on the clock face.

1. 3:30 — The hour hand will be halfway between 3 and 4. The minute hand will be on 6.
2. 9:30 — The hour hand will be halfway between 9 and 10. The minute hand will be on 6.
3. 11:30 — The hour hand will be halfway between 11 and 12. The minute hand will be on 6.

Use with Lesson 6-4. 67

Practice On Level

Telling and Writing Time to the Half Hour P 6-4

Write the time shown on each clock.

1. 3:30
2. 9:30
3. 5:30
4. 8:30
5. 1:30
6. 4:30

Problem Solving *Visual Thinking*

7. Show 1 o'clock on the first clock. On the second clock show the time it will be in 30 minutes.

Use with Lesson 6-4. 67

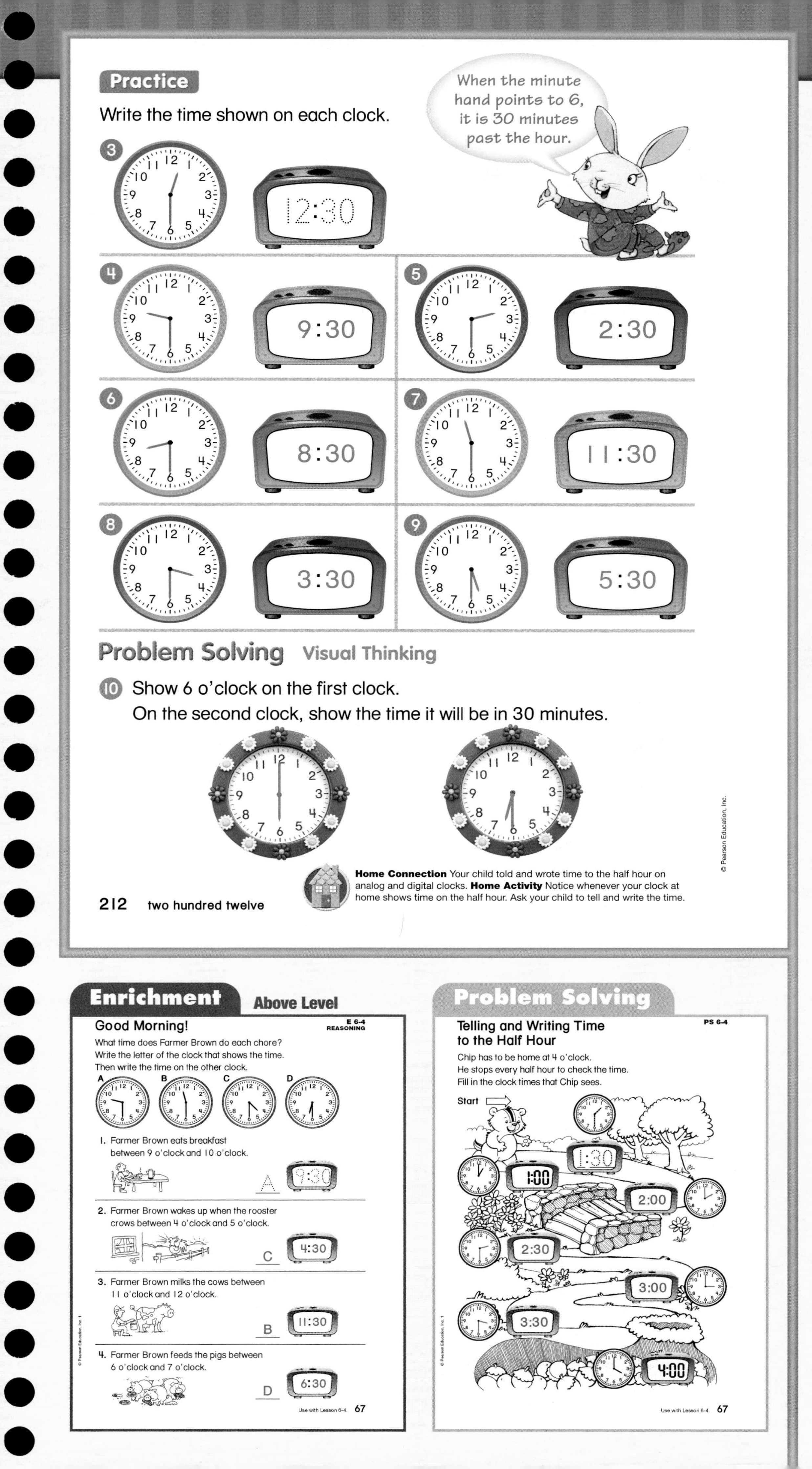

Practice

Write the time shown on each clock.

When the minute hand points to 6, it is 30 minutes past the hour.

3. 12:30
4. 9:30
5. 2:30
6. 8:30
7. 11:30
8. 3:30
9. 5:30

Problem Solving Visual Thinking

10. Show 6 o'clock on the first clock.
On the second clock, show the time it will be in 30 minutes.

Home Connection Your child told and wrote time to the half hour on analog and digital clocks. **Home Activity** Notice whenever your clock at home shows time on the half hour. Ask your child to tell and write the time.

Enrichment Above Level

E 6-4 REASONING

Good Morning!

What time does Farmer Brown do each chore?
Write the letter of the clock that shows the time.
Then write the time on the other clock.

1. Farmer Brown eats breakfast between 9 o'clock and 10 o'clock. A 9:30
2. Farmer Brown wakes up when the rooster crows between 4 o'clock and 5 o'clock. C 4:30
3. Farmer Brown milks the cows between 11 o'clock and 12 o'clock. B 11:30
4. Farmer Brown feeds the pigs between 6 o'clock and 7 o'clock. D 6:30

Use with Lesson 6-4. 67

Problem Solving

PS 6-4

Telling and Writing Time to the Half Hour

Chip has to be home at 4 o'clock.
He stops every half hour to check the time.
Fill in the clock times that Chip sees.

Start 1:00 1:30 2:00 2:30 3:00 3:30 4:00

Use with Lesson 6-4. 67

3 Practice

Point out that both the clock face and the digital clock should show the same time.

Reading Assist: Vocabulary Clarify the meaning of *between* by placing an object between two other objects.

Leveled Practice

Below Level Determine where the hour hand is and circle it before completing each exercise.

On Level Complete all exercises as written.

Above Level Write the time it will be 30 minutes after each time shown on the page.

Early Finishers Have a child set a clock face to a time on the hour. The partner tells what time it will be one half hour later.

4 Assess

Journal Idea Invite children to draw a clock face to show the time it will be one half hour after 1 o'clock and 3 o'clock. Have them write the times.

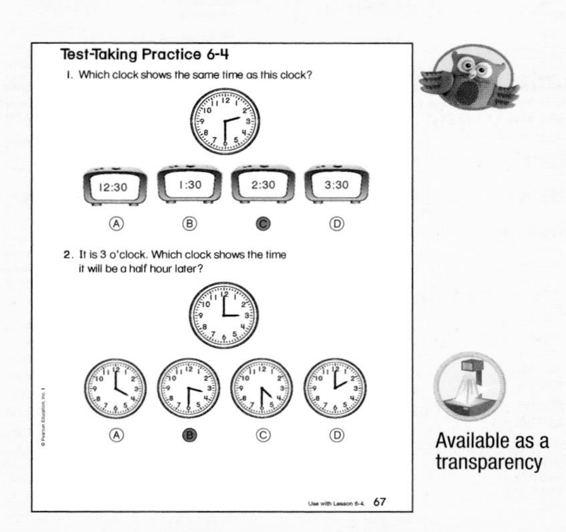

Test-Taking Practice 6-4

1. Which clock shows the same time as this clock?
Ⓐ 12:30 Ⓑ 1:30 Ⓒ 2:30 Ⓓ 3:30
2. It is 3 o'clock. Which clock shows the time it will be a half hour later?
Ⓐ Ⓑ Ⓒ Ⓓ

Use with Lesson 6-4. 67

Available as a transparency

Reading for Math Success

Purpose Show children how to apply the reading skill, *Visualize,* to their math work. Help prepare children for the problem-solving strategy lesson, *Act it Out,* which follows.

Using Student Page 213

Reading Skills and Math Understanding Children learn to visualize details, characters, and settings to help them comprehend the action in a story. Children can also visualize events in a story problem. They can imagine events that last for one hour, and they can visualize how the duration of one hour is represented by the movement of the hands on a clock.

Model the Process Tell children that they will read problems about activities that last for one hour. Model how to visualize situations in story problems: **When I read a problem, I make pictures in my mind of what is happening. If the problem is about time, I think about how long something takes. If the time in the problem is a minute, I know that it is a short amount of time. If the time in the problem is an hour, I know that it is a longer amount of time. I picture some things that can happen during an hour. I also picture how the hands of a clock show that an hour has gone by.**

Guide the Activity Read the problem at the top of the page. Encourage children to visualize the action in the problem to help them understand that it involves elapsed time. Read Exercises 1 and 2. Review the ways that time can be written: *8:00* and *8 o'clock.* Then use a clock with moveable hands and set it to show 8:00. Show how the minute hand circles the clock and the hour hand moves from the 8 to the 9 to show that 1 hour has gone by. Then have children complete the exercises on the page.

Think About It Help children use the vocabulary words *minute hand* and *hour hand* as they provide explanations. If they need help, have them use a clock with moveable hands to explain how each hand moves.

Name_______________

Reading for Math Success

Visualize

Read this math problem. Picture what is happening.

The bus picks up the children at 8:00.
It takes 1 hour to get to school.
What time do the children arrive at school?

1. Show the starting time on your clock.
Draw hands to show the time on the first clock.
Write the time below it.

2. Move the hands on your clock to show that 1 hour has passed.
Draw hands to show the time on the second clock.
Write the time below it.

8 o'clock ——→ 1 hour ——→ 9 o'clock

3. What time did the children get to school? 9:00

Think About It Reasoning
How do the hands on a clock show that 1 hour has gone by?

The hour hand moves to the next number. The minute hand moves all the way around the clock one time.

Chapter 6 two hundred thirteen 213

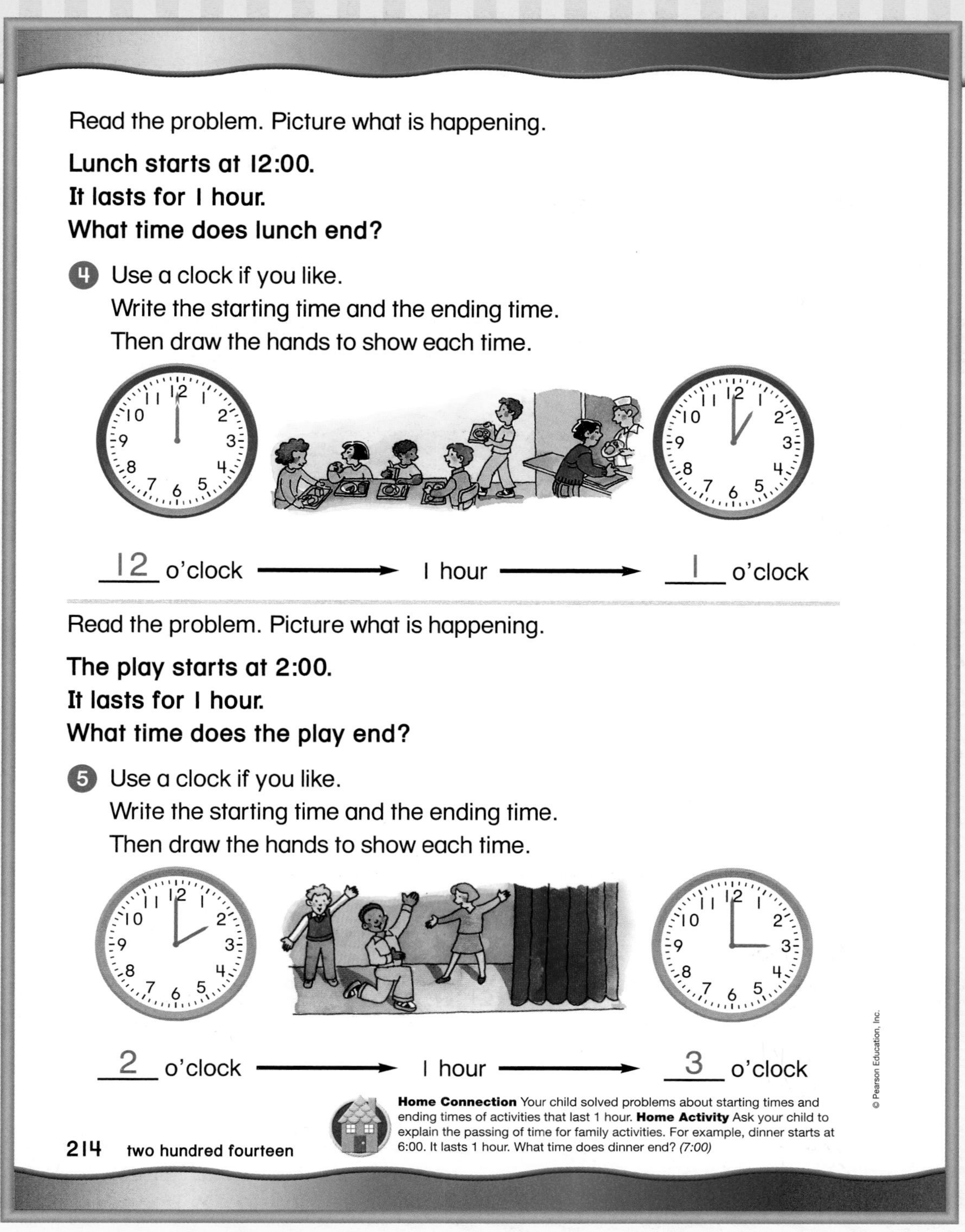

Read the problem. Picture what is happening.

Lunch starts at 12:00.
It lasts for 1 hour.
What time does lunch end?

4. Use a clock if you like.
Write the starting time and the ending time.
Then draw the hands to show each time.

12 o'clock ⟶ 1 hour ⟶ 1 o'clock

Read the problem. Picture what is happening.

The play starts at 2:00.
It lasts for 1 hour.
What time does the play end?

5. Use a clock if you like.
Write the starting time and the ending time.
Then draw the hands to show each time.

2 o'clock ⟶ 1 hour ⟶ 3 o'clock

Home Connection Your child solved problems about starting times and ending times of activities that last 1 hour. **Home Activity** Ask your child to explain the passing of time for family activities. For example, dinner starts at 6:00. It lasts 1 hour. What time does dinner end? *(7:00)*

Using Student Page 214

Tell children that the problems on this page are similar to the problem on page 213. Have children independently read the problems and write the starting and ending times for each problem. Encourage them to make pictures in their minds to help them solve the problems. Allow them to use a clock with moveable hands if necessary.

When children have completed the page, have them act out each problem for other children in a small group, explaining the question and using a clock with moveable hands to show the elapsed time.

Error Intervention

If children are having difficulty visualizing,

then have them draw pictures to show what is happening in a story problem. After children finish their drawings, ask them to explain how they can use their pictures to solve the problem. Then have children close their eyes and picture their drawings in their minds. Give children another story problem and have them decide whether to draw a picture or to visualize to find the answer.

Journal Idea Have children write their own story problems involving activities that last for 1 hour. Then have them draw clock faces that indicate the starting and ending times for their activities.

Act It Out

Lesson Organizer

Quick Lesson Overview

Objective Solve problems by acting out given situations.

Math Understanding One strategy that can be used to solve a problem is to act it out.

Materials for Student Pages *(per child)* Clock Face (Teaching Tool 22)

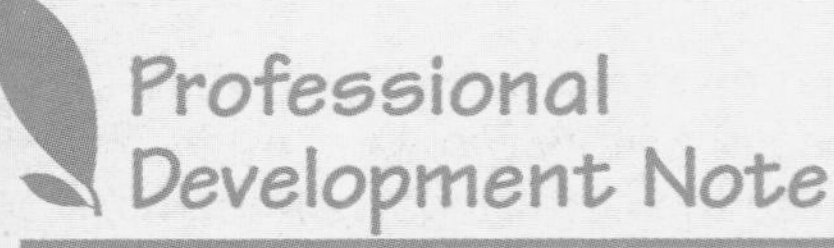

Math Background Children need to become familiar with a variety of problem-solving strategies. One strategy is to physically act out a problem or use manipulatives to model the situation. In this lesson, children will use a clock to act out problems about elapsed time.

NCTM Standards

- Measurement

(For a complete correlation to the NCTM Standards and Grades Pre-K through 2 Expectations, see Pages 203G and 203H.)

Spiral Review

Read Aloud A totem pole is a pole carved and painted with animals and plants. Many cultures in North America make totem poles and then put them in front of their homes. The owner of this totem pole wants 5 red faces. How many red faces need to be added?

Topics Reviewed

- Addition and subtraction
- Problem-Solving Skill: One-Step Problem

Answer Two red faces would have to be added to the totem pole; $5 - 3 = 2$ and $3 + 2 = 5$.

Spiral Review and Test Prep 6-5

1. Which figure below shows a line of symmetry for this rectangle?

Ⓐ Ⓑ Ⓒ Ⓓ

2. What is the missing number in the pattern?

2, 4, 6, ___, 10, 12

Ⓐ 4 Ⓑ 7 Ⓒ 8 Ⓓ 10

3. Show 9 o'clock on the first clock. Then show the time it will be a half hour later.

68 Use with Lesson 6-5.

Available as a transparency and as a blackline master

Topics Reviewed

1. Symmetry
2. Look for a Pattern
3. Telling and Writing Time to the Half Hour

Investigating the Concept

What Time Will It Be?

15–20 MIN **Logical/Mathematical/Kinesthetic** WHOLE CLASS

Materials Overhead Clock; *(per child)* Clock Face (Teaching Tool 22)

What to Do

- Using an overheard clock, show 10 o'clock. **This is the time we go to the library. We stay for 1 hour. What time will it be when we leave the library?** Allow children to guess the ending time.
- Act out the problem by moving the hands on the clock face to show 1 hour passing, as children follow with their clock faces. Check the new time against children's predictions.
- Repeat with several similar problem situations using elapsed times of 1, 2, and 3 hours.

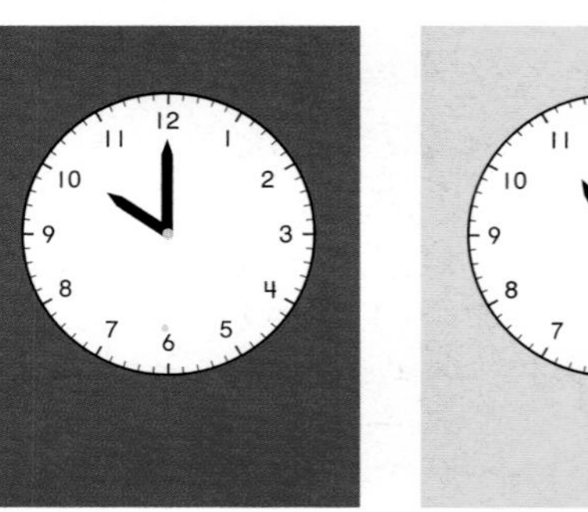

Ongoing Assessment

For each story problem, ask:

- **Reasoning What do you need to find out?** *(What time it will be when the activity ends)*
- **What can you do to solve the problem?** *(Act it out with the clock.)*

Reaching All Learners

Math and Literature

Time Around the World

15–20 MIN **Logical/Mathematical**

Materials *Nine O'Clock Lullaby* by Marilyn Singer (Scott Foresman, 1993); Clock Face (Teaching Tool 22)

- Share this book about the changing time zones around the world.
- After children have learned how times change from place to place, write "Brooklyn, NY" below one clock, and ask children to show 9:00 with the hands on the clock.
- Post two more clocks. Choose locations from the book and have children show the times in those locations.

Extend Language

English Language Learners

Math Story Language

10–15 MIN **Linguistic**

Materials *(per child)* Clock Face (Teaching Tool 22)

- Practice vocabulary involving time by writing this story outline on the board,

  "_____ starts at _:__.
  It lasts for 1 hour.
  It ends at _:__."
- Do repeated readings of the story, filling in classroom activities and times to the hour. Use actual activities and times, if possible.
- Act out the activities using an overhead transparency of the clock face to demonstrate the starting times.
- Have children show the ending times.

Reteaching

Acting It Out

10–15 MIN **Linguistic**

Materials *(per child)* Clock Face (Teaching Tool 22)

- Tell a story such as the following:

  A birthday party starts at 6:00.
  It lasts 1 hour.
  At what time will the party be over?
- Show 6:00 on your clock. Then have a child show the time 1 hour later.
- Continue to make up stories. Encourage children to tell stories about events that last one, two, or three hours. Give every child a chance to show a beginning or ending time on a clock.

Math and Technology

Time Museum

15–20 MIN **Linguistic/Visual/Spatial**

- Discuss how the technology of telling time has changed.
- Show books with old timepieces, or if possible, bring in old clocks, watches, and hourglasses. Briefly discuss how they work, including how older clocks had to be wound.
- Compare these old methods of telling time with modern digital clocks and computer clocks.
- You may wish to make a museum display of old timepieces that you and the children bring in from home.

Objective Solve problems by acting out given situations.

1 Warm Up

Activate Prior Knowledge Review acting out a subtraction story. Invite 6 children to the front of the room. Have them act out the following situation: **6 birds are in a cage. 2 fly away. How many are left?** Continue with other subtraction story problems.

2 Teach

Learn!

Read aloud the problem-solving steps: Read and Understand, Plan and Solve, Look Back and Check. Have children use their clock faces to act out the problem. Discuss how acting out the problem can help them solve it.

Ongoing Assessment

Talk About It

- **What do you need to find out?** *(What time it will be 1 hour after 7:00)*
- **What plan can you use to solve the problem?** *(Act it out.)*
- **How can you check your answer?** *(By looking at the new time on the clock)*

If children do not understand elapsed time,

then write down the times seen on the classroom clock before and after children participate in an hour-long activity.

Check

Error Intervention

If children have difficulty solving the problem,

then have them follow as you act it out on the clock face. *(Also see* Reteaching, *Page 215B.)*

Think About It Have children move their clocks from 2 o'clock to 4'oclock. **How many times did the minute hand move around the clock?**

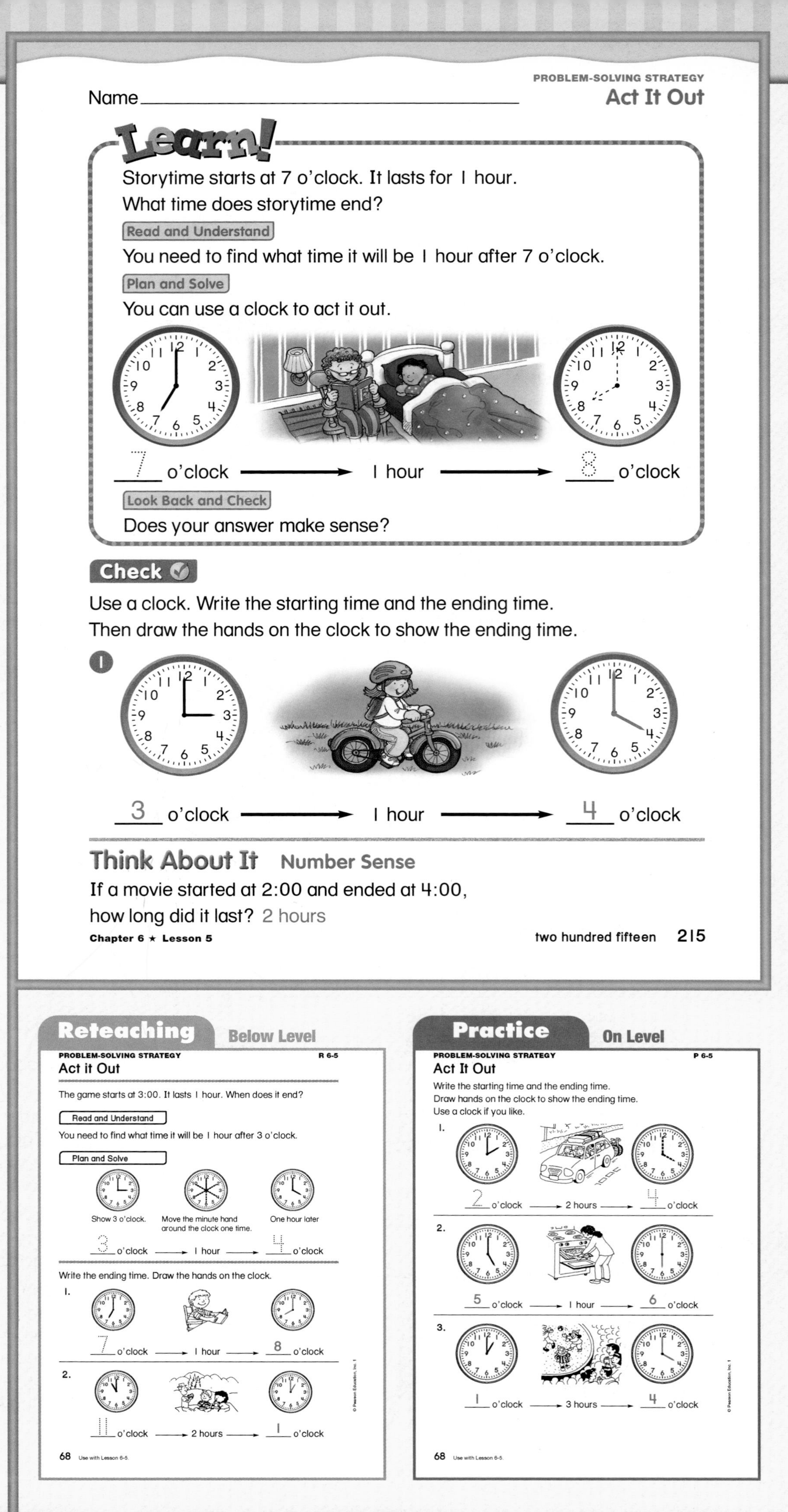

Name ____________

PROBLEM-SOLVING STRATEGY
Act It Out

Learn!

Storytime starts at 7 o'clock. It lasts for 1 hour.
What time does storytime end?

Read and Understand

You need to find what time it will be 1 hour after 7 o'clock.

Plan and Solve

You can use a clock to act it out.

7 o'clock → 1 hour → 8 o'clock

Look Back and Check

Does your answer make sense?

Check

Use a clock. Write the starting time and the ending time.
Then draw the hands on the clock to show the ending time.

1. 3 o'clock → 1 hour → 4 o'clock

Think About It Number Sense

If a movie started at 2:00 and ended at 4:00, how long did it last? 2 hours

Chapter 6 ★ Lesson 5 — two hundred fifteen 215

Reteaching Below Level

PROBLEM-SOLVING STRATEGY — R 6-5
Act it Out

The game starts at 3:00. It lasts 1 hour. When does it end?

Read and Understand

You need to find what time it will be 1 hour after 3 o'clock.

Plan and Solve

Show 3 o'clock. — Move the minute hand around the clock one time. — One hour later

3 o'clock → 1 hour → 4 o'clock

Write the ending time. Draw the hands on the clock.

1. 7 o'clock → 1 hour → 8 o'clock

2. 11 o'clock → 2 hours → 1 o'clock

68 Use with Lesson 6-5.

Practice On Level

PROBLEM-SOLVING STRATEGY — P 6-5
Act It Out

Write the starting time and the ending time.
Draw hands on the clock to show the ending time.
Use a clock if you like.

1. 2 o'clock → 2 hours → 4 o'clock

2. 5 o'clock → 1 hour → 6 o'clock

3. 1 o'clock → 3 hours → 4 o'clock

68 Use with Lesson 6-5.

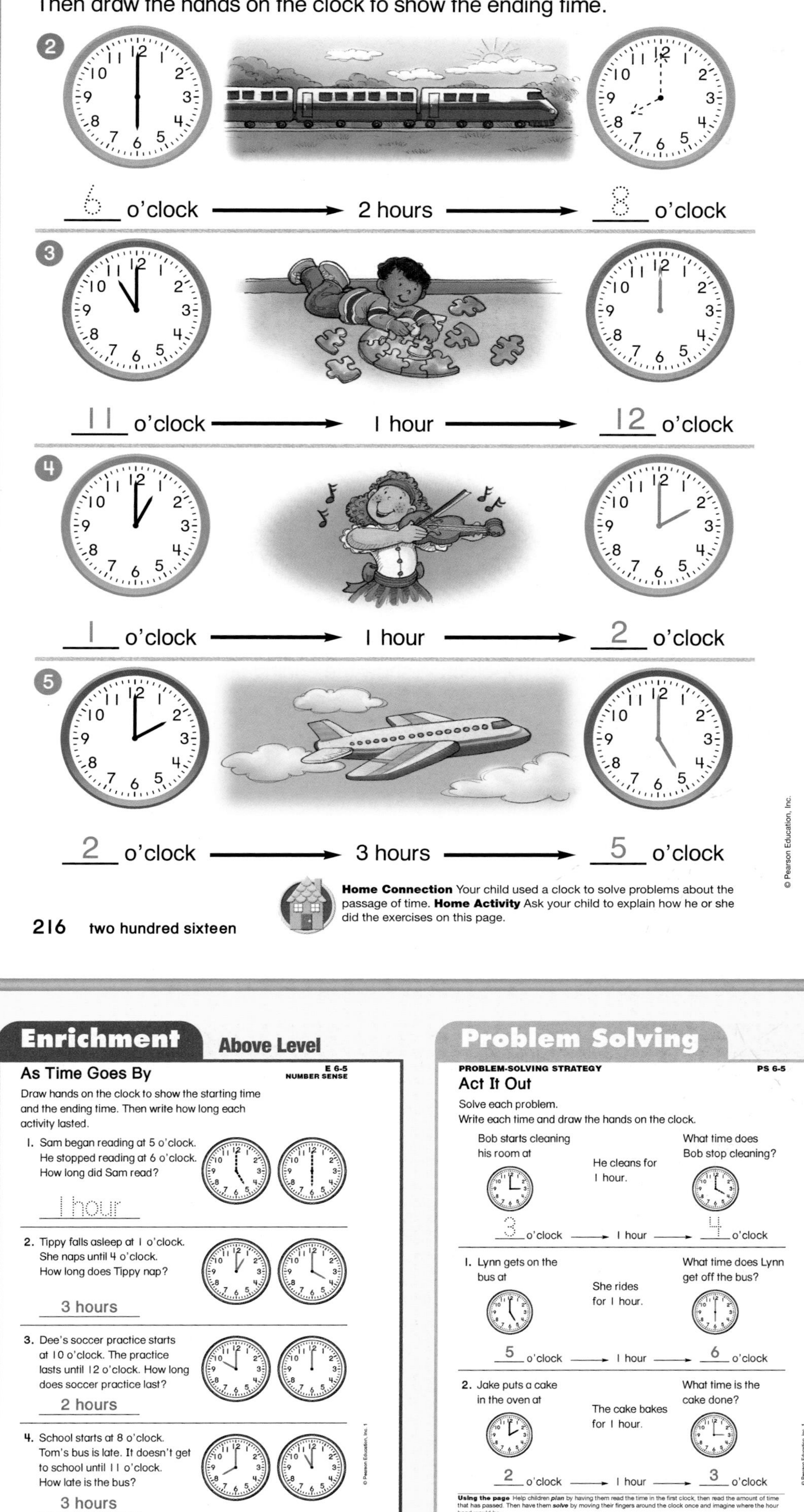

Practice

Use a clock. Write the starting time and the ending time.
Then draw the hands on the clock to show the ending time.

2. 6 o'clock → 2 hours → 8 o'clock

3. 11 o'clock → 1 hour → 12 o'clock

4. 1 o'clock → 1 hour → 2 o'clock

5. 2 o'clock → 3 hours → 5 o'clock

Home Connection Your child used a clock to solve problems about the passage of time. **Home Activity** Ask your child to explain how he or she did the exercises on this page.

216 two hundred sixteen

Enrichment Above Level

As Time Goes By E 6-5 NUMBER SENSE

Draw hands on the clock to show the starting time and the ending time. Then write how long each activity lasted.

1. Sam began reading at 5 o'clock. He stopped reading at 6 o'clock. How long did Sam read? 1 hour
2. Tippy falls asleep at 1 o'clock. She naps until 4 o'clock. How long does Tippy nap? 3 hours
3. Dee's soccer practice starts at 10 o'clock. The practice lasts until 12 o'clock. How long does soccer practice last? 2 hours
4. School starts at 8 o'clock. Tom's bus is late. It doesn't get to school until 11 o'clock. How late is the bus? 3 hours

68 Use with Lesson 6-5.

Problem Solving

PROBLEM-SOLVING STRATEGY PS 6-5

Act It Out

Solve each problem.
Write each time and draw the hands on the clock.

Bob starts cleaning his room at 3 o'clock. He cleans for 1 hour. What time does Bob stop cleaning? 4 o'clock

1. Lynn gets on the bus at 5 o'clock. She rides for 1 hour. What time does Lynn get off the bus? 6 o'clock
2. Jake puts a cake in the oven at 2 o'clock. The cake bakes for 1 hour. What time is the cake done? 3 o'clock

Using the page Help children *plan* by having them read the time in the first clock, then read the amount of time that has passed. Then have them *solve* by moving their fingers around the clock once and imagine where the hour hand would be.

68 Use with Lesson 6-5.

3 Practice

Help children follow the three-step strategy: Read and Understand, Plan and Solve, Look Back and Check.

Leveled Practice

Below Level Work in pairs to complete all exercises as written.

On Level Work individually to complete all exercises as written.

Above Level Complete all exercises without using clocks, then use clocks to check the answers.

Early Finishers Have pairs write riddles about how long an activity takes, then trade and solve each other's riddles. Provide this frame for the riddles. "I started at __:___. I ended at __:___. How long did it take?"

4 Assess

Journal Idea On the board, write, "Starting time: 12:30. Ending time: 2:30." Have children draw a picture of something they could do in the elapsed time and label the picture with the amount of time that passed.

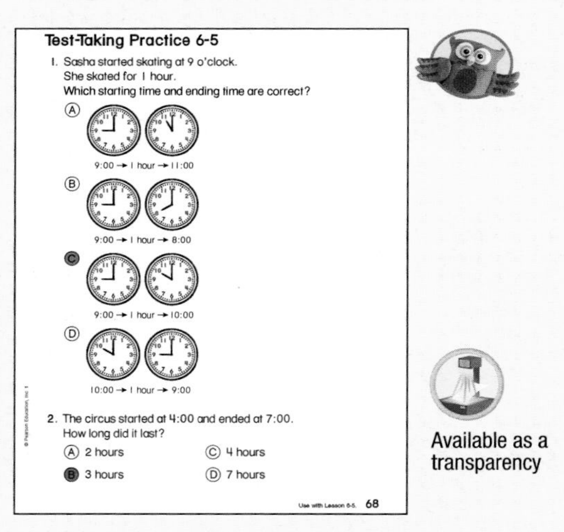

Test-Taking Practice 6-5

1. Sasha started skating at 9 o'clock. She skated for 1 hour. Which starting time and ending time are correct?
   - Ⓐ 9:00 → 1 hour → 11:00
   - Ⓑ 9:00 → 1 hour → 8:00
   - Ⓒ 9:00 → 1 hour → 10:00
   - Ⓓ 10:00 → 1 hour → 9:00
2. The circus started at 4:00 and ended at 7:00. How long did it last?
   - Ⓐ 2 hours
   - Ⓑ 3 hours
   - Ⓒ 4 hours
   - Ⓓ 7 hours

Use with Lesson 6-5. 68

Available as a transparency

Diagnostic Checkpoint

Purpose Provide assessment of children's progress to date by checking their understanding of key content covered in the previous section.

Vocabulary Review

You may wish to review these vocabulary terms before assigning the page:

half hour A unit of time equal to 30 minutes *(pp. 211–212)*

hour A unit of time equal to 60 minutes *(pp. 207–208)*

hour hand The short hand on a clock; the hand that shows hours *(pp. 207–208)*

minute A unit of time equal to 60 seconds *(pp. 205–206)*

minute hand The long hand on a clock; the hand that shows minutes *(pp. 207–208)*

o'clock By the clock; according to the clock *(pp. 207–208)*

Activities for this section are available in the Math Vocabulary Kit.

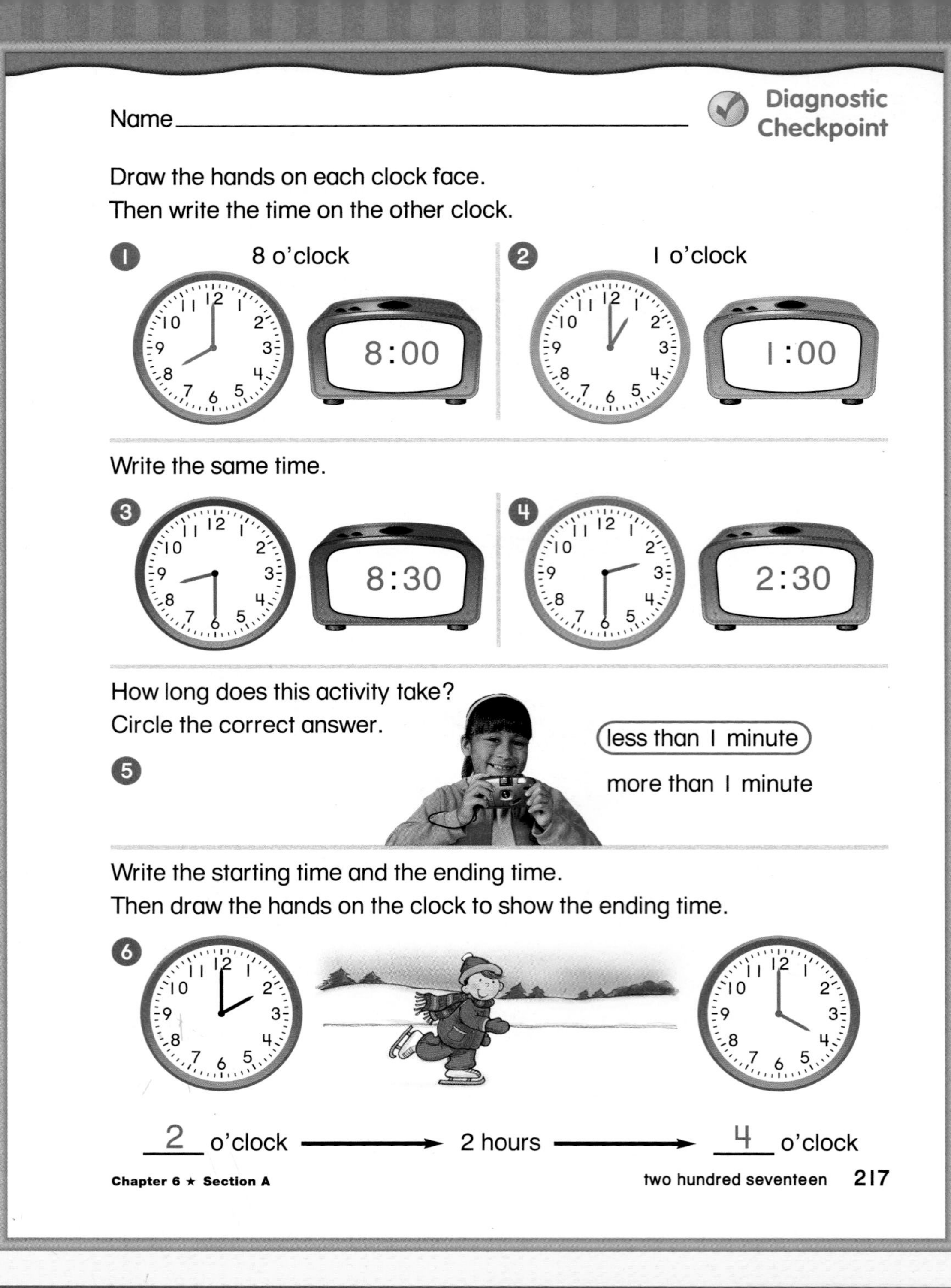

Name ____________________ Diagnostic Checkpoint

Draw the hands on each clock face.
Then write the time on the other clock.

1. 8 o'clock — 8:00
2. 1 o'clock — 1:00

Write the same time.

3. 8:30
4. 2:30

How long does this activity take?
Circle the correct answer.

5. less than 1 minute / more than 1 minute

Write the starting time and the ending time.
Then draw the hands on the clock to show the ending time.

6. 2 o'clock → 2 hours → 4 o'clock

Chapter 6 ★ Section A — two hundred seventeen 217

Item Analysis for Diagnosis and Intervention

Objective	Items	Student Book Pages*	Intervention System
Identify the hour hand and the minute hand on a clock and tell time to the hour.	1–2	207–208	D4
Tell and write time to the hour on an analog clock and on a digital clock.	1–2	209–210	D5
Tell and write time to the half hour.	3–4	211–212	D6
Determine if an event takes more or less than one minute.	5	205–206	D3
Solve problems by acting out given situations.	6	215–216	E30

*For each lesson, there is a *Reteaching* activity in *Reaching All Learners* and a *Reteaching* master.

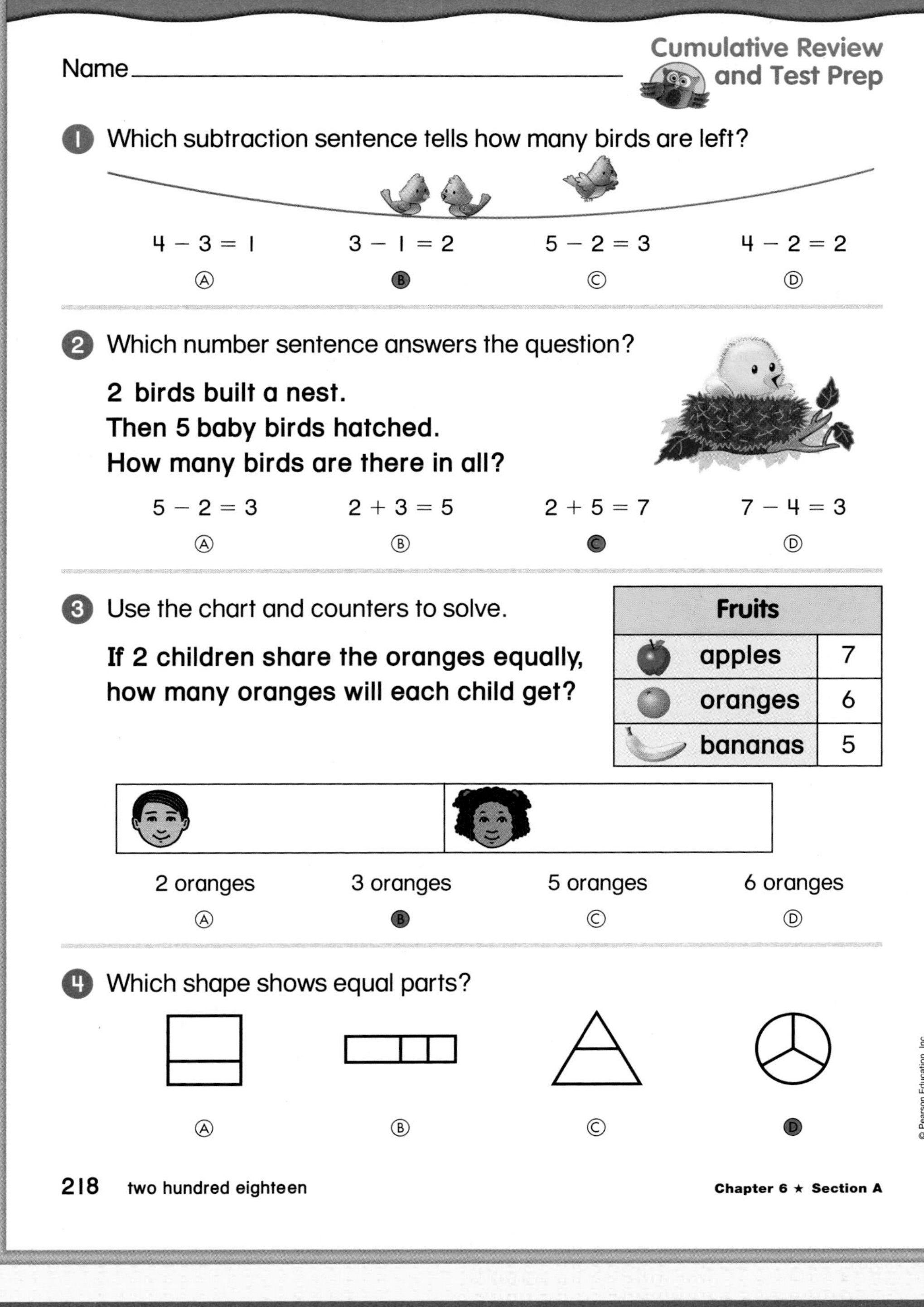

Name ______________________

Cumulative Review and Test Prep

1. Which subtraction sentence tells how many birds are left?

$4 - 3 = 1$ Ⓐ $3 - 1 = 2$ Ⓑ $5 - 2 = 3$ Ⓒ $4 - 2 = 2$ Ⓓ

2. Which number sentence answers the question?

2 birds built a nest.
Then 5 baby birds hatched.
How many birds are there in all?

$5 - 2 = 3$ Ⓐ $2 + 3 = 5$ Ⓑ $2 + 5 = 7$ Ⓒ $7 - 4 = 3$ Ⓓ

3. Use the chart and counters to solve.

If 2 children share the oranges equally, how many oranges will each child get?

Fruits	
apples	7
oranges	6
bananas	5

2 oranges Ⓐ 3 oranges Ⓑ 5 oranges Ⓒ 6 oranges Ⓓ

4. Which shape shows equal parts?

Ⓐ Ⓑ Ⓒ Ⓓ

Cumulative Review and Test Prep

Purpose Provide children with a review of math concepts. Items appear as they would on a standardized test so children become familiar with that format.

Item Analysis for Diagnosis and Intervention

Objective	Items	Student Book Pages*	Intervention System
Write a subtraction sentence to find the difference in a separating situation.	1	65–66	B12
Solve a problems by choosing addition or subtraction.	2	143–144	E4
Solve a problem using data from a chart.	3	191–192	E1
Determine whether a shape has been divided into equal or unequal parts and if applicable, count the number of equal parts into which it has been divided.	4	181–182	A59

*For each lesson, there is a *Reteaching* activity in *Reaching All Learners* and a *Reteaching* master.

6-6 Ordering Events

Lesson Organizer

Quick Lesson Overview

Objective Determine whether an event takes place in the morning, afternoon, or night.

Math Understanding The time an event takes place can be labeled with the terms *morning, afternoon,* or *night.*

Vocabulary Morning, afternoon, night

Professional Development Note

Research Base

Children begin their understanding of a varying quantity, such as time, by representing it along a continuum, like a mental number line (Griffin, Case, & Siegler, 1998). In these lessons, children build this continuous model for time by ordering events linearly from first to last.

NCTM Standards

- Measurement

(For a complete correlation to the NCTM Standards and Grades Pre-K through 2 Expectations, see Pages 203G and 203H.)

Getting Started

Spiral Review

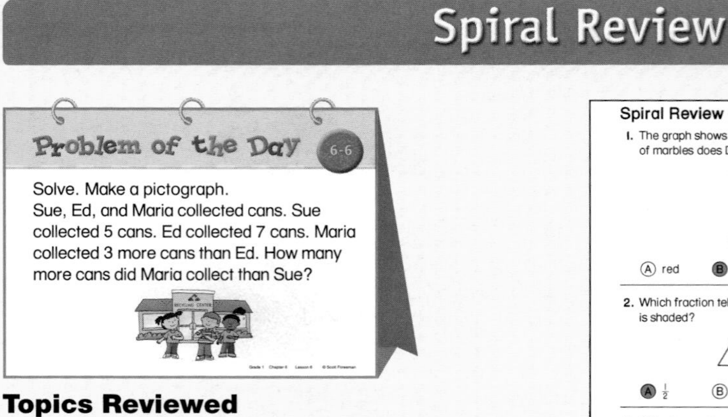

Problem of the Day 6-6
Solve. Make a pictograph.
Sue, Ed, and Maria collected cans. Sue collected 5 cans. Ed collected 7 cans. Maria collected 3 more cans than Ed. How many more cans did Maria collect than Sue?

Topics Reviewed

- Pictographs; addition; subtraction
- Problem-Solving Strategy: Make a Graph

Answer Maria collected 5 more cans than Sue. Check children's graphs.

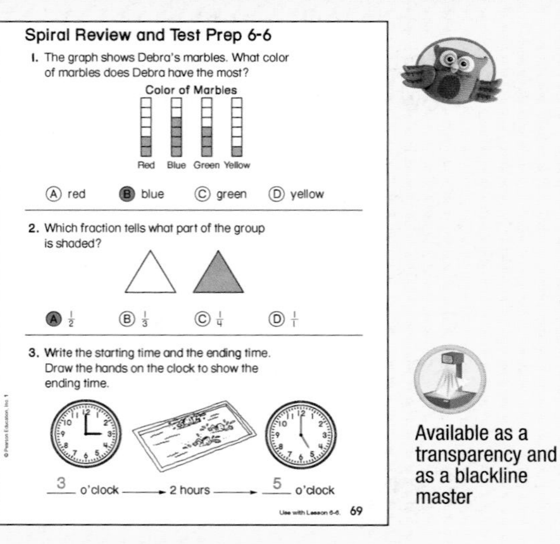

Spiral Review and Test Prep 6-6

1. The graph shows Debra's marbles. What color of marbles does Debra have the most?

Color of Marbles

Red Blue Green Yellow

Ⓐ red Ⓑ blue Ⓒ green Ⓓ yellow

2. Which fraction tells what part of the group is shaded?

Ⓐ $\frac{1}{2}$ Ⓑ $\frac{1}{3}$ Ⓒ $\frac{1}{4}$ Ⓓ $\frac{1}{1}$

3. Write the starting time and the ending time. Draw the hands on the clock to show the ending time.

3 o'clock → 2 hours → 5 o'clock

© Pearson Education, Inc. 1

Use with Lesson 6-6. 69

Available as a transparency and as a blackline master

Topics Reviewed

1. Real Graphs
2. Fractions of a Set
3. Act It Out

Investigating the Concept

Morning, Afternoon, and Night

SMALL GROUP

Materials 3 pieces of construction paper labeled *morning, afternoon,* and *night; (per group)* drawing paper; crayons

What to Do

- Divide the class into three groups. Distribute one of the labeled pieces of construction paper to each group. Invite children to talk with each other about things they do during the morning, afternoon, and night. Have them draw pictures that show activities done at that time.
- Collect the finished pictures and display them beside their respective labels. Invite volunteers to name each activity.

Ongoing Assessment

- **Reasoning Which time comes just after morning?** *(Afternoon)* **Which time comes just before night?** *(Afternoon)*
- **What is something you can do in the morning or in the afternoon?** *(Sample responses: Play a game, skate, draw a picture, color)*

Reaching All Learners

Oral Language in Math

Morning, Afternoon, and Night Activities

10–15 MIN **Linguistic**

- Write the following heads on the board: "Things I Do in the Morning," "Things I Do in the Afternoon," and "Things I Do at Night."
- Share something you did yesterday morning, afternoon, and night. Write each thing you did under the appropriate heading.
- Then ask children to tell some things they did, or usually do, at these times, using the words *morning, afternoon,* and *night.*

Things I Do in the Morning	Things I Do in the Afternoon	Things I Do at Night
brush my teeth	eat lunch	go to sleep

Extend Language

English Language Learners

When Do I ...?

5–10 MIN **Linguistic/Kinesthetic** SMALL GROUP

- Write the words "morning," "afternoon," and "night" on the board.
- Point to *morning* as you say the word, and act out rising from bed. Say: **I get up.**
- As you say and point to *afternoon* and *night,* mime and name activities typical of those times of day.
- Have children take turns pantomiming an activity that is done at a particular time of day for others to guess.

Reteaching

Time-of-Day Riddles

5–10 MIN **Auditory/Linguistic** SMALL GROUP

- Remind children that we can do some things at any time. For example, we can read in the morning, afternoon, or evening.
- Explain that certain other activities are generally done in the morning, afternoon, or at night. For example, we usually sleep at night. Have children give other examples.
- Ask children to make up time-of-day riddles and present them to the group to solve, for instance, "When people eat lunch, it's ____ ." *(Afternoon)*

When people eat lunch, it's ...

Math and Health

Breakfast, Lunch, and Dinner

15–20 MIN **Visual/Spatial**

Materials *(per child)* Crayons or markers; paper

- Talk about healthy foods eaten at different times of the day. Discuss that eating breakfast is done in the morning, eating lunch is done in the afternoon, and eating dinner is done at night.
- Ask children to fold a sheet of paper in thirds and label each part: *Breakfast, Lunch,* and *Dinner.*
- In each section of their papers, have children draw their ideas of healthy breakfasts, lunches, and dinners.

Objective Determine whether an event takes place in the morning, afternoon, or night.

1 Warm Up

Activate Prior Knowledge Review activities that children might do in a day. Have children pantomime as you say: **I get up. I get dressed. I have breakfast. I ride the school bus. I work in school. I eat lunch. I build with blocks. I ride the bus. I eat dinner. I take a bath. I put on pajamas. I go to sleep.**

2 Teach

Learn!

Draw children's attention to the pictures. Ask volunteers to tell what is happening in each picture. Discuss clues in each of the pictures that help children tell the time of day each takes place, morning, afternoon, and night.

Ongoing Assessment

Talk About It

- **Which time comes after morning?** *(Afternoon)* **What did the girl do at that time?** *(She ate lunch.)*
- **How can you tell that a picture shows night.** *(Sample response: I see the moon and stars.)*

If children confuse the terms,

then say each time of day and give examples of activities that are typically done at that time.

Check

Error Intervention

If children do not match the pictures correctly,

then then talk about what is happening in each picture and what clues there are to the time of day. *(Also see* Reteaching, *Page 219B.)*

Think About It Help children recognize that the events in Exercises 1–3 all happen during the same day. Ask questions to guide children through the question.

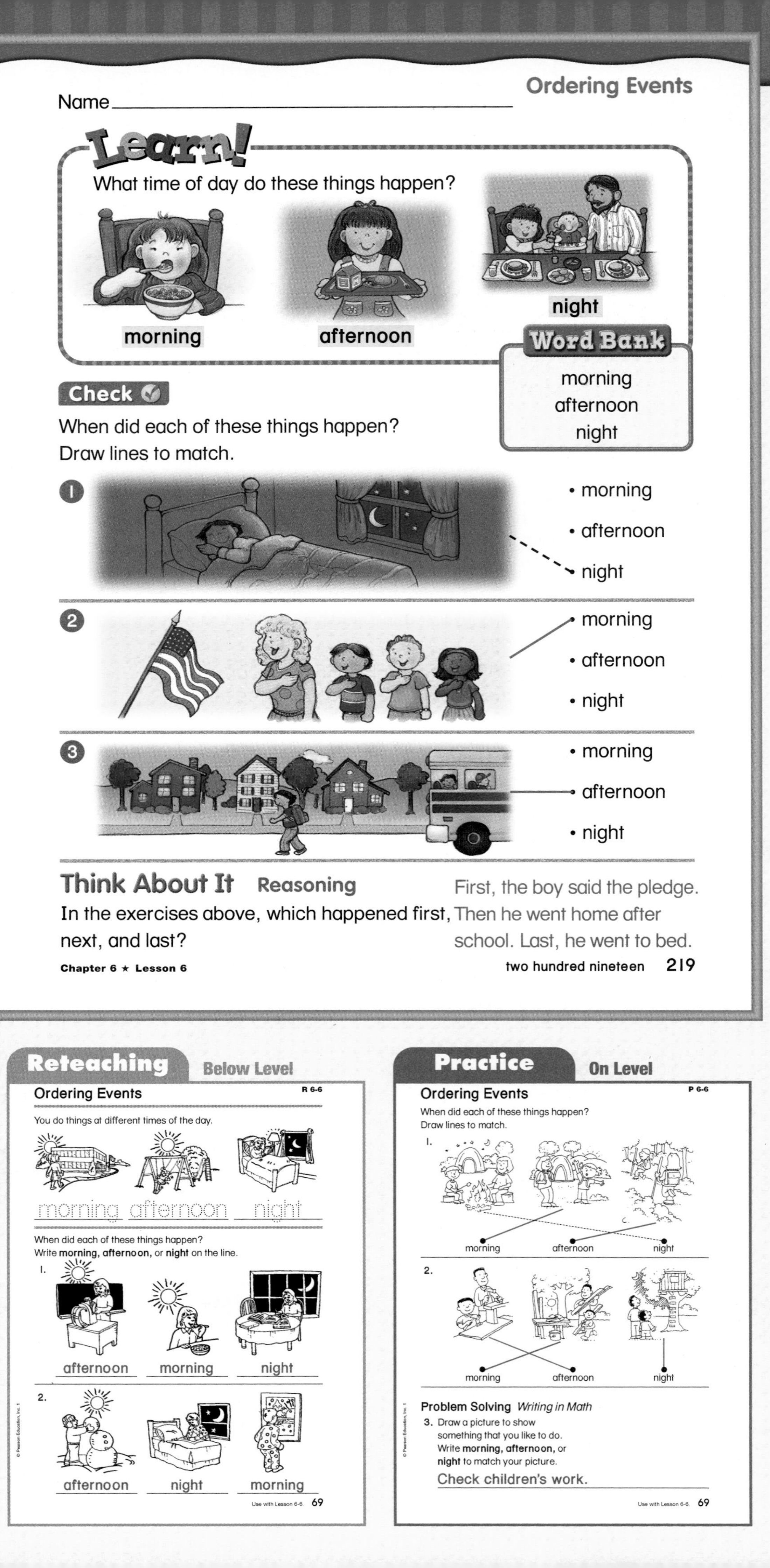

Name ______________________ Ordering Events

Learn!

What time of day do these things happen?

morning afternoon night

Word Bank
morning
afternoon
night

Check

When did each of these things happen?
Draw lines to match.

1. • morning • afternoon • night
2. • morning • afternoon • night
3. • morning • afternoon • night

Think About It Reasoning
In the exercises above, which happened first, next, and last?
First, the boy said the pledge. Then he went home after school. Last, he went to bed.

Chapter 6 ★ Lesson 6 two hundred nineteen 219

Reteaching Below Level

Ordering Events R 6-6

You do things at different times of the day.

morning afternoon night

When did each of these things happen?
Write **morning, afternoon,** or **night** on the line.

1. afternoon morning night
2. afternoon night morning

Use with Lesson 6-6. 69

Practice On Level

Ordering Events P 6-6

When did each of these things happen?
Draw lines to match.

1. morning afternoon night
2. morning afternoon night

Problem Solving *Writing in Math*
3. Draw a picture to show something that you like to do. Write **morning, afternoon,** or **night** to match your picture.
Check children's work.

Use with Lesson 6-6. 69

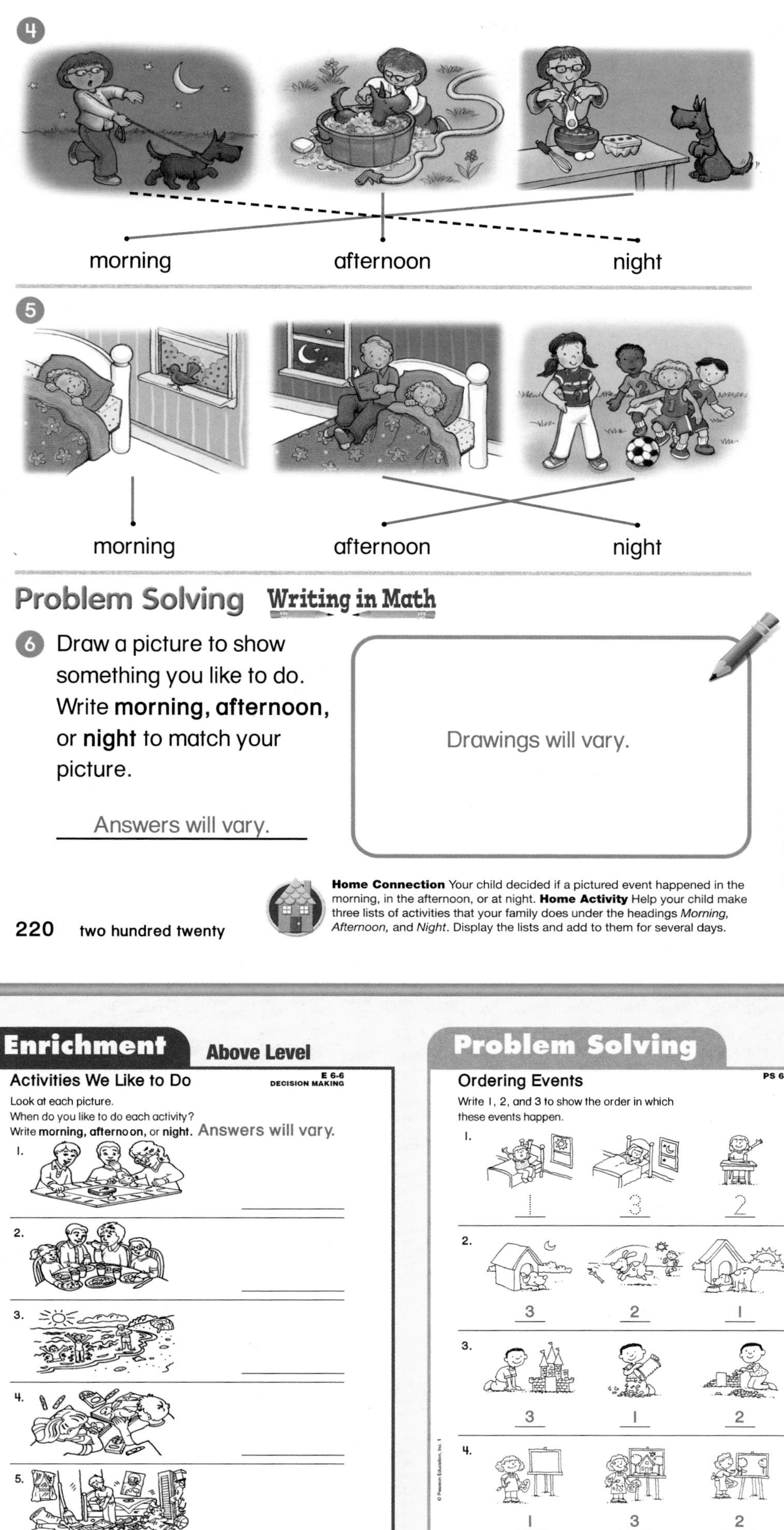

Practice

When did each of these things happen?
Draw lines to match.

4
morning afternoon night

5
morning afternoon night

Problem Solving

Writing in Math

6 Draw a picture to show something you like to do. Write **morning, afternoon,** or **night** to match your picture.

Answers will vary.

Drawings will vary.

Home Connection Your child decided if a pictured event happened in the morning, in the afternoon, or at night. **Home Activity** Help your child make three lists of activities that your family does under the headings *Morning, Afternoon,* and *Night*. Display the lists and add to them for several days.

220 two hundred twenty

Enrichment Above Level

Activities We Like to Do — E 6-6 DECISION MAKING

Look at each picture.
When do you like to do each activity?
Write **morning, afternoon,** or **night.** Answers will vary.

1.
2.
3.
4.
5.

Use with Lesson 6-6. 69

Problem Solving

Ordering Events — PS 6-6

Write 1, 2, and 3 to show the order in which these events happen.

1. 1 3 2
2. 3 2 1
3. 3 1 2
4. 1 3 2

Use with Lesson 6-6. 69

3 Practice

Have children share and discuss the pictures they drew for Exercise 6.

Reading Assist: Vocabulary Help children understand the terms *night* and *evening.* Explain that evening refers to the end of afternoon until night begins. Tell children that *night* refers to the time after sunset and before sunrise.

Leveled Practice

Below Level Listen as the teacher describes each activity.

On Level Circle the clue to the time in each picture before completing each exercise.

Above Level Complete all exercises as written.

Early Finishers Give children drawing paper folded in thirds and labeled *morning, afternoon,* and *night.* Have them draw pictures showing activities done at each time.

4 Assess

Journal Idea Have children write sentences with the words *morning, afternoon,* or *night.*

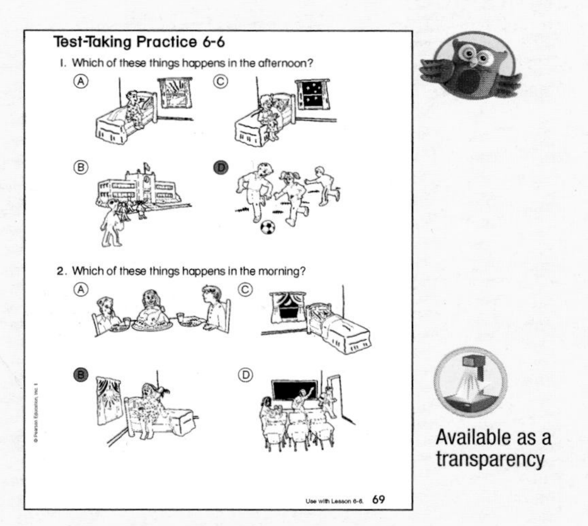

Test-Taking Practice 6-6

1. Which of these things happens in the afternoon?

2. Which of these things happens in the morning?

Use with Lesson 6-6. 69

Available as a transparency

6-7 Estimating Lengths of Time

Lesson Organizer

Quick Lesson Overview 

Objective Compare and estimate the length of time it takes for each of three activities.

Math Understanding The duration of two or more events can be compared.

Math Monster Videos
Use Episode 8: *Time* with or anytime after Lesson 6-7.

Professional Development Note

Math Background Children have had experience with exact measures of time to the hour and to the half hour. In this lesson, they will be asked to estimate time using inexact terms. They will determine *about* how long an activity takes and which of three activities take the *least* and *greatest* amount of time.

NCTM Standards

- Measurement

(For a complete correlation to the NCTM Standards and Grades Pre-K through 2 Expectations, see Pages 203G and 203H.)

Getting Started

Spiral Review

Problem of the Day 6-7

On Pet Day the children in Ms. Dennis' room brought 6 dogs, 3 cats, and 7 guinea pigs. How many fewer cats than dogs did the children bring?

Topics Reviewed

- Subtraction

Answer The children brought 3 fewer cats than dogs.

Spiral Review and Test Prep 6-7

1. Which shape is a square?
   Ⓐ Ⓑ ● Ⓓ
2. Gina has 3 goldfish. She has 2 guppies. How many fish does she have in all?
   Ⓐ 6 fish ● 5 fish Ⓒ 4 fish Ⓓ 3 fish
3. Tell one thing that you do during each time of the day. Answers will vary.
   Morning ______
   Afternoon ______
   Night ______

70 Use with Lesson 6-7.

Available as a transparency and as a blackline master

Topics Reviewed

1. Identifying Plane Shapes
2. Choose an Operation
3. Ordering Events

Investigating the Concept

A Minute, an Hour, or a Day

Materials Pieces of construction paper labeled with the following activities: *hiking up a tall mountain, playing piano, exercising,* and *passing out papers;* index cards labeled *1 minute, 1 hour,* and *1 day*

What to Do

- Display the labels. Have a child choose an activity card and pantomime the activity. After classmates guess the activity, have a volunteer choose a label that tells about how long the activity probably takes.
- Repeat with each activity card.

Ongoing Assessment

- **Reasoning How could you prove that an activity takes about 1 minute?** *(Sample response: Do the activity and use a clock to time yourself as you do it.)*
- **Would you use minutes, hours, or days to tell how long it takes to read a few sentences?** *(Minutes)*

Reaching All Learners

Reading in Math

Good Times

10–15 MIN **Linguistic**

- Discuss the games and activities children enjoy. Write these activities on the board. Have children think about the time each activity takes.
- Write children's estimates for how long each activity takes. Then have them decide which activities take minutes, which take hours, and which take days.
- Then have children determine which activity takes the least amount of time and which activity takes the greatest amount of time.

Reteaching

Minutes, Hours, Days

10–15 MIN **Logical/Mathematical**

Materials Magazines

- Write *"hour," "minute,"* and *"day"* on the board. Have children tell you which word represents the shortest amount of time, which word represents the next longest, and which represents the longest amount of time.
- Show children pictures from magazines that feature people doing various activities.
- Have children give an estimate of the time each activity takes. Encourage children to suggest similar activities that would take about the same amount of time.

Access Content

English Language Learners

It's About Time

5–10 MIN **Visual/Spatial/Linguistic**

SMALL GROUP

Materials Clock Face (Teaching Tool 22); classroom calendar

- Practice the words *minute, hour,* and *day* with children.
- Have children close their eyes. When 1 minute has passed, say: **A minute is up!** Have children repeat.
- Put the hour hand on the clock at 3. Move the hand to 4. **That is 1 hour.** Have children repeat.
- Point to today's date on the calendar. Move your finger to tomorrow's date. **That is 1 day.** Have children repeat.
- Guide children to list activities that take each amount of time.

Advanced Learners

How Long Does It Take?

15–20 MIN  **Visual/Spatial**

PAIRS

Materials *(per pair)* Crayons or markers; posterboard

- Challenge children to think of activities that take weeks, months, and years to accomplish.
- Ask children to work together to make a poster with the headings: "Weeks," "Months," and "Years."
- Have them list activities of varying lengths of time in the appropriate columns on the poster.

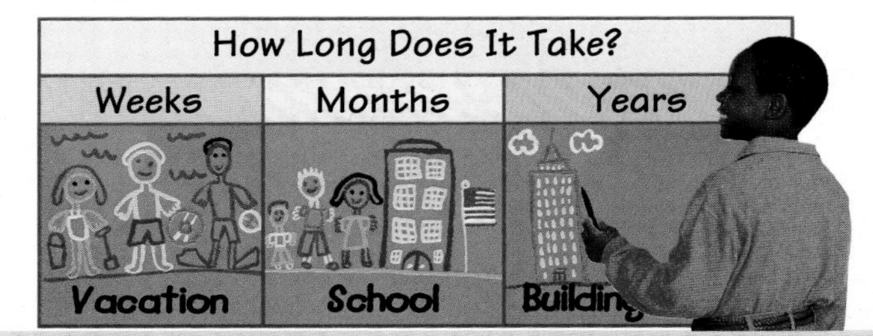

Objective Compare and estimate the length of time it takes for each of three activities.

1 Warm Up

Activate Prior Knowledge Review comparing times to 1 minute by having children determine if certain activities take more than or less than 1 minute.

2 Teach

Learn!

Discuss the activities pictured on the student page. Read aloud to the children how long each activity takes. Invite children to tell other activities that take about 1 minute, about 1 hour, and about 1 day.

Ongoing Assessment

Talk About It

- **Would it take about 3 minutes or about 3 days to build a doghouse? Explain.** *(Sample response: 3 days; because there are many steps to follow)*
- **Why is the word *about* in front of each unit of time?** *(It is not the exact amount of time. It is an estimate.)*

If children do not grasp the meaning of the word *about*,

then explain that they are estimating the time, not giving the exact amount.

Check

Error Intervention

If children make errors in matching,

then have them tell which activities take the least and greatest amounts of time and mark them first. *(Also see* Reteaching, *Page 221B.)*

Think About It Ask questions to guide children's thinking. **Which is the shortest period of time: 2 minutes, 2 hours, or 2 days? the longest?**

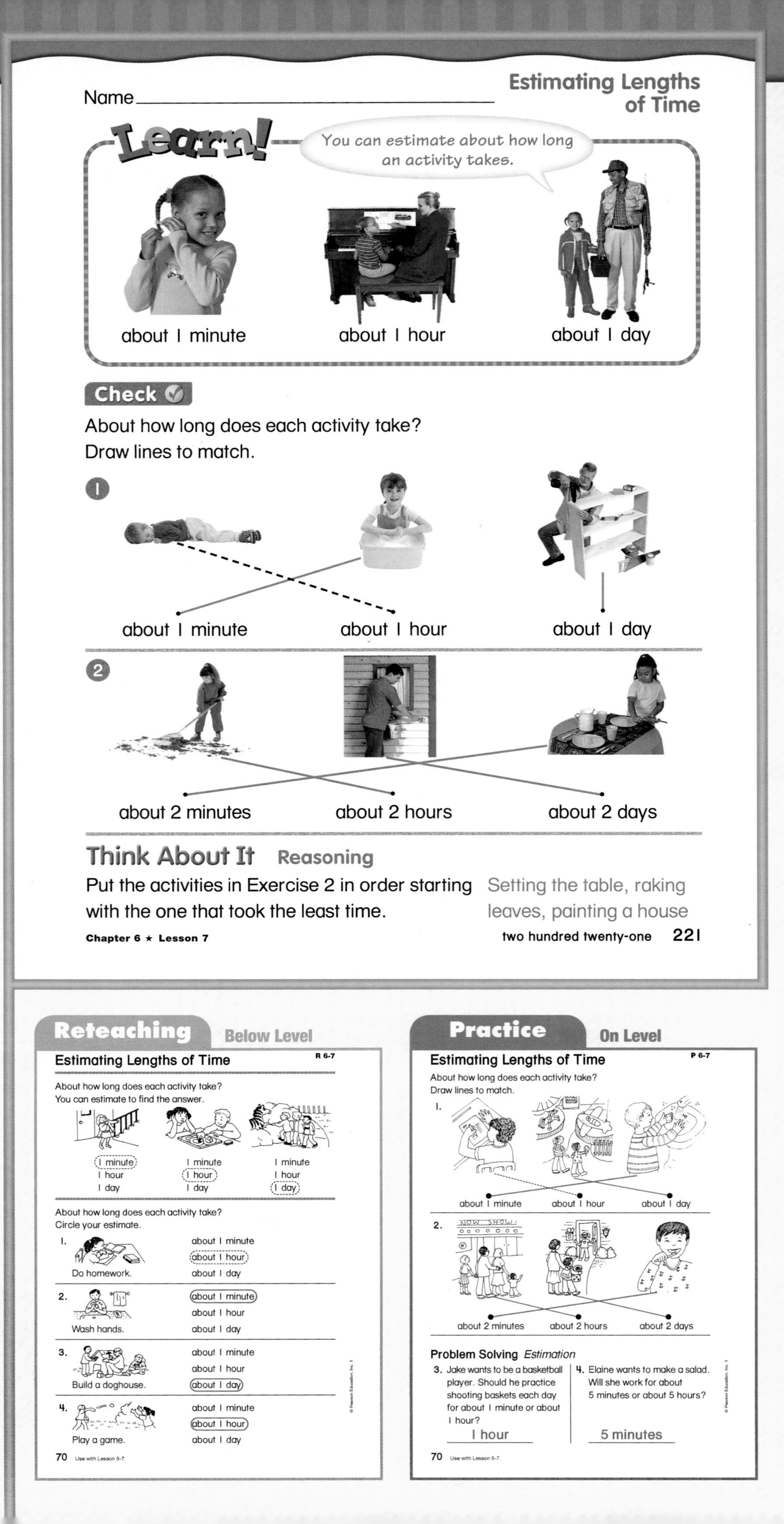

Name ______________________

Estimating Lengths of Time

Learn!

You can estimate about how long an activity takes.

about 1 minute | about 1 hour | about 1 day

Check

About how long does each activity take?
Draw lines to match.

1. about 1 minute | about 1 hour | about 1 day

2. about 2 minutes | about 2 hours | about 2 days

Think About It Reasoning

Put the activities in Exercise 2 in order starting with the one that took the least time. Setting the table, raking leaves, painting a house

Reteaching Below Level

Estimating Lengths of Time R 6-7

About how long does each activity take?
You can estimate to find the answer.

1 minute / 1 hour / 1 day — 1 minute / 1 hour / 1 day — 1 minute / 1 hour / 1 day

About how long does each activity take?
Circle your estimate.

1. Do homework. — about 1 minute / about 1 hour / about 1 day
2. Wash hands. — about 1 minute / about 1 hour / about 1 day
3. Build a doghouse. — about 1 minute / about 1 hour / about 1 day
4. Play a game. — about 1 minute / about 1 hour / about 1 day

70 Use with Lesson 6-7.

Practice On Level

Estimating Lengths of Time P 6-7

About how long does each activity take?
Draw lines to match.

1. about 1 minute | about 1 hour | about 1 day

2. about 2 minutes | about 2 hours | about 2 days

Problem Solving *Estimation*

3. Jake wants to be a basketball player. Should he practice shooting baskets each day for about 1 minute or about 1 hour? 1 hour

4. Elaine wants to make a salad. Will she work for about 5 minutes or about 5 hours? 5 minutes

70 Use with Lesson 6-7.

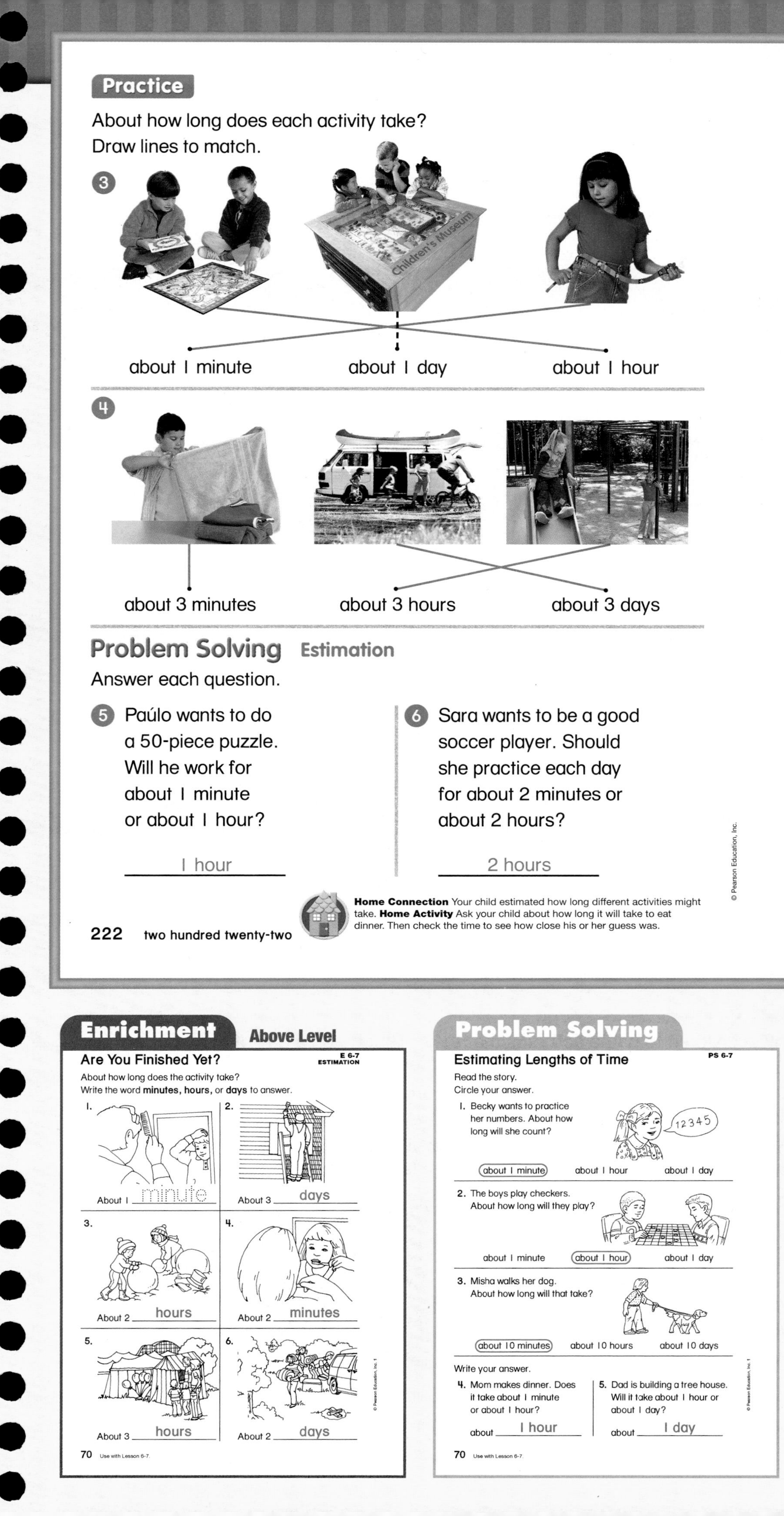

Practice

About how long does each activity take?
Draw lines to match.

3

about 1 minute | about 1 day | about 1 hour

4

about 3 minutes | about 3 hours | about 3 days

Problem Solving Estimation

Answer each question.

5 Paúlo wants to do a 50-piece puzzle. Will he work for about 1 minute or about 1 hour?

1 hour

6 Sara wants to be a good soccer player. Should she practice each day for about 2 minutes or about 2 hours?

2 hours

Home Connection Your child estimated how long different activities might take. **Home Activity** Ask your child about how long it will take to eat dinner. Then check the time to see how close his or her guess was.

Enrichment Above Level

Are You Finished Yet? E 6-7 ESTIMATION

About how long does the activity take?
Write the word **minutes**, **hours**, or **days** to answer.

1. About 1 minute
2. About 3 days
3. About 2 hours
4. About 2 minutes
5. About 3 hours
6. About 2 days

70 Use with Lesson 6-7.

Problem Solving

Estimating Lengths of Time PS 6-7

Read the story.
Circle your answer.

1. Becky wants to practice her numbers. About how long will she count?
   (about 1 minute) about 1 hour about 1 day
2. The boys play checkers. About how long will they play?
   about 1 minute (about 1 hour) about 1 day
3. Misha walks her dog. About how long will that take?
   (about 10 minutes) about 10 hours about 10 days

Write your answer.

4. Mom makes dinner. Does it take about 1 minute or about 1 hour?
   about 1 hour
5. Dad is building a tree house. Will it take about 1 hour or about 1 day?
   about 1 day

70 Use with Lesson 6-7.

3 Practice

Invite children to talk about what each picture shows before doing the page.

Reading Assist: Sequence After children have completed Exercise 4, have them put the activities and times in sequence from least to greatest.

Leveled Practice

Below Level Circle the activity that takes the least amount of time.

On Level Complete all exercises as written.

Above Level Name another activity that takes about the same amount of time as each activity.

Early Finishers Have children draw three activities: one that takes less than 1 hour, one that takes about 1 hour, and one that takes more than 1 hour.

4 Assess

Journal Idea Ask children to think of an activity that would take about 3 minutes and draw a picture to illustrate it.

Test-Taking Practice 6-7

1. About how long does it take to blow up a balloon?
   - Ⓐ about 1 minute
   - Ⓑ about 1 hour
   - Ⓒ about 2 hours
   - Ⓓ about 2 days
2. Marcus has T-ball practice. About how long will practice last?
   - Ⓐ about 3 minutes
   - Ⓑ about 3 days
   - Ⓒ about 1 day
   - Ⓓ about 1 hour

Use with Lesson 6-7. 70

Available as a transparency

Use Data from a Schedule

Lesson Organizer

Quick Lesson Overview

Objective Solve problems by reading and using the information in a schedule.

Math Understanding A time schedule is a table that is useful for solving problems.

Professional Development Note

Math Background Reading a schedule provides a real-world opportunity for children to connect time and measurement concepts to their own lives. They also expand their knowledge of how to read, organize, and interpret data that is presented in table form, thus supporting children's abilities for making connections across mathematics.

NCTM Standards

- Data Analysis and Probability
- Measurement

(For a complete correlation to the NCTM Standards and Grades Pre-K through 2 Expectations, see Pages 203G and 203H.)

Getting Started

Spiral Review

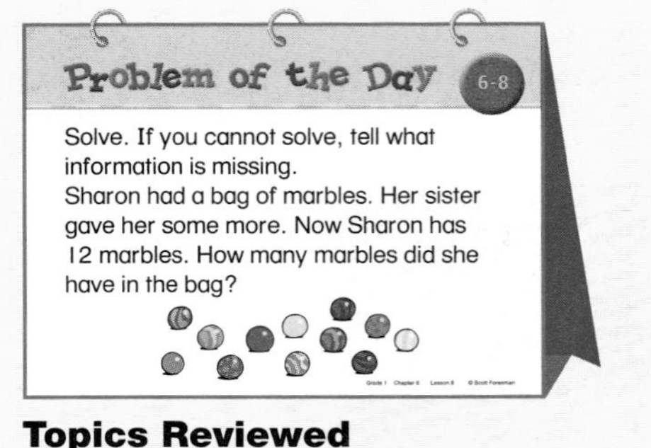

Problem of the Day 6-8
Solve. If you cannot solve, tell what information is missing.
Sharon had a bag of marbles. Her sister gave her some more. Now Sharon has 12 marbles. How many marbles did she have in the bag?

Topics Reviewed

- Meaning of addition and subtraction
- Problem-Solving Skill: Extra or Missing Information

Answer The missing information needed to solve the problem is the number of marbles that Sharon's sister gave her.

Spiral Review and Test Prep 6-8

1. About how long does it take to brush your teeth?
   Ⓐ about 2 minutes Ⓒ about 2 hours
   Ⓑ about 1 hour Ⓓ about 1 day
2. Which fraction tells how much is shaded?
   Ⓐ $\frac{1}{3}$ Ⓑ $\frac{2}{3}$ Ⓒ $\frac{3}{4}$ Ⓓ $\frac{1}{4}$
3. Circle **add** or **subtract**. Then write a number sentence.
   Jeff has 10 postcards. He mails 6 postcards. How many postcards does Jeff have left?
   add (subtract)
   10 ⊖ 6 = 4

Use with Lesson 6-8. 71

Available as a transparency and as a blackline master

Topics Reviewed

1. Estimating Lengths of Time
2. Non-Unit Fractions
3. Choose an Operation

Investigating the Concept

Make a Schedule

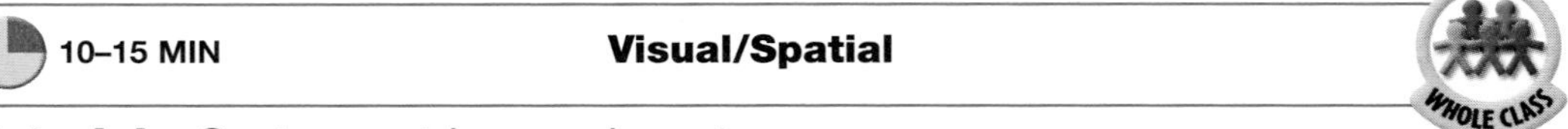

Materials Sentence strips; markers; tape

What to Do

- Invite children to name activities that they might do on a day off from school. Write 4–5 of the activities on sentence strips.
- Discuss with the children what might be a good order in which to do the activities. Have children tape the strips in that order on the board.
- Help children agree on times for each activity to start. On separate sentence strips, write the times and tape them beside each activity. Tell children that this is called a *schedule.*

1:00 Eat a Lunch.
2:00 Do a puzzle.

3:00 Go to the playground.

Ongoing Assessment

- **Reasoning What information do you learn from a schedule?** *(The time and order in which things happen)*
- **Why might you change the times on this schedule?** *(You might want to start earlier or later or spend more or less time doing something.)*

Reaching All Learners

Reading in Math

Using Picture Clues

5–10 MIN **Visual/Spatial**

- Copy the schedule on Student Page 224 onto the board.
- Have children tell what each of the four symbols stands for. **What do these pictures show? How do the pictures help you understand the Class Schedule?**
- Discuss why the picture of a book is a clue for the word reading. Ask children to imagine that science and math were added to the schedule. Have children suggest simple drawings to represent these subjects.

science
math

English Language Learners

Extend Language

Read the Schedule

10–15 MIN **Linguistic**

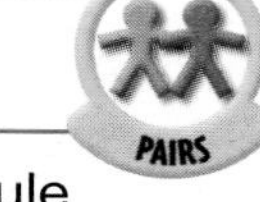

Materials *(per pair)* A copy of a typical schedule for a child at your school

- With the class, review the meanings of *before* and *after*. Ask a few questions about the schedule, such as: **What class is before recess? What class is after math? What begins at 9:00?** Guide children to use the schedule to point to the answer and say it.
- Partners can ask and answer similar questions.

Reteaching

Our Class Schedule

10–15 MIN **Visual/Spatial**

SMALL GROUP

Materials Chart paper; markers

- Write the word *"schedule"* on the board. Ask children to discuss what a schedule is and why people use schedules.
- Invite children to create an actual class schedule with you. Write your name or your room number at the top of the schedule. List the lesson times and activities below. Have children illustrate the schedule.
- If you already have a class schedule posted, create a different schedule and plan special activities for the day.

Math and Social Studies

All Kinds of Schedules

15–20 MIN **Visual/Spatial**

WHOLE CLASS

Materials Collection of schedules such as television guides, after-school club schedules, camp schedules, or train schedules

- Ask children to think about different types of schedules they have seen and what kind of information is included in those schedules.
- Explain that schedules show what programs are on television and when trains or buses arrive. Hold up examples and identify each.
- Copy a modified version of one of these schedules on the board. Discuss the information that is included in the schedule.

Time	Show
5:00	Cartoons
5:30	The News
6:00	The Game Show

Objective Solve problems by reading and using the information in a schedule.

1 Warm Up

Activate Prior Knowledge Review *before* and *after*. List numbers in order from 0 to 10 on the board. **Which number comes just after 6?** *(7)* **Which number comes just before 5?** *(4)*

2 Teach

Learn!

Explain that a schedule shows the time and order of activities. Model how to use a schedule. **If I want to know which activity starts at 3:30, I find 3:30 listed under the times. Then I read to the right of the time to see which activity is listed.**

Ongoing Assessment

Talk About It

- **How can you find which activity comes just before sports?** *(Look on the schedule to see which activity is listed just above sports.)*
- **How can you find how long reading lasts?** *(See what time it starts. Then see what time the next activity starts. Tell how much time passed.)*

If children need help interpreting the schedule,

then read and discuss each time and activity.

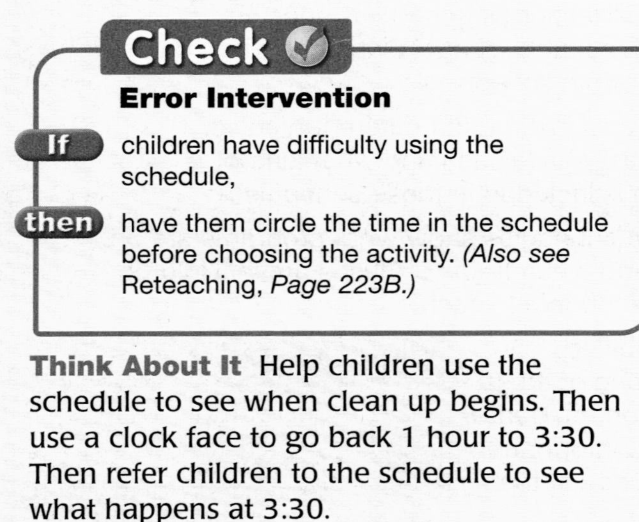

Check

Error Intervention

If children have difficulty using the schedule,

then have them circle the time in the schedule before choosing the activity. *(Also see Reteaching, Page 223B.)*

Think About It Help children use the schedule to see when clean up begins. Then use a clock face to go back 1 hour to 3:30. Then refer children to the schedule to see what happens at 3:30.

PROBLEM-SOLVING SKILL

Use Data from a Schedule

Name ____________________

Learn!

Community Center After-School Schedule	
Time	**Activity**
3:00	Reading
3:30	Art
4:00	Sports
4:30	Clean Up

This schedule shows the time at which each activity starts.

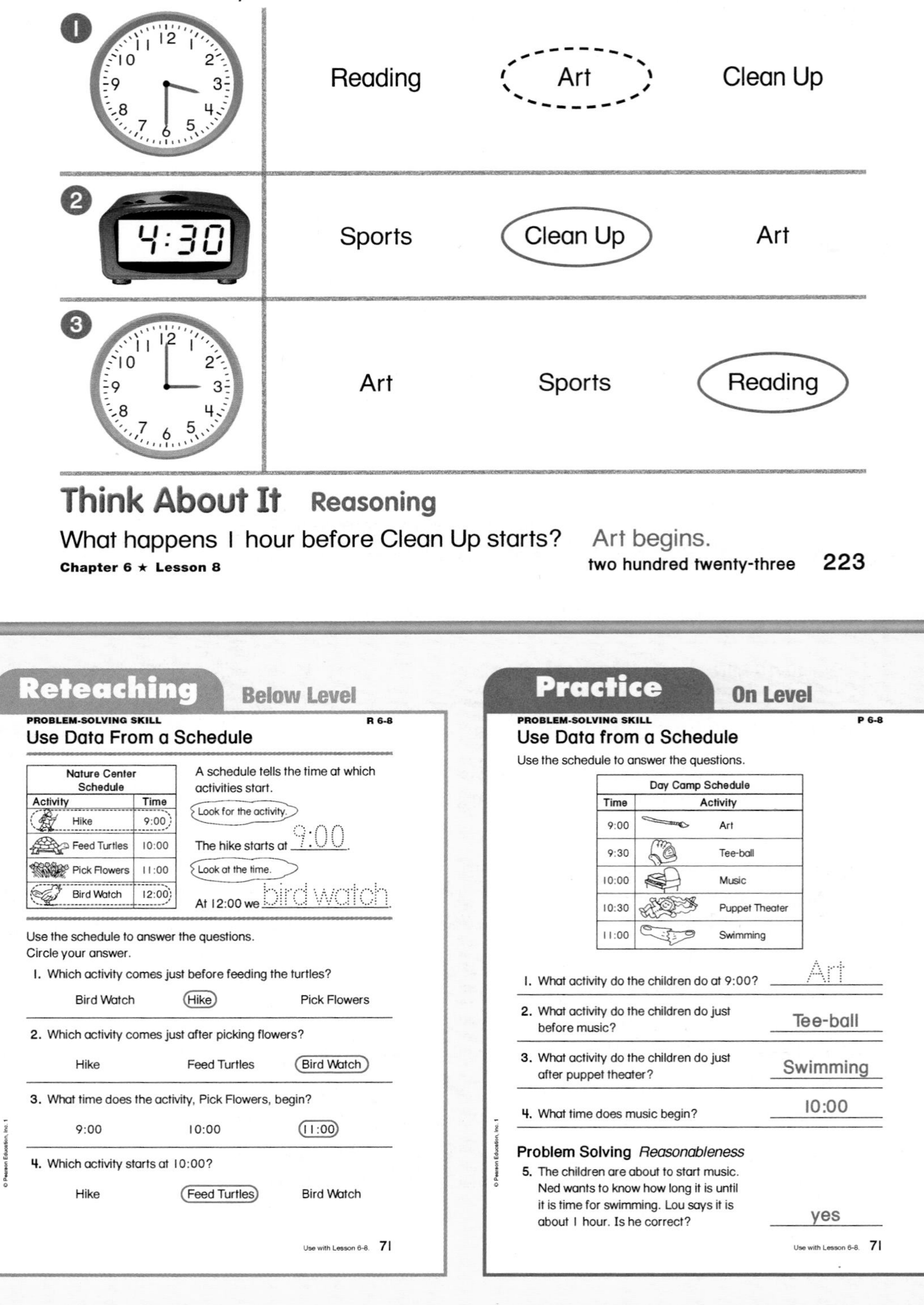

Check

Circle the activity that starts at the time shown on each clock.

1. Reading | Art | Clean Up
2. 4:30 — Sports | Clean Up | Art
3. Art | Sports | Reading

Think About It Reasoning

What happens 1 hour before Clean Up starts? Art begins.

Reteaching Below Level

PROBLEM-SOLVING SKILL R 6-8

Use Data From a Schedule

Nature Center Schedule	
Activity	Time
Hike	9:00
Feed Turtles	10:00
Pick Flowers	11:00
Bird Watch	12:00

A schedule tells the time at which activities start.

Look for the activity.

The hike starts at 9:00.

Look at the time.

At 12:00 we bird watch.

Use the schedule to answer the questions. Circle your answer.

1. Which activity comes just before feeding the turtles?
   Bird Watch | Hike | Pick Flowers
2. Which activity comes just after picking flowers?
   Hike | Feed Turtles | Bird Watch
3. What time does the activity, Pick Flowers, begin?
   9:00 | 10:00 | 11:00
4. Which activity starts at 10:00?
   Hike | Feed Turtles | Bird Watch

Use with Lesson 6-8. 71

Practice On Level

PROBLEM-SOLVING SKILL P 6-8

Use Data from a Schedule

Use the schedule to answer the questions.

Day Camp Schedule	
Time	Activity
9:00	Art
9:30	Tee-ball
10:00	Music
10:30	Puppet Theater
11:00	Swimming

1. What activity do the children do at 9:00? Art
2. What activity do the children do just before music? Tee-ball
3. What activity do the children do just after puppet theater? Swimming
4. What time does music begin? 10:00

Problem Solving *Reasonableness*

5. The children are about to start music. Ned wants to know how long it is until it is time for swimming. Lou says it is about 1 hour. Is he correct? yes

Use with Lesson 6-8. 71

 EC NTL 12 11 10 9

Practice

Use the schedule to answer the questions.

Mrs. Lopez's Class Schedule	
Time	**Activity**
8:00	Calendar Time
8:30	Reading
9:00	Centers
9:30	Math
10:00	Recess

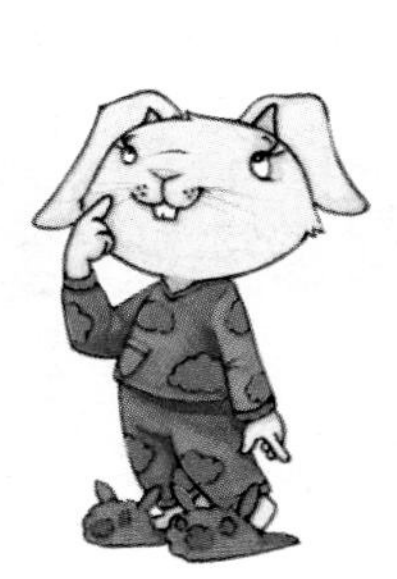

4. What activity do children do just before recess?

   Math

5. What does the class do just after reading?

   Centers

6. What time does math begin?

   9:30

Reasonableness

Use the schedule to solve the problem.

7. The class is about to start centers.
   Jan wants to know how long it is until recess.
   Peg says it is 2 hours.
   Is she correct?

   no

Home Connection Your child used a schedule to answer questions. **Home Activity** Work with your child to make a schedule of activities that you might do on a Saturday afternoon.

3 Practice

Read the questions aloud to the children before they complete the page.

Reading Assist: Draw Conclusions Look at the schedule together. **What conclusion can you draw about how long reading lasts in Mrs. Lopez's class?**

Leveled Practice

Below Level Work in pairs to complete all exercises as written.

On Level Complete all exercises as written.

Above Level Beside each activity on the schedule, write how long it lasts.

Early Finishers Have children work with partners to create a class schedule. Ask them to list five activities the class does while in school and write a time for each one.

4 Assess

Journal Idea Invite children to write a schedule of things to do after school. Have them begin their schedule at the time when school ends.

Test-Taking Practice 6-8

Use the schedule to solve the problems.

Kids-Fit Class Schedule	
Time	Activity
2:00	Swimming
2:30	Bicycling
3:00	Running
3:30	Stretching

1. What do the children do at 2:30?
   - (A) swimming
   - (B) running
   - (C) stretching
   - (D) bicycling
2. If the kids are swimming, how long is it until they go running?
   - (A) 2 hours
   - (B) 1 minute
   - (C) 1 hour
   - (D) 2 days
3. What do the children do at 3:30?
   - (A) running
   - (B) stretching
   - (C) swimming
   - (D) bicycling

Use with Lesson 6-8. 71

Available as a transparency

Enrichment Above Level

Fun at the Fair

E 6-8 DATA

Look at the schedule for the school fair.
Each activity comes right after the one before it.

Fair Schedule	
Activity	**Time**
Puppet Show	11:30
Make Your Own Bracelet	12:30
Dig for Toy Dinosaurs	1:00
Face Painting	2:00
Clown Fun	2:30
Bingo	3:30

1. List the activities that take a half hour.

   Make Your Own Bracelet, Face Painting

2. List the activities that take 1 hour.

   Puppet Show, Dig for Toy Dinosaurs,
   Clown Fun

3. Bingo is over at 4:30.
   How long does Bingo last? 1 hour

4. Lisa leaves her house at 10:00 to go to the fair.
   Peg says it will take about an hour to get there.
   Will Lisa have enough time? yes

Use with Lesson 6-8. 71

Problem Solving

PROBLEM-SOLVING SKILL PS 6-8

Use Data from a Schedule

This movie schedule shows the names of the movies and the time each movie starts.

Movie Schedule	
Time	**Movie**
1:00	Dinosaurs and Dragons
2:30	Pokey the Pony
4:00	Haunted Hill
5:30	Volcano!

Use the schedule to answer the questions.

1. What time does Dinosaurs and Dragons start? 1:00
2. Circle the movie that starts at the time shown on the clock.

   Haunted Hill   Volcano!   (Pokey the Pony)

3. Ruth wants to know how long it is from the beginning of Dinosaurs and Dragons to the beginning of Haunted Hill. Jed says 1 hour. Is he right? no
4. What movie starts at 5:30? Volcano!
5. What movie starts right after Pokey the Pony? Haunted Hill

Using the page Help children ***read*** the chart by showing them how to run their fingers horizontally from a movie title to the time it begins. You may even suggest that they hold a straight edge beneath them. This technique will help children ***understand*** how to answer time-related questions.

Use with Lesson 6-8. 71

Days of the Week

Lesson Organizer

Quick Lesson Overview

Objective Read and use a calendar to name the days of the week.

Math Understanding A calendar is a chart listing the days of the month in order, grouped into weeks.

Vocabulary Calendar, day, month, week

Professional Development Note

Effective Questioning Techniques
On a daily basis, continue to ask structured questions that guide children to discover how the days of the week are related to each other and to the numbers on the calendar. For example: **What day comes two days after Monday? What day of the week is November 28?**

NCTM Standards

• Measurement
(For a complete correlation to the NCTM Standards and Grades Pre-K through 2 Expectations, see Pages 203G and 203H.)

Getting Started

Spiral Review

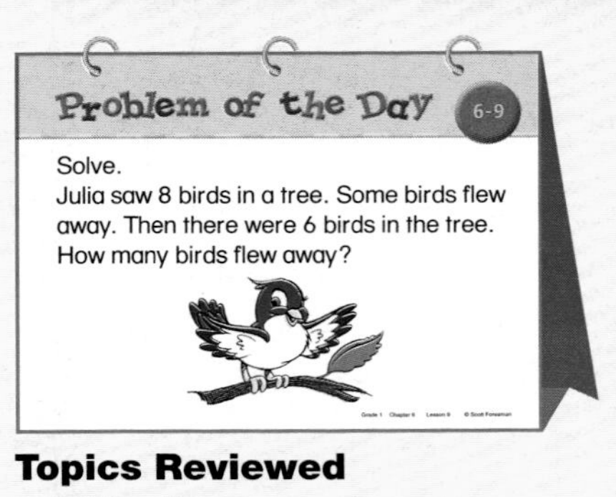
Problem of the Day 6-9

Solve.
Julia saw 8 birds in a tree. Some birds flew away. Then there were 6 birds in the tree. How many birds flew away?

Topics Reviewed
- Subtraction
- Problem-Solving Skill: One-Step Problem

Answer 2 birds flew away; 8 – 6 = 2.

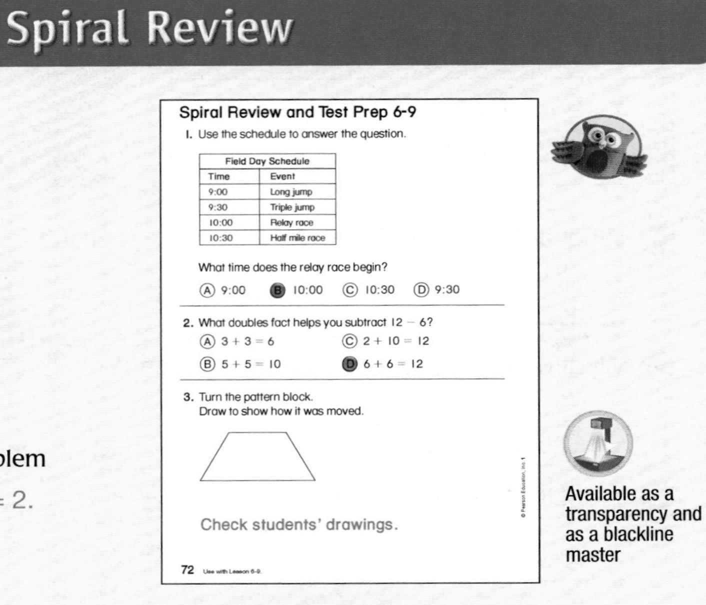
Spiral Review and Test Prep 6-9

1. Use the schedule to answer the question.

Field Day Schedule	
Time	Event
9:00	Long jump
9:30	Triple jump
10:00	Relay race
10:30	Half mile race

What time does the relay race begin?
Ⓐ 9:00 Ⓑ 10:00 Ⓒ 10:30 Ⓓ 9:30

2. What doubles fact helps you subtract 12 – 6?
Ⓐ 3 + 3 = 6 Ⓒ 2 + 10 = 12
Ⓑ 5 + 5 = 10 Ⓓ 6 + 6 = 12

3. Turn the pattern block.
Draw to show how it was moved.

Check students' drawings.

72

Available as a transparency and as a blackline master

Topics Reviewed
1. Use Data from a Schedule
2. Using Doubles to Subtract
3. Slides, Flips, and Turns

Investigating the Concept

On the Calendar

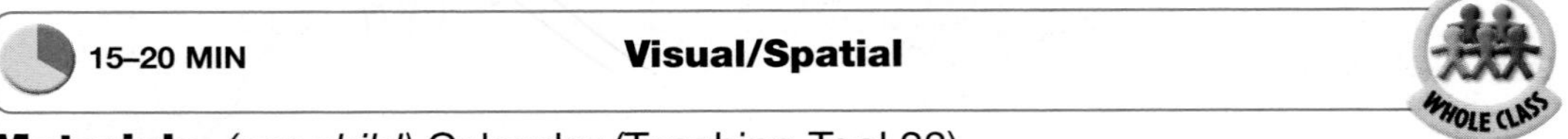

Materials *(per child)* Calendar (Teaching Tool 23)

What to Do
- Give each child a calendar and explain that when the calendar is completed, it will show one month. Help children write the name of the current month at the top of their calendars.
- Point out that the calendar shows the names of each of the days of the week in order. Name the days aloud together.
- Help children begin the calendar by putting 1 on the first day of the month. Then have them fill in the numbers to the end of the month.

Ongoing Assessment
- **Reasoning What are the names of the days of the week in order?** *(Sunday, Monday, Tuesday, Wednesday, Thursday, Friday, Saturday)*
- **What day was yesterday? What day will it be tomorrow?** *(Answers will vary.)*

November						
S	M	T	W	T	F	S
	1	2	3	4	5	6
7						

Reaching All Learners

Oral Language in Math

Days-of-the-Week Rhyme

5–10 MIN **Auditory/Linguistic**

- Write the following rhyme on the board and recite it to children.

  Sneeze

  Sneeze on Monday, sneeze for danger;
  Sneeze on Tuesday, meet a stranger;
  Sneeze on Wednesday, get a letter;
  Sneeze on Thursday, wetter weather;
  Sneeze on Friday, sneeze for sorrow;
  Sneeze on Saturday, play tomorrow;
  Sneeze on Sunday, wait! It's fun day.

- Have children recite the rhyme with you. Use a calendar to point to days of the week as you say the rhyme in unison.

Access Content

English Language Learners

Learn the Days

5–10 MIN **Auditory/Linguistic**

Materials Calendar for current month

- Write the days of the week on the board. Point to each day as you name it. Have children repeat.
- Discuss the days of the week. **There are seven days of the week. Saturday and Sunday are not school days.**
- Show this month's calendar and have volunteers point at and say what today is, yesterday was, and tomorrow will be.

Sunday
Monday
Tuesday
Wednesday
Thursday
Friday
Saturday

Reteaching

Days on a Calendar

Materials Large monthly calendar

- Display the current month on a classroom wall calendar.
- Point to each day of the week as you and the children read it together. **What is the first day of the week? What day is it today?**
- Focus on the days of the month. **How many days are in (month's name)? How many days are left in (month's name)?**
- Have children make up questions about the days of the week and the month to present to the group.

December						
S	M	T	W	T	F	S
			1	2	3	4
5	6	7	8			1
12	13	14	15	1		8
19	20	21	22	23		
26	27	28	29	30		

Students with Special Needs

Living Days of the Week

10–15 MIN **Linguistic/Kinesthetic**

SMALL GROUP

Materials *(per child)* Construction paper; markers

- Write the name of each day of the week on a separate sheet of paper. Make enough sheets so that each group member has one. Then write the days of the week on the board.
- Give each child a sheet of paper. Have children line up in order, using the list on the board for help.
- In turn, have children hold up their papers and recite the days.

Sunday Monday

Objective Read and use a calendar to name the days of the week.

1 Warm Up

Activate Prior Knowledge Review counting to 31. Write the numbers from 1 to 31 on the board as children count. Then erase some of the numbers. Have volunteers take turns filling in the missing numbers.

2 Teach

Learn!

Direct children's attention to the calendar at the top of the student page. Explain that a calendar is a chart that shows the name of the month and the days of the week. Read the days of the week aloud together.

Ongoing Assessment

Talk About It

- **What day of the week comes before Friday?** *(Thursday)*
- **How can you find what day tomorrow will be?** *(Find today, then look at the next day.)*

If children have trouble identifying yesterday, today, and tomorrow,

then on their calendars have them circle today, underline yesterday, and put a box around tomorrow.

Check ✓

Error Intervention

If children are having trouble locating days on the calendar,

then have them color each column of days a different color. *(Also see* Reteaching, *Page 225B.)*

Think About It Explain that the day following the end of one month is the first day of the next month. Have children point to the last day of November. **What day is it? Which day comes next?**

Name ______________________

Learn!

This **calendar** shows the **days** and **weeks** in the **month** of November.

November						
Sunday	Monday	Tuesday	Wednesday	Thursday	Friday	Saturday
	1	2	3	4	5	6
7	8	9	10	11	12	13
14	15	16	17	18	19	20
21	22	23	24	25	26	27
28	29	30				

Word Bank
calendar
day
week
month

Check ✓

Use the calendar above to answer the questions.

1. How many days are in 1 week? 7
2. How many days are in November? 30
3. On what day does this November begin? Monday
4. If today is Thursday, what day will tomorrow be? Friday
5. If today is Tuesday, what day was yesterday? Monday

Think About It Reasoning

On what day of the week will the next month begin? Explain.

Wednesday, because November ends on Tuesday

Reteaching Below Level

Days of the Week

R 6-9

March

There are 7 days in a week.

1st day	2nd day	3rd day	4th day	5th day	6th day	7th day
Sunday	Monday	Tuesday	Wednesday	Thursday	Friday	Saturday
		1	2	3	4	Y 5
6	B 7	8	9	10	11	Y 12
13	B 14	15	16	17	18	Y 19
20	B 21	22	23	24	25	Y 26
27	B 28	29	30	31		

Use the calendar to answer the questions.

1. Write the days of the week in order.
   Sunday, Monday, Tuesday, Wednesday, Thursday, Friday, Saturday
2. Color all the Saturdays yellow. yellow
3. Color all the Mondays blue. blue

Problem Solving *Visual Thinking*

4. Find the pattern.
   Then write the day of the week that comes next.
   Wednesday, Thursday, Friday, Saturday
5. Monday, Tuesday, Wednesday, Thursday

Practice On Level

Days of the Week

P 6-9

1. Circle the names of the days of the week.
2. Color the Mondays blue and Wednesdays red.

April						
Sunday	Monday	Tuesday	Wednesday	Thursday	Friday	Saturday
	B 1	2	R 3	4	5	6
7	B 8	9	R 10	11	12	13
14	B 15	16	R 17	18	19	20
21	B 22	23	R 24	25	26	27
28	B 29	30				

3. Write the days of the week in order.
   Sunday, Monday, Tuesday, Wednesday, Thursday, Friday, Saturday

Problem Solving *Visual Thinking*

Find the pattern. Then write the day that comes next.

4. Wednesday Thursday Friday Saturday
5. Friday Saturday Sunday Monday

Practice

6. Circle the names of the days of the week.
7. Color the Sundays green and the Thursdays blue.
8. Write the days of the week in order.

Sunday, Monday,

Tuesday, Wednesday,

Thursday, Friday, Saturday

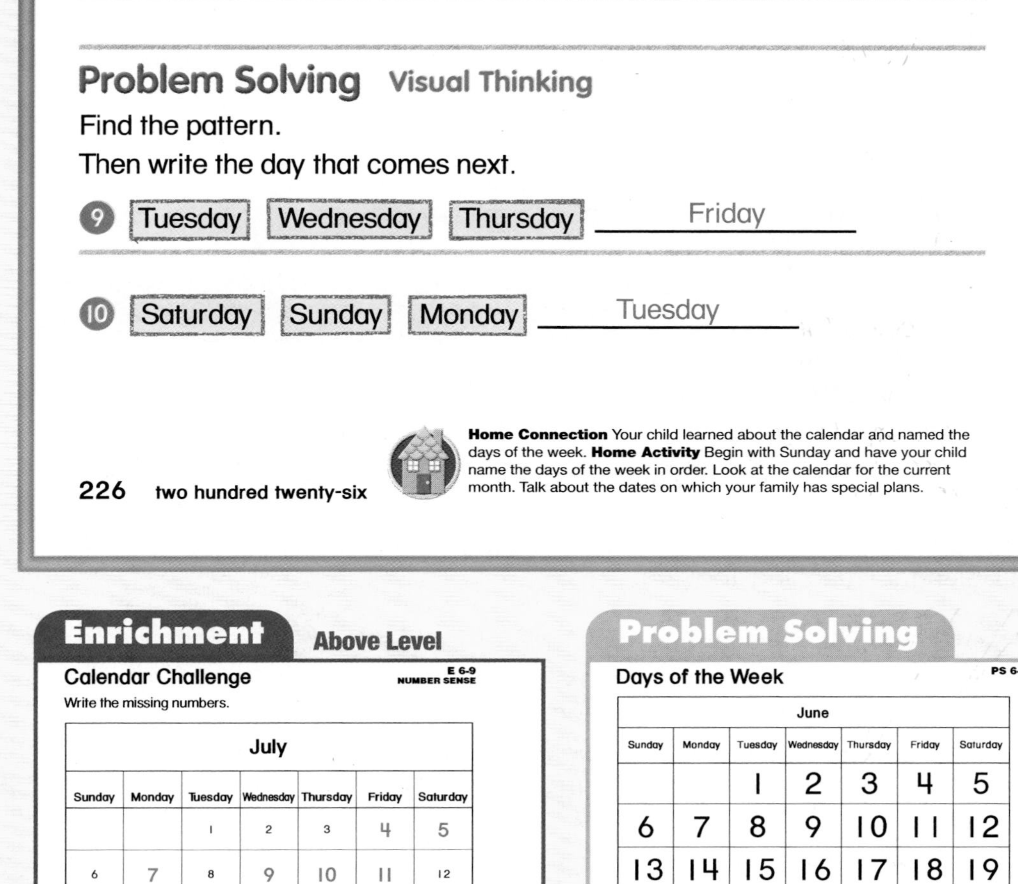

May						
Sunday	Monday	Tuesday	Wednesday	Thursday	Friday	Saturday
						1
2	3	4	5	6	7	8
9	10	11	12	13	14	15
16	17	18	19	20	21	22
23 / 30	24 / 31	25	26	27	28	29

green

blue

Problem Solving Visual Thinking

Find the pattern.
Then write the day that comes next.

9. Tuesday Wednesday Thursday Friday

10. Saturday Sunday Monday Tuesday

Home Connection Your child learned about the calendar and named the days of the week. **Home Activity** Begin with Sunday and have your child name the days of the week in order. Look at the calendar for the current month. Talk about the dates on which your family has special plans.

3 Practice

Ask children to draw a box around the day of the week that is their favorite.

Reading Assist: Classify Help children distinguish between the meanings of *date* and *day*. List examples of both on the board and have children classify each.

Leveled Practice

Below Level For Exercise 8, say the days of the week in order rather than write them.

On Level Complete all exercises as written.

Above Level Write the next three days in order for Exercises 9 and 10.

Early Finishers Write the following on the board and have children use the calendar on Student Page 226 to write each day of the week: May 4– ____; May 12– _____; May 20– _____.

4 Assess

Journal Idea Ask children to name something they do weekly. Have them illustrate their activities and write the name of the day of the week below the picture.

Test-Taking Practice 6-9

Use the calendar to solve the problems.

July						
S	M	T	W	T	F	S
		1	2	3	4	5
6	7	8	9	10	11	12
13	14	15	16	17	18	19
20	21	22	23	24	25	26
27	28	29	30	31		

1. On what day does this July end?
   - (A) Sunday
   - (B) Tuesday
   - (C) Thursday
   - (D) Saturday
2. If today is Friday, what day is tomorrow?
   - (A) Sunday
   - (B) Saturday
   - (C) Monday
   - (D) Thursday
3. On what day does July start?
   - (A) Monday
   - (B) Tuesday
   - (C) Wednesday
   - (D) Thursday

Use with Lesson 6-9. 72

Available as a transparency

Enrichment Above Level

Calendar Challenge

E 6-9 NUMBER SENSE

Write the missing numbers.

July						
Sunday	Monday	Tuesday	Wednesday	Thursday	Friday	Saturday
		1	2	3	4	5
6	7	8	9	10	11	12
13	14	15	16	17	18	19
20	21	22	23	24	25	26
27	28	29	30	31		

Now use the calendar to answer the questions.

1. How many Mondays are in this month? 4
2. How many Tuesdays are in this month? 5
3. On what day is July 4th? Friday
4. What is the date of the first Sunday in this month? July 6

72 Use with Lesson 6-9.

Problem Solving

Days of the Week

PS 6-9

June						
Sunday	Monday	Tuesday	Wednesday	Thursday	Friday	Saturday
		1	2	3	4	5
6	7	8	9	10	11	12
13	14	15	16	17	18	19
20	21	22	23	24	25	26
27	28	29	30			

Use the calendar to answer the questions.

1. Tuesday is the first day in June. What was the last day of the month before June? Monday
2. If today is Tuesday and Tony has a game the next day, what day is the game? Wednesday
3. The last day of June is on a Wednesday. Mike goes to camp on the day before. What day does Mike go to camp? Tuesday
4. Write the day that comes next. Thursday, Friday, Saturday, Sunday

72 Use with Lesson 6-9.

6-10 Months of the Year

Lesson Organizer

Quick Lesson Overview 

Objective Identify and order the months of the year.

Math Understanding The months of the year, like the days of the week, appear in a specific order.

Vocabulary Year

Professional Development Note

Effective Questioning Techniques
To help children master the names and order of the months, each day display the year calendar and have children recite the names of the months in order. Ask questions similar to the following: **What are the first three months of the year? What month comes after January?**

NCTM Standards

- Measurement

(For a complete correlation to the NCTM Standards and Grades Pre-K through 2 Expectations, see Pages 203G and 203H.)

Getting Started

Spiral Review

Topics Reviewed

- Subtraction
- Problem-Solving Skill: One-Step Problem

Answer Juan has 8 toy planes; $11 - 3 = 8$ and $8 + 3 = 11$

Spiral Review and Test Prep 6-10

1. Add to find the sum.

   $8 + 3 =$ ____

   Ⓐ 9 Ⓑ 10 Ⓒ 11 Ⓓ 12

2. Which shape shows 8 equal parts?

   Ⓐ Ⓑ Ⓒ Ⓓ

3. Use the calendar to answer the question.

May						
Sunday	Monday	Tuesday	Wednesday	Thursday	Friday	Saturday
			1	2	3	4
5	6	7	8	9	10	11
12	13	14	15	16	17	18
19	20	21	22	23	24	25
26	27	28	29	30	31	

Write the day that comes next.

Friday, Saturday, Sunday, Monday

Use with Lesson 6-10. 73

Available as a transparency and as a blackline master

Topics Reviewed

1. Adding 1, 2, or 3
2. Equal Parts
3. Days of the Week

Investigating the Concept

Order the Months

10–15 MIN Visual/Spatial WHOLE CLASS

Materials 12 index cards each labeled with the name of a month; 12-Month Calendar (Teaching Tool 24)

What to Do

- Read each card, as you give one to each of 12 children. Invite children to place the cards on the board ledge. Arrange them in random order.
- Display the 12-month calendar. Explain that this calendar shows 12 months (one year). Recite the names of the months in order. Point out the number of days in each month.
- Then have children take turns moving only one card at a time until all of the cards are in the correct order.

Ongoing Assessment

- **Reasoning Which month comes before September?** *(August)*
- **Which is the month with the fewest days?** *(February)*

Reaching All Learners

Reading in Math

What Month Am I?

5–10 MIN **Auditory/Visual/Spatial**

Materials 12-Month Calendar (Teaching Tool 24)

- Have children use the 12-month calendar to help them answer riddles about the months, such as the following examples. **I am the first month of the year. What month am I? I begin with the letter *N*. What month am I? I rhyme with the word *say*. What month am I?**
- Invite children make up riddles to challenge their classmates. The child who correctly guesses the answer gets to be the next riddle-maker.

August
S M T W T F S
1 2 3 4
5 6 7 8 11
12 13 14 15 18
19 20 21 22 25
26 28

Access Content

English Language Learners

Reading a Calendar

10–15 MIN **Auditory/Linguistic**

Materials *(per pair)* 12-Month Calendar (Teaching Tool 24)

- Display a 12-month calendar. **These are the twelve months of the year.** Have children repeat the names of the months. Guide children to identify the current month, then the months containing 30 days, 28 days, and 31 days.
- Have each pair use their calendar to take turns following instructions like these: **Put an X on the month after February. Circle the month before November. Write your name on your birthday month.**

Reteaching

Fill in the Months

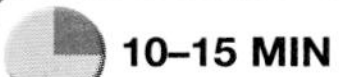

10–15 MIN **Visual/Spatial**

Materials *(per group)* 12-Month Calendar (Teaching Tool 24)

- Post a 12-month calendar at the front of the class and pass out copies of a partly filled-in 12-month calendar to each child.
- Ask children to fill in the remaining names of the months of the year on the copies.
- Have children compare their work to make sure they have written the months in the same order.
- Children can clear up any discrepancies by comparing their copies with the posted 12-month calendar.

Advanced Learners

Months Around the World

15–20 MIN **Linguistic**

Materials *(per group)* Computer with Internet access

- Ask children to find the names for the months of the year in a language other than English.
- Let children consult with the school librarian or an adult who can help them search the Internet for this information.
- Have children present their findings in charts that list the months in English and in the language they chose.
- Post the charts in the classroom for everyone to read.

English	español
January	enero
February	febrero
March	marzo

Objective Identify and order the months of the year.

1 Warm Up

Activate Prior Knowledge Review the current month's calendar with children. Have them name the month and recite the names of the days of the week in order. Then have children find the first day and the last day of the month.

2 Teach

Learn!

Look at the calendar at the top of the student page and explain that it shows 12 months (one year). Together recite the names of the months in order. Encourage children to name their birthday months, the summer months, the months they like best, and the months of their favorite holidays.

Ongoing Assessment

Talk About It

- **What is the greatest number of days that a month can have?** *(31)* **What is the least number of days?** *(28)*
- **Which month comes between April and June?** *(May)*

If children do not know where to look on the calendar to show *before* and *after* a month,

then color the current month, the one that comes before it, and the one that comes after it.

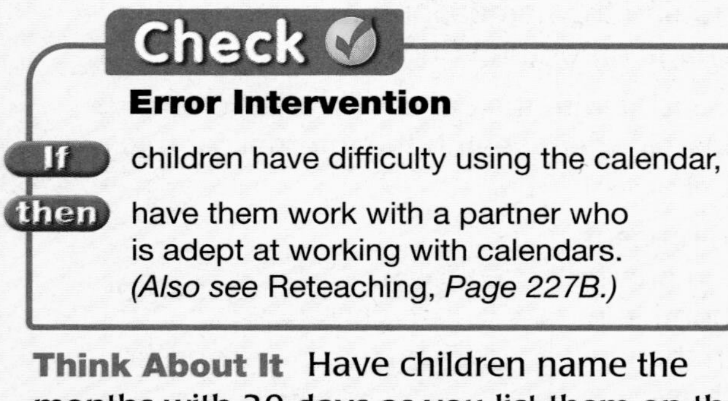

Check

Error Intervention

If children have difficulty using the calendar,

then have them work with a partner who is adept at working with calendars. *(Also see* Reteaching, *Page 227B.)*

Think About It Have children name the months with 30 days as you list them on the board. Repeat for the months with 31 days. Have them compare the lists to answer the question.

Name ______________________

Months of the Year

Learn!

There are 12 months in one **year**.

January

S	M	T	W	T	F	S
				1	2	3
4	5	6	7	8	9	10
11	12	13	14	15	16	17
18	19	20	21	22	23	24
25	26	27	28	29	30	31

February

S	M	T	W	T	F	S
1	2	3	4	5	6	7
8	9	10	11	12	13	14
15	16	17	18	19	20	21
22	23	24	25	26	27	28

March

S	M	T	W	T	F	S
1	2	3	4	5	6	7
8	9	10	11	12	13	14
15	16	17	18	19	20	21
22	23	24	25	26	27	28
29	30	31				

April

S	M	T	W	T	F	S
			1	2	3	4
5	6	7	8	9	10	11
12	13	14	15	16	17	18
19	20	21	22	23	24	25
26	27	28	29	30		

May

S	M	T	W	T	F	S
					1	2
3	4	5	6	7	8	9
10	11	12	13	14	15	16
17	18	19	20	21	22	23
24/31	25	26	27	28	29	30

June

S	M	T	W	T	F	S
	1	2	3	4	5	6
7	8	9	10	11	12	13
14	15	16	17	18	19	20
21	22	23	24	25	26	27
28	29	30				

July

S	M	T	W	T	F	S
			1	2	3	4
5	6	7	8	9	10	11
12	13	14	15	16	17	18
19	20	21	22	23	24	25
26	27	28	29	30	31	

August

S	M	T	W	T	F	S
						1
2	3	4	5	6	7	8
9	10	11	12	13	14	15
16	17	18	19	20	21	22
23/30	24/31	25	26	27	28	29

September

S	M	T	W	T	F	S
		1	2	3	4	5
6	7	8	9	10	11	12
13	14	15	16	17	18	19
20	21	22	23	24	25	26
27	28	29	30			

October

S	M	T	W	T	F	S
				1	2	3
4	5	6	7	8	9	10
11	12	13	14	15	16	17
18	19	20	21	22	23	24
25	26	27	28	29	30	31

November

S	M	T	W	T	F	S
1	2	3	4	5	6	7
8	9	10	11	12	13	14
15	16	17	18	19	20	21
22	23	24	25	26	27	28
29	30					

December

S	M	T	W	T	F	S
		1	2	3	4	5
6	7	8	9	10	11	12
13	14	15	16	17	18	19
20	21	22	23	24	25	26
27	28	29	30	31		

Word Bank

year

Check

Use the calendar above to answer the questions.

1. How many months are in one year? 12
2. Which month comes before May? April
3. Which month comes between January and March? February
4. How many months have 31 days? 7

Think About It Number Sense

Are there more months with 30 days or 31 days? There are more months with 31 days.

Reteaching Below Level

Months of the Year R 6-10

January is the first month of the year. February is the month before March. March is the third month. April is the month after March.

Use the calendar to answer the questions.

1. What are the names of the months?
   January, February, March, April, May, June, July, August, September, October, November, December
2. Count the months. How many months are in a year? 12
3. Which month is the first month of the year? January
4. Which month comes after May? June
5. Which month comes before September? August

Use with Lesson 6-10. 73

Practice On Level

Months of the Year P 6-10

1. Write the names of the missing months.
   January, February, March, April, May, June, July, August, September, October, November, December

Problem Solving *Number Sense*

You can show the date two ways.

April 19, 2004 or **4/19/04**

The 4 tells that April is the 4th month.

2. Draw lines to match the dates.

August 22, 2004 — 8/22/04

May 9, 2004 — 5/9/04

Use with Lesson 6-10. 73

Practice

January

S	M	T	W	T	F	S
		1	2	3	4	5
6	7	8	9	10	11	12
13	14	15	16	17	18	19
20	21	22	23	24	25	26
27	28	29	30	31		

February

S	M	T	W	T	F	S
					1	2
3	4	5	6	7	8	9
10	11	12	13	14	15	16
17	18	19	20	21	22	23
24	25	26	27	28		

March

S	M	T	W	T	F	S
					1	2
3	4	5	6	7	8	9
10	11	12	13	14	15	16
17	18	19	20	21	22	23
24/31	25	26	27	28	29	30

April

S	M	T	W	T	F	S
	1	2	3	4	5	6
7	8	9	10	11	12	13
14	15	16	17	18	19	20
21	22	23	24	25	26	27
28	29	30				

May

S	M	T	W	T	F	S
			1	2	3	4
5	6	7	8	9	10	11
12	13	14	15	16	17	18
19	20	21	22	23	24	25
26	27	28	29	30	31	

June

S	M	T	W	T	F	S
						1
2	3	4	5	6	7	8
9	10	11	12	13	14	15
16	17	18	19	20	21	22
23/30	24	25	26	27	28	29

July

S	M	T	W	T	F	S
	1	2	3	4	5	6
7	8	9	10	11	12	13
14	15	16	17	18	19	20
21	22	23	24	25	26	27
28	29	30	31			

August

S	M	T	W	T	F	S
				1	2	3
4	5	6	7	8	9	10
11	12	13	14	15	16	17
18	19	20	21	22	23	24
25	26	27	28	29	30	31

September

S	M	T	W	T	F	S
1	2	3	4	5	6	7
8	9	10	11	12	13	14
15	16	17	18	19	20	21
22	23	24	25	26	27	28
29	30					

October

S	M	T	W	T	F	S
		1	2	3	4	5
6	7	8	9	10	11	12
13	14	15	16	17	18	19
20	21	22	23	24	25	26
27	28	29	30	31		

November

S	M	T	W	T	F	S
					1	2
3	4	5	6	7	8	9
10	11	12	13	14	15	16
17	18	19	20	21	22	23
24	25	26	27	28	29	30

December

S	M	T	W	T	F	S
1	2	3	4	5	6	7
8	9	10	11	12	13	14
15	16	17	18	19	20	21
22	23	24	25	26	27	28
29	30	31				

5. Write the names of the missing months.
Then say the names of the months in order.

January, February, March, April,

May, June, July, August,

September, October, November, December

Problem Solving Number Sense

You can show the date two ways.

January 12, 2004 or **1/12/2004**

The 1 tells that January is the 1st month!

6. Draw lines to match the dates.

April 21, 2004 — 4/21/2004

June 20, 2004 — 6/20/2004

Home Connection Your child used a calendar to find and name the months. **Home Activity** Look at a one-year calendar and take turns saying the names of the months in order. Ask your child to name the 5th month and the 7th month. *(May; July)*

Enrichment Above Level

Mixed-Up Months E 6-10 PATTERNS

Write the months in order on the calendar.

January, February, March, April, May, June, July, August, September, October, November, December

March	August	October	June
April	December	July	February
November	May	January	September

1. Jeri's 8th birthday is on 5/14/2004. Write that date another way. May 14, 2004
2. It is September. Juan's birthday will be in two months. Which month is Juan's birthday in? November

Use with Lesson 6-10. 73

Problem Solving

Months of the Year PS 6-10

Use the calendar to answer the questions.

1. Mike's birthday is in the third month of the year. What month is that? March
2. The last month of the year is Karen's favorite month. What month is that? December
3. Kevin visits his Grandma the month after July. What month is that? August
4. Thanksgiving Day is in November. What month comes before November? October
5. What is another way to write each date? Draw a line to match the dates.
May 10, 2005 — 5/10/2005
September 3, 2005 — 9/3/2005

Use with Lesson 6-10. 73

3 Practice

Before children complete Exercise 6, show them two ways to write the date. Explain that the first number stands for the month, the second number stands for the day, and the third number is the year.

Leveled Practice

Below Level Work in pairs to complete the page.

On Level Complete all exercises as written.

Above Level Complete all exercises as written. Then practice naming the months in order.

Early Finishers Have children work in pairs. One partner takes a self-stick note and covers a month on the page while the other child looks away. The partner then tries to name the hidden month. Partners exchange roles and repeat.

4 Assess

Journal Idea Ask children to choose a month and write its name. Then ask them to draw a picture of something that usually happens, or something they usually do, in that month.

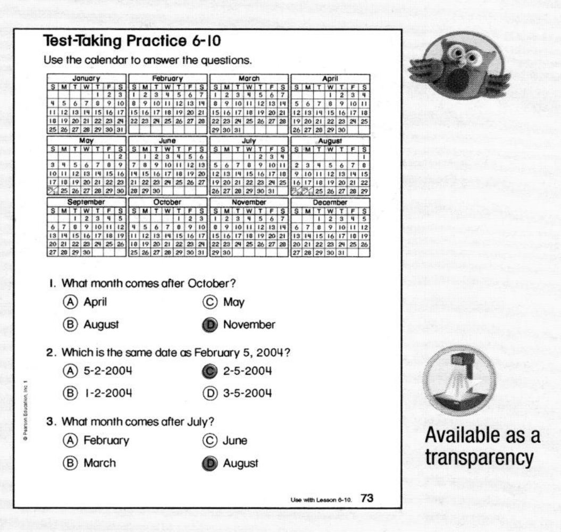

Test-Taking Practice 6-10

Use the calendar to answer the questions.

1. What month comes after October?
Ⓐ April Ⓒ May
Ⓑ August Ⓓ November
2. Which is the same date as February 5, 2004?
Ⓐ 5-2-2004 Ⓒ 2-5-2004
Ⓑ 1-2-2004 Ⓓ 3-5-2004
3. What month comes after July?
Ⓐ February Ⓒ June
Ⓑ March Ⓓ August

Use with Lesson 6-10. 73

Available as a transparency

What's Inside the Egg?

Lesson Organizer

Quick Lesson Overview

Objective Review and apply concepts, skills, and strategies learned in this and previous chapters.

Math Understanding Some real-world problems can be solved using known concepts, skills, and strategies.

Professional Development Note

Math Background Children apply what they know about telling time to solve new problems. If a child has difficulty solving a problem, determine if the child does not understand the concepts of time or does not understand the question posed in the problem. To help children better understand the content, read problems aloud to them.

NCTM Standards

- Number and Operations
- Measurement

(For a complete correlation to the NCTM Standards and Grades Pre-K through 2 Expectations, see Pages 203G and 203H.)

Getting Started

Spiral Review

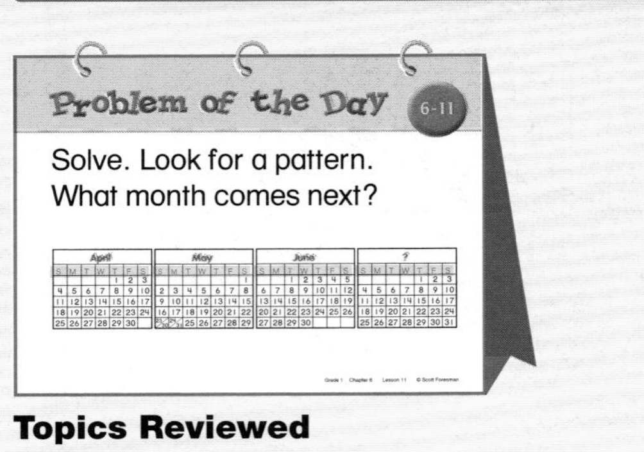
Problem of the Day
6-11
Solve. Look for a pattern.
What month comes next?
April
May
June
?

Topics Reviewed

- Months of the year
- Problem-Solving Strategy: Look for a Pattern

Answer July is the next month. It comes after June when the months are named in order.

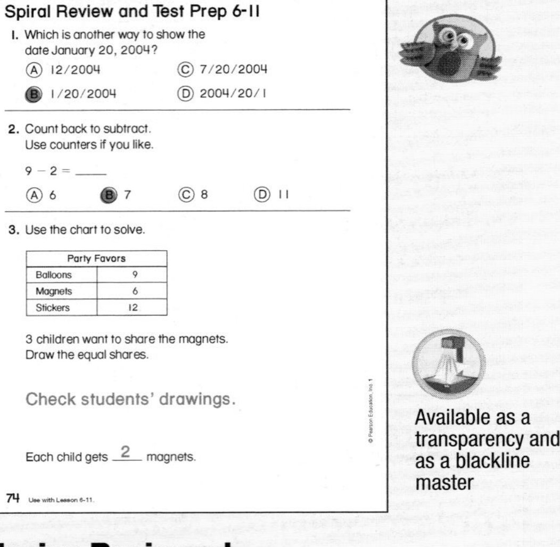

Spiral Review and Test Prep 6-11

1. Which is another way to show the date January 20, 2004?
   Ⓐ 12/2004 Ⓒ 7/20/2004
   Ⓑ 1/20/2004 Ⓓ 2004/20/1
2. Count back to subtract. Use counters if you like.
   9 − 2 = ____
   Ⓐ 6 Ⓑ 7 Ⓒ 8 Ⓓ 11
3. Use the chart to solve.

Party Favors	
Balloons	9
Magnets	6
Stickers	12

3 children want to share the magnets. Draw the equal shares.

Check students' drawings.

Each child gets 2 magnets.

74 Use with Lesson 6-11.

Available as a transparency and as a blackline master

Topics Reviewed

1. Months of the Year
2. Counting Back
3. Use Data from a Chart

Investigating the Concept

Reviewing Time

10–15 MIN **Logical/Mathematical/Kinesthetic** WHOLE CLASS

Materials *(per child)* Clock Face (Teaching Tool 22)

What to Do

- Ask children to listen as you tell the following story problem: **Ken started watching TV at 4:00 on Monday afternoon. He watched for 1 hour. At what time did Ken stop watching?**
- **What kind of problem is this?** *(A problem about time)*
- Retell the problem and have children use their clocks to act it out. Compare clocks and determine that Ken stopped watching TV at 5:00.
- Repeat, telling similar problems that children can solve by manipulating their clocks.

Ongoing Assessment

- **If Ken has a soccer game the next afternoon, on what day will his soccer game be played?** *(On Tuesday)*
- **Reasoning What word do we use to tell time on the hour? on the half hour?** *(O'clock; thirty)*

Reaching All Learners

Math and Literature

Story Time

10–15 MIN **Linguistic**

Materials Books that involve a time sequence

- Share books that show a sequence of events happening over a day or a week, such as *Biscuit* by Alyssa Satin Capucilli (1996 HarperCollins) or "The Garden" from *Frog and Toad Together* by Arnold Lobel (1972 HarperCollins).
- Read about Biscuit and his attempts to delay bed time.
- Have children suggest the time at which certain events might occur. **At what time does Biscuit have his snack?** *(6:30)* **At what time does Biscuit hear a story?** (*7:00*)

Activate Prior Knowledge/Build Background

English Language Learners

Concept Review

10–15 MIN **Linguistic**

- Give each group a problem that reviews a different concept. Examples: Group 1: **What do you do in the morning? afternoon?** Group 2: **What takes less than 1 minute to do? more than 1 minute?** Group 3: **Draw 2:30 on a clock. What is on your schedule at 2:30?** Group 4: **Name the days of the week. What day comes after Wednesday?** Group 5: **Name the months of the year. What month comes before May?**
- Groups can share answers with the rest of the class.

Reteaching

Real Time

10–15 MIN **Logical/Mathematical** SMALL GROUP

Materials Clock Face (Teaching Tool 22)

- Present real situations set at home and in the classroom for which children calculate time to the hour and to the half hour.
- Here is a suggestion for discussion: **You have to get to school at 9:00. The bus ride is 1 hour, what time do you have to leave home? Show it on the clock.**

Math and Science

Shadows and Time

10–15 MIN **Kinesthetic** WHOLE CLASS

- On a sunny day, let children discover how the shapes of their shadows change with the time of day.
- At morning, midday, and afternoon take children outside to observe the lengths of their shadows.
- Each time, have children write the time and draw pictures of themselves and their shadows.
- Children will discover that their shadows are long in the morning and afternoon, and short in the middle of the day.

Objective Review and apply concepts, skills, and strategies learned in this and previous chapters.

1 Warm Up

Activate Prior Knowledge Review telling time to the half hour. Use a clock and show children different times to the half hour. Have children take turns writing the digital time for each time shown.

2 Teach

Explain to children that they will use what they already know about telling time to solve the problems on the student page. Have children do Exercise 1 independently. Then read Exercise 2 aloud.

Ongoing Assessment

Talk About It

- **What do we need to do to solve Exercise 2?** *(Show 4:30 on both clocks.)*
- **What do we know?** *(We say* thirty *when the longer hand points to the 6.)*
- **How can we solve this problem?** *(Draw the minute hand to point at 6; draw the hour hand between 4 and 5; write 4 and 30.)*

If children do not know how to show time on an analog clock,

then review the positions of the hands for different times.

Error Intervention

If children do not write the same time on both clocks,

then have them tell the time on each clock. Then remind them that both should say 4:30. *(Also see* Reteaching, *Page 229B.)*

Name ______________________

PROBLEM-SOLVING APPLICATIONS
What's Inside the Egg?

Dorling Kindersley

Do You Know...
that a mother tortoise digs a hole and lays her eggs in the warm soil?

Fun Fact!
Caterpillars hatch from eggs and become butterflies.

1. Before this egg began to hatch, it looked like a table tennis ball. What shape was the egg?
   sphere

2. At 4:30 this baby tortoise began to bite the shell to make the hole bigger. Show 4:30 on both clocks.

3. The mother tortoise laid 12 eggs. 6 of the eggs have hatched. How many eggs have not hatched?
   12 − 6 = 6 eggs

Chapter 6 ★ Lesson 11 two hundred twenty-nine 229

Reteaching Below Level

PROBLEM-SOLVING APPLICATIONS R 6-11
What's Inside the Egg?

1. Jane uses a telescope to look at the birds. What shape is the telescope? cylinder
2. At 3 o'clock Jane sees a baby bird. Write the time on both clocks. 3:00
3. On Monday 1 bird egg hatches. The next day 2 bird eggs hatch. On what day do the 2 bird eggs hatch? Tuesday

Writing in Math

4. It is April. In 2 months Jane will get a pet bird for her birthday. In what month is Jane's birthday? June

74 Use with Lesson 6-11.

Practice On Level

PROBLEM-SOLVING APPLICATIONS P 6-11
What's Inside the Egg?

1. The zoo keeps baby tortoises in this tank. What shape is the tank? rectangular prism
2. Joan went to the zoo to see the baby tortoises. She left the zoo at 4:30. Show the time on both clocks. 4:30
3. Joan wanted to go to the zoo on Monday. Her mother took Joan the next day. On which day did Joan go to the zoo? Tuesday

Writing in Math

4. Joan visited the zoo in April. After 3 months, she will go back to see how much the baby tortoises have grown. Use a calendar to find which month she will return to the zoo. July

74 Use with Lesson 6-11.

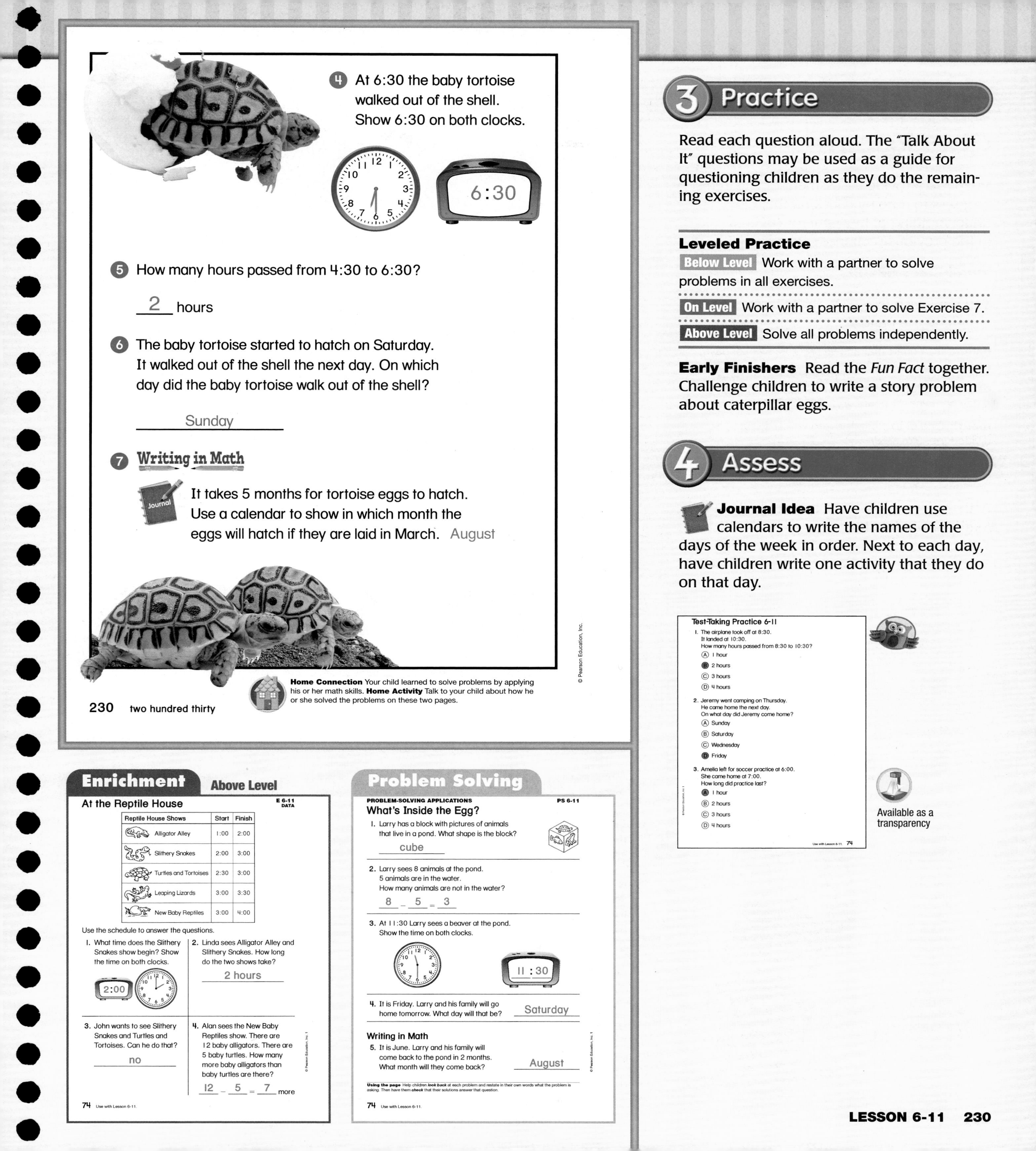

4. At 6:30 the baby tortoise walked out of the shell. Show 6:30 on both clocks.

6:30

5. How many hours passed from 4:30 to 6:30?

2 hours

6. The baby tortoise started to hatch on Saturday. It walked out of the shell the next day. On which day did the baby tortoise walk out of the shell?

Sunday

7. **Writing in Math**

It takes 5 months for tortoise eggs to hatch. Use a calendar to show in which month the eggs will hatch if they are laid in March. August

Home Connection Your child learned to solve problems by applying his or her math skills. **Home Activity** Talk to your child about how he or she solved the problems on these two pages.

3 Practice

Read each question aloud. The "Talk About It" questions may be used as a guide for questioning children as they do the remaining exercises.

Leveled Practice

Below Level Work with a partner to solve problems in all exercises.

On Level Work with a partner to solve Exercise 7.

Above Level Solve all problems independently.

Early Finishers Read the *Fun Fact* together. Challenge children to write a story problem about caterpillar eggs.

4 Assess

Journal Idea Have children use calendars to write the names of the days of the week in order. Next to each day, have children write one activity that they do on that day.

Test-Taking Practice 6-11

1. The airplane took off at 8:30. It landed at 10:30. How many hours passed from 8:30 to 10:30?
   - Ⓐ 1 hour
   - Ⓑ 2 hours
   - Ⓒ 3 hours
   - Ⓓ 4 hours
2. Jeremy went camping on Thursday. He came home the next day. On what day did Jeremy come home?
   - Ⓐ Sunday
   - Ⓑ Saturday
   - Ⓒ Wednesday
   - Ⓓ Friday
3. Amelia left for soccer practice at 6:00. She came home at 7:00. How long did practice last?
   - Ⓐ 1 hour
   - Ⓑ 2 hours
   - Ⓒ 3 hours
   - Ⓓ 4 hours

Use with Lesson 6-11. 74

Available as a transparency

Enrichment Above Level

At the Reptile House E 6-11 DATA

Reptile House Shows	Start	Finish
Alligator Alley	1:00	2:00
Slithery Snakes	2:00	3:00
Turtles and Tortoises	2:30	3:00
Leaping Lizards	3:00	3:30
New Baby Reptiles	3:00	4:00

Use the schedule to answer the questions.

1. What time does the Slithery Snakes show begin? Show the time on both clocks. 2:00
2. Linda sees Alligator Alley and Slithery Snakes. How long do the two shows take? 2 hours
3. John wants to see Slithery Snakes and Turtles and Tortoises. Can he do that? no
4. Alan sees the New Baby Reptiles show. There are 12 baby alligators. There are 5 baby turtles. How many more baby alligators than baby turtles are there? 12 − 5 = 7 more

74 Use with Lesson 6-11.

Problem Solving

PROBLEM-SOLVING APPLICATIONS PS 6-11

What's Inside the Egg?

1. Larry has a block with pictures of animals that live in a pond. What shape is the block? cube
2. Larry sees 8 animals at the pond. 5 animals are in the water. How many animals are not in the water? 8 − 5 = 3
3. At 11:30 Larry sees a beaver at the pond. Show the time on both clocks. 11:30
4. It is Friday. Larry and his family will go home tomorrow. What day will that be? Saturday

Writing in Math

5. It is June. Larry and his family will come back to the pond in 2 months. What month will they come back? August

Using the page Help children *look back* at each problem and restate in their own words what the problem is asking. Then have them *check* that their solutions answer that question.

74 Use with Lesson 6-11.

Diagnostic Checkpoint

Purpose Provide assessment of children's progress to date by checking their understanding of key content covered in the previous section.

Vocabulary Review

You may wish to review these terms before assigning the page:

calendar A chart that shows months, weeks, days, and dates *(pp. 225–226)*

day The period of time from midnight to midnight; a day contains 24 hours. *(pp. 225–226)*

month One of the 12 parts into which the year is divided *(pp. 225–226)*

year A period of 365 or 366 days divided into 12 months *(pp. 227–228)*

Activities for this section are available in the Math Vocabulary Kit.

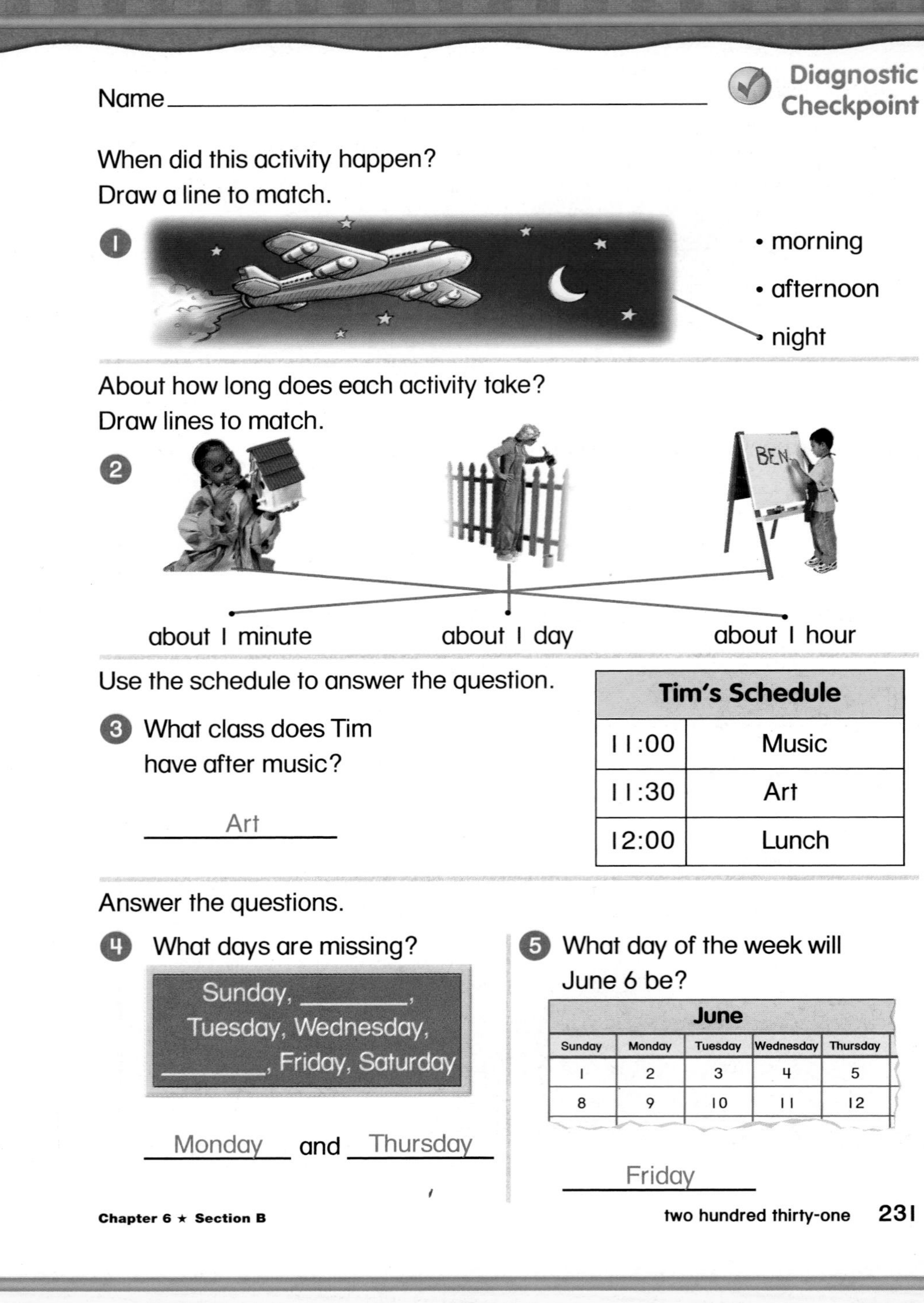

Name ____________________

Diagnostic Checkpoint

When did this activity happen?
Draw a line to match.

1 • morning • afternoon • night

About how long does each activity take?
Draw lines to match.

2 about 1 minute about 1 day about 1 hour

Use the schedule to answer the question.

3 What class does Tim have after music?

Art

Tim's Schedule	
11:00	Music
11:30	Art
12:00	Lunch

Answer the questions.

4 What days are missing?

Sunday, ________, Tuesday, Wednesday, ________, Friday, Saturday

Monday and Thursday

5 What day of the week will June 6 be?

June				
Sunday	Monday	Tuesday	Wednesday	Thursday
1	2	3	4	5
8	9	10	11	12

Friday

Chapter 6 ★ Section B   two hundred thirty-one 231

Item Analysis for Diagnosis and Intervention

Objective	Items	Student Book Pages*	Intervention System
Determine whether an event takes place in the morning, afternoon, or night.	1	219–220	D7
Compare and estimate the length of time it takes for each of three activities.	2	221–222	D7
Solve problems by reading and using the information in a schedule.	3	223–224	E1
Read and use a calendar to name the days of the week.	4–5	225–226	D8

*For each lesson, there is a *Reteaching* activity in *Reaching All Learners* and a *Reteaching* master.

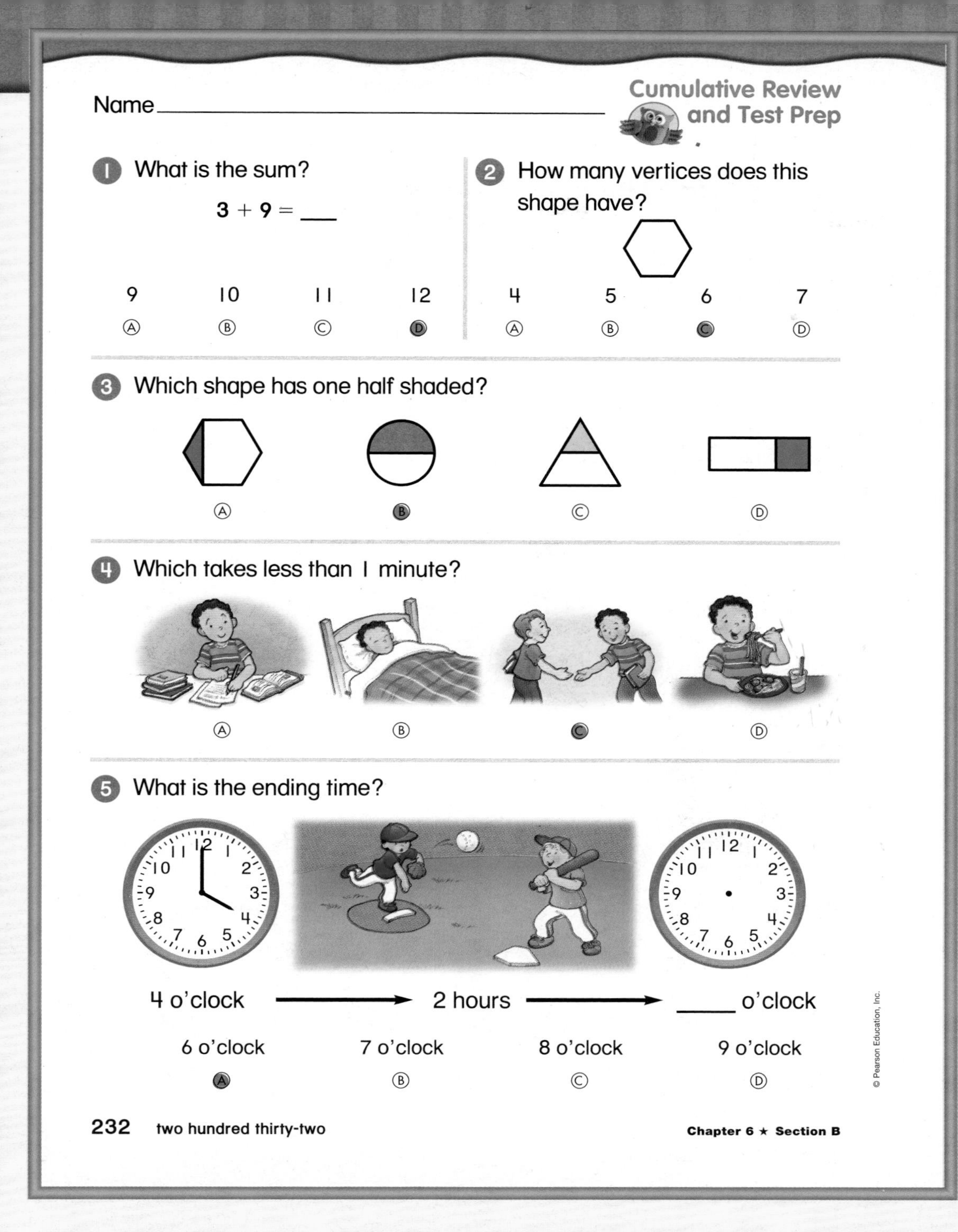

Name
Cumulative Review and Test Prep
1 What is the sum?
3 + 9 = ___
9 10 11 12
2 How many vertices does this shape have?
4 5 6 7
3 Which shape has one half shaded?
4 Which takes less than 1 minute?
5 What is the ending time?
4 o'clock
2 hours
___ o'clock
6 o'clock
7 o'clock
8 o'clock
9 o'clock
© Pearson Education, Inc.
232 two hundred thirty-two
Chapter 6 ★ Section B

Item Analysis for Diagnosis and Intervention

Objective	Items	Student Book Pages*	Intervention System
Count on 1, 2, or 3 to add, starting with the greater number.	1	95–96	B19
Sort plane shapes and identify their properties.	2	167–168	D49, D50
Identify and show halves of a region.	3	183–184	A60
Determine if events take more or less than 1 minute.	4	205–206	D3
Solve problems by acting out given situations.	5	215–216	E30

*For each lesson, there is a *Reteaching* activity in *Reaching All Learners* and a *Reteaching* master.

Cumulative Review and Test Prep

Purpose Provide children with a review of math concepts. Items appear as they would on a standardized test so children become familiar with that format.

Enrichment

Purpose Provide children with related mathematical topics and applications beyond the basic chapter content.

Using Student Page 233

Remind children that they have already learned how to tell time to the hour and half hour. Say that on this page, they will make decisions about the *elapsed time* for some activities.

Before having children work through the page, you may want to use Clock Faces (Teaching Tool 22) to review how to draw hands on a clock to show the time. Tell children to pretend that they began eating dinner at 6:00 and to show this time by drawing the hands on a clock. Ask if they think that eating dinner might last about an hour or a half hour. Have children show dinner's ending time on a second clock. Repeat the process several times for other activities, such as playing a game or having art class. Encourage children to note patterns in the clocks for the starting and finishing times for different activities. For example, if the activity lasts an hour, the minute hand has moved completely around the clock and is in the same position for the starting and ending times. If the activity lasts half an hour, the minute hand moves halfway around the clock.

When children are comfortable with the process, read the directions on the page and make sure children understand how to complete the exercises.

When drawing the hands on the clock to show the ending time, children should focus on two things: the activity's starting time and its predicted duration. Have children review how the hour and minute hands look when the clock shows times to the hour and when it shows times to the half hour.

Name ______________________________

Learning with Technology

Create a Schedule Using a Computer

You can use a computer to show the times that you start your after-school activities.

1. Make a list of 5 things you do after school. Write the activities in order on a separate sheet of paper.
2. On a computer, go to the Time eTool.
3. Choose a start time for your first activity by setting the hands of the clock.
4. Check the digital clock to make sure that it shows the time you want your first activity to start. Write this time next to the first activity on your sheet of paper.
5. Repeat Steps 3 and 4 for your other after-school activities.

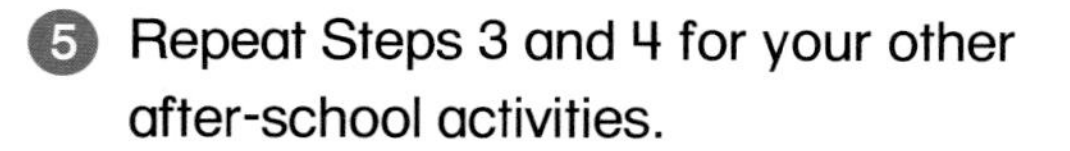

Think About It Reasoning

On which activity do you spend the greatest amount of time? On which activity do you spend the least amount of time?

Answers will vary.

Home Connection Your child used a computer to show the starting times of different after-school activities and created a schedule for those activities. **Home Activity** Ask your child questions about his or her weekday and weekend schedules.

Learning with Technology

Purpose Use a computer program to show time.

Using Student Page 234

You will need the Time eTool to do this activity.

Give children ideas to use for their after-school activities. Once they have their activities ordered on a sheet of paper, demonstrate the features of the Time eTool on your computer. Tell children what time you do your first after-school activity, and have them describe where you should put the hands on the clock.

Once children are settled at their computers, allow them to practice moving the hands on the clock. Before the activity begins, remind children to write down the time on the digital clock once they have set the hands on the analog clock. You may also have them draw the analog clock from the screen for each activity.

Think About It Help children determine how long each activity lasts. Help them understand that the time that their second activity begins is the time that their first activity ends. You may wish to have them draw analog clocks for each activity, and use the clocks to determine the number of minutes they spent on each activity. Children can use the elapsed time field and the digital clock on their computers to check their work.

Test Talk

Purpose Teach children a particular test-taking strategy and help them become more comfortable with the language and format used on standardized tests

Using Student Page 235

This page is designed to give children practice in understanding test questions.

Children often have difficulty on standardized tests not because they haven't been introduced to the concept or skill being tested, but because they fail to understand what they are being asked to do or how they are being asked to do it. This page can help with both the what and the how.

Discuss the question in Exercise 1. Ask for volunteers to restate the question in their own words, and in statement form: "I think this question means ..." Then ask children how they would get information from the table to answer the question. *(Sample answer: I would find the column with Time at the top. Then I would read down that column to find a time before 1:30. Then I would read across that row to find the name of the activity that started at 1:00.)* Then discuss why *Beanbag Toss* is the correct answer.

Have children complete Exercise 2 independently. When they have finished, ask children to explain how they used the table to answer the question. *(Sample answer: I found the column with Activity at the top. Then I read down that column until I found the Cake Sale. Then I read across that row to find out what time the Cake Sale started.)* Then discuss why 2:00 is the correct answer.

Name ____________________

Chapter 6 Test Talk

Read Together

Get Information for the Answer

You can get information from a table to help you solve math problems.

Test-Taking Strategies
- Understand the Question
- **Get Information for the Answer**
- Plan How to Find the Answer
- Make Smart Choices
- Use Writing in Math

1. Which activity will Megan miss if she comes to the fair at 1:30?
   - Ⓐ Beanbag Toss
   - Ⓑ Face Painting
   - Ⓒ Cake Sale
   - Ⓓ Musical Chairs

School Fun Fair	
Activity	**Time**
Beanbag Toss	1:00
Face Painting	1:30
Cake Sale	2:00
Musical Chairs	2:30

Find the activity that starts before 1:30. Fill in the answer bubble.

Your Turn

Use the table to solve this problem. Fill in the answer bubble.

2. At what time should Frank come to the fair if he does not want to miss anything?
   - Ⓐ 1:00
   - Ⓑ 1:30
   - Ⓒ 2:00
   - Ⓓ 2:30

Home Connection Your child prepared for standardized tests by using information from a table to solve math problems. **Home Activity** Ask your child to explain how he or she used the table to solve the problem in Exercise 2.

Test-Taking Strategies

Understand the Question
- Look for important words.
- Turn the question into a statement: "I need to find out ..."

Get Information for the Answer
- Get information from text.
- Get information from pictures, maps, diagrams, tables, graphs.

Plan How to Find the Answer
- Think about problem-solving skills and strategies.
- Choose computation methods.

Make Smart Choices
- Eliminate wrong answers.
- Try working backward from an answer.
- Check answers for reasonableness; estimate.

Use Writing in Math
- Make your answer brief but complete.
- Use words from the problem and use math terms accurately.
- Describe the steps in order.
- Draw pictures to explain your thinking.

Name ____________________

Discover Math in Your World

DISCOVERY CHANNEL SCHOOL

Read Together

Time for Math!

Do you know at what time you wake up, have breakfast, and go to school? Do you know at what time you get home from school?

Right now it's time to do some math!

What Time Is It?

1. Carlos wakes up at 7:00 each morning. He arrives at school 1 hour later. At what time does Carlos get to school?

   8:00

2. At school, lunch begins at noon. It is now 10:00. In how many hours will lunch begin?

   2 hours

3. Jennifer gets home from school at the time shown on the clock. She will play for 1 hour. At what time will she finish playing?

   4:30

Take It to the NET
Video and Activities
www.scottforesman.com

Home Connection Your child solved problems about daily activities by telling time on analog (dial) and digital clocks. **Home Activity** Ask your child to tell at what time three daily activities begin or end, using both analog and digital clocks.

Discover Math in Your World

Purpose Help children connect math content to everyday applications.

Using Student Page 236

This page is designed to help children relate telling time to everyday activities and to find the elapsed time for some of those activities.

To introduce children to this activity, use a clock with moveable hands to model elapsed time. Set the clock at 1:00, and have children move the hands to show the passage of 2 hours, watching what happens to the minute hand and the hour hand. Then, with the clock still set at 3:00, tell children to imagine that they will eat dinner at 5:00. Help them figure out in how many hours dinner will begin by moving the clock's hands. *(2 hours)*

Read through the introductory information on the page and discuss with children the times that they do certain activities each day. Since the questions ask children to give either a time or a number of hours as answers, children may become confused. If so, have them circle the important word *(time* or *hour)* in the question before answering it. Then read through each problem and ask for volunteers to give the answers. If children need extra help, have them use a clock with moveable hands.

Take It to the NET
Video and Activities
www.scottforesman.com

The video includes pre-viewing and post-viewing questions. A Discovery Channel Blackline Master is also provided.

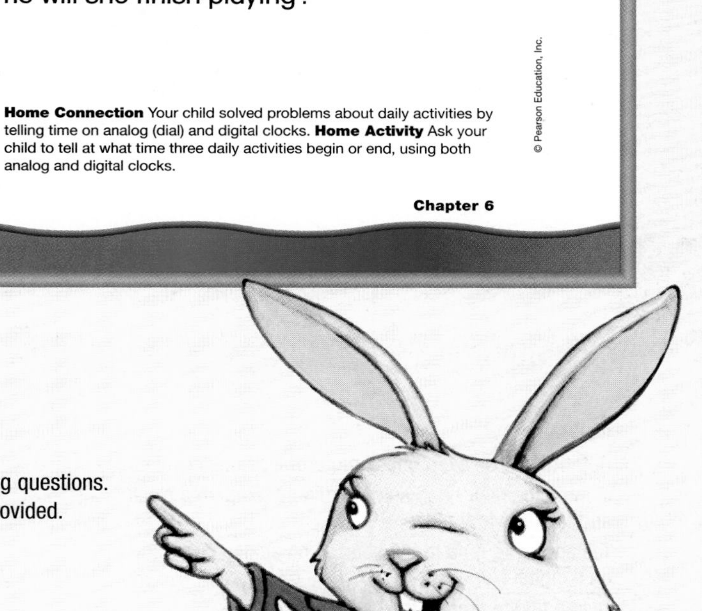

Chapter Test

Purpose Assess children's progress by checking their understanding of the concepts and skills covered in Chapter 6. Use as a review, practice test, or chapter test.

MindPoint Quiz Show CD-ROM Use *MindPoint Quiz Show* for additional practice on Chapter 6.

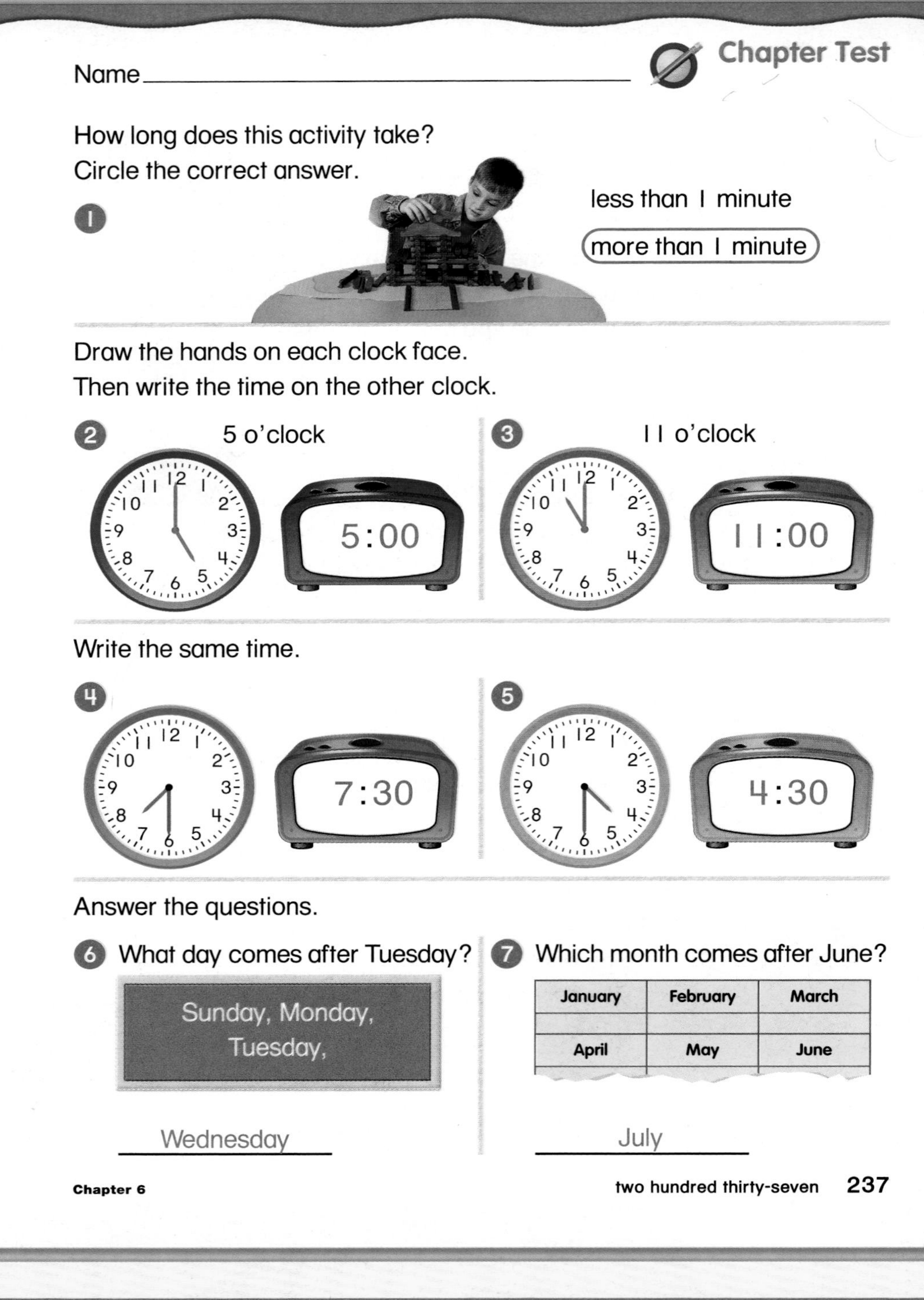

Name ____________________

Chapter Test

How long does this activity take?
Circle the correct answer.

1

less than 1 minute

more than 1 minute

Draw the hands on each clock face.
Then write the time on the other clock.

2 5 o'clock

5:00

3 11 o'clock

11:00

Write the same time.

4 7:30

5 4:30

Answer the questions.

6 What day comes after Tuesday?

Sunday, Monday, Tuesday,

Wednesday

7 Which month comes after June?

January	February	March
April	May	June

July

Chapter 6

two hundred thirty-seven 237

Item Analysis for Diagnosis and Intervention

Objective	Items	Student Book Pages*	Intervention System
Determine if an event takes more or less than 1 minute.	1	205–206	D3
Identify the hour hand and the minute hand on a clock and tell time to the hour.	2–3	207–208	D4
Tell and write time to the hour on an analog clock and on a digital clock.	2–3	209–210	D5
Tell and write time to the half hour.	4–5	211–212	D6
Read and use a calendar to name the days of the week.	6	225–226	D8
Identify and order the months of the year.	7	227–228	D8

*For each lesson, there is a *Reteaching* activity in *Reaching All Learners* and a *Reteaching* master.

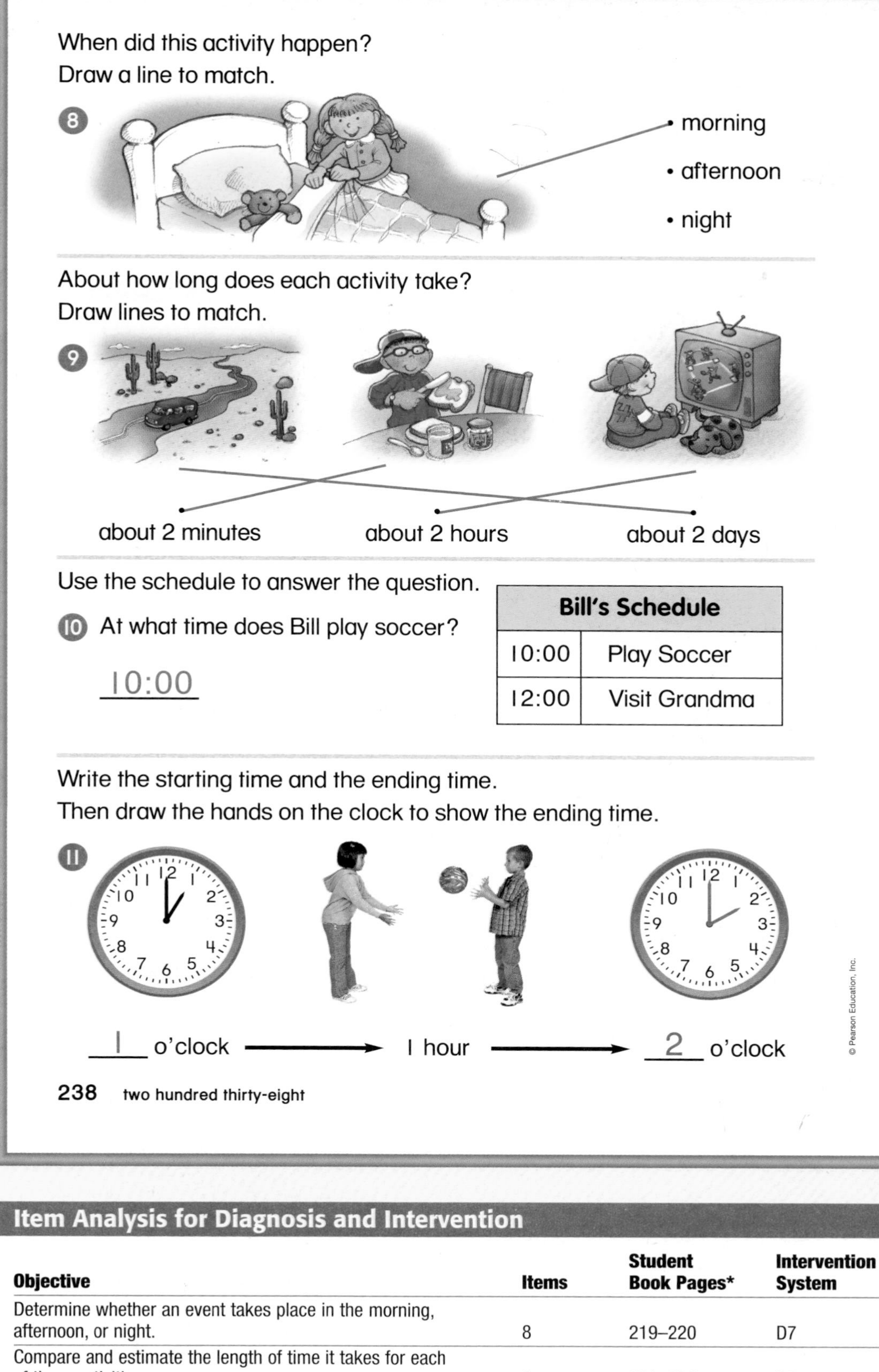

When did this activity happen?
Draw a line to match.

8
• morning
• afternoon
• night

About how long does each activity take?
Draw lines to match.

9
about 2 minutes
about 2 hours
about 2 days

Use the schedule to answer the question.

10 At what time does Bill play soccer?

10:00

Bill's Schedule	
10:00	Play Soccer
12:00	Visit Grandma

Write the starting time and the ending time.
Then draw the hands on the clock to show the ending time.

11

1 o'clock → 1 hour → 2 o'clock

Item Analysis for Diagnosis and Intervention

Objective	Items	Student Book Pages*	Intervention System
Determine whether an event takes place in the morning, afternoon, or night.	8	219–220	D7
Compare and estimate the length of time it takes for each of three activities.	9	221–222	D7
Solve problems by reading and using the information in a schedule.	10	223–224	E1
Solve a problems by acting out a given situation.	11	215–216	E30

*For each lesson, there is a *Reteaching* activity in *Reaching All Learners* and a *Reteaching* master.

Assessment Sourcebook

These additional assessment options may be found in the *Assessment Sourcebook:*

- Chapter 6 Free-Response Test (Forms A and B)
- Chapter 6 Multiple-Choice Test (Forms C and D)
- Chapter 6 Performance Assessment
- Chapters 1–6 Cumulative Test

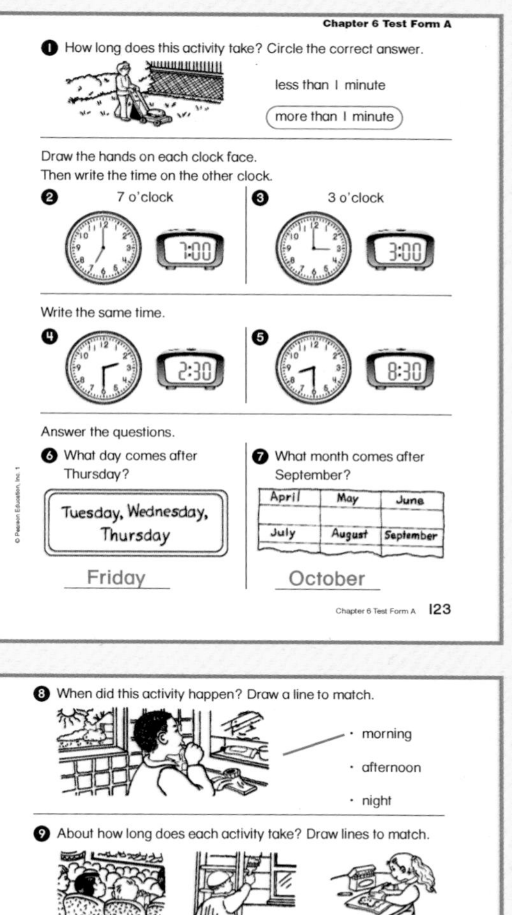

Chapter 6 Test Form A

1 How long does this activity take? Circle the correct answer.

less than 1 minute
more than 1 minute

Draw the hands on each clock face.
Then write the time on the other clock.

2 7 o'clock 7:00
3 3 o'clock 3:00

Write the same time.

4 2:30
5 8:30

Answer the questions.

6 What day comes after Thursday?
Tuesday, Wednesday, Thursday
Friday

7 What month comes after September?

April	May	June
July	August	September

October

Chapter 6 Test Form A 123

8 When did this activity happen? Draw a line to match.
• morning
• afternoon
• night

9 About how long does each activity take? Draw lines to match.
about 2 minutes
about 2 hours
about 2 days

10 Use the schedule to answer the question.
At what time does Sue go to see Aunt Leona?
6:00

Sue's Schedule	
4:00	Dance Class
6:00	Visit Aunt Leona

11 Write the starting time and the ending time.
Then draw the hands on the clock to show the ending time.

3 o'clock → 1 hour → 4 o'clock

124 Chapter 6 Test Form A

Cumulative Review and Test Prep

Purpose Provide children with a review of math concepts. Items on page 238A appear as they would on a standardized test so children become familiar with that format.

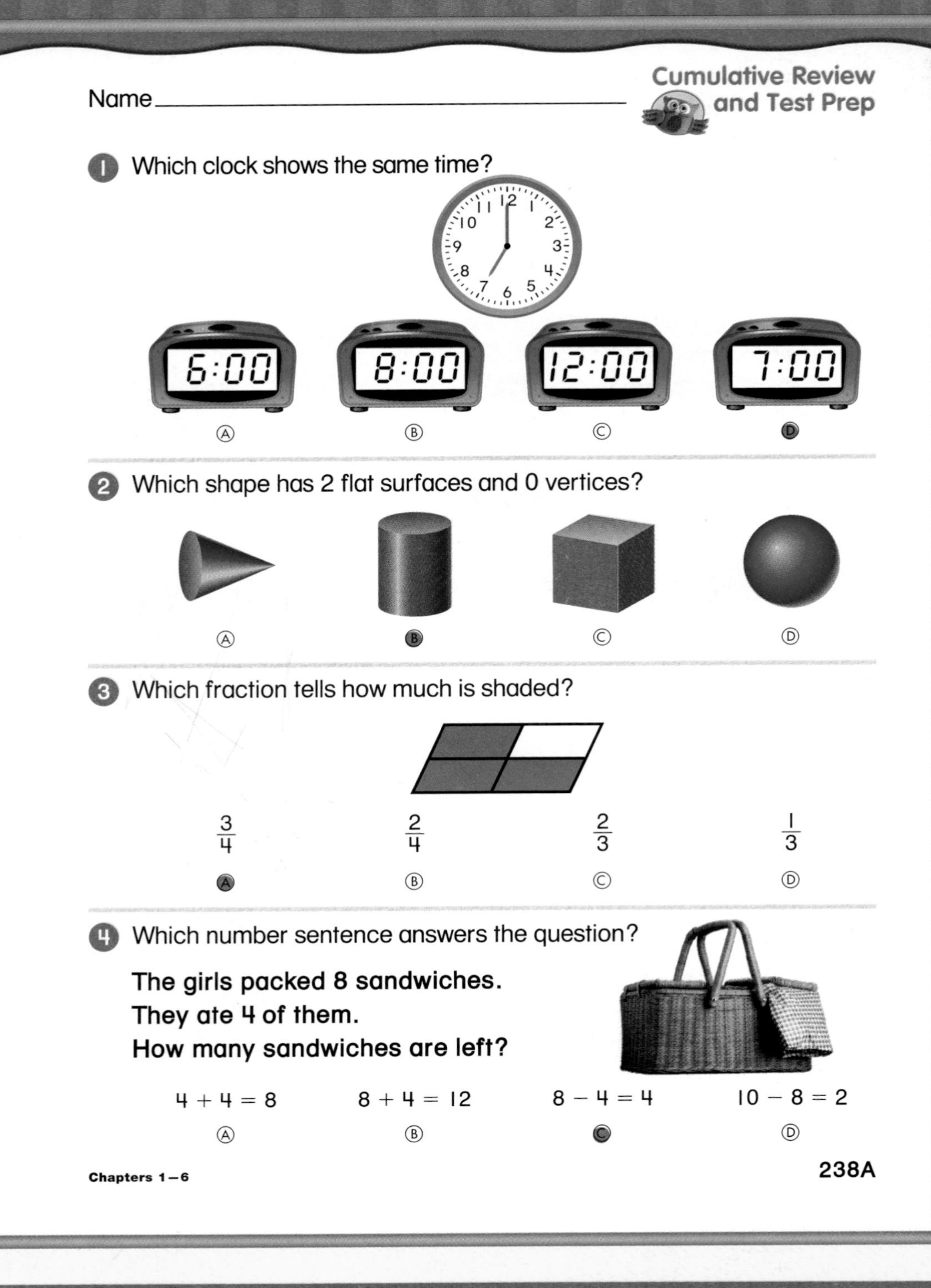

Name ______________________

Cumulative Review and Test Prep

1. Which clock shows the same time?

6:00 Ⓐ 8:00 Ⓑ 12:00 Ⓒ 7:00 Ⓓ

2. Which shape has 2 flat surfaces and 0 vertices?

Ⓐ Ⓑ Ⓒ Ⓓ

3. Which fraction tells how much is shaded?

$\frac{3}{4}$ Ⓐ $\frac{2}{4}$ Ⓑ $\frac{2}{3}$ Ⓒ $\frac{1}{3}$ Ⓓ

4. Which number sentence answers the question?

The girls packed 8 sandwiches.
They ate 4 of them.
How many sandwiches are left?

$4 + 4 = 8$ Ⓐ $8 + 4 = 12$ Ⓑ $8 - 4 = 4$ Ⓒ $10 - 8 = 2$ Ⓓ

Chapters 1–6 238A

Item Analysis for Diagnosis and Intervention

Objective	Review Items	Student Book Pages*	Intervention System
Tell and write time to the hour on an analog clock and on a digital clock.	1	209–210	D5
Count the number of flat surfaces and vertices on geometric solids.	2	159–160	D46
Identify and show non-unit fractions of a region or set.	3	189–190	A62
Solve problems by choosing addition or subtraction.	4	143–144	E4

*For each lesson, there is a *Reteaching* activity in *Reaching All Learners* and a *Reteaching* master.

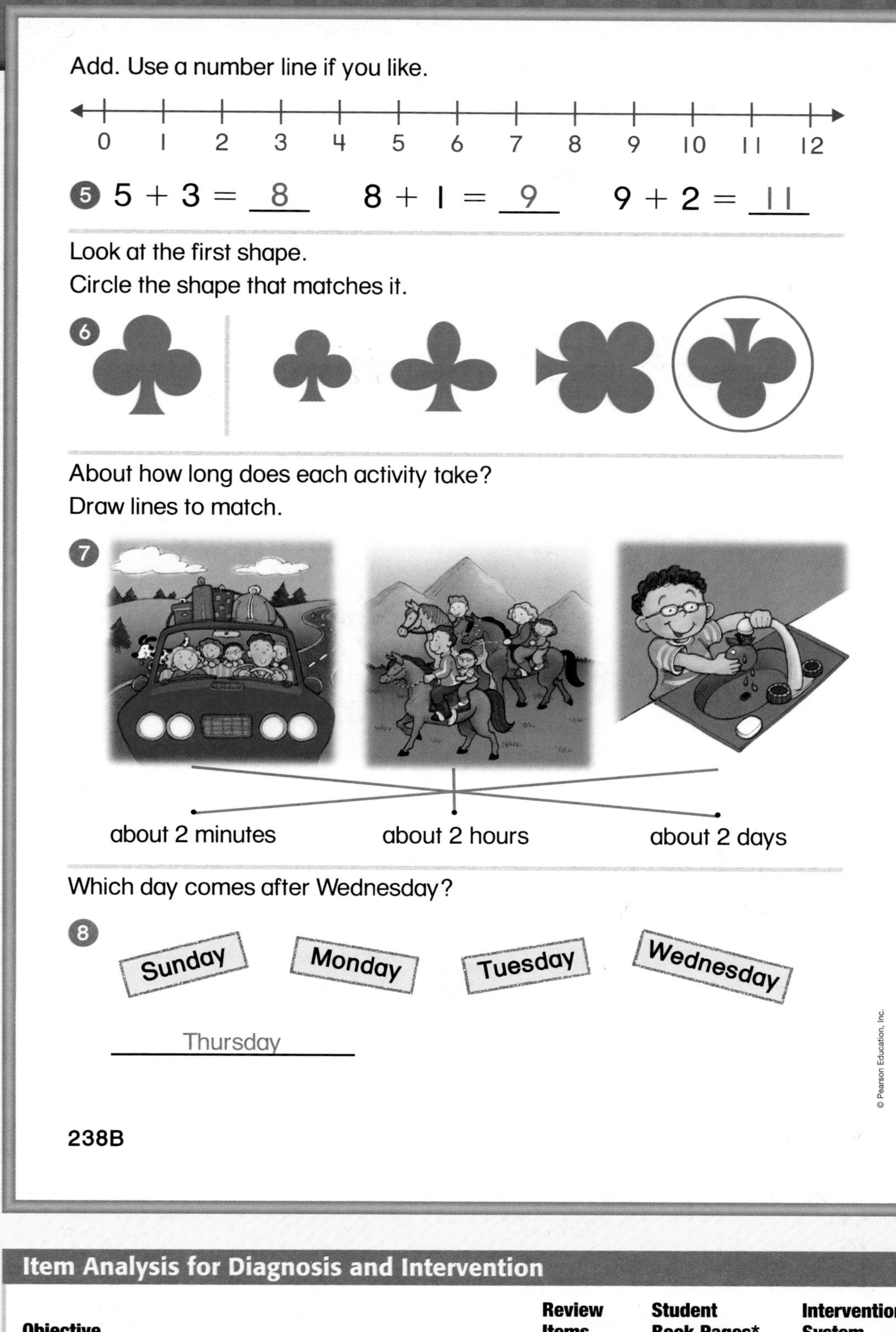

Add. Use a number line if you like.
0 1 2 3 4 5 6 7 8 9 10 11 12
5 5 + 3 = 8 8 + 1 = 9 9 + 2 = 11
Look at the first shape.
Circle the shape that matches it.
6
About how long does each activity take?
Draw lines to match.
7
about 2 minutes
about 2 hours
about 2 days
Which day comes after Wednesday?
8
Sunday
Monday
Tuesday
Wednesday
Thursday
© Pearson Education, Inc.
238B

Item Analysis for Diagnosis and Intervention

Objective	Review Items	Student Book Pages*	Intervention System
Use a number line to count on 1, 2, or 3.	5	97–98	B20
Identify and create figures that are the same size and the same shape.	6	169–170	D51
Compare and estimate the length of time it takes for each of three activities.	7	221–222	D7
Read and use a calendar to name the days of the week.	8	225–226	D8

*For each lesson, there is a *Reteaching* activity in *Reaching All Learners* and a *Reteaching* master.

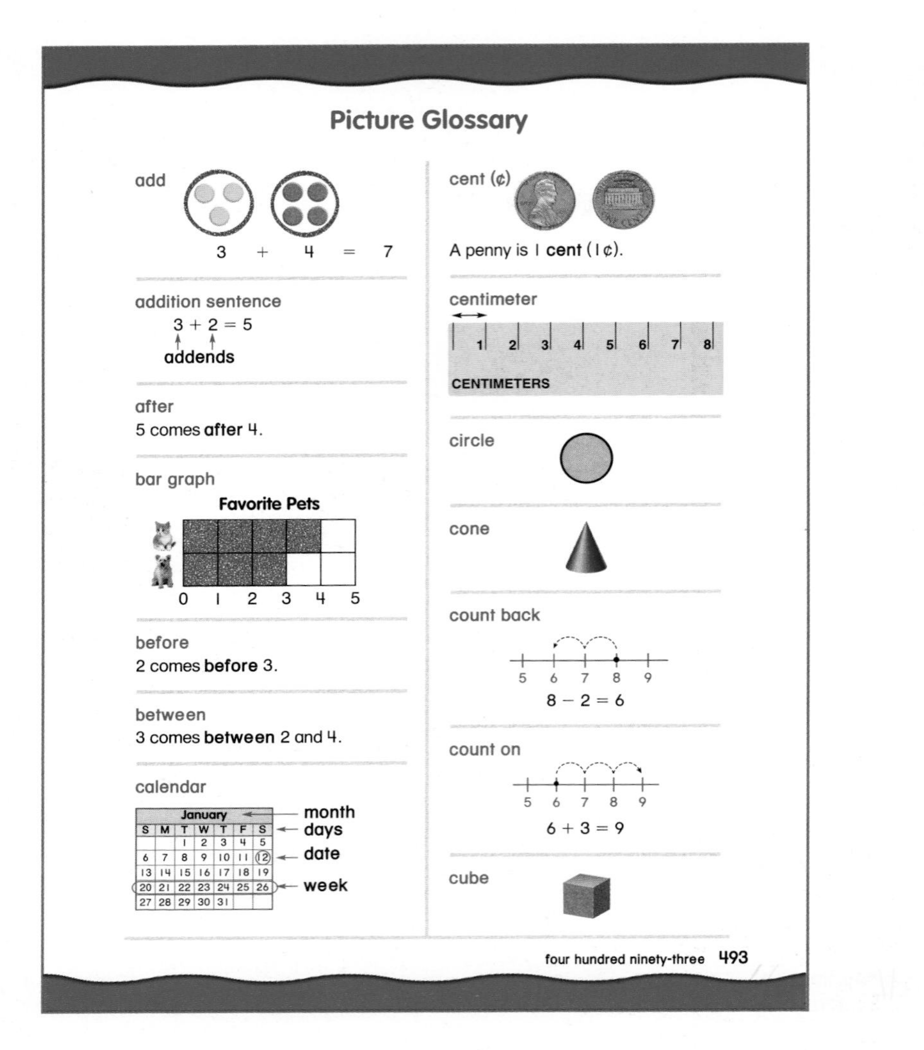

Picture Glossary

add

3 + 4 = 7

addition sentence

3 + 2 = 5

addends

after

5 comes **after** 4.

bar graph

before

2 comes **before** 3.

between

3 comes **between** 2 and 4.

calendar

cent (¢)

A penny is 1 **cent** (1¢).

centimeter

circle

cone

count back

8 − 2 = 6

count on

6 + 3 = 9

cube

four hundred ninety-three 493

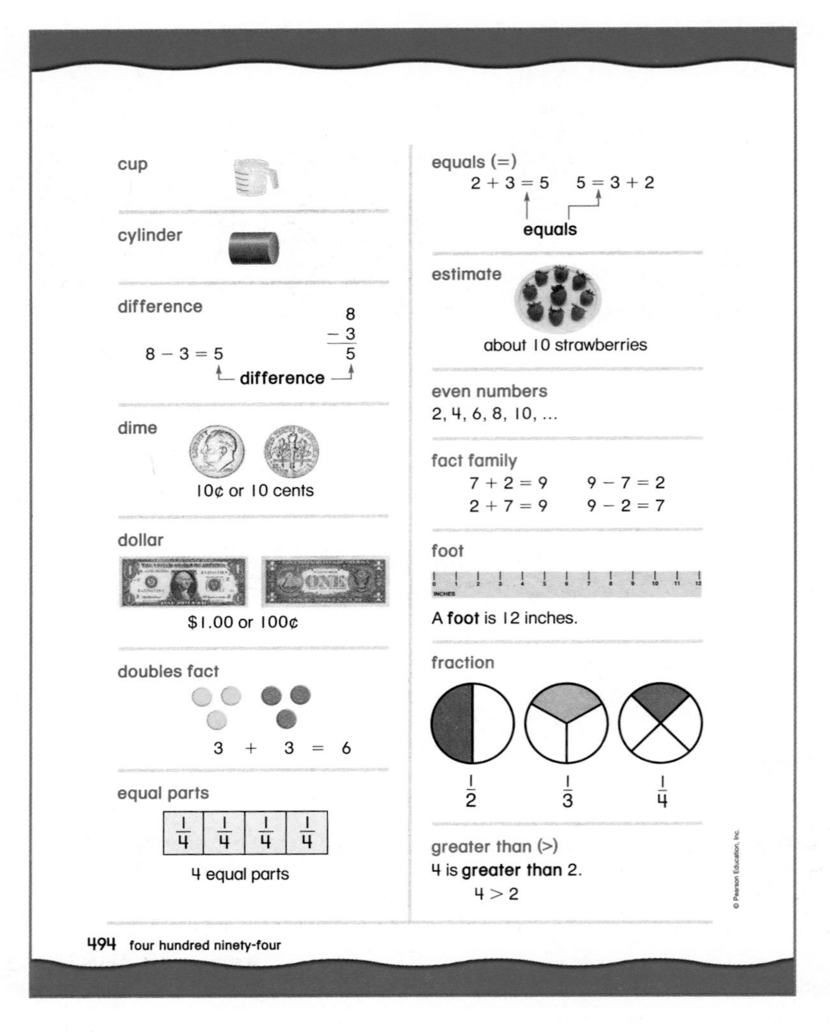

cup

cylinder

difference

8 − 3 = 5

8
− 3
5

difference

dime

10¢ or 10 cents

dollar

$1.00 or 100¢

doubles fact

3 + 3 = 6

equal parts

1/4	1/4	1/4	1/4

4 equal parts

equals (=)

2 + 3 = 5   5 = 3 + 2

equals

estimate

about 10 strawberries

even numbers

2, 4, 6, 8, 10, ...

fact family

7 + 2 = 9   9 − 7 = 2
2 + 7 = 9   9 − 2 = 7

foot

A **foot** is 12 inches.

fraction

$\frac{1}{2}$ $\frac{1}{3}$ $\frac{1}{4}$

greater than (>)

4 is **greater than** 2.

4 > 2

© Pearson Education, Inc.

494 four hundred ninety-four

 EC NTL 12 11 10 9 8 7 6 5

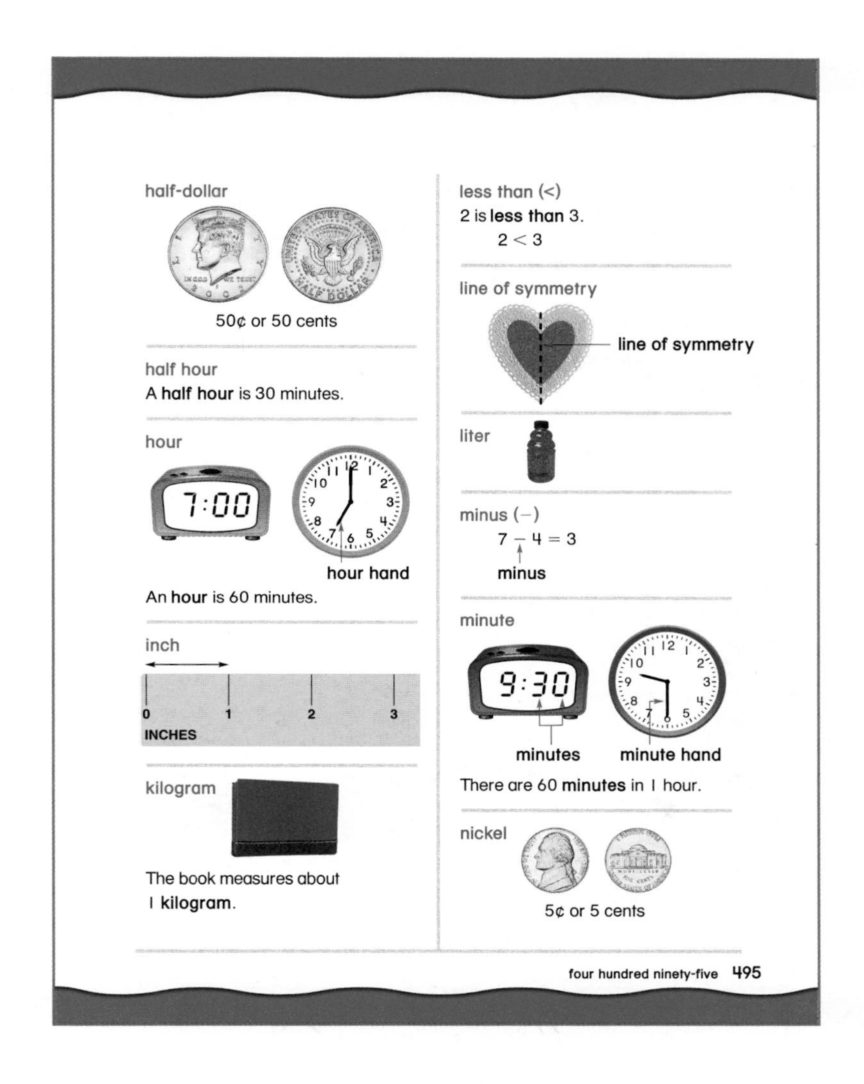

half-dollar

50¢ or 50 cents

half hour

A **half hour** is 30 minutes.

hour

An **hour** is 60 minutes.

inch

kilogram

The book measures about 1 **kilogram**.

less than (<)

2 is **less than** 3.

$2 < 3$

line of symmetry

liter

minus (−)

$7 - 4 = 3$

minute

There are 60 **minutes** in 1 hour.

nickel

5¢ or 5 cents

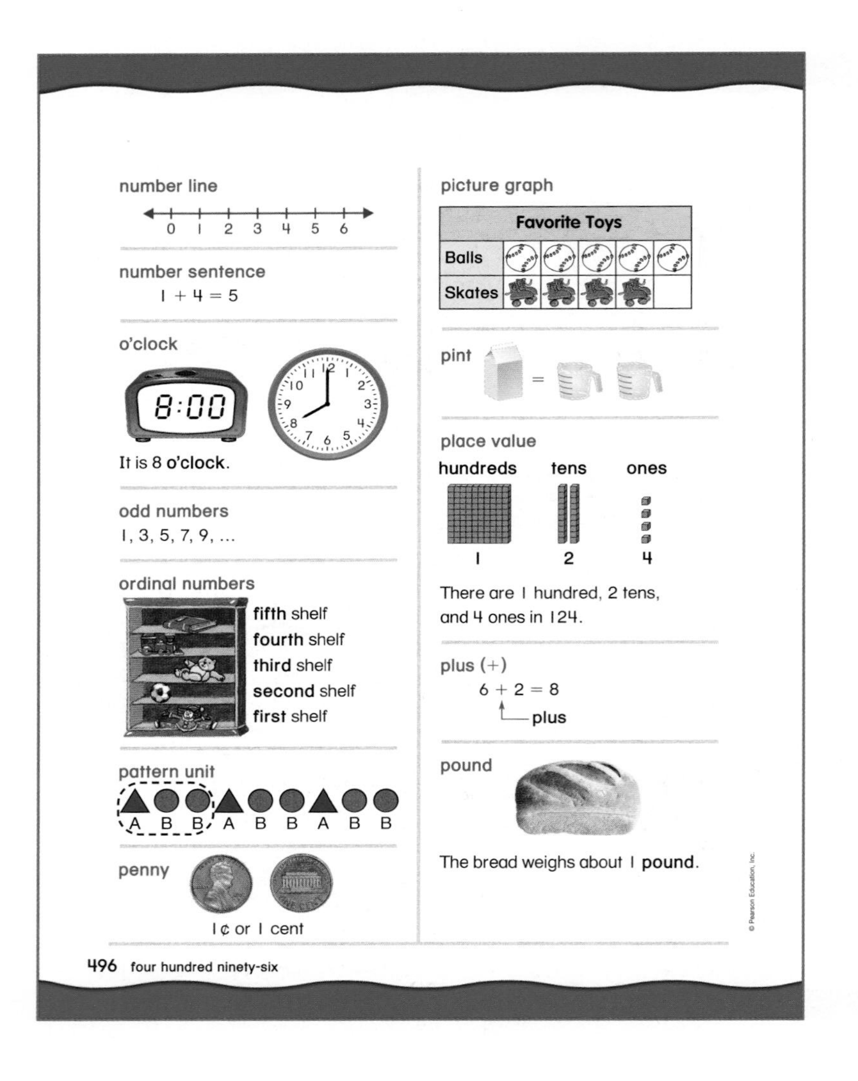

number line

0 1 2 3 4 5 6

number sentence

1 + 4 = 5

o'clock

8:00

It is 8 **o'clock**.

odd numbers

1, 3, 5, 7, 9, ...

ordinal numbers

fifth shelf
fourth shelf
third shelf
second shelf
first shelf

pattern unit

A B B A B B A B B

penny

1¢ or 1 cent

picture graph

Favorite Toys					
Balls	⚾	⚾	⚾	⚾	⚾
Skates	🛼	🛼	🛼	🛼	

pint

place value

hundreds	**tens**	**ones**
1	2	4

There are 1 hundred, 2 tens, and 4 ones in 124.

plus (+)

6 + 2 = 8

plus

pound

The bread weighs about 1 **pound**.

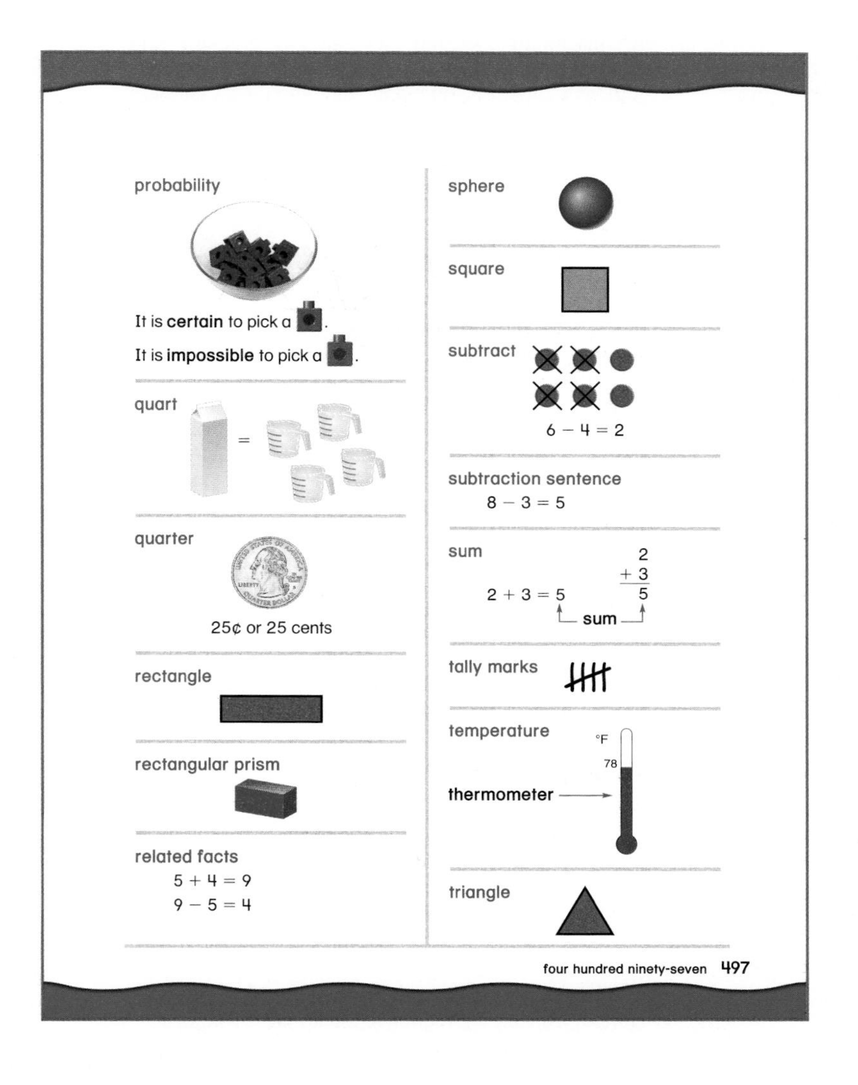

probability

It is **certain** to pick a ■.

It is **impossible** to pick a ■.

quart

quarter

25¢ or 25 cents

rectangle

rectangular prism

related facts

$5 + 4 = 9$

$9 - 5 = 4$

sphere

square

subtract

$6 - 4 = 2$

subtraction sentence

$8 - 3 = 5$

sum

$2 + 3 = 5$

$\begin{array}{r} 2 \\ + 3 \\ \hline 5 \end{array}$

sum

tally marks

temperature

°F

78

thermometer

triangle

four hundred ninety-seven 497

Credits

Cover: Jose Pardo

Text

Dorling Kindersley (DK) is an international publishing company specializing in the creation of high-quality reference content for books, CD-ROMs, online materials, and video. The hallmark of DK content is its unique combination of educational value and strong visual style. This combination allows DK to deliver appealing, accessible, and engaging educational content that delights children, parents, and teachers around the world. Scott Foresman is delighted to have been able to use selected extracts of DK content within this Scott Foresman Math program.

33–34: *Flip-Flap* by Sandra Jenkins. Copyright ©1995 by Dorling Kindersley Limited; 79–80: *Bugs! Bugs!* Bugs! by Jennifer Dussling. Copyright ©1998 by Dorling Kindersley Limited; 113–114: *Rabbit* by Mark Evans. Text copyright ©1992 by Mark Evans. Foreword copyright ©1992 by Roger Caras. Copyright ©1992 by Dorling Kindersley Limited; 145–146: *Puppies* by Carey Scott. Copyright ©1997 by Dorling Kindersley Limited; 193–194: *My Very First Colors, Shapes, Sizes, and Opposites Book* by Angela Wilkes. Copyright ©1993 by Dorling Kindersley Limited; 229–230: *Egg* by Robert Burton, photographed by Jane Burton and Kim Taylor. Copyright ©1994 by Dorling Kindersley Limited; 269–270: *My First Math Book* by David and Wendy Clemson. Copyright ©1994 by Dorling Kindersley Limited; 319–320: *My First Number Book* by Marie Heinst. Copyright ©1992, 1999 by Dorling Kindersley Limited; 353–354: *Counting Book* photographed by Dave King. Copyright ©1998 by Dorling Kindersley Limited; 405–406: *Children's Quick & Easy Cookbook* by Angela Wilkes. Text copyright ©1997 by Angela Wilkes. Copyright ©1997 by Dorling Kindersley Limited; 447–448: *A Day at Greenhill Farm* by Sue Nicholson. Copyright ©1998 by Dorling Kindersley Limited; 483–484: *Kitten* by Mark Evans. Text copyright ©1992 by Mark Evans. Foreword copyright ©1992 by Roger Caras. Copyright ©1992 by Dorling Kindersley Limited

Illustrations:

R2 **Carly Castillon** R3, R4 **Marisol Sarrazin** 1A, 1B, 1C, 1D, 1E, 1F, 2, 6, 11, 14, 16, 18, 21, 22, 25, 26, 28, 30, 35, 37 **Carly Castillon** 2A, 2B, 2C, 2D, 2E, 2F, 43, 44, 47, 48, 52, 63, 69, 70, 75, 76, 77, 342, 382 **Kathi Ember** 3A, 3B, 3C, 3D, 3E, 3F, 89, 90, 92, 93, 95, 97, 98, 101, 105, 106, 107, 108, 109, 111, 117 **John Patience** 4A, 4B, 4C, 4D, 4E, 4F, 80, 123, 124, 125, 126, 139, 140, 141, 142, 429, 430 **Karen Stormer Brooks** 4, 10, 12, 393, 394 **Janet Skiles** 5A, 5B, 5C, 5D, 5E, 5F, 155, 156, 157, 158, 166, 167, 168, 170, 171, 172, 173, 183, 184, 185, 189, 190 **Will Terry** 6A, 6B, 6C, 6D, 6E, 6F, 203, 204, 207, 208, 211, 212, 213, 217, 224, 226, 227, 228 **Jason Wolff** 7A, 7B, 7C, 7D, 7E, 7F, 240, 242, 251, 265, 266, 273 **Amy Vangsgard** 7, 8, 9, 32 **Remy Simard** 8A, 8B, 8C, 8D, 8E, 8F, 279, 280, 283, 284, 287, 288, 297, 300, 313, 323, 324 **Cameron Eagle** 9A, 9B, 9C, 9D, 9F, 329, 330, 333, 335, 336, 337, 338, 345, 357 **Laura Ovresat** 10A, 10B, 10C, 10D, 10E, 10F, 363, 364, 369, 370, 372, 377, 378, 395, 398, 403 **Bridget Starr Taylor** 11A, 11B, 11C, 11D, 11E, 11F, 415, 416, 417, 419, 420, 421, 425, 426, 427, 431, 432, 437, 440, 443, 444, 452 **Diane Greenseid** 12A, 12B, 12C, 12D, 12E, 12F, 459, 462, 463, 464, 471, 472, 473, 475, 476, 477, **Jackie Snider** 19, 20, 102, 109, 110, 116, 180, 197, 418 **Rose Mary Berlin** 45, 46, 61, 62, 65, 66, 88, 215, 216, 217, 219, 220, 231, 232, 238, 238B, 328A **Suwin Chan** 50, 57, 58, 59, 60, 82 **Jane Maday** 71, 72, 73, 218 **Paul Sharp** 94 **Terry Taylor** 103, 104 **Claudine Gevry** 108, 223, 224, 285, 286, 293, 309, 310, 311, 312, 321, 327, 328, 414A, 492B **Mike Dammer** 117, 349, 350, 456 **Rusty Fletcher** 122, 367, 368, 413 **Chi Chung** 127, 128, 130, 135, 153, 295, 296, 305 **Maryn Roos** 188, 191 **Ginna Magee** 213, 214 **George Ulrich** 244, 272, 278, 437, 438, 449 **Reggie Holladay** 257, 258, 395, 396, 399 **Margeaux Lucas** 257, 258, 408 **Eldon Doty** 259, 260 **Thomas Taylor** 261, 262 **John Sandford** 267, 268 **Linda Howard Bittner** 289, 290 **Nan Brooks** 301, 302, 305, 327 **Joe Stites** 315, 316, 317, 318, 321, 328, 400 **Donna Catanese** 326 **Carolyn Croll** 479, 480 **Jane Miles Smith ©2005 edition** R 15, R16 **Mike Dammer** 3, 8, 14, 22, 30 **Carly Castillon** 6 **Janet Skiles** 31 **Eldon Doty**

Photographs:

Every effort has been made to secure permission and provide appropriate credit for photographic material. The publisher deeply regrets any omission and pledges to correct errors called to its attention in subsequent editions. Unless otherwise acknowledged, all photographs are the property of Scott Foresman, a division of Pearson Education.

Photo locators denoted as follows: Top (T), Center (C), Bottom (B), Left (L), Right (R), Background (Bkgd)

1, 4 (BCL), 36 (TL, BR), 49 (T), 60, 67 (BR), 88A, 88B, 89, 102 (T), 116, 136, 143 (B), 144 (TC, BC, B), 154A, 154B, 157, 162 (All Other), 164, 176 (L), 187 (TL, TR, CR, BL), 202, 236 (CL), 238A, 271, 291 (T), 322, 328B, 339, 340 (BL, TR), 341, 366, 373, 374 (C), 376 (T, B), 384, 386, 387, 388 (TR), 391 (CR), 392 (CL, TR), 397, 398 (T, CC, CL, BL), 399 (TL, CL, CR), 408, 412 (TR), 414B (TL, TR), 431, 439 (TT, TB, CLT, CLB, BLT, BLB), 440, 450, 456 (T, C), 470, 472, 486, 492A, 492, 493 (TL), 496 (BR) Hemera Technologies 4 (TL, TR, BL, BC, BR), 10, 18, 36 (BC), 49 (CL), 51, 59 (R), 67 (TL, TR, CL, CR, BL), 68, 81, 87, 99, 100 (T, C), 101 (B), 102 (B), 111, 112 (BC), 115, 121, 133, 136, 144 (T), 154, 175, 187 (CL, BR), 276, 372, 374 (BL, BR), 375 (BL), 376 (C, BL, BR), 390, 391 (CL, BL), 392 (BL, CR, BR), 399 (BL, BCL, BCR, BR), 414B (BR), 434, 439 (CRT, BRT, BRB), 446 (B, T), 456 (BL, BR), 468 (T), 492B, 493 (BL) Getty Images 4 (TC, BCR), 33 (TL, CL), 34, 56, 79, 80 (TL, TR), 86, 100 (B), 113, 114, 142, 143 (T), 145, 146, 152, 193, 194, 221, 229, 230, 236 (TL), 269, 270, 319, 320, 353, 354, 388 (CRT), 405, 406, 439 (CRB), 445 (B), 446 (C), 447, 448, 483, 484 ©Dorling Kindersley 33 (BR) Philip Dowell/©Dorling Kindersley Artville 36 (TR), 49 (CR, BL, BR), 59 (L), 375 (CL) ©Comstock Inc. 73 (L, R), 101 (T), 112 (TC), 162 (CTR), 254, 340 (TC), 398 (TC), 80 (CR) Brian Kenney 222 ©John Lamb/Getty Images 375 (TL, B), 381, 385 Corbis 412 (TC) Digital Stock 445 (T) Tracy Morgan/©Dorling Kindersley WM1, WM3 Getty Images 347 (TR), 357 (TL, CL, BL, BC) Golden Dollar Obverse. 1999 United States Mint. All rights reserved. Used with permission/United States Mint. ©2005 edition R1 Getty Images, Brand X Pictures R2 Getty Images, Brand X Pictures R5 Getty Images R7 Getty Images R8 Getty Images 1 Hemera Technologies 14 Getty Images, Rubberball Productions 27 Rubberball Productions 33,34 ©Dorling Kindersley 36 Getty Images

Teacher's Edition Credits

Acknowledgements:

11B: "Ten potatoes in a pot" from TEN POTATOES IN A POT AND OTHER COUNTING RHYMES, Selected by Michael Jay Katz, p. 10. Copyright © 1990 by Michael Jay Katz. Reprinted by permission of HarperCollins Publishers.

Illustrations:

27B (©2005, 19B), 287B **Donna Catanese;** 33B, 97B, 113B, 191A, 193B, 205B, 229B, 243B, 261B, 267A **Bari Weissman;** 47B, 57B, 63B, 67B, 127B, 139B, 249A, 263A, 263B **Roberta Polfus;** 61B, 91B **Wendy Edelson;** 71B, 207B, 245B **Steve Henry;** 224 **Jason Wolff;** 291B, 309A **Reggie Holladay;** 303A **Lynda Calvert Weyant;** 313B, 315A, 317B **Linda Howard Bittner;** 369B, 397B, 401B **Jane Maday;** 377B **Deborah Borgo;** 421B, 471A, 473B **Janet Skiles**

Photographs:

209B (BR) Hemera Technologies, 395A (BR) Getty Images

Index

*Teacher's Edition references are in italics.

D

E

Index

 EC NTL 12 11 10 9